D1592377

Criminal Justice and the Mentally Disordered

The International Library of Criminology, Criminal Justice and Penology
Series Editors: Gerald Mars and David Nelken

Titles in the Series:

Integrative Criminology
Gregg Barak

The Origins and Growth of Criminology
Piers Beirne

Issues in Comparative Criminology
Piers Beirne and David Nelken

Criminal Detection and the Psychology of Crime
David V. Canter and Laurence J. Alison

Offender Rehabilitation
Francis T. Cullen and Brandon K. Applegate

International Criminal Law and Procedure
John Dugard and Christine van den Wyngaert

Crime and the Media
Richard V. Ericson

Psychological Explanations of Crime
David P. Farrington

Penal Abolition
Johannes Feest

State Crime, Vols I & II
David O. Friedrichs

Terrorism
Conor Gearty

Criminal Careers, Vols I & II
David F. Greenberg

Fear of Crime
Christopher Hale

Social Control: Aspects of Non-State Justice
Stuart Henry

Professional Criminals
Dick Hobbs

Crime, Deviance and the Computer
Richard C. Hollinger

Race, Crime and Justice
Barbara A. Hudson

Fraud: Organization, Motivation and Control
Michael Levi

Violence
Michael Levi

Radical Criminology
Michael J. Lynch

Serial Murder
Elliott Leyton

Street Crime
Mike Maguire

Occupational Crime
Gerald Mars

Theoretical Traditions in Criminology
Ross Matsueda

Alternatives to Prison
Roger Matthews

The Sociology of Punishment
Dario Melossi

Gender, Crime and Feminism
Ngaire Naffine

White-Collar Crime
David Nelken

Comparative Criminal Justice
David Nelken and Richard K. Vogler

Crime and Risk Management
Pat O'Malley

Organized Crime
Nikos Passas

Transnational Crime
Nikos Passas

Uses and Abuses of Criminal Statistics
Kenneth Pease

Criminal Justice and the Mentally Disordered
Jill Peay

Policing, Vols I & II
Robert Reiner

Victimology
Paul Rock

Criminal Policy Making
Andrew Rutherford

Prosecution in Common Law Jurisdictions
Andrew Sanders

Politics, Crime Control and Culture
Stuart A. Scheingold

Drugs, Crime and Criminal Justice, Vols I & II
Nigel South

Youth Crime, Deviance and Delinquency, Vols I & II
Nigel South

Crime and Political Economy
Ian Taylor

Rape and the Criminal Justice System
Jenny Temkin

The Sentencing Process
Martin Wasik

Sex Crimes
Donald West

Criminal Justice and the Mentally Disordered

Edited by

Jill Peay

London School of Economics

Ashgate

DARTMOUTH

Aldershot • Brookfield USA • Singapore • Sydney

Published by
Ashgate Publishing Limited
Gower House
Croft Road
Aldershot
Hants GU11 3HR
England

Ashgate Publishing Company
Old Post Road
Brookfield
Vermont 05036
USA

British Library Cataloguing in Publication Data
Criminal justice and the mentally disordered. – (The
international library of criminology, criminal justice and
penology)
1. Mentally handicapped offenders
I. Peay, Jill
364.3'8

Library of Congress Cataloguing-in-Publication Data
Criminal justice and the mentally disordered / edited by Jill Peay.
p. cm. – (The international library of criminology, criminal
justice and penology)
Includes bibliographical references.
ISBN 1–85521–962–X (hb)
1. Mentally handicapped offenders–United States. 2. Criminal
justice. Administration of–United States. I. Peay, Jill.
II. Series. III. Series : International library of criminology,
criminal justice & penology.
HV6791.C75219 1998
364.3'8'0973–dc21 98–2546
CIP

ISBN 1 85521 962 X

Printed and bound by Athenaeum Press, Ltd.,
Gateshead, Tyne & Wear.

Contents

PART III ASPECTS OF PROCESS

PART IV THE ETHICS OF FORENSIC PSYCHIATRY: SHOULD PSYCHIATRISTS ENGAGE WITH THE CRIMINAL COURTS?

PART V DANGEROUSNESS/PSYCHOPATHIC DISORDER AND THE PREDICTION OF VIOLENCE

Acknowledgements

The editor and publishers wish to thank the following for permission to use copyright material.

American Medical Association for the essay: Sheilagh Hodgins (1992), 'Mental Disorder, Intellectual Deficiency, and Crime: Evidence from a Birth Cohort', *Archives of General Psychiatry*, **49**, pp. 476–83.

American Psychiatric Association for the essay: John Monahan (1977), 'John Stuart Mill on the Liberty of the Mentally Ill: A Historical Note', *American Journal of Psychiatry*, **134**, pp. 1428–29. Copyright © 1977, the American Psychiatric Association. Reprinted by permission.

American Psychological Association for the essay: John Monahan (1992), 'Mental Disorder and Violent Behaviour: Perceptions and Evidence', *American Psychologist*, **47**, pp. 511–21. Copyright © 1992 by the American Psychological Association, Inc.

Blackwell Publishers Ltd for the essays: Elizabeth Burney and Geoffrey Pearson (1995), 'Mentally Disordered Offenders: Finding a Focus for Diversion', *The Howard Journal*, **34**, pp. 291–313. Copyright © 1995 Blackwell Publishers Ltd; Philip W.H. Fennell (1994), 'Mentally Disordered Suspects in the Criminal Justice System', *Journal of Law and Society*, **21**, pp. 57–71. Copyright © 1994 Blackwell Publishers Ltd.

British Medical Journal for the essays: Deborah Brooke, Caecilia Taylor, John Gunn and Anthony Maden (1996), 'Point Prevalence of Mental Disorder in Unconvicted Male Prisoners in England and Wales', *British Medical Journal*, **313**, pp. 1524–27. Copyright © British Medical Journal; John Gunn, Anthony Maden and Mark Swinton (1991), 'Treatment Needs of Prisoners with Psychiatric Disorders', *British Medical Journal*, **303**, pp. 338–41. Copyright © 1991 British Medical Journal.

Cambridge University Press for the essay: Aubrey Lewis (1974), 'Psychopathic Personality: A Most Elusive Category', *Psychological Medicine*, **4**, pp. 133–40.

Chiltern Publishing for the essay: Herschel Prins (1990), 'Mental Abnormality and Criminality – An Uncertain Relationship', *Medicine, Science and Law*, **30**, pp. 247–59. Copyright © British Academy of Forensic Sciences.

Elsevier Science Ltd for the essays: Nigel Eastman (1992), 'Psychiatric, Psychological, and Legal Models of Man', *International Journal of Law and Psychiatry*, **15**, pp. 157–69.

Copyright © 1992 Pergamon Press Ltd; Sheilagh Hodgins (1995), 'Assessing Mental Disorder in the Criminal Justice System: Feasibility Versus Clinical Accuracy', *International Journal of Law and Psychiatry*, **18**, pp. 15–28. Copyright © Elsevier Science Ltd; Linda A. Teplin and Nancy S. Pruett (1992), 'Police as Streetcorner Psychiatrist: Managing the Mentally Ill', *International Journal of Law and Psychiatry*, **15**, pp. 139–56. Copyright © 1992 Pergamon Press Ltd; Simon N. Verdun-Jones (1989), 'Sentencing the Partly Mad and Partly Bad: The Case of the Hospital Order in England and Wales', *International Journal of Law and Psychiatry*, **12**, pp. 1–27. Copyright © 1989 Maxwell Pergamon Macmillan Plc; Stephen L. Golding (1990), 'Mental Health Professionals and the Courts: The Ethics of Expertise', *International Journal of Law and Psychiatry*, **13**, pp. 281–307. Copyright © 1990 Pergamon Press Plc; Michel Foucault (1978), 'About the Concept of the "Dangerous Individual" in 19th-Century Legal Psychiatry', *International Journal of Law and Psychiatry*, **1**, pp. 1–18. Published in *Dits et Écrits* (1994), 'L'Évolution de la notion d' "individu dangereux" dans la psychiatrie légale du XIXe siècle' by Michel Foucault. Copyright © Editions Gallimard, 1994, reprinted by permission; Alan A. Stone (1994), 'Revisiting the Parable: Truth Without Consequences', *International Journal of Law and Psychiatry*, **17**, pp. 79–97. Copyright © 1994 Elsevier Science Ltd.

Kluwer Law International for the essay: L. H. Leigh (1991), 'Reason, Emotion and Criminal Responsibility', *Coexistence*, **28**, pp. 23–43, with kind permission from Kluwer Law International. Copyright © 1991 Kluwer Academic Publishers.

Melbourne University Law Review for the essay: C. S. Lewis (1953), 'The Humanitarian Theory of Punishment', *Res Judicatae: University of Melbourne Law Review*, **6**, pp. 224–30.

Oxford University Press for the essays: Adrian Grounds (1991), 'The Transfer of Sentenced Prisoners to Hospital 1960–1983: A Study in One Special Hospital', *British Journal of Criminology*, **31**, pp. 54–71; Keith Hawkins (1983), 'Assessing Evil: Decision Behaviour and Parole Board Justice', *British Journal of Criminology*, **23**, pp. 101–27.

Plenum Publishing Corporation for the essays: David B. Wexler (1992), 'Putting Mental Health in Mental Health Law: Therapeutic Jurisprudence', *Law and Human Behavior*, **16**, pp. 27–38. Copyright © 1992 Plenum Publishing Corporation; Robert Menzies, Christopher D. Webster, Shelley McMain, Shauna Staley and Rosemary Scaglione (1994), 'The Dimensions of Dangerousness Revisited: Assessing Forensic Predictions About Violence', *Law and Human Behavior*, **18**, pp. 1–28. Copyright © 1994 Plenum Publishing Corporation.

Royal College of Psychiatrists for the essays: John Gunn (1977), 'Criminal Behaviour and Mental Disorder', *British Journal of Psychiatry*, **130**, pp. 317–29; Paul E. Mullen (1991), 'Jealousy: The Pathology of Passion', *British Journal of Psychiatry*, **158**, pp. 593–601; P. D. Scott (1977), 'Assessing Dangerousness in Criminals', *British Journal of Psychiatry*, **131**, pp. 127–42; A. T. Grounds (1987), 'Detection of "Psychopathic Disorder" Patients in Special Hospitals: Critical Issues', *British Journal of Psychiatry*, **151**, pp. 474–78.

Routledge for the essays: Steffano Ferracuti (1996), 'Cesare Lombroso (1835–1907), *Journal of Forensic Psychiatry*, **7**, pp. 130–49. Copyright © 1996 Routledge; Ronnie Mackay (1995), 'Insanity and Fitness to Stand Trial in Canada and England: A Comparative Study of Recent Developments', *Journal of Forensic Psychiatry*, **6**, pp. 121–38. Copyright © 1995 Routledge; Bohdan Solomka (1996), 'The Role of Psychiatric Evidence in Passing "Longer than Normal" Sentences', *Journal of Forensic Psychiatry*, **7**, pp. 239–55. Copyright © 1996 Routledge.

Sweet and Maxwell Limited for the essays: Daniel Maier-Katkin and Robbin Ogle (1993), 'A Rationale for Infanticide Laws', *Criminal Law Review*, pp. 903–14; David Wood (1988), 'Dangerous Offenders, and the Morality of Protective Sentencing', *Criminal Law Review*, pp. 424–33.

University of London for the essay: Lord Mustill (1992), 'The Mentally Disordered Offender: A Call for Thought', *The King's College Law Journal*, **3–4**, pp. 1–28.

Whurr Publishers Ltd for the essay: S. Wessely and P. J. Taylor (1991), 'Madness and Crime: Criminology versus Psychiatry', *Criminal Behaviour and Mental Health*, **1**, pp. 193–228. Copyright © 1991 Whurr Publishers Ltd.

Every effort has been made to trace all the copyright holders, but if any have been inadvertently overlooked the publishers will be pleased to make the necessary arrangement at the first opportunity.

Series Preface

The International Library of Criminology, Criminal Justice and Penology, represents an important publishing initiative designed to bring together the most significant journal essays in contemporary criminology, criminal justice and penology. The series makes available to researchers, teachers and students an extensive range of essays which are indispensable for obtaining an overview of the latest theories and findings in this fast changing subject.

This series consists of volumes dealing with criminological schools and theories as well as with approaches to particular areas of crime, criminal justice and penology. Each volume is edited by a recognised authority who has selected twenty or so of the best journal articles in the field of their special competence and provided an informative introduction giving a summary of the field and the relevance of the articles chosen. The original pagination is retained for ease of reference.

The difficulties of keeping on top of the steadily growing literature in criminology are complicated by the many disciplines from which its theories and findings are drawn (sociology, law, sociology of law, psychology, psychiatry, philosophy and economics are the most obvious). The development of new specialisms with their own journals (policing, victimology, mediation) as well as the debates between rival schools of thought (feminist criminology, left realism, critical criminology, abolitionism etc.) make necessary overviews that offer syntheses of the state of the art. These problems are addressed by the INTERNATIONAL LIBRARY in making available for research and teaching the key essays from specialist journals.

GERALD MARS
Professor in Applied Anthropology, University of Bradford School of Management

DAVID NELKEN
Distinguished Research Professor, Cardiff Law School, University of Wales, Cardiff

Introduction

The field of criminal justice and the mentally disordered is dogged by ambiguity, uncertainty, myth and fear. It is also a field which challenges criminologists to examine their conceptions about the causes of crime and the merits of intervening in the lives of those who have been caught and/or prosecuted and/or convicted. It even requires us to think about the legitimacy of intervention where a crime may not yet have been committed or where the demand for punishment has already been met, with the intention of preventing further offending. To confuse the situation further, the boundaries of the field are blurred – blurred partly because of the changing fashions in the psychiatrization of offending, but partly also because of a growing recognition of the levels of distress, damage and disorder amongst incarcerated ('normal') populations. There are also questions arising out of the conjunction of mental disorder and justice: is it possible properly to weigh the responsibility of 'normal' offenders, let alone their abnormal counterparts, where the causes of offending are multi-faceted and the debate about free will is impossible to resolve? In this context, do mentally disordered offenders receive justice, when they may be dealt with as much on the basis of who they are rather than what they have done? Moreover, *should* such offenders be subject to treatment moderated by the benefit of enhanced procedural safeguards? Finally, where mental disorder is defined by experts but frequently used in the vernacular by laypeople and embraced or rejected by offender–sufferers, sometimes according to utilitarian considerations, there is likely to be little practical consistency in its application. Where crime is accepted to be a culturally constructed concept, and thus as malleable as the notion of mental disorder, bringing together these two arenas will encompass a huge literature.

Faced with the dilemma of too much choice, my inclination as an empiricist (to say nothing of my propensity to indolence) was to approach the task not by ploughing through 50 years of journal essays, but rather to seek the advice of friends and colleagues. Which, I asked them, were their three favourite essays? Some found this task impossible and never returned my calls; others showed a surprising degree of conformity, whilst one, whom I will not embarrass, sent me a list of ten – a selection of such excellence that I almost felt obliged to hand over the editorship to him. I thank them all for their efforts.

One further caveat is necessary. In 1989 Richard Freeman and Ronald Roesch edited a special issue of the *International Journal of Law and Psychiatry* devoted to the topic of 'Mental Disorder and the Criminal Justice System'. I have tried not to replicate the themes they pursued, for the special issue stands as a significant contribution to the domain and is worthy of inspection in its entirety. However, it is notable that they conclude their introductory review by calling for better delineation of the problems posed by mentally ill offenders, arguing that, until this is achieved, they will be 'as much at risk from society as they will be a risk to society' (1989:114). The contribution in that volume by Saleem Shah is extraordinarily helpful in clarifying *how* such progress might be made. Not only did he set out how, where the mentally disordered offender is concerned, both the state's coercive police powers and *parens patriae* rationales are interweaved, but his analysis also importantly stressed the need to think about mental disorder in a more sophisticated way. Shah recognized it was not a 'once and for all purposes' label, but that one always needed to think about the severity of the disorder in the context of the nature of the criminal justice intervention; as with physical fitness, one may be fit enough to walk three miles on a Sunday afternoon on the flat, but insufficiently fit to tackle Mount Everest. Similarly, with mental fitness, issues of justice and fairness need to be judged in their appropriate context; they will not always be impeded by a particular level of disorder. Equally, the strictness with which definitions are applied should be compatible with the purpose being pursued; inclusionary criteria may be acceptable where a benefit is to be gained but, where an offender is to suffer an unusual detriment, then exclusionary criteria would be more apt. Over and above these acute observations, I should like to pay tribute here to Saleem Shah's contribution to the whole field. It was, in short, invaluable, not only in terms of his own work, but also in the way in which he generously encouraged young researchers. I myself have benefited enormously from the warmth of his support. That his life should have been cut tragically short in a car accident caused by a drunken driver left many bereft and much work uncompleted.

The lengthy selection in this volume, which asks, rather than answers, questions, is divided into five Parts. Part I tries to examine the nature of the relationship between offending and mental disorder; in essence, how much is causation, how much correlation and what consequences follow? This is a division impossible to draw with any accuracy and the Part concludes with two essays which adopt a fundamentally different approach to the policy question arising from this uncertain relationship: namely, do the mentally disordered deserve their just measure of punishment and, alternatively, can the justice process itself, where appropriate procedural safeguards are in-built, be therapeutic to those with such needs? Part II addresses some of the conceptual and methodological problems which impede a full understanding of the issues and finds those who would seek to explain criminal behaviour on the basis of individual factors at odds with those who locate explanatory force in more general social processes. Part III takes a look at the way in which the justice process deals with the mentally disordered, from early involvement by the police, through assorted diversion schemes and special defences, via the problems of sentencing and the prevalence of disorder within incarcerated populations. At each stage it is evident that the degree of discretion operating, the variability in resources available and the diffuse conceptual imperatives and limitations on the understanding of the key human actors, all contribute to a concertina-like effect. This can both include, and then exclude, some mentally disordered offenders from the benefits and disadvantages of special processing. But it is also a concertina which operates like a lottery, so that there is inconsistency in whether any particular individual will end up on either side of the inclusionary/exclusionary divide. This issue has also been reviewed elsewhere and in too much detail for inclusion here (see, for example, Morse 1978, 1985; Ennis and Litwack 1974). Ironically, even individual commentators have changed their positions over the years as to the appropriateness of the location of mentally disordered offenders at any given stage in the process, testament to the challenging nature of the problems posed. Part IV examines the ethical and moral problems which arise when psychiatrists involve themselves with the criminal process and, in particular, in the use of preventive 'longer than normal' sentences. This touches on the same debate more starkly drawn over whether psychiatrists should be involved, however tenuously, with the death penalty. Certifying an offender as sufficiently sane to be killed may readily be agreed to be 'off-limits', but would involvement in the treatment of the disordered, who face the death penalty if they recover, offend psychiatric morality? This debate is also too complex for inclusion here, but has been dealt with elsewhere (see, for example, Bloche 1993). The final Part deals with the ever-popular topic of dangerous mentally disordered offenders. In so doing, the selection of essays seeks to expose some of the mythology around this topic concluding, in essence, that dangerousness, like beauty, lies primarily in the eye of the beholder.

Mental Disorder and Crime: Causation, Correlation and Consequences

The selection of essays is eclectic – with the first two seeking to demonstrate that even dearly held misconceptions can still be misconceptions. John Monahan, noted for the libertarian flavour to his own work, observes in Chapter 2 that a closer reading of John Stuart Mill establishes that the limits to the libertarian tradition exclude the mentally disordered. Similarly, a more detailed analysis in Chapter 1 by Stefano Ferracuti of the work of Lombroso, much beloved as the humorous starting point to courses on 'what is the relationship between offender and offending?', reveals Lombroso to have been interested *both* in the association between biological factors and offending (suggesting an absence of free will) *and*, in his later work, in the influence of environmental factors on offending. His contribution to the libertarian tradition (if to be exempt from punishment is to be liberated – itself a contentious point) is to note that, if crime is the expression of the personality and nature of the individual, then we ought to exclude the 'irresponsible' from punishment.

Of course, to exempt from formal punishment is not to be spared from intervention, and treatment itself can be as punishing and as prolonged to he or she who endures it unwillingly. Here, the contribution of Lewis with his 'Humanitarian Theory of Punishment' (Chapter 7) is crucial; 'humanity' he argues, is a dangerous illusion and 'disguises the possibility of cruelty and injustice without end' (p. 89). To treat removes offenders from the sphere of justice – whose primary concern is with what the offender deserves – and places them into the hands of technical experts who do not give primacy to notions of rights or justice. Lewis makes the important point that where crime and disease are to be regarded as the same thing, it follows that any state of mind which our masters choose to call disease can be treated as crime and compulsorily 'cured' (see p. xix on jealousy). Thus, the 'Humanitarian Theory' is to be resisted at all costs, for it carries a semblance of mercy which is wholly false. On the other hand, but not necessarily incompatible with this approach, David Wexler (Chapter 8) espouses the concept of therapeutic justice, arguing that involvement with the law and the behaviour of legal actors may both improve therapeutic outcomes without sacrificing the interests of justice.

The three essays by Gunn, Prins and Hodgins (Chapters 3, 4 and 5 respectively) look primarily at the unrelatedness of mental disorder and crime. Although Hodgins is concerned with relatedness, she concludes by comparing the contribution to the totality of offending; the proportion perpetrated by the mentally disordered is insignificant. Curiously, John Gunn, a psychiatrist, focuses on the social end of the relationship between crime and mental disorder (or lack of it, for his central premise is that we may be mistaken in looking for an overall relationship between what are two heterogenous populations), whilst Herschel Prins, from the social work tradition, looks at the more clinical end and the possibilities of intervention: he too concludes that 'Most psychiatric disorders are only very occasionally associated with criminality' (p. 48). Hodgins' work, which takes a birth cohort and is methodologically more rigorous, still suffers from the disadvantage of using recorded crime as an index. But what perhaps is most telling is the association in respect of violence; women with major disorders were 27 times more likely to be registered for a violence *conviction*; for their male counterparts the figure was only four times as likely to have such a conviction as men with no major mental disorder. But does this tell us about a causal relationship, or about the strength of that relationship when mental disorder is present in women (namely, that disordered women when violent are very violent), or about the culturally determined responses of society, law enforcers and the courts to women who challenge our notions of femininity by being both disordered and violent?

Finally, Lord Mustill makes an impassioned plea in Chapter 6 that 'provision for the mentally disordered offender is unsystematic, unfocused and short-winded' (p. 63). He argues that it is the professionals who are in large measure to blame, for, amongst other matters, not only have we failed to analyse why the problems exist, we have also failed effectively to relate psychiatry and law. He documents the gulf between the training, inclination and professional aims of those who practise within the two systems. Of course, our thinking should start with a clear penal policy, but this is difficult before we can agree on which offenders are to be included within the ambit of the 'mentally disordered offender' (a conception that has changed over time) and what we are aiming to achieve by their inclusion. Mustill asks what it is about mental illness that allows us to think that these offenders should be extracted from the criminal justice system whereas their physically ill counterparts are not. Similarly, what is it about particular aberrant acts (for example, the theft of underwear in the course of burglary) which causes us to deem them driven by disorder? In short, his is a call for the avoidance of caprice in the criminal justice process.

Methodological and Conceptual Problems: Conflicting Legal and Historical Models

The two contributions by Nigel Eastman and Leonard Leigh (Chapters 9 and 10) illustrate well the dilemmas that arise due to the incongruous legal and psychiatric models of man employed by law and psychiatry. The law's adherence to a rationalistic model of human behaviour as the basis for legal rules is in sharp contrast to the many and varied models employed by medicine. As Eastman points out, these discontinuities are much less marked at the sentencing stage; however, to ignore psycho-legal disjunctions in the preconviction process would offend our sense of fairness and justice towards those with mental disorders. Indeed, the law explicitly recognizes man-made notions encompassing '"*automatic*", "*irrational*", "*mentally diseased*", "*mentally abnormal*", or "*mentally unbalanced*" *mens*"' (p. 122) – and, one might add, 'diminished'. Leigh's essay further explores the moral quicksand, for he is interested in the gap between the law's rationality and psychiatry's irrationality – a gap which he fills with the emotions, like stress, that can and do afflict us all. In this context, Barbara Wootton's 'anguished rationality' or Leigh's argument that although 'The hero may be our exemplar; he cannot readily be our daily standard' (p. 142) require a model of man that recognizes that we may have opportunities for calm deliberation and yet still exercise imperfect control over our emotional reactions. Hence, the mentally disordered and their extended subgroup, mentally disordered offenders, may be more far-reaching (quite rightly) than some current narrow ambit.

In a sense, Paul Mullen's contribution (Chapter 11) illustrates this theme by tracing the way in which the social, ethical and interpersonal meaning has been stripped away from jealousy, leaving it as a piece of individual psychopathology. Other human experiences – despair, guilt, fear and nostalgia – may, he argues, be equally at risk. Creating symptoms from phenomena may have both theoretical and pragmatic justifications, but their potential to warp the processes of the assessment of guilt are evident where the law has progressively entered the arena of sexual politics and domestic violence. These are muddy waters.

Conceptual problems are complemented by methodological ones. In Chapter 12 Hodgins concludes from studies which she regards as methodologically rigorous that the mentally disordered are overrepresented in incarcerated offender populations (supported by evidence from Brooke *et al.* and Gunn *et al.* in Chapters 21 and 22). However, this is only the first stage in documenting the problem. She comprehensively illustrates how much there is still to understand, not only about the various mental disorders, but also about the effects of various combinations of disorder as well as disorders in the context of other life experiences – whether they be drug and alcohol abuse or other social ills such as homelessness, family breakdown or unemployment.

Finally, in Chapter 13 Wessely and Taylor combine the criticisms of methodological rigour and conceptual difficulties, although they define the latter as the difference between the individual focus of psychiatry (particularly in respect of violence) and the criminological focus on populations and general offending. Crucially, Wessely and Taylor observe (echoing Lombroso) that the 'substantial differences in age of onset of criminal behaviours between mentally ill and non-mentally ill samples suggests that social adversity consequent upon mental illness may be a mediator between illness and the observed increased rates of offending' (p. 183); on this basis they advocate greater use of longitudinal studies. Equally, the relationship between mental illness and abnormal behaviour is dynamic (unlike, for example, cases where the prognosis of cancer is determined by the level of initial exposure); accordingly 'the single most effective preventive measure would be a better standard of after-care' (p. 200).

Aspects of Process

Involvement of the mentally disordered with the criminal justice process is problematic, both in terms of what should happen and what actually does. The debate encompasses those who would *absolve* the mentally disordered from the brutality of process; those who would take proceedings in order to *obtain* special services for the mentally disordered; those who believe that involvement with the criminal justice process will result in a *denial* of certain specialized (community) services to the mentally disordered; and those who take the view that the mentally disordered are as *entitled* to their measure of just deserts as any other offender. And then there are variants of those positions. All of these perspectives can serve to include or exclude the mentally disordered offender from the criminal justice system. Practitioners involved at different stages mix and match these philosophies, without necessarily paying any great heed to that to which the law subscribes. In Chapter 14 Teplin and Pruett's study of the exercise of discretion by police officers in a Midwestern US city well illustrates the point, for, of 1396 police–citizen encounters involving the mentally ill, over 70 per cent were dealt with informally – that is, not by arrest or resort to hospitalization. This is consistent with Bittner's (1967) seminal study of how the police used their discretion; this was structured around their own informal operative code and not the formal legal structure. At a time when the mentally ill are being, or have already been, substantially deinstitutionalized, the encounters between the mentally disordered and those with less than adequate training in and/or understanding of mental health issues will be critical, for not only do they act as the gatekeepers to the criminal process, they are also in a position to diffuse or inflame citizen–citizen interactions. Where the police do pursue official action, Burney and Pearson's contribution (Chapter 15) builds on some of Lord Mustill's themes by looking at a court-based scheme to assess the mentally disordered and, where appropriate, divert them from further involvement with the criminal justice process. Again, a picture emerges not of the courts being swamped by the demands of this 'group', but of the relative rarity with which such offenders emerge at court. However, when people with mental disorder are identified, what is striking is the multiplicity of needs which they display – for example, problems of homelessness and drug misuse plague them as much as 'normal' offenders. Moreover, the higher proportions of mentally disordered offenders appearing before the courts on charges of relatively minor violence, testify, the authors assert, to the relative lack of confidence of the police or public in dealing with these issues. The early appearance of such systematic biasing factors is notable.

In Chapter 16 Fennell documents the problematic position of the mentally disordered suspect; procedural safeguards for such vulnerable individuals are themselves vulnerable when operated by practitioners not fully wedded to, or understanding, the need for such special safeguards. As a statement of principle, the *Report of the Royal Commission on Criminal Justice* in the UK recognized that 'the protection of suspects from unfair or unreasonable pressure is just as important to the criminal justice system as the thoroughness with which the police carry out their investigations' (1993:25). Yet, what is unfair has to be assessed against the background of the person subject to the procedures; the already sorry procession of miscarriages of justice involving false confessions by the mentally disordered is likely, in Fennell's view, to continue. This assessment will surely be further substantiated where the mentally disordered are demonized rather than dealt with empathetically. The undermining of clear safeguards for all – such as the 'right to silence' – impacts differentially against vulnerable groups. Ensuring that special legal safeguards achieve their objectives is also a theme pursued by Mackay (Chapter 17), who compares and contrasts legal reforms in Canada and England in respect of insanity and unfitness to plead provisions. In so doing, he lays bare some of the illogicalities, inconsistencies and difficulties which bedevil the field – for example, sleepwalking in Canada is not a disease of the mind, so offences committed in this mental state can lead to complete acquittal, whereas in England sleepwalking has been held to arise from a sleep disorder and hence results in the insanity verdict. Canada has adopted substantive law reform; England has merely tinkered with the procedures. Canada has both reduced stigma by adopting a verdict that 'the accused committed the act or omission but is not criminally responsible on account of mental disorder' (p. 274) (that is, making no mention of insanity) but has, at the same time, introduced further stigmatization of certain groups of the mentally disordered – to be known as 'dangerous mentally disordered accused' (p. 278). He calls for more research (especially in Canada) to monitor the actual use of the new provisions: in England their usage remains disappointingly low, suggesting that dearly held beliefs about 'insanity' are extremely hard to combat even amongst professionals.

The existence of English infanticide laws, serving to protect a woman who kills her child (under 12 months of age) from the harshness of a murder conviction, also straddle the cusp of normal–abnormal offending. Psychiatrists maintain that puerperal psychosis is a demonstrable condition; criminologists argue that the killing of neonates is commonplace across time and culture and that its primary causes are likely to be social and cultural rather than rooted in any imbalance in a woman's mind. Yet, there are compelling arguments, as Máier-Katkin and Ogle review in Chapter 18, for retaining special and lenient provisions in such circumstances. Perhaps the more challenging questions concern why such provisions tempering justice with mercy are not extended to fathers who kill babies (they rather receive the brunt of society's demonizing forces) or babysitters/au pairs/nannies who do likewise? Again, mental disorder appears to be a peg upon which we can hang only some of the innocent (to mix metaphors). These themes, of the mad, bad, dangerous to know and combinations of the three are pursued by Verdun-Jones in his analysis of sentencing principles (Chapter 19). Is it sufficient, he asks, to settle for a pragmatic compromise which neglects issues of responsibility in the knowledge that the discretion exercised by the judge can put it all right at the stage of disposal? The answer is seemingly not, particularly where, in the real world, issues of perceived and attributed dangerousness can prevent even those meriting hospital treatment from being offered care – with the result that incarceration follows. Writing before both the amendments to Canadian and English insanity law, he asks whether it would not be more just to attempt to resolve the prior problematic issue of the mentally disordered offender's criminal responsibility.

The inappropriate disposal of the mentally disordered to prison rather than hospital – or the development of disorder amongst 'normal' offenders once incarcerated – requires provision for transfer for treatment in hospital since such treatment is often not appropriate, even if possible, in prison. Grounds' study of receptions to one secure hospital during one historical period, reproduced as Chapter 20, was an indictment of the inequities and iniquities of such transfers. Only this quality of thorough research can help us understand the complexities of the varied decision-making paths followed by mentally disordered offenders, bridging, as they do, systems with competing imperatives. For example, when the numbers of transfers rise should we view this as an index of the declining mental health of the prison population? Or as reflecting more punitive attitudes on the part of a judiciary failing to use therapeutic alternatives at the point of sentence? Or as a greater preparedness on the part of the caring professions to seek to treat those offenders regarded by some as either intransigent in behaviour or too difficult and disruptive to care for amongst a non-offending population?

The final two chapters in Part III comprise the two most recent surveys of the psychiatric health of the prison and remand populations in England. Both surveys are perturbing, documenting, as they do, not only the variety and depth of disorder, but also its inclusiveness. Amongst the sentenced population Gunn and his colleagues found a population of whom 37 per cent had diagnosable psychiatric disorders (Chapter 22); whilst Brooke and her colleagues found a staggering 63 per cent amongst the remand population (Chapter 21). Here, then, is not the 'needle in the haystack' of the first court appearance, or the problems which result from diversion schemes, but the problem of a custodial population being swamped by the psychiatrically disturbed. Perhaps most worryingly, the surveys establish levels of psychosis ranging from 2 per cent in the sentenced population to 5 per cent in the remand population. Significant selective forces must have been at work to concentrate disturbance at these levels in the prison population when both official policy and the law have been designed to produce a countervailing pressure – namely, to keep the mentally disordered out of prison populations.

The Ethics of Forensic Psychiatry: Should Psychiatrists Engage with the Criminal Courts?

The short section devoted to the ethics of forensic psychiatry addresses the invidious position in which doctors can find themselves when they become involved in the sentencing process. One focus for this has been the debate between Paul Appelbaum (see, most recently, Appelbaum 1997) and Alan Stone – the parameters of which are outlined in Stone's essay, reproduced as Chapter 24. In essence, when a psychiatrist assesses an offender with a view to writing a report for the court, to what extent is it appropriate for information derived from the offender, possibly under the guise of a 'therapeutic' relationship, to be passed on to the court, which may in turn result in the offender receiving a more punitive sentence? In Stone's view, never: in Appelbaum's, provided sufficient warnings are given to the offender about the nature of the assessment process, the therapeutic hat may be removed. This debate is not merely academic. One practical manifestation of it arises in Solomka's review of the new provisions for 'longer than normal' sentences in England and Wales (Chapter 25); indeed, the ethical problems are writ large both in respect of the involvement of psychiatry with the death penalty and with the shifting emphasis towards mixed punishment–therapy orders. Although such an approach may have jurisprudential logic (why should not those who are 'mad and bad' be subject to both 'therapy and punishment'?), it gives rise to all kinds of practical and moral difficulties. In turn, Stephen Golding, in Chapter 23, takes the debate from the specific to the general by offering an analysis of ethical issues germane to all forensic mental health professionals who find themselves acting as experts in court. Finally, in Chapter 26 David Wood examines the territory between those who would detain on protective grounds (even if only on a civil basis) the dangerous non-offender and those who believe that such detention can never be justified. He finds both positions wanting.

Dangerousness/Psychopathic Disorder and the Prediction of Violence

The involvement of mentally disordered offenders with the criminal justice system cannot be seen in isolation from the public's perceptions of the mentally disordered. Citizens' actions in reporting crimes, pursuing them in the role of victims and/or witnesses, their preparedness to tolerate released offender-patients and their influence generally upon the political climate (and, therefore, the changing statutory arrangements) are the same or greater than is the influence which they exert in respect of normal offenders. Yet, their perception is overwhelmingly negative – a perception to some extent created and sustained by the actions of the press where other agendas may dominate ('obtaining services for mentally ill by noting how poorly they are supported in the community' – for which, read the 'risk' posed). Part V attempts to address the validity of these stereotypes of 'the dangerous individual' and looks in particular at those possibly most feared – the so-called psychopaths. The use of the vernacular may be inherently misleading and damaging, for these offenders with severe personality disorder are as likely as those suffering from affective disorders to take their own lives; it is just that the personality-disordered are more likely to commit suicide at a younger age.

The essay by Foucault (Chapter 27) sets the historical context, by charting the shift from an era when 'the criminal had been no more than the person to whom a crime could be attributed and who could therefore be punished' to one where 'the crime tends to be no more than the event which signals the existence of a dangerous element....in the social body' (p. 432). Foucault attributes psychiatry's *desire* to dominate this domain to a yearning to secure and justify a further modality of power; their *success* in so doing he attributes to the phenomenon of legal punishment being used as a technique for transforming the individual. By shifting the focus from the act to the danger inherent in the individual, Foucault asserts that there was a move away from classical juridical notions to those that can only function in a technical knowledge system – in this case, monopolized by psychiatry. In turn, this gives the state rights over an individual based not on what she or he has done, but on the basis of what they are by nature, constitution or pathology. Foucault sees real dangers inherent in this.

Two further seminal essays follow. The first by Scott (Chapter 28), reviews the difficulties of defining and predicting dangerousness; he advocates the maintenance of good communication and personal relationships as a way of managing the potentially dangerous patient. Curiously, the theoretical shifts through which the literature on dangerousness has most recently gone – from dangerousness *per se* to risk prediction to risk management – anticipated by Scott's recommended practices, still do not seem to have been learnt by some as basic lessons. In the current era when care (and punishment) of offenders and patients has shifted into the community, it is a matter of genuine concern that the spate of 'Inquiries after Homicide' (Peay 1996) repeatedly find tragic incidents arising in the context of poor communication and/or patient management. In Chapter 29 Aubrey Lewis fleshes out one explanation for these problems by detailing the struggles that psychiatric nosologists throughout Europe have had since 1801 in *describing* and *defining* what was ultimately to become known as the psychopathic personality (my own favourite from amongst those he cites is Edward Glover's suggestion in 1955 that they were prepsychotic or 'larval'). Even in 1974, when Lewis was writing, the additional difficulties psychiatrists would have in agreeing on which sufferers required, or were susceptible to, treatment was recognized; these judgements would inevitably be subjective and inconsistent. Another 20 years on, Cope's (1993) survey suggests that (in the UK at least) forensic psychiatrists are little the wiser about treatability.

In Chapter 31 Adrian Grounds continues the critique of the concept of psychopathic disorder – a pseudo-diagnosis – by looking at the problematic position of these patients within a secure hospital system where they may be detained on an indeterminate basis. He argues, given the uncertainties around the concept and its application, that such detention is unjust. Advocating the greater use of *transfer* for time-limited treatment for those sentenced to imprisonment, he anticipates by almost a decade the introduction of an order explicitly for psychopaths in England and Wales to achieve a mixed punishment–therapy outcome. It is evident that the literature reflects not only the inherent ambiguities associated with those who both offend and are disordered, but also the additional polluting influence that public conceptions and misconceptions about this troublesome group can have: psychopaths do not readily attract the sympathetic understanding which may much more readily be accorded the mentally ill offender.

John Monahan's 1992 review of the relationship between mental disorder and violent behaviour, presented as Chapter 30, is refreshingly candid. As a former advocate of the body of opinion that no such relationship exists, he revises his view, in this essay, to one where current mental disorder may be a modest risk factor for the occurrence of violence. He recognizes the field to be empirically complex and politically controversial, but nonetheless comes to that conclusion on the basis of empirical evidence and the inferences that can reliably be drawn therefrom. It is a model answer from perhaps the leading exponent in the field and it provides both a critique of the methodology employed by much of the prior (misleading) literature and an agenda for future research and policy. Monahan also makes the crucial point that, even if a modest relationship exists, it needs to be seen in the context of its magnitude; for, overwhelmingly, people with mental disorders are not violent, and those who are, are violent only spasmodically. As a risk factor, mental disorder bears no comparison with youth, male gender, lower socioeconomic class and, most importantly, alcohol and drug abuse. Moreover, mental disorder is too generic a term – it needs to be unpacked, for example, in terms of specific symptoms and offender–victim interactions. Thus, Monahan echoes Shah's theme that we need to think in a more sophisticated fashion and not in stereotypes, broad classifications or diagnoses. It is to be hoped that the range, depth and quality of work only just emerging from the MacArthur project will help develop some of these critical issues.

Since so much of the acceptability of forms of special intervention hang on the ability reliably to predict dangerousness, one might expect empirically sound research establishing the ability (or inability) of clinicians to do this to be determinative of future policy. One of the best studies to date is that of the Canadian work of Menzies *et al.* included as Chapter 32 of this volume. Their earlier 1985 work indicated low prediction–outcome correlations, but at that stage the authors stopped short of recommending the wholesale abolition of dangerousness predictions in forensic settings. They remained cautiously optimistic that a refined replication study might yield better results, and it is these that they report in the essay reproduced in this volume. However, even with considerably greater methodological sophistication, the results yielded were disappointing and little better than the earlier study. As the authors conclude:

> Whereas some assessors were able to predict some people, under limited temporal and contextual conditions, some of the time, under no circumstances could even the most encouraging performances be mustered as an argument for clinical or psychometric involvement in the identification of potentially violent clinical or correctional subjects. (p. 515)

Yet this pessimistic and negative conclusion is recognized even by the authors as unlikely to dent the momentum enjoyed by the power of dangerousness predictions and related ideas about psychiatric pathology and individual violence. One wonders how that momentum would have been affected by positive findings, if negative findings cannot touch the central preoccupation of the criminal justice process with the potential violence of the mentally disordered.

Keith Hawkins' detailed analysis of the decision-making of one North American Parole Board in one case (Chapter 33) serves to illustrate just how crucial are the perceptions and attitudes of the individual decision-makers in the construction of the potential dangerousness (and wickedness) of individual offenders. It is a timely reminder that, for all the empirical research and attempts to crystallize out factors associated with good and bad risks in groups of similar offenders, that, ultimately, decisions in the criminal justice process are made on a case-by-case basis by individual decision-makers. Structuring their discretion can only go so far in achieving consistency; ultimately, human decision-makers will find ways and means of applying rules and guidelines to serve their own ends. This, then, is why the perception of mentally disordered offenders is of central importance: right through the criminal process, dealings with them by agents of the official process, whether therapeutically or punitively minded, will be influenced by those individuals' perceptions and misperceptions and by their beliefs, whether well- or ill-informed. As Hawkins observes, decisions are not made in an ideological vacuum. Moreover, filling that vacuum shifts the perception of crime as rational as adopted by the criminal law (and hence the pre-trial and trial processes) to one that sees punishment as instrumental, aiming to change offenders. Foucault had already referred to the untenable paradox that results: psychologically determined acts are those for which you would be found legally responsible; yet gratuitous acts are excused on grounds of an absence of responsibility. Thus, he asserted, the interplay between penal responsibility and psychological determinism becomes the cross of legal and medical thought. Of course, mentally disordered offenders seemingly require, are susceptible to, and worthy of so much more 'changing' than their 'normal' counterparts. This makes them more vulnerable to positivist inspired intervention. It is their lot to inhabit Mustill's Martian landscapes of logical positivism – 'stimulating to visit but impossible to inhabit' (p. 69). Finally, as Hawkins notes, central to the processing of 'deviants' is their moral status and 'the degree to which it is tainted by evil deserving of punishment' (p. 532), but for the mentally disordered offender this judgement is doubly difficult, for how is the issue of their responsibility for their offending to be weighed in any reliable or satisfactory fashion? Justice, for the mentally disordered offender, does not readily make sense, and the attempt to do so involves an infinite regression through cause and effect in the offender's psyche, history and family history.

Conclusion

Why it is so difficult to make sense of any of this? Perhaps the reason is that we are posing the wrong question. Rather than asking 'Can we design a system of criminal justice which recognizes the special position of mentally disordered offenders?', should we be asserting 'Those matters which distinguish mentally disordered offenders are less pressing than those which they share with ordered offenders'? If a study of the place of the mentally disordered offender in the justice process has lessons, they are arguably lessons for all offenders, not just for some ill-defined, and perhaps artificially constructed, group.

References

Appelbaum P. (1997), 'A Theory of Ethics for Forensic Psychiatry', *Journal of the American Academy of Psychiatry and the Law*, **25**, pp. 233-47.

Bittner E. (1967), 'Police Discretion in Emergency Apprehension of Mentally Ill Persons', *Social Problems*, **14**, 278–92.

Bloche M.G. (1993), 'Psychiatry, Capital Punishment, and the Purposes of Medicine', *International Journal of Law and Psychiatry*, **16**, 301–57.

Cope R. (1993), 'A Survey of Forensic Psychiatrists' Views on Psychopathic Disorder', *Journal of Forensic Psychiatry*, **4**, 215–35.

Ennis B.J. and Litwack T.R. (1974), 'Psychiatry and the Presumption of Expertise: Flipping Coins in the Courtroom', *California Law Review*, **62**, 693–752.

Freeman R.J. and Roesch R. (1989), 'Mental Disorder and the Criminal Justice System: A Review', *International Journal of Law and Psychiatry*, **12**, 105–15.

Menzies R.J., Webster C.D. and Sepejak D.S. (1985), 'The Dimension of Dangerousness: Evaluating the Accuracy of Psychometric Predictions of Violence among Forensic Patients', *Law and Human Behavior*, **9**, 35–56.

Morse, S.J. (1978), 'Crazy Behavior, Morals and Science: An Analysis of Mental Health Law', *Southern California Law Review*, **51**, 527–645.

Morse S.J. (1985), 'Excusing the Crazy: The Insanity Defence Reconsidered', *Southern California Law Review*, **58**, 777–836.

Peay J. (ed.) (1996), *Inquiries after Homicide*, London: Duckworth.

Report of the Royal Commission on Criminal Justice (1993), Cm. 2263, London: HMSO.

Shah S.A. (1989), 'Mental Disorder and the Criminal Justice System: Some Overarching Issues', *International Journal of Law and Psychiatry*, **12**, 231–44.

Wootton B. (1981), *Crime and the Criminal Law – Reflections of a Magistrate and Social Scientist*, (2nd edn), London: Sweet and Maxwell.

Part I

Mental Disorder and Crime: Causation, Correlation and Consequences

[1]

Cesare Lombroso (1835–1907)

STEFANO FERRACUTI

ABSTRACT The Italian physician Cesare Lombroso, one of the first scientific criminologists and a forensic psychiatrist, was an outstanding exponent of positivistic naturalism. His work engendered unending controversies, especially for the aspects concerning the absence of free will. Although Lombroso related criminal behaviour primarily to biological factors such as atavism, epilepsy and moral insanity, he increasingly recognized the importance of environmental influences in causing crime. As this review underlines, in tracing the development of his thought during the course of his life, Lombroso partly changed his theories on criminality. In some aspects yet their influence still persists today. An attempt of a reinterpretation of the positivistic thought in 'criminal anthropology' is proposed.

Keywords: Lombroso, criminal anthropology, positivism, atavism

Cesare Lombroso's thought had an indelible influence on the development of criminology and forensic psychiatry. His theories on the absence of free will and on the organic causes of criminality have provoked endless debates. Even today Lombroso remains a controversial figure. Equally controversial were many of his choices and his frequent changes of opinion. He was a representative of evolutionist and naturalistic positivism (Abbagnano, 1993). At the age of 31, in 1866 he translated Moleschott's *Kreislauf des Lebens* (Circulation of Life). Moleschott, a German philosopher and physiologist, wrote that 'evil is a phenomenon of nature' and that 'to understand everything means to forgive everything' (Bulferetti, 1975: 205). Lombroso's interests ranged from cretinism to spiritualism. He also devoted much of his research to the cause of pellagra.

Lombroso's criminological theory asserted that delinquency stems from an individual's abnormal physical constitution; hence, crime is a natural phenomenon. The delinquents are therefore not responsible for their behaviour, and must be kept in conditions in which they cannot harm society.

The Journal of Forensic Psychiatry Vol 7 No 1 May 1996 130–149

ISSN 0958-5184

An unpublished photograph of Lombroso, courtesy of Professor Ugo Fornari

This theory formed the basis of the '*Scuola Positiva*' (the Positive School), which contributed decisively to reviewing penal law.

Another of Lombroso's theses identified genius with madness and, in general, with an attitude regarded by others as exceptional. This idea goes back to Aristotle (Klibansky *et al.*, 1983). The development of this hypothesis has been summarized elsewhere (Mora, 1964).

Lombroso's research was based on an anatomical, physical and chemical examination of the individual, not unlike Freud's first experimental researches. One of Lombroso's scholars, Morselli, attempted adapting Freud's positions to Lombroso's clinical explanations (Morselli, 1926a, 1926b).

Lombroso was deeply concerned about social life. He was the first physician in Italy to speak about the necessity of 'a complete handbook of medical geography of the country, a kind of hygienic map of the peninsula'. In looking at Lombroso's work we need to remember that Lombroso was a socialist reformer, and that his theories were often influenced by his ideals.

THE LIFE

Lombroso's family originated from Spain. They were Sephardic Jews who emigrated first to Tunisia and then to Italy. Lombroso's parents, Aronne Lombroso and Zefora Levi, belonged to well-off families of traders (Bulferetti, 1975). Ezechia Marco Lombroso, called Cesare, was born in Verona on 6 November 1835, the third-born child. Apparently he was such a sensitive child that he even had mystical visions (Gina Lombroso-Ferrero, 1921: 9). Especially after his sister Pasquetta's death, Lombroso's mother had a strong influence over her son, which in part changed his personality. In his youth, he met a maternal cousin, David Levi, a writer and a patriot, a follower of Mazzini's republican ideals, from whom he took his intellectual restlessness.

Lombroso's father was an extremely pious man, who expected his son to lead a more religious style of life. Perhaps this explains why Cesare isolated himself, spending his time writing poems and a tragedy, later lost. While attending high school in the city of Verona (then under Austro-Hungarian domination) he began to behave as 'free-thinker', laying down the foundations of his atheist beliefs. Because of his rebellious character his parents removed him from school and educated him privately, a special emphasis being placed on humanities, to which he seemed to have a strong inclination. Inspired by the ideas of the eighteenth-century philosopher Vico, in 1850 Lombroso wrote an 'Essay on the History of the Roman Republic', discussing a common base of civilization. Soon afterwards he wrote the 'Sketches of Ancient Agriculture in Italy', which contained many linguistic annotations. His interests in linguistics led him to review a work by Paolo Marzolo, a physician who had written a handbook about the origin of languages and about comparisons between them. Although Lombroso probably already knew Marzolo, his hagiographers recount that, impressed by the review, Marzolo asked to meet the young author (Baima-Bollone, 1992). Under Marzolo's influence, in 1852 Lombroso decided to study medicine at Pavia University, where he had professors such as Bartolomeo Panizza (1785–1867) and Paolo Mantegazza (1831–1910).

While still a medical student he entered into correspondence with F. A. Maury, the author of a well-known book about dreams. In 1855 Lombroso published an article entitled 'Sulla pazzia di Cardano' (On Cardan's Madness). Jerome Cardan was a sixteenth-century Italian physician, philosopher and outstanding mathematician. He supported the biological equivalence of men, and argued against the death penalty and torture. In his numerous publications he maintained a distinction between the behaviour of the abnormal personalities, the mentally ill, those in emotional and passionate states, and the habitual and occasional delinquents. Cardano had an oniric and unstable temperament (Grieco and Mancia, 1989; Grieco, 1993). And it is in the article on Cardano that Lombroso writes first about the link between genius and madness, a link that, in his opinion, can be detected especially in dreams. Lombroso interpreted

Cardano's reliance on dreams as a 'regredent metamorphosis, a sort of cerebral modification that can awaken . . . the instincts and ideas of the primitive man'.

After an unhappy love affair, Lombroso left Pavia and moved to Vienna, where he completed the fourth year (1855–6) of medicine. On returning to Pavia in 1857, he began to study cretinism, concluding that it originated from a disease of the thyroid glands.

Lombroso graduated in medicine in 1858 at Pavia University, and in surgery in 1859 at Genoa. He then entered the medical corps in the Piedmontese army, and participated in the Second Italian War for Independence. As he had successfully treated wounds with alcohol compresses, he was asked to re-enlist in the army. He published a prize-winning book on 'wounds by fire-arms', and started anthropological observations of soldiers. While stationed in Calabria, where the army was involved in the fight against banditry, Lombroso remained deeply shocked by the poor standards of hygiene in the region. In 1863, back in Genoa, he worked on homeopathy with Gaiter, a doctor from Verona. In April, the same year, he was transferred to the army hospital in Pavia, where Panizza invited him to start a course on psychiatry. He left the army in 1865.

Lombroso published a series of clinical observations, describing, in particular, two forms of mania found in patients with diphtheria. Suggesting that diphtheria might affect organs other than the larynx, he foresaw the possibility of a vaccine (Baima-Bollone, 1992). From 1868 Lombroso concentrated his attention on pellagra, which at the time was endemic in the maize-growing areas of northern Italy, and a major health problem. He became convinced that the disease originated from a toxin-producing alteration of maize grains. Throughout his academic life Lombroso was embittered by a controversy, which was partly connected with his pellagra theory. This conflict influenced his professional career choices, eventually persuading him to leave Pavia and accept the chair of legal medicine in Turin in 1876 (Bulferetti, 1975). Gina Lombroso-Ferrero's biography passionately describes all the stages of the debate between Lombroso and his opponents. Even though Lombroso never succeeded in identifying the true causes of pellagra his studies and his fights on this matter had a strong social influence. In 1902 Italy passed a law which prohibited the sale or possession of unripe or damaged maize and forbade trading in it. His work persuaded public opinion that the disease could be prevented (De Bernardi, 1984). Lombroso was designated *Cavaliere d'Italia* for his studies on pellagra.

In 1866 Lombroso became full professor of psychiatry in Pavia. In April 1870 he married Nina De Benedetti, the marriage being celebrated with both Jewish and civil rites. In 1871 their first child, Paola Marzola, was born, followed 18 months later by Gina, then Arnaldo in 1874, Leo in 1876 and Ugo in 1877. Leo died of diphtheria at 6, and Arnaldo of typhus fever at 20.

In 1871 Lombroso was invited for a year to direct the psychiatric hospital in Pesaro, where he enjoyed the close collaboration of the public authorities. It was in Pesaro that he conceived the idea of creating psychiatric hospitals for authors of crime who were 'very young or lacking in judgement' ('*di tenera età o tenue discernimento*'). As director of the hospital, he notably improved the environment, organized recreational activities for the patients, and started a mental hospital newspaper. During that period, Lombroso examined more than 400 criminals, collecting their family histories, their biographies, anthropometrical data, physiognomic components and psycho-physical characteristics.

In 1876 after he won the university competition for a chair in legal medicine in Turin he moved there. In 1886 he was appointed prison physician, and in 1890 became professor of psychiatry. In Turin he organized a laboratory of criminal anthropology and started a museum, to which he gave all the material he had collected for years, and where he also kept the skulls that began arriving from all over the world. In 1884 Lombroso had organized an exhibition of skulls, drawings, masks, tattoos, weapons, marked playing-cards and works by the inmates. The exhibition was enlarged and repeated on the occasion of the first Congress of Criminal Anthropology in Rome, in 1885. In 1892 Lombroso enriched his museum with an important collection of anatomical pieces and material evidence, which he took from the Roman prison of Regina Coeli.

In 1878 Lombroso published *Pensiero e meteore* (Thought and Meteors), in which he discussed relationships between meteorological phenomena and criminal activities; later (1886–7) he also took a great interest in hypnotism.

In 1888, after publishing an article in which he criticized belief in spiritualism, Lombroso was invited to Naples to meet the famous medium Eusapia Palatino. He accepted with reluctance. Yet, having attended the spiritualist sessions and observed the unusually disconcerting phenomena accompanying the medium's trances, Lombroso partially changed his mind about spiritualism and began publishing on the topic, mainly on telepathy. Despite the fact that the scientific content of these articles was low, they aroused the interest of the scientific and social community, because Lombroso was known to be utterly against all kinds of irrationality.

In 1897 Lombroso went to Moscow for a congress, and on that occasion wanted to meet Tolstoy. Gina Lombroso-Ferrero describes the encounter as follows:

> The meeting was not very dramatic; the two men did not understand each other. While pertaining to the same generation, both being intuitive, sensitive, artistic and idealist, Lombroso and Tolstoy were morally poles apart. . . . On the other hand Tolstoy, biased against Lombroso and fearful that he might declare him crazy, did not let him penetrate into his soul . . . and Lombroso left . . . convinced that Tolstoy confirmed his theories about genius. (Gina Lombroso-Ferrero, 1921: 351–2)

Lombroso died on the morning of 19 October 1909, of cardio-circulatory complications. At his wish, a few days later his body was submitted to autopsy and his skeleton donated to the criminal anthropology museum.

THE METHODS

Since the work of Goring (1913–72), Lombroso's methods have been strongly criticized. His ideas lie buried amid a multitude of somehow confused data; his sources often remain unreported, and his observations and statistics pile up in a disorganized fashion. According to Gina Lombroso-Ferrero, her father used to keep at hand a copy of *La donna delinquente* for jotting down research data, chance observations, discussions with colleagues and any event he considered interesting. Others (Aschaffenburg, 1913) commented on his lack of critical sense and on the haphazard way in which he collected the material for his works, indiscriminately mixing statistical data, anecdotes and proverbs, inscriptions from prison walls, individual and collective data.

Not until 1871, at the age of 36, did Lombroso become interested in criminality. According to his daughter Gina, it was only when he became director of Pesaro Mental Hospital in that year that he had some of the rooms transformed into laboratories of criminal anthropology. In this environment

> hospital attendants were going back and forth with criminals' skulls and documentation; patients writing down what he dictated, drawing the figures and calculating the statistics. (Lombroso-Ferrero, 1921: 137)

Even so, Lombroso believed firmly in the advantages of quantitative methods. When teaching in Pavia, he wrote:

> Only figures and precision instruments have allowed science to make the enormous advances we admire, advances which have allowed us to dominate nature. Why do we not apply this magnificent method also to psychiatry, for the mental insane is made up not of the spirit alone, but also of the body. For all changes in psychic forces, hence of the spirit, must be accompanied by changes in the body. (quoted by Bulferetti, 1975: 138)

In his comprehensive review of Lombroso's methods, Wolfgang (1972) states: 'In general terms it may be said that Lombroso used both clinical and historical methods in the collection of factual data from which emerged deductively his theories of atavism and degeneration.' Among his criticism of Lombroso's work Wolfgang lists the following drawbacks: the use of an often anecdotal approach and analogies; the developing of philosophical deduction based on unrelated facts; subjectivism in his anatomical-pathological methods; the lack of an acceptable control group of normals to meet statistical demands; the lack of a clear definition of the 'criminal'; and the lack of a clear cut-off number to classify the born criminal.

Nevertheless Wolfgang concludes that, beside the limitations, Lombroso 'manifested imaginative insight, good intuitive judgement, intellectual honesty, awareness of some of his limitations', plus a willingness to use control groups, and a desire to have his theories tested impartially. This evaluation of Lombroso's methods holds true even today.

THE THEORY OF THE GENESIS OF CRIMINAL BEHAVIOUR

Lombroso's thought underwent notable changes from the first to the fifth edition of *L'uomo delinquente*. In the first two editions (1876, 1878), his analysis of criminality is centred basically on a single type: the habitual delinquent, explained with the atavic degeneration theory (the 'born delinquent' according to Ferri's definition). From the third edition onwards (1884) Lombroso uses Ferri's definition. In the third edition he added the hypothesis of 'moral insanity', only to abandon it in the fourth edition (1889) in favour of criminal or 'latent' epilepsy.

In the fourth edition Lombroso perfected his personal typology. Together with the born delinquent, he described other categories of criminals, and extended the concepts related to the exogenous causes of crime (already mentioned in the first edition). The fifth edition had more or less the same structure as the fourth. Publications in various languages of the third volume of the fifth edition as a separate work (*Crime: Its Causes and Remedies*) have created confusion in the sequence of his writings.

As mentioned before, Lombrosian theory is based mainly on three concepts: atavic degeneration (atavism); 'moral insanity'; and criminal or 'latent' epilepsy.

Atavism

Lombroso states that the born criminal is classifiable as 'an anomaly, partially pathologic and partially atavic, a kind of rebirth of the primitive man' (preface to *Criminal Man according to the Classification of Cesare Lombroso*, by Gina Lombroso-Ferrero, 1911: xxii). Lombroso had elaborated this idea in 1872, while examining the skull of Vilella, a 70-year-old brigand from Calabria. Instead of the internal occipital crest, the skull had a smooth-bottomed cavity. In the opening session of the sixth International Congress of Criminal Anthropology (1906), Lombroso stated: 'Looking at that dimple, I suddenly saw, like a wide plain under an infinite horizon, the solution to the problem of delinquency: the delinquent was reproducing, in our times, primitive man's characteristics.'

According to Lombroso, the presence in the criminal of ancestral characteristics – i.e. the phenomenon of reappearance of the ancient in the modern – could explain the existence of analogies between delinquents, uncivilized people, insane persons and prehistoric races. These ancestral characteristics simply demonstrate that for those individuals development stopped at a previous stage of evolution. Lombroso thought his idea had been confirmed when he gave an expert opinion on a 20-year-old peasant, Verzeni. Pellagrous, an idiot and the son of a idiot,

Verzeni was charged with killing many women, with sucking their blood, and with getting pleasure from eating them. According to Lombroso such brutal behaviour could be explained only by atavism, i.e. the return to the primitive, to a subhuman condition.

Thus Lombroso defines the delinquent as a non-progressed creature, a person whose development stopped in the past. Such a person's body structure induces him or her 'naturally' to act in a way which could be acceptable in the age to which their body belongs, but which in the present time inevitably leads to conflict with modern society.

The 'atavistic' theory underwent a progressive evolution in the various editions of *L'uomo delinquente*. In the second edition Lombroso considered suicide as a factor showing the delinquent's lack of instinct of self-preservation, his lack of foresight and his impatience. Moreover, he considered tattoos a clear sign of intrinsic atavism, of a tendency to conform with wild and primitive behaviours. Lombroso then started to analyse criminals' use of slang. In some of these linguistic expressions he again found modalities of primitive man, even if he admitted that peculiar forms of slang were by no means exclusive to criminals.

Besides, Lombroso remained convinced that neither crime nor punishment was peculiar to humans. They were present also in the animal and vegetable kingdom. In the third edition of the *L'uomo delinquente* Lombroso added a chapter on 'Embryology of Crime', giving examples from botany and animal behaviour. The analysis of 'savage' populations made him think, for example, that theft was punished or sexual promiscuity sanctioned when leaders decided to keep the prey or save the best females for themselves. From these 'facts' Lombroso argued that morality and punishment are a consequence of crime.

In the fourth and fifth editions of *L'uomo delinquente* he enlarged the section about 'Embryology of Crime' and the analysis of physical factors. Lombroso thought that prognathism, facial asymmetry, an attitude of face similar to that of the opposite sex, a sparse beard, a deformed nose, thick hair, protruding cheekbones, a squint, a receding forehead and pointed ears, were all criminal traits. These elements may combine to set up various distinct somatic types, each related to a particular form of criminal activity. For example, a thief will have a lively facial mimickry, a small beard, small mobile eyes, thick close eyebrows, a twisted snub nose and a small receding forehead. A rapist will have brilliant eyes, delicate features, swollen lips and scroll ears. A murderer will have wide cheekbones, a sparse beard, well-developed canine teeth, thin lips, a cold and motionless look, a bloody eye, a large, hooked nose, strong jaws and thick frizzy hair. A fraud will be fat and pale, with a long twisted nose and small, downward-looking eyes.

Having discussed the anthropometrical and physiognomic features of criminals, Lombroso writes about the physiology and psychology of the born delinquent, describing his sensitivity to pain and touch, his colour sense, his visual and auditory acuity, his sense of smell and taste, his sensitivity to magnetism and weather conditions, and his strength and agility. Lombroso thought that the left-handedness frequently found in delinquents corresponded to the ambidextrousness found in children and primitives. In the second volume of the fifth edition Lombroso also elaborated a classification of criminals.

Moral madness

Lombroso equated the 'moral insane' with the born delinquent (*L'uomo delinquente*, 4th edn: 631–2). The idea of 'moral madness' was not Lombroso's own. It went back to Thomas Abercromby's definition of moral madness as a state in which all good and right sentiments are suppressed, while intelligence remains unimpaired (Antonini, 1900). Galzigna writes: 'What Prichard has called the idea of moral madness, capable of producing a catastrophe of will, but consistent with preservation of intellectual faculties' was such that it allowed the presence in the author of a crime of 'a damage of will, which makes the author of a crime incapable of acting in full possession of his moral freedom'. It is this concept which originally paved the way for forensic psychiatry (Galzigna, 1988). In 1801 Pinel (*Medico-Philosophical Handbook of Mental Alienation*) developed this thesis. In 1867 (9 years before the first edition of the *L'uomo delinquente*) Maudsley published two works, *The Physiology of Mind* and *The Pathology of Mind*, in which he stated that a lack of moral sense was due to a pathological mental condition. In 1874 he published *Responsibility in Mental Disease*, in which he defined the criminal as 'morally' insane and established the existence of an intermediate area between disease and normality, an area that probably corresponded to delinquency. The basic element of 'moral madness' was the concept that the 'morally insane' individual is incapable of understanding the difference between 'good' and 'evil'. This description corresponded to selfish, lazy and immoral delinquents who were indifferent to imprisonment and had no feelings of guilt for the crimes they had committed. In some ways similar to the atavism theory, it hypothesized the existence of the primitive mentality, a kind of common ground, far from rational thought and scientific mentality (Manuel, 1959; Rossi, 1969). Speaking about this category in the third edition of *L'uomo delinquente* Lombroso admitted that it was not his own idea. He thought that moral insanity was confirmed by the behaviour of children, who also spontaneously act in a violent, obscene and cruel manner, behaviours which are controlled only by fear of punishment, habit and convenience. If these factors are inadequate (because of lack of education) or if the individual is refractory (constitutionally or because of an acquired disease), we will have a 'moral childhood', called 'moral madness'.

From the fourth edition, Lombroso began to elaborate on the theory of moral madness, stating that 'moral madness is a variety of epileptoid delirium', because he found between 'the moral insane and the epileptic a complete parallelism in skull morphology and in physiognomy, and a completely equal proportion in degenerative anomalies (including left-handedness)' (*L'uomo delinquente*: 633).

Development of this parallelism allowed Lombroso to link the 'moral' and physical fields. Later he gradually and progressively gave up the moral madness thesis, in favour of the epileptic thesis, which he thought was based upon more solid and reliable organic evidence (preface to *Criminal Man* . . . by Gina Lombroso-Ferrero, 1911: xxiii).

Epilepsy

Yet Lombroso was not completely convinced of the 'atavic' origin of delinquency, because in some criminals he had observed the presence of 'many characteristics not attributable to atavism, including facial asymmetry, cerebral sclerosis, impulsivity and periodicity of criminal acts' (preface to *Criminal Man* . . . by Gina Lombroso-Ferrero, 1911: xxvi).

The case of the soldier Misdea (who had killed seven officers, wounded another three, then fallen into a sound sleep for 12 hours before waking up completely amnesic) suggested to Lombroso that the factors that could not be explained with atavism were 'morbid characteristics common to epilepsy' (preface to *Criminal Man* . . . by Gina Lombroso-Ferrero, 1911: xxvi; 1889: II, 53 *et seq*.). Gina Lombroso-Ferrero states that the connection between epilepsy and criminality is derived, not identical. 'The born criminal is an epileptic, because he has the physical, psychological and moral characteristics of clear epilepsy. . . . Nevertheless he has other peculiar characteristics, in particular a desire to hurt somebody, a feeling unknown to normal epileptics' (Gina Lombroso-Ferrero, 1911: 69–70).

The main reason why Lombroso looked for another causal factor for criminal behaviour was not the existence of crimes that could not be explained with the atavistic hypothesis, but the fact that many somatic and behavioural traits of the 'born criminal' could not be explained with the concept of regression. Accepting the 'epileptic' hypothesis, therefore, means necessarily accepting the concept of atavism.

When Lombroso talked of epilepsy, he did not mean the clinical entity known as such at the time, but a 'latent' or 'criminal' form of epilepsy. According to Lombroso, the symptoms in subjects suffering from that kind of epilepsy are similar to those in subjects suffering from overt epilepsy. But, unlike overt epileptics, criminal epileptics do not present tonic-clonic seizures (convulsions). In Lombroso's pattern, 'convulsions' are substituted by uncontrollable explosions of rage and violence (in the words of Gina Lombroso-Ferrero: 'Sometimes the attack manifests itself only with paroxysms of rage or with primitive impulses'; 1911: 58–9). Lombroso was writing before the invention of EEG, at a time when knowledge of epileptic syndromes was scarce. Because he did not recognize convulsions as a diagnostic criterion for the presence of epilepsy,

Lombroso automatically renounced the sole diagnostic element available at that time. He used the term 'epilepsy' in a metaphorical way, but attributed to this metaphor moral values (for example, the urge to hurt somebody). Besides, epistemologically it is impossible to falsify the basic reasoning in Lombroso's statement, that evidence of 'latent' epilepsy is the crime itself, with its exceptional brutality and monstrosity.

ENVIRONMENTAL FACTORS AND FEMALE CRIMINALITY

Although Lombroso's interest centred on 'organic' constitutional aspects, his theory is not based only on biological factors. In the first edition of *L'uomo delinquente* he indicates that the environment, together with poverty, cost of food, alcoholism, criminal activity of gangs, and corruption, are arousing factors of crime. In the second edition he deepens his analysis of environmental factors to encompass direct and indirect hereditary factors, as well as meteorological and climatic variables. Too much food would increase sexual stimuli, while alcohol and drugs would increase crimes against the person, indecent behaviour and rebellion. Sex and age influence the genesis of crime (crime is more frequent in men, especially men aged between 20 and 30 years), while education and profession affect the type of crime.

In Lombroso's opinion poverty contributes to crime because it promotes degenerative diseases. These incite men to be criminal because they put them in a condition where it is easier to commit crimes and not be punished. Prison detention also promotes crime, because it increases the chance of meeting other criminals.

In the third volume of the fifth edition, Lombroso reviews the environmental causes of crime. Among possible methods of crime prevention he suggests avoiding living in huge urban agglomerates, a better distribution of wealth and elimination of torture. He criticizes exacerbation of punishments for preventive purposes, deeming 'real preventive measures' more suitable. He exhorts banks to exercise their functions and says that the privileges of the political class have to be eliminated. Lombroso foresees a better selection of public officers and a more efficient fight against corruption. For the prevention of alcoholism he outlines a social programme envisaging the establishment of special deintoxication centres. He underlines the importance of the family in the prevention of criminality. Rather than serving as a corrective, the detention of minors encourages them to emulate the criminal behaviours of their elders. Lombroso supports individual treatment in prisons, and criticizes the isolation regimen. Nevertheless, he thinks that correction of an inmate in a prison environment is an artificial measure that will never allow the individual to be amended.

In the same volume Lombroso makes suggestions for juridical reform. In particular, he stresses the paramount importance of assessing the individual's intention at the moment of the criminal act, believing that a punishment based on the severity of the lesions is wholly inappropriate. Lombroso supports indeterminate detention, especially for offenders evaluated as mentally insane; criticizes the role of the judges, because of their scarce knowledge of criminology; suggests possible alternatives to detention; believes that fines should be proportionate to the condemned person's property; and thinks it appropriate to introduce probation. According to Lombroso, abortion and adultery are not to be considered crimes.

Lombroso verifies that few delinquent stigmas are present in women. In women, prostitution is the equivalent of crime and degeneration, an opinion already given by Locatelli (Baima-Bollone, 1992: 138). The subject will be treated more profoundly in Ferrero's work *La donna delinquente*. Born delinquents and prostitutes would have in common

> the lack of moral sense; the same 'hard heart'; the same early taste for evil; the same indifference to social shame, which makes them bear their condition; the same lack of foresight, the same mobility, the same laziness; the same taste for easy pleasures, for orgy, for alcohol; and the same vanity. Prostitution is merely the female aspect of criminality. Prostitution and criminality resemble one another so closely that their extremes merge. Hence the frequent association of prostitution with slight crimes such as theft, blackmail, and wounding. Psychologically the prostitute is a criminal: if she does not commit crimes it is because her physical weakness, her poor intelligence, the ease with which she can obtain anything she wants . . . exempt her . . . because criminal women are always extraordinarily abnormal, and, more than men, show an extreme malice, or male characteristics (also biological). (*La donna delinquente*, 1883: 467–70)

The third volume includes a discussion about political crime, which we will review later.

CRIMINAL TYPOLOGY AND POLITICAL CRIME

In Wolfgang's words, 'Lombroso became convinced that rather than being a variation from the norm the criminal was practically a special species, a subspecies of man, having distinct physical and mental characteristics' (1972: 250). Lombroso concluded that although the epileptic criminal, the 'insane criminal' and the born criminal were distinct types, they had a common epileptoid base. This allows the various criminal types to be grouped into anthropological typologies (see above).

Later Lombroso also defined the 'occasional delinquent', who has no connections with atavism or epilepsy. In this category he included pseudocriminals, unintentional criminals, those who become criminals to protect their person, their honour, or their family, and who do not upset community morals, and criminaloids, those who become criminals for environmental reasons or opportunities. The latter have a less strong organic tendency to criminality than born criminals, but long periods of detention may make them look like born criminals (apart from minor somatic stigmata).

A third group of occasional delinquents is that of habitual criminals, born with no significant physical predisposition, but who became delinquents because their poor education made them revert to primitive tendencies. In this latter group would belong members of criminal organizations (such as the Mafia).

Another group of criminals without a common epileptic base are delinquents who commit violent crimes not because of an organic predisposition, but because of an irresistible strength which, according to Lombroso, originates from 'anger, platonic or filial love, offended honour, which are usually generous and often sublime passions'. This category also includes political criminals, a group with a high rate of suicide, indicative of an altered function of mind.

Political criminals always posed a problem for Lombroso (Ferracuti and Cortellessa, 1988; Di Re, 1982). The topic is deeply discussed in his book *Gli Anarchici*. According to Lombroso, political delinquents 'are men who embrace ideas of progress'. Political delinquents include geniuses, the insane, saints and criminals. In this work Lombroso states the principle that the will of the majority decides whether a fact is qualified as criminal. 'Indeed, the first condition for an action to be considered antisocial, i.e. a crime, is that it is accomplished by a minority. When the majority approves it, it will become a normal act.'

Lombroso quotes St Thomas to justify 'insurrection against a power which does not act for the common good', but qualifies anarchists as criminals, trying to fit together the notion of deviance with the notion of violation of criminal law. Nevertheless, Lombroso still looks for physical stigmata in anarchists. Yet on other occasions he calls them 'beautiful'. Lombroso classifies anarchists as criminals because of their passion, 'the antithesis of born criminals'. He presents anarchy as a 'regression' through atavism. In the anarchists' behaviour, however, Lombroso sees a notable demand for justice. He thinks that a moderate socialism might prevent their behaviour, rather than increasing it as police repression does. Political crime would be the expression of the conflict with misoneism, a term used to indicate a sentiment of hatred of novelty and of innovations in social, political, cultural and scientific spheres (Ferrarotti, 1972). Lombroso shows the same ambiguous position in assessing Passanante, an anarchist who made an attempt on the life of King Umberto I in 1878. Lombroso thought he had regressive characteristics, his real purpose in attempting the king's life being to commit homicide-suicide. In addition he also presented characteristics which put him in the criminaloid (*mattoidi*) category. Instead, the expert opinion ordered at the time judged Passanante sound of mind (Ferracuti and Cortellessa, 1988).

Lombroso thought that the most effective means to prevent political crime was the presence of democratic systems, an independent magistracy and a healthy economic system.

THE SCHOOL OF PENAL LAW

The Positive School of Criminal Anthropology published two journals, *La Rivista di Filosofia Scientifica* and the *Archivio di Psichiatria, Scienze Penali e Antropologia Criminale*. The first, published between 1881 and 1891, was edited by Morselli. Its aim was 'to work for the victory of the experimental method and for the final connection of philosophy and science in Italy'. This journal produced the best of what positivist culture had to offer in Italy, at the same time trying to generalize philosophy connected with science. When founded by Lombroso, Ferri and Garofalo in 1880 the 'Archives of Psychiatry, Penal Sciences and Criminal Anthropology' announced the following programme:

> Few scholars will deny that psychiatry and criminal sciences are bound with everlasting ties. But how tight those ties are is shown by the fact that the psychiatric publications are devoting more and more of their space to criminality, and penal and penitentiary publications are devoting more of their space to mental alienation. . . . We thought it was time to pick up the fruits of that union in a journal which encompasses all the journals of psychiatry and forensic medicine, penitentiary and penal disciplines which honour our country.

Both journals accepted articles written by thinkers of a completely contrary ideology.

The School of Criminal Anthropology clearly shows the desire to unify scientific knowledge and to make political use of research findings in order to promote legislation governing the renewal of psychiatric hospitals and penitentiaries, and to increase awareness of the serious hygienic and sanitary conditions in Italy. As we have seen, Lombroso called for many kinds of social, penitentiary and judicial reform. All these ideas were taken up again and enlarged on by his scholars, in particular Ferri (Sellin, 1972) and Garofalo (Allen, 1972). Whereas Garofalo admitted that a pure 'psychic' criminal, without somatic characteristics, might exist, Ferri in his *Sociologia Criminale* admitted that crime encompassed a multiplicity of causal factors. He thus elaborated the concept of 'penal substitutes', i.e. social conditions and legislative provisions aimed to reduce crime-inducing factors. Ferri firmly denied the existence of free will, and prepared a completely positivist plan for penal code reforms. Like Compte, Ferri maintained sociology's supremacy, stating that penal law is a 'branch of sociology'.

According to the Positive School, society does not have the right to punish. It merely finds it necessary to punish, in order to defend itself from that peculiar disease known as crime and to prevent further crimes. Hence penality is then not a punishment but a kind of social defence, and the sole object of penal law is prevention. According to Lombroso, criminal trial must be a scientific assessment. The ideology of the Positive School was partially incorporated in the 1931 penal code still in force today in Italy (Fornari and Ferracuti, 1995; Ferracuti and Marasco, 1994).

CONCLUSIONS

From the history of ideas, errors cannot be excluded. So despite the fact that Lombroso's work is unquestionably full of methodological and conceptual errors, he cannot be ignored. Sometimes he can even be defined as racist (*L'uomo bianco e l'uomo di colore*, 1871), and his work contributed to the development of eugenics (Forshaw and Rollin, 1990).

Lombroso's work remains as a testimony of the links between the physical and the psychic personality of man. Because his theory is principally a biological one that asserts the link between certain physical features and peculiar behaviours, it should be verified on a biological level. While Lombroso was not the first to formulate the conception of crime as the expression of the personality and nature of the criminal – a subject already discussed in France at the beginning of the nineteenth century (Galzigna, 1984) – Lombroso helped to spread this idea. Throughout the western world, also at a legislative level, Lombroso and the Positive School promoted a vision of crime which was not linked only to moral causes and violations of legal norms. To Lombroso's work and to the Positive School of Criminology we owe the willingness of modern legislation 'to understand' the criminal and to try to exempt the 'irresponsible' and the mentally ill from sanctions. As underlined by Wolfgang (1972), this perspective is present whenever research studies distinguish between delinquent and non-delinquent. Obviously today nobody measures in detail hundreds of skulls, or analyses tattoos for taxonomic purposes. Yet the multifactorial conceptualization of peculiar patterns of behaviour – including the search for a previous conduct disorder possibly related to an attentional-neurological dysfunction in the antisocial personality – is a Lombrosian formulation of causality in forensic psychiatry. The value of biotypological studies has been reshuffled. But modern publications still abound with papers searching for biochemical (Shalling, 1993; Virkkunen and Linnoila, 1993), hereditary (Brennan *et al.*, 1993), neurologic (Wong *et al.*, 1994), or, in general, organic (Fishbein, 1990; Blake *et al.*, 1995) factors, to explain the greater frequency of aggressive behaviours in selected populations. Lombroso is still quoted in studies on the influence of weather changes on aggressive behaviour (Anderson *et al.*, 1995), and the connection of weather and homicide is the subject of contemporary research (Cheatwood, 1995).

That Lombroso did not have an exclusively organicistic interest, should be evident from the number of 'social' concepts in use today that were originally expressed in his works. In assessing the influence of social factors on Lombroso, Kurella (1910, quoted by Wolfgang) wrote: 'It became necessary for him to prove . . . that nature makes the criminal, but that society provides the condition in which the criminal commits crimes.'

What Sellin stated in 1937 is still valid: 'Any scholar who succeeds in driving hundreds of fellow students to search for the truth, and whose ideas after half a century possess vitality, merits an honourable place in the history of thought.' And Wolfgang (1972) expressed the opinion that 'Lombroso has illuminated the scientific study of criminal behaviour with many provocative ideas, and deserved a place of honour in his own field'.

To these opinions we would like to add a reflection on certain aspects of Lombroso's thought that maintain a speculative broadmindedness that is still up-to-date. Like Freud's theory, Lombroso's theory embodies a strict materialism, a determinism, an atheism, an awareness both of the lack of responsibility in the abnormal individual and of the possibility of a therapy.

Despite proposals advocating empiricism the deterministic doctrine base and its implications still prevail in criminology (Agnew, 1995). From a cultural point of view, it is interesting to note that psychoanalytical determinism has obtained wide consensus in heterogeneous environments, while criminal anthropology has been fought especially for its deterministic view. According to Pirella (1971) Lombrosian ideology is an attempt 'to deny hope, to kill with the law'.

Moreover Lombroso, like Freud, acknowledged the value of the concept of 'regression' within Darwin's optimistic vision; although Lombroso denied it, his thought was influenced by Darwinism. The 'atavism' which Freud abandoned, from the Lombrosian standpoint is to be considered as a phenomenon of natural protection from certain traumatizing factors (such as alcohol, climate, heredity and meteors), and, as Lombroso said, a 'return to the ancient'. Besides, at that time the atavistic theory did not apply exclusively to criminals (Gelb, 1995). Even his final comprehensive hypothesis of epilepsy, which permitted Lombroso to add a pathological factor to atavic degeneration and to 'explain' abnormal phenomena, was interpreted by Lombroso in a post-Freudian direction. Indeed, by epilepsy Lombroso meant only a series of psychic unconscious activities. The term served to explain a condition of greater 'cerebral irritability', but which could express itself in various ways, depending on constitution, on intelligence and on a multitude of other factors.

As has been observed, 'Lombroso broadened the biological, social and cultural role of the epileptic by accepting Moreau de Tours' transformation of the ancient doctrine of the great melanconic. . . . Most important perhaps was the alleged analogy between the epileptic attack and the moment of inspiration which the genius experienced' (Temkin, 1971: 366–7). In this way Lombroso established a connection not only between epilepsy and criminal behaviour, but also between epilepsy and the idea of genius itself. The concept spread in literature – for example, in Zola's famous novel *The Human Beast* (1890) – and was taken up again also by Nietzsche (Temkin, 1971).

Generally, historiography presents Lombroso as a follower of the positivism of the nineteenth century, a man linked to a linear conception of progress, based on the concept that scientific advancement is indissolubly linked to a moral and social progress. This progress is the result of a fight, a constituent element of progress itself. The concept of 'degeneration' reached its height in Lombroso, who applied it to so broad a category of persons as delinquents. In Lombroso, as in Maudsley, Morel, Scighele, Tarde and Taine, whom Lombroso defined as his real inspirer (Mongardini, 1985), the potential degeneration of European society became a biological, empirically demonstrable fact (Pick, 1989). The development of mass psychology permeates Lombroso's ideology (Van Ginneken, 1991).

This should be enough for us to reconsider a less linear and oversimplified reading of Lombroso's thought. For his criminological theses, discredited and opposed by generations of scholars, have often been reduced to a naive and sometimes discriminatory vision of the 'different'.

Yet it is just because of this intrinsic ambiguity, because Lombroso conceives the idea of a 'moral' advancement of man in spite of his biological 'stigmata', that his work continues to offer us a source of meditation. Lombroso's work continually reminds us that the choice between irrational and rational behaviour (and thought) will never be definitively completed in our time. Nor could it ever be, because behaviour and thought are intrinsically linked with human nature. Perhaps the optimism of the modern positivists (Gottfredson and Hirshi, 1987) cannot be fully justified.

Stefano Ferracuti, MD, Dipartimento di Scienze Psichiatriche e Medicina Psicologica, Università 'La Sapienza', Piazzale Aldo Moro 5, 00185 Rome, Italy

REFERENCES

Abbagnano, N. (1993) 'Il positivismo evoluzionistico'. In *Storia della Filosofia*, Vol. 3. Turin: UTET, pp. 362–7.

Agnew, R. (1995) 'Determinism, Indeterminism, and Crime: an Empirical Evaluation'. *Criminology*, 33: 83–109.

Allen, F. A. (1972) 'Raffaele Garofalo'. In Mannheim, H. (ed.) *Pioneers in Criminology*. Montclair NJ: Patterson Smith, 1972, pp. 318–40.

Anderson, C. A., Deuser, W. E. and DeNeve, K. M. (1995) 'Hot Temperatures, Hostile Affect, Hostile Cognition, and Arousal: Test of a General Model of Affective Aggression'. *Personality and Social Psychology Bulletin*, 21: 434–48.

Antonini, G. (1900) *I precursori di Cesare Lombroso*. Turin: Fratelli Bocca.

Aschaffenburg, G. (1913) *Crime and its Repression*. New York: Little, Brown.

Baima Bollone, P. G. (1992) *Cesare Lombroso ovvero il principio dell'irresponsabilità*. Turin: Società Editrice Internazionale.

Blake, P. Y., Pincus, J. H. and Buckner, C. (1995) 'Neurologic Abnormalities in Murderers'. *Neurology*, 45: 1641–7.

Brennan, P. A., Mednick, B. R. and Mednick, S. A. (1993) 'Parental Psychopathology, Congenital Factors, and Violence'. In Hodgins, S. (ed.) *Mental Disorder and Crime*. Newbury Park: Sage, pp. 244–62.

Bulferetti, L. (1975) *Cesare Lombroso*. Turin: UTET.

Cheatwood, D. (1995) 'The Effects of Weather on Homicide'. *Journal of Quantitative Criminology*, 11: 51–70.

Dabbs, J. M., Carr, T. S., Frady, R. L. and Riad, J. K. (1995) 'Testosterone, Crime, and Misbehaviour among 692 Male Prison Inmates'. *Personality and Individual Differences*, 18: 627–33.

De Bernardi, A. (1984) 'Pellagra e scienza medica: la curabilità impossibile'. In Della Peruta, F. (ed.) *Storia di Italia. Annali 7. Malattia e medicina*. Turin: Einaudi.

Di Re, M. (1982) 'Lombroso rivisitato: lo strano problema degli anarchici'. *L'Indice Penale*, 3: 669–75.

Ferracuti, F. and Cortellessa, D. (1988) preface to Parente, Antonio, *Giovanni Passanante. Anarchico o Mattoide?* Rome: Bulzoni, pp. 9–17.

Ferracuti, S. and Marasco, M. (1994) 'The Criminal Responsibility of Drug and Alcohol Abusers'. *Journal of Drug Issues*, 24: 679–86.

Ferrarotti, F. (1972) preface to Lombroso, Cesare, *Gli Anarchici*. Rome: Napoleone Editore, pp. 9–15.

Fishbein, D. (1990) 'Biological Perspectives in Criminology'. *Criminology*, 28: 27–72.

Fornari, U. and Ferracuti, S. (1995) 'Special Judicial Hospitals in Italy and the Shortcomings of the Mental Health Law'. *Journal of Forensic Psychiatry*, 6: 381–92.

Forshaw, D. and Rollin, H. (1990) 'The History of Forensic Psychiatry in England'. In Bluglass, R. and Bowden, P. (eds) *Principles and Practice of Forensic Psychiatry*. Edinburgh: Churchill Livingstone, pp. 61–102.

Galzigna, M. (1984) preface to the reprint of Georget, E. J., *Il Crimine e la Colpa*. Venice: Marsilio. A translation of (1826) *Discussion médico-légale sur la folie ou aliénation mentale* . . . Paris: Chez Migneret.

Galzigna, M. (1988) *La malattia morale. Alle origini della psichiatria moderna*. Venice: Marsilio, pp. 219–44.

Gelb, S. A. (1995) 'The Beast in Man: Degenerationism and Mental Retardation, 1900–1920'. *Mental Retardation*, 33: 1–9.

Goring, C. (1972[1913]) *The English Convict: A Statistical Study*, reprint. Montclair, NJ: Patterson Smith.

Gottfredson, M. R. and Hirshi, T. (1987) 'The Positive Tradition'. In Gottfredson, M. R. and Hirshi, T. (eds) *Positive Criminology*. Newbury Park: Sage, pp. 9–23.

Grieco, A. (1993) 'Immagine e narrazione', preface to the reprint of Cardano, Gerolamo, *Sogni*. Padua: Marsilio.

Grieco, A. and Mancia, M. (1989) preface to the reprint of Cardano, Gerolamo, *Sul Sogno e sul Sognare*. Padua: Marsilio.

Klibansky, R., Panowsky, E. and Saxl, F. (1983) *Saturno e la melanconia. Studi di storia della filosofia naturale, religione ed arte*. Turin: Einaudi. Translated as *Saturn and Melancholy. Studies in the History of Natural Philosophy, Religion and Art*. London: Thomas Nelson.

Kurella, H. (1910) *Cesare Lombroso: A Modern Man of Science*. New York: Rebman.

Lombroso-Ferrero, Gina (1911) *Criminal Man According to the Classification of Cesare Lombroso*. Preface by C. Lombroso. Reprinted (1972) Montclair, NJ: Patterson Smith.

Lombroso-Ferrero, Gina (1921) *Cesare Lombroso. Storia della vita e delle opere*, 2nd edn. Bologna: Zanichelli.

Manuel, F. (1959) *The Eighteenth Century Confronts the Gods*. Cambridge, MA: Harvard University Press.

Maudsley, H. (1867a) *The Physiology of Mind*. London: Macmillan.

Maudsley, H. (1867b) *The Pathology of Mind*. London: Macmillan.

Maudsley, H. (1874) *Responsibility in Mental Disease*. London: Macmillan.

Mongardini, C. (1985) *Storia e sociologia di H. Taine*. Milan: Giuffré.

Mora, G. (1964) 'One Hundred Years from Lombroso's First Essay "Genius and Insanity"'. *American Journal of Psychiatry*, 121: 562–71.

Morselli, E. (1926a) *La Psicanalisi*. Vol. I, *La Dottrina*. Turin: Fratelli Bocca.

Morselli, E. (1926b) *La Psicanalisi*. Vol. II, *La Pratica*. Turin: Fratelli Bocca.

Pick, D. (1989) *Faces of Degeneration. A European Disorder 1848–1918*. Cambridge: Cambridge University Press.

Pirella, A. (1971) preface to Lombroso, Cesare, *L'uomo di genio*. Rome: Napoleone Editore, p. xi.

Rossi, P. (1969) *Le sterminate antichità: Studi vichiani*. Pisa: Nisi Lischi, pp. 81–164.

Sellin, T. (1937) 'The Lombrosan Myth in Criminology'. *American Journal of Sociology*, 42: 897–9.

Sellin, T. (1972) 'Enrico Ferri'. In Mannheim, H. (ed.) *Pioneers in Criminology*. Montclair, NJ: Patterson Smith, pp. 361–84.

Shalling, D. (1993) 'Neurochemical Correlates of Personality, Impulsivity, and Disinhibitory Suicidality'. In Hodgins, S. (ed.) *Mental Disorder and Crime*. Newbury Park: Sage, pp. 208–26.

Temkin, O. (1971) *The Falling Sickness. An History of Epilepsy from the Greeks to the Beginning of Modern Neurology*, 2nd edn. Baltimore, MA: Johns Hopkins University Press.

Van Ginneken, J. (1991) *Folla, psicologia e politica*. Rome: Pieraldo Editore.

Virkkunen, M. and Linnoila, M. (1993) 'Serotonin in Personality Disorders with Habitual Violence and Impulsivity'. In Hodgins, S. (ed.) *Mental Disorder and Crime*. Newbury Park: Sage, pp. 227–43.

Wolfgang, M. E. (1972) 'Cesare Lombroso'. In Mannheim, H. (ed.) *Pioneers in Criminology*. Montclair, NJ: Patterson Smith, pp. 232–91.

Wong, M. T. H., Lumsden, J., Fenton, G. W. and Fenwick, P. B. (1984) 'Electroencephalography, Computed Tomography and Violence Ratings of Male Patients in a Maximum Security Mental Hospital'. *Acta Psychiatrica Scandinavica*, 90: 97–101.

BIBLIOGRAPHY

A bibliography of Lombroso with a curriculum vitae is included at the end of Gina Lombroso's book. Lombroso was a prolific writer, his name appearing on over 1,000 publications in various languages.

L'uomo bianco e l'uomo di colore. Padua: Sacchetto, 1871.

Pensiero e meteore. Milan: Fratelli Dumolard, 1878.

Palimsesti dal carcere. Raccolta unicamente destinata ad uomini di scienza. Turin: Fratelli Bocca, 1888.

(with L. Laschi) *Il delitto politico e le rivoluzioni*. Turin: Fratelli Bocca, 1890.

Gli anarchici. Reprinted with a new introduction by Franco Ferracuti. Millwood, NY: Kraus. Original edition Turin: Fratelli Bocca, 1895.

Genio e follia, 4th edn. Turin: Fratelli Bocca, 1882. A translation published as *The Man of Genius*. London: Walter Scott, 1891.

Nuovi studi sul genio. Da Colombo a Manzoni. Milan: Remo Sandron, 1902.

(with G. Ferrero) *La donna delinquente. La prostituta e la donna normale*. Turin: Fratelli Bocca, 1903 [1893]. A translation published as *The Female Offender*. London: Fisher Unwin, 1895.

L'uomo delinquente, studiato in rapporto all'antropologia, alla medicina legale e alle discipline carcerarie, 1st edn. Milan: Hoepli, 1876.

L'uomo delinquente, studiato in rapporto all'antropologia, alla medicina legale e alle discipline carcerarie, 2nd edn. Turin: Fratelli Bocca, 1878.

L'uomo delinquente in rapporto all'antropologia, alla giurisprudenza ed alle discipline carcerarie. Delinquente nato e pazzo morale, 3rd edn. Turin: Fratelli Bocca, 1884.

L'uomo delinquente. Delinquente nato e pazzo morale, 4th edn. Vol. I. Turin: Fratelli Bocca, 1889.

L'uomo delinquente. Delinquente epilettico, d'impeto, pazzo, criminaloide, 4th edn. Vol. II. Turin: Fratelli Bocca, 1889.

L'uomo delinquente, 5th edn. Vol. I. Turin: Fratelli Bocca, 1896.

L'uomo delinquente, 5th edn. Vol. II. Turin: Fratelli Bocca, 1896.

L'uomo delinquente, 5th edn. Vol. III, with an atlas. Turin: Fratelli Bocca, 1897. A translation published as *Crime: Its Causes and Remedies*. Boston, MA: Little, Brown, 1913. Reprinted Montclair, NJ: Patterson Smith, 1968.

L'uomo delinquente in rapporto all'antropologia, alla giurisprudenza ed alle discipline carcerarie, ed. Gina Lombroso sull'ultima edizione 1897–1900. Turin: Fratelli Bocca, 1924.

Delitti vecchi e delitti nuovi. Turin: Fratelli Bocca, 1902.

The Spiritualism. Boston, MA: Little, Brown, 1914.

Delitto, Genio, Follia. Selected Readings, ed. D. Frigessi, F. Giacanelli and L. Mangoni. Turin: Boringhieri, 1995.

[2]

John Stuart Mill on the Liberty of the Mentally Ill: A Historical Note

BY JOHN MONAHAN, PH.D.

The author discusses the quote from Mill's On Liberty *that is often cited by libertarians in opposition to involuntary commitment of the mentally ill. This quote has been taken out of context; other statements in the document indicate that Mill excluded from his libertarian credo those "without the ordinary amount of understanding," i.e., those people who would now be considered mentally ill.*

IN THE continuing debate on the involuntary commitment of persons diagnosed as mentally ill and believed to be suicidal, gravely disabled, or otherwise a danger to themselves, one passage has been quoted repeatedly by libertarians to provide historical and philosophical support for their position. It is the credo of John Stuart Mill in *On Liberty*:

> the only purpose for which power can be rightfully exercised over any member of a civilized community, against his will, is to prevent harm to others. His own good, either physical or moral, is not a sufficient warrant. He cannot rightfully be compelled to do or forbear because it will be better for him to do so, because it will make him happier, because, in the opinions of others, to do so would be wise, or even right. (1, p. 22)

This eloquent statement of the libertarian tradition in its most pure and classic form is cited in virtually every legal, psychiatric, and psychological treatise on the right of the mentally ill to decline intervention that others believe would benefit them (e.g., references 2–4). The statement is interpreted as indicating that to be a true libertarian, one must eschew all involuntary treatment of the mentally ill that is justified by a *parens patriae* concern for their welfare.

The purpose of this communication is to suggest that a fuller reading of Mill's work would lead to the contrary conclusion that he specifically excluded those who would now be called "mentally ill" from the scope of his argument. One is, of course, free to hold that Mill was in error when he declined to apply his libertarian thesis to the mentally ill, much as we today would object to his exclusion of "barbarians" (see below). Yet it should be recognized that Mill himself found nothing inconsistent in applying libertarianism only to those lacking a mental disorder. Quoting Mill in support of the abolition of civil commitment is done out of context and has the effect of distorting the historical record.

In the paragraph following the one typically cited, Mill notes the first exception to his libertarian thesis that only harm involving others is subject to state action:

> It is, perhaps, hardly necessary to say that this doctrine is meant to apply only to human beings *in the maturity of their faculties*. We are not speaking of children, or of young persons below the age which the law may fix as that of manhood or womanhood. Those who are still *in a state to require being taken care of by others* must be protected against their own actions as well as against external injury. (1, p. 22, emphasis added here and in following quotes).

In its most narrow reading, this exemption applies only to children, but it may also be read as applying to others who lack "the maturity of their faculties" and are "in a state to require being taken care of by others." That Mill intended the broader reading can be judged from his next sentences, which constitute a startling example of the colonial racism of the mid-nineteenth century:

> For the same reason, we may leave out of consideration those backward states of society in which the race itself may be considered in its nonage. . . . Despotism is a legitimate mode of government in dealing with barbarians, provided the end be their improvement, and the means justified by actually effecting that end. Liberty, as a principle, has no application to any state of things anterior to the time when mankind have become *capable of being improved by free and equal discussion*. Until then, there is nothing for them but implicit obedience to an Akbar or a Charlemagne, if they are so fortunate as to find one. (1, p. 23)

Later in *On Liberty*, Mill makes the exemption of individuals who would now be regarded as mentally ill more explicit.

> As soon as any part of a person's conduct affects prejudicially the interest of others, society has jurisdiction

When this paper was written, Dr. Monahan was a Fellow in Law and Psychology at Harvard Law School. He is now Assistant Professor, Program in Social Ecology and Department of Psychiatry and Human Behavior, University of California, Irvine, Calif. 92717.

The author wishes to thank Louis McGarry for suggesting the topic and Stephen Morse, John Robson, and Michael Hindus for their comments.

over it, and the question whether the general welfare will or will not be promoted by interfering with it, becomes open to discussion. But there is no room for entertaining any such question when a person's conduct affects the interests of no person's conduct besides himself, or needs not affect them unless they like (all persons concerned being of full age, and *the ordinary amount of understanding*). (1, p. 135)

Finally, toward the end of his treatise, Mill directly addressed the issue of persons who engage in behavior "dangerous to self," clearly holding that the psychologically disordered constitute an exception to his general rule of nonintervention:

If either a public officer or anyone else saw a person attempting to cross a bridge which had been ascertained to be unsafe, and there was no time to warn him of his danger, they might seize him and turn him back, without any real infringement of his liberty; for liberty consists of doing what one desires, and he does not desire to fall into the river. Nevertheless, when there is not a certainty, but only a danger of mischief, no one but the person himself can judge of the sufficiency of the motive which may prompt him to incur the risk; in this case, therefore, (unless he is a child, *or delirious or in some state of excitement or absorption incompatible with the full use of the reflecting faculty*), he ought, I conceive, to be only warned of the danger; not forcibly prevented from exposing himself to it. (1, p. 172)

The full record, therefore, indicates that Mill was quite aware of limits to his libertarian philosophy. He chose to exclude from its range of application those not "in the maturity of their faculties," those "in a state to require being taken care of by others," those without "the ordinary amount of understanding," those not "capable of being improved by free and equal discussion," and those whose behavior was "incompatible with the full use of the reflecting faculty"—in short, those who today would be regarded as mentally ill. Use of the partial citation to the contrary is historically inaccurate.

REFERENCES

1. Mill JS: On Liberty, 2nd ed. London, Parker, 1859
2. Kittrie N: The Right To Be Different: Deviance and Enforced Therapy. Baltimore, Johns Hopkins University Press, 1971
3. Miller K: Managing Madness: the Case Against Civil Commitment. New York, Free Press, 1976
4. Szasz T: Law, Liberty, and Psychiatry. New York, Macmillan Publishing Co., 1963

[3]

Brit. J. Psychiat. (1977), **130**, 317–29

Review Article

Criminal Behaviour and Mental Disorder

By JOHN GUNN

The main problem in discussing any relationship between criminal behaviour and mental disorder is that the two concepts are largely unrelated. We are all aware that the very existence of mental illness has been challenged (Szasz, 1962) and that definitions are extremely difficult to formulate (see e.g. Lewis, 1953 and Clare, 1976). Yet most of us believe that somewhere in the confusion there is a biological reality of mental disorder, and that this reality is a complex mixture of diverse conditions, some organic, some functional, some inherited, some learned, some acquired, some curable, others unremitting. It would be surprising if such a mélange had a clear-cut relationship with any social parameter, specially one which is arbitrarily determined by legislation. Criminal behaviour is simply the breaking of the criminal laws in force at any particular time. Crimes embrace everything from murder and treason to riding a bicycle without lights. Over 60 per cent of all crimes dealt with by British courts concern motoring, and almost 6 per cent concern drunkenness. As attitudes change so do laws; suicide attempts were criminal offences until recently in the United Kingdom, male homosexual behaviour was once illegal under all circumstances.

Most discussions on the mentally abnormal offender concentrate on either those who are resident in hospitals or prisons, or on serious offenders, especially those who are violent or sexually deviant. In view of the complexities mentioned above, this selectivity is understandable, but it should always be remembered that it excludes the majority of the mentally disordered and the majority of criminals.

Prison Populations

Prisons are institutions. This truism has to be emphasized, because although prisons are part of the penal system they also form part of the institutional network of most countries, and their population contains a disproportionate number of people in need of chronic institutional care (Gunn, 1974a). Penrose is often quoted as proving that mental hospital and prison populations are inversely related. He did not quite demonstrate that (Penrose, 1939); he simply showed that, before the Second World War in Europe, countries with a large prison population had a small mental hospital population and *vice versa*. To be exact, he found that the homicide rate, the number of prisoners, the birth rate, the suicide rate, and the general death rate were all negatively correlated with the level of mental hospitalization. He concluded that attention to mental health may help to prevent the occurrence of serious crimes, particularly homicide. In Britain 'Penrose's Law' is often cited because as mental hospital populations have fallen since the Second World War so prison populations have risen sharply.

There are surprisingly few systematic studies of the health of British prison populations, but those that have been carried out all indicate high levels of mental disorder. Rarely is the reason for this discussed. It could be due to an association between serious crime and mental disorder. More likely, as Penrose implied, many psychiatric patients and potential psychiatric patients are diverted from one institutional system to another. There could also be an element of prison conditions generating their own psychopathology. A long prison sentence is very debilitating, and few people can take any form of imprisonment with total equanimity.

In 1963 Professor Gibbens published his survey of 200 borstal lads aged 17–21 years. Although all but one psychotic lad had been screened out before sentencing, Gibbens regarded 27 per cent of the population as requiring psychiatric treatment. At about the same time, West (1963) examined 100 long-term prisoners and found 2 of them to be epileptic, 10 to be or to have been psychotic and a further 9 to have a history of previous hospitalization. More recently my colleagues and I also examined a consecutive cohort of long-term prisoners taken into the allocation unit of the South East Region of the prison service. The demographic details of this survey have been reported elsewhere (Gunn *et al*, 1973), but it is of interest that we found that 17 of the 90 men examined (19 per cent) had made one or more suicide attempts, and 16 (18 per cent) had at some previous point been admitted to a psychiatric hospital. We diagnosed 33 (37 per cent) as suffering from alcoholism, and using the criteria of Goldberg *et al* (1970) we estimated that 30 or one-third had abnormalities in their mental state, at the time of interview, which required psychiatric attention. In an M.D. thesis, Bluglass (1966) sampled one in four of the total admissions of convicted prisoners to Perth Prison for eleven months. He diagnosed 138 out of 300 (46 per cent) as having a psychiatric disorder, 6 (2 per cent) were psychotic, 7 (2 per cent) were neurotic, 40 (13 per cent) were called 'psychopathic', 33 (11 per cent) were alcoholic, 1 was drug addicted, 43 (14 per cent) were subnormal or borderline subnormal, 3 (1 per cent) were epileptic, and 5 (2 per cent) had other organic states. This is a wide range of pathology and matches our own findings from another survey, this time a census by questionnaire of a 10 per cent sample of all the convicted prisoners in the South East Region of the English prison service (Gunn *et al*, in press). We sent questionnaires to 811 men, randomly selected by the Home Office Research Unit, and received 629 satisfactory replies. The questionnaires were validated against 106 interviews conducted by a team of 11 senior trainee psychiatrists. We devised a weighted system of case identification taking into account desire for treatment, previous psychiatric history, and neurotic symptoms detected on the self-rating GHQ (see Goldberg, 1972). Using this method, we estimated that 31 per cent of the convicted prisoners in the South East Region prisons could be regarded as psychiatric cases. We made no attempt to estimate mental subnormality, as this diagnosis is partially dependent on social variables and partially on cognitive ones, neither of which we could measure. The diagnostic labels given to the 35 psychiatric cases ascertained by the interviewing psychiatrists included 2 psychoses, 9 neuroses, 3 sexual deviations, 13 alcoholic, and 22 personality disorders. (Several patients had more than one diagnosis.) These figures have to be set against the estimate of 14 per cent of the general population consulting their doctors for psychiatric reasons made by Shepherd and his colleagues (1966).

During the course of our census we took the opportunity to examine the data for a possible relationship between neurotic symptomatology and crime. All the information collected was put together with social and criminal data collected by the Home Office Research Unit. A principal components analysis was carried out, and two independent factors emerged: (a) psychiatric disturbance, and (b) recidivism. We were particularly interested in the positions of the various categories of offending. Property offences tended to load highly on the recidivist dimension and not at all on the psychiatric, whereas violence offences, sexual offences, and especially drug offences loaded highly on the psychiatric dimension. This suggests that for a prison population stealing has little to do with psychiatric disturbance, although it should be remembered that this is a statistical statement and individual exceptions will be found.

These British findings have been to some extent reinforced by a series of American studies carried out in Missouri by Guze and his colleagues (Guze, 1976). He studied 223 consecutive male and 66 female felons (serious offenders) as they left prison, both 'parolees' and 'flat timers' (no remission). Using a standard interview and criteria set out in his book, he diagnosed 90 per cent of the male population as having a psychiatric disorder, but 70 per cent of the population he described as 'sociopathic'. Even so, he regarded 52 per cent of the population as suffering from a psychiatric disorder other than sociopathy.

Schizophrenia was detected in only 1 per cent of the men, epilepsy in 1 per cent and mental deficiency in less than 1 per cent. Approximately 85 per cent were described as sociopathic, alcoholic, or drug dependent. Figures for the female felons were of a similar order in that only 12 per cent were regarded as having no psychiatric diagnosis, but this time 41 per cent of the population were regarded as suffering from hysteria, which Guze regards as a female equivalent of sociopathy. He concludes that sociopathy, alcoholism and drug dependence are the disorders associated with serious crime, whereas schizophrenia, affective disorders, neuroses, and brain syndromes are not. Sexual deviations in his estimation, in the absence of sociopathy, alcoholism or drug dependence, are not associated with serious crime.

Court Cohorts

Obviously the best way to determine the level of psychiatric disturbance in a criminal population is to examine a consecutive group of people convicted of criminal offences at a particular court or series of courts. As most convicted offenders are given non-custodial sentences, such as fines, this would be immensely difficult. As far as I know, this type of study waits to be done.

An examination of a recent issue of the criminal statistics for England and Wales (Home Office, 1975) can tell us something about the way in which courts see the relationship between crimes and mental disorder for the more serious offences (Table I). We can see immediately that more violent offenders and fewer property offences are put on hospital orders, and that both sexual offences and criminal damage (which includes arson) are disproportionately dealt with by hospitals. This kind of analysis however, can only tell us how courts, lawyers, and doctors are prepared to dispose of certain types of offender; furthermore it must be appreciated that probation orders with conditions of medical treatment are not included, nor are the bulk of offences because they are less serious (non-indictable). In 1974 there were 107,884 people convicted under intoxicating liquor laws, 6 per cent of the total criminal picture.

Table I

Numbers of offences reported in 1974 compared with the numbers of hospital orders made in the same year

	No. of offences per 100,000 popn*	%	No. of hospital orders (S.60 & S.65)	%
Homicide ..	1	—	50	5·9
Other personal violence	128	3·2	168	19·8
Sexual offences ..	50	1·3	75	8·8
Burglary ..	983	24·6	109	12·9
Robbery ..	18	0·5	8	0·9
Theft and handling	2,419	60·6	182	21·5
Fraud and forgery	238	6·0	48	5·7
Criminal damage	136	3·4	203	23·9
Other offences	17	0·4	5	0·6
Total	3,990	100	848	100

* These totals ×492·2 will give an approximation of the absolute figures, except for homicide where 600 cases were reported.

In 1973 Walker and McCabe published their analysis of a one-year cohort of hospital order cases collected some ten years previously. They showed that approximately 41 per cent were diagnosed schizophrenic, 35 per cent subnormal, 12 per cent personality disordered and 8 per cent affectively disordered.

The Criminality of Psychiatric Populations

It is a surprising fact that in spite of the common belief that crime and mental disorder are related there are very few systematic data available about the criminality of psychiatric populations. There is some information about the criminality of the general population in Britain, and that information suggests that for there to be a special association between crime and mental illness there would have to be a very high level of criminality among psychiatric patients. For example, we learn from the criminal statistics that 374,918 people were convicted of an indictable (serious) offence in England and Wales, and 1,558,731 were convicted of lesser or non-indictable offences in 1974. Taking the population of England and Wales in that year as 49·2 million (which, of course, includes children below the age of criminal responsibility) this gives a crime rate of approximately 8/1,000 persons for indictable offences, 32/1,000 for non-indictable offences and 39/1,000 overall. McClintock and Avison (1968) calculated the cumulative risk of being convicted during a life span. They estimated that approximately 1 in 3 of the male population and 1 in 12 of the female population would be convicted of a standard list offence at some time during their life span. The standard list of offences includes all indictable offences and those non-indictable offences which are regarded as of a similar nature to the indictable ones, in other words is a list of serious offences.

Taking these figures as a rough guideline, it would be surprising indeed if, for example, mental hospitals did not contain a large number of patients with a criminal record. No doubt there are good ethical objections to the data collection process involved, but it is a serious omission in our understanding of the population we treat as psychiatrists that we do not know accurately what proportion have been in conflict with the law, and for what reasons.

In 1974 Guze *et al* published an analysis they carried out of 500 patients attending a psychiatric clinic in the United States. They selected their patients to represent a cross-section of the psychiatric clinic population, and found that 22 patients had a history of at least one felony (serious offence); this represented 4 per cent of the total (10 per cent of the males and 1 per cent of the females). The offences committed varied from burglary and robbery (11 cases) to exhibitionism (4 cases) and child molestation (1 case). The offenders were labelled sociopathic (13 cases), alcoholic (9 cases), sexually deviant (6 cases), drug dependent (3 cases), and anxious (1 case). It is very unlikely that these figures are above those expected for an age, class, sex matched United States general population.

One piece of British information we can obtain is the number of patients who are formally admitted to psychiatric hospitals in England and Wales under Part V of the Mental Health Act, 1959. Part V deals with patients convicted of an offence (indictable or non-indictable) but handed over to the Health Service for ordinary in-patient care. The patients are detained under Sections 60, 65, 71 or 72 and are admitted to mental illness hospitals, mental handicap hospitals, or Special Hospitals. The Department of Health and Social Security's Mental Health Enquiry has kindly supplied me with the appropriate figures for 1974. These are given in Table II, from which it can be seen that only 0·7 per cent are admitted in this way. Even if we add the Section 136 admissions (i.e. the direct police admissions of unconvicted patients), the figure only rises to 1·5 per cent, but of course most of the Section 136 patients would not appear in a court of law. It has also to be remembered that these figures do not include those who were given conditional discharges in court so that they could obtain psychiatric treatment, nor those who received probation orders with a condition of medical treatment. Table III breaks down the 1,260 Part V admissions into the type of hospital to which they were sent. Nearly one-fifth went to Special Hospitals, and almost two-thirds went to mental illness hospitals. However, it is clear that mental handicap hospitals were admitting Part V patients at three times the rate of mental illness hospitals. This association between Part V admissions and mental handicap is borne out by an examination of the population of the Special Hospitals, which predominantly take Part V patients. The Special Hospitals Research Unit case register indicates that during the years 1972–74 inclusive 1,007 patients (704 males and 243 females) were admitted, 349 (35 per cent) classified psychopathic, 441 (44 per cent) classified mentally ill, and 257 (26 per cent) classified as subnormal or severely subnormal (the figures do not add up to 1,007 or 100 per cent because some of the cases were

TABLE II

Admissions to psychiatric hospitals 1974

Informal admits	159,533 (87·1%)
Part IV admits	20,708 (11·3%)
Part V admits	1,260 (0·7%)
Sect 136 admits	1,542 (0·8%)
Other admits	222 (0·1%)
Total admits	183,265 (100%)

TABLE III

The disposal of Part V cases in 1974

	Total admits	Part V cases	Proportion of Part V cases
Mental illness hospitals	170,827 (93·2%)	823 (65·3%)	0·5%
Mental handicap hospitals ..	12,132 (6·6%)	203 (16·1%)	1·7%
Special hospitals	306 (0·2%)	234 (18·6%)	76·5%
Total	183,265 (100%)	1,260 (100%)	0·7%

unclassified and others had more than one designation).

THE STAGE ARMY

By now it is clear that disorders such as 'psychopathy', alcoholism, drug addiction, and mental subnormality have particular associations with criminal behaviour, although those associations are not clear cut and refer, on the whole to serious offences. Many a hospital psychiatrist will, however, believe that schizophrenia plays a substantial part in the story of the mentally abnormal offender. This is because there is an important group of patients, mainly men, whose basic problem is that their disorder, whether it is alcoholism, personality disorder or schizophrenia, leaves them vulnerable and in need of asylum in the broadest sense. These men constitute the 'social litter' (Rollin, 1969) of our modern cities, and they move from hospital to prison, to doss house and back again, like a stage army tramping round and round, making a much greater impression than their numbers warrant simply because we have no facilities for them (Gunn, 1974a). They usually commit trivial offences, but serious crimes are not unknown from this group. Horton Hospital, Epsom, near London, has a special problem because it serves a part of the capital that collects more than its fair share of the nation's 'social litter'. Rollin studied the population admitted in 1961 and 1962 (Rollin, 1969), and found that the typical mentally abnormal offender admitted was a man aged 30–50 years, single, of no fixed abode, and very likely suffering from schizophrenia (83 per cent of the sample). He looked in more detail at the unprosecuted offenders, i.e. those admitted directly from the street by the police. Of the 78 cases admitted, 10 per cent had committed sexual offences, almost always indecent exposure, 13 per cent had committed violence, often assaults against the police, and 9 per cent were thieves, but 57 per cent committed offences against public order such as ripping aerials off cars, walking naked down the street, entering the Houses of Parliament to dispense justice and other such clearly 'mad' behaviour.

It emerged, after admission, that 40 per cent of the patients had a previous criminal record, 36 per cent being recidivists. The prosecuted offenders, admitted under Part V of the Mental Health Act 1959, were more often found to be thieves (41 per cent), but again 4 per cent were exhibitionists, 15 per cent were violent and 40 per cent offended against public order by begging, wandering abroad and so on. Of the prosecuted group 63 per cent had previous convictions and 44 per cent had previously served prison sentences.

In 1970 Tidmarsh and Wood (1972 and 1973) conducted a survey of the largest Reception Centre in London. Reception centres are operated by the Department of Health and Social Security, as the successors of the old casual wards, and are supposed to provide temporary accommodation to persons without a settled way of life. In practice they admit the destitute and homeless. Tidmarsh and Wood studied 8,000 cases referred to the centre, 4,000 of whom were old cases who had been there before. Of the old cases, 79 per cent had had convictions and 58 per cent had been in prison. Tidmarsh made psychiatric assessments and found that about 1,200 men diagnosed as mentally ill or mentally subnormal used the centre each year. Only just over one-quarter were said to have no psychiatric disorder. Of special relevance to this review is the fact that men with no psychiatric abnormalities were the least likely to have had convictions. Furthermore it emerged that most of those without prison sentences had not been in hospital, and most of whose who had not been in hospital had not been in prison either, while conversely those who had been in either type of institution had usually been in both.

THE ROLE OF THE FORENSIC PSYCHIATRIST

These statistical studies are tantalizingly inconclusive. Nevertheless there are a few general beliefs that seem to be supported by the figures. It appears that criminal behaviour is more likely to occur in patients with personality problems, social problems, mental handicap and addictions, especially alcoholism, in other words, those parts of the psychiatric spectrum that border on to social inadequacy and volitional or habit disorders. Does this mean that the forensic psychiatrist is one who specializes in personality problems, mental handicap, sexual problems, alcoholism, and the like? He is going to be a busy man if he takes on the totality of that work! Why not add adolescent behaviour disorders, since they also frequently lead a patient into conflict with the law? Clearly it would be nonsensical to try to separate off this vast lump of general psychiatry and call it forensic psychiatry, and yet there is a growing danger that this could happen. The sub-specialty of forensic psychiatry seems to have mushroomed in the last few years, albeit without an adequate academic base. This has coincided with the demand for 'security' to be re-introduced into the National Health Service. Both the DHSS working party on security units (known as the Glancy Report) and the combined Home Office/DHSS Report of the Committee on Mentally Abnormal Offenders (known as the Butler Report) have recommended that security units should be built in each National Health Service Region and that these units should be directed by forensic psychiatrists. Thus there is a danger that forensic psychiatry will be regarded as that part of psychiatry which is concerned with locking patients up. There is also the danger that hard-pressed general psychiatrists will increasingly say that the difficult cases of personality disorder, alcoholism and the like are somebody else's problem.

A close examination of these two important reports reveals that neither intended these interpretations to be put on their recommendations. Such interpretations would defeat the objectives of the Committees, because if carried too far they would mean that a tiny sub-specialty would have to deal with a large and difficult slice of general psychiatry in a few security units. Indeed the Butler Committee state categorically that the 'main emphasis in forensic psychiatric services . . . should be on community care and out-patient work . . . (area) psychiatric hospitals should continue to provide a wide range of facilities for forensic patients'. It is worth noting what the holder of the first Chair in Forensic Psychiatry in England and Wales had to say on this subject nearly a decade ago—'whether forensic psychiatry is a sub-specialty on its own is a debatable question . . . the well-trained consultant psychiatrist is as competent as anyone else to deal with the majority of problems in forensic psychiatry, especially of the more serious kind . . . any claim to specialization must lie in being able to cross . . . social and administrative boundaries, as well as in the specialized studies of particular mental conditions' (Gibbens, 1968). Professor Gibbens on more than one occasion has been concerned to stress the educational tasks of the forensic psychiatrist. In the paper just referred to he concludes by emphasizing the importance of all psychiatrists having the opportunity to learn about various penal institutions and methods of social control, and he particularly stresses the importance of close connections between forensic psychiatry and adolescent psychiatry, seeing that crime (other than motoring offences) is principally an adolescent activity.

The major difficulty in discussing forensic psychiatry or the relationship between crime and mental disorder is that neither the sub-specialty, nor the relationship can be defined in biological terms. It is not simply a matter of defining age limits, as in child psychiatry, or of defining a group of disorders, as in organic psychiatry. Medico-legal problems are determined socially and administratively, and they are steeped in legal concepts which are alien to biology. The most significant of these is responsibility.

Criminal Responsibility

In English law accused persons are presumed to be 'responsible' for their actions unless they can show that this is untrue for any particular act. The factors which will remove criminal responsibility (except in cases of strict liability), if they can be proved by the defence and are present in sufficient degree, are mistake, accident, provocation, duress, and insanity (Whitlock, 1963). A law of strict liability is one in which these factors are no defence; responsibility is always present. Hence, although criminal responsibility is linked to the concepts of free will and choice, in practice it means liability to punishment. Some legal systems (e.g. the Italian) acknowledge this by calling the concept 'imputability'.

As the Butler Committee (Home Office and DHSS, 1975) has indicated, 'the extent to which mental disorder constitutes a defence to a charge or a reason for convicting of a lesser offence depends at present on a complex body of law represented by M'Naghten's case, the defence of diminished responsibility, infanticide and the doctrine of non-insane automatism'. McNaughton was a psychotic who believed he was being persecuted by the Tory party. In 1843 he shot the Prime Minister's secretary, mistaking him for the Prime Minister. He himself was found not guilty by reason of insanity, but the verdict caused a public outcry and the Judges were asked to draw up rules of guidance. (An excellent account of this is to be found in Walker (1968). The famous Rules tell us that 'to establish a defence on the grounds of insanity, it must be clearly proved that at the time of the committing of the act the party accused was labouring under such a defect of reason, from disease of the mind, as not to know the nature and quality of the act he was doing, or if he did know it, that he did not know he was doing wrong'.

These Rules have always been difficult if not impossible to apply indeed it seems likely that McNaughton himself would not have passed the criteria if stringently applied! One of the basic problems, from the psychiatrist's point of view, is that the legal concept of responsibility seems to be all or none, you either have it or you don't, whereas, of course, mental disorder forms a continuum. However, when flexible sentencing is available to the judge insanity is rarely pleaded as a defence against conviction; mental disorder is usually used by the defence to plead mitigation of sentence. In murder, the major crime which still commands a mandatory sentence, some acknowledgement of the continuum of sanity and hence responsibility has been forthcoming in English law in recent years by the introduction of the concept of 'diminished responsibility'. The Homicide Act, 1957 states that where a person kills or is a party to the killing of another, he shall not be convicted of murder 'if he was suffering from such abnormality of mind (whether arising from a condition of arrested or retarded development of mind or any inherent causes or induced by disease or injury) as substantially impaired his mental responsibility for his acts and omissions'. As with the plea of insanity, diminished responsibility has to be raised and proved by the defence. A successful plea has the effect of reducing the charge from murder to manslaughter and thereby giving discretionary sentencing back to the judge.

In British courts in these days questions of responsibility have largely given way to questions of the type and degree of any mental abnormality present, its treatability, its possible mitigating effects on the sentence, and the management problems presented by the offender.

Alcohol and Alcoholism

No matter from which angle the relationship between crime and mental disorder is viewed, the problem of alcoholism always stands out. It will be recalled that Bluglass regarded 11 per cent of his Scottish prisoners as alcoholic; Guze *et al* (1974) reported that of 70 alcoholic out-patients, 13 per cent had committed a felony, and in his book Guze (1976) reported that 43 per cent of a consecutive series of male felons were alcoholic. Added to this there are in England and Wales over 100,000 convictions for drunkenness which usually do not result in custodial or serious penalties. Edwards *et al* (1971) reviewed the literature, which showed that the reported prevalence of alcoholism among prisoners varies between 10 per cent and 56 per cent, and they enumerated five basic research problems in this type of epidemiological work. Three of these problems are worth reiterating here because they are central to all aspects of the relationship between crime and mental disorder. Firstly, precise definitions of the disorder in question are hard to come by, Secondly, different samples give different data. e.g. Gibbens and Silberman (1970) showed that different types of prison have different rates of alcoholism. Thirdly, control data concerning the general levels of disorders are often lacking.

A special problem relating to alcoholism is the consideration of whether it should be regarded as mental disorder at all. Certainly it can produce severe illnesses such as liver cirrhosis, brain damage, peripheral neuritis, and the like. Certainly it can exacerbate mental illnesses such as schizophrenia and depression. Certainly a small proportion of alcoholics take themselves to doctors pleading for assistance and saying that they cannot control their drinking. Alcoholism presents conceptual difficulties which it shares with other addictions. If it is a disorder, it is a habit disorder, perhaps a behaviour disorder, and volition is a very significant factor. This poses difficult problems for the psychiatrist and for the courts. Firstly, there is the question of responsibility. If a man gets drunk and reckless and then commits an offence he may argue 'I'm innocent, I didn't know what I was doing'. Occasionally he will be successful in his plea if he can prove that he was so drunk as to be incapable of forming an intent (see Edwards, 1961, for a discussion). However, such a defence is difficult to sustain and courts show reluctance in allowing drunkenness to be an excuse for antisocial behaviour, mainly because the temporary mental derangement of drunkenness was 'voluntarily' acquired. The Butler Committee faced this problem squarely and pointed out that if the rule about drunkenness were logically applied a person who is habitually violent in drink would escape any criminal charge, and they recommended that courts should be given power to convict those who became violent when voluntarily intoxicated. 'The object', they said 'is not necessarily to punish them. An alcoholic or drug addict may after conviction be persuaded to accept treatment. But not all these offenders are addicts . . . and in any case powers of punishment are necessary for those who will not accept treatment and who cannot otherwise be controlled.'

At this point the Butler Committee were commenting on the second major problem in relation to alcoholism: treatment. As the law stands it could be argued (although it rarely is) that an unwilling drunken person needs compulsory detention in hospital for his own protection or the protection of others. Twenty-four hours later such an argument would be much harder to sustain in the face of a sober patient who says that he knows what he is doing, feels reasonably well, and wishes to decide for himself whether he will drink or not —thank you very much. Many of the severest alcoholics deny their problems when they are sober and even if they accept their drinking as a problem are unwilling to submit to a treatment programme which is irksome and involves abstinence. Some such people may be potential or actual offenders when drunk or in relation to drinking (e.g. stealing money for more drink). Why not regard an habitual drunken offender as suffering from a form of 'psychopathy' and therefore admit him to hospital compulsorily, after conviction, under Section 60 of the Mental Health Act 1959? The Butler Committee is opposed to such an expedient and suggests that much of the problem would be eased if the recommendations of the Weiler Committee (Home Office, 1971) were implemented and more hostels were provided, together with detoxification units. In these arguments the Butler Report is clearly taking the volitional element of drinking disorders into account, accepting the undesirability and the impracticality of forcing treatment for behaviour disorders on unwilling patients, and allowing the ordinary social (penal) control measures to operate for those patients who express their preference for that method by refusing treatment. This is quite a long way from the paternalistic notion that alcoholism is a disease which must necessarily be treated for the good of the patient.

If this view can be applied to the alcoholic, how much more can it be applied to the 'psychopath'?

Psychopathic Disorder

A review of the vexing subject of psychopathic disorder could well occupy a monograph. All that can be done here is to outline one or two special problems. So far no one has come up with a satisfactory definition for the diagnosis or category, and to make matters worse there are two distinct uses of the term, legal and clinical, which do not necessarily coincide although they affect one another. The legal use is almost entirely confined to England and Wales. Scotland has escaped the problem: the term 'psychopathic disorder' is not used in the Mental Health (Scotland) Act, 1960, although similar distinctions regarding admission and discharge exist for patients described by the same words as define 'psychopathic disorder' in the English Act.

The Mental Health Act definition of psychopathic disorder is somewhat circular 'a persistent disorder or disability of mind (whether or not including subnormality of intelligence) which results in abnormally aggressive or seriously irresponsible conduct on the part of the patient, and requires or is susceptible to medical treatment'. Lady Wootton (1959) has suggested that the psychopath 'makes nonsense of every attempt to distinguish the sick from the healthy delinquent' because 'mental abnormality is inferred from antisocial behaviour while antisocial behaviour is explained by mental abnormality'. Walker and McCabe (1973) point out that this is not entirely fair, as the psychiatrist does not necessarily use matters brought before the court to determine whether or not the patient has a disability of mind. Nevertheless, it must be admitted that there is a serious danger of circular reasoning, a danger that in certain circumstances could lead to very illiberal consequences. There is no evidence in this country of social nuisances who have no psychiatric abnormality being locked up in mental hospitals; on the contrary, psychopaths find that they cannot get into hospital, even when they want to go there (Gunns 1974b). But the point does illustrate the need for vigilance in the interpretation of mental health laws. Walker and McCabe see the main weakness of the legal definition to be the stultifying influence which a supposedly generic legal category has had on the diagnostic habits of psychiatrists.

The Butler Committee believes that so much confusion has arisen over the use of the term that 'personality disorder' should be substituted in the Act for 'psychopathic personality' provided stringent safeguards are included to prevent mere eccentrics being detained compulsorily. In taking its evidence the Butler Committee was confronted with six major arguments for the removal of the clauses about psychopaths from the English Act: (1) psychiatrists disagree about its meaning; (2) it has a circular definition; (3) it is used by some people as a medico-scientific explanation for antisocial behaviour; (4) it stigmatizes those so labelled; (5) the Act covers all 'mental disorder' and therefore specific clauses for psychopaths are redundant; (6) in the Scottish and Northern Irish Acts the term is not used. Nevertheless, the Department of Health has proposed, in its recent consultation document on the Mental Health Act (D.H.S.S., 1976), that the category should remain.

One of the best recent reviews of the clinical use of the term is that by the late Sir Aubrey Lewis (1974); he tells us: 'For 150 years the diagnostic concept called "moral insanity" has been troubling psychiatric nosologists'. He concludes his article: 'The diagnostic groupings of psychiatry seldom have sharp and definite limits. Some are worse than others in this respect. Worst of all is psychopathic personality, within its wavering confines. Its outline will not be firm until much more is known about its genetics, psychopathology, and neuropathology.' Walker and McCabe point out that in clinical terms a diagnostic label can have one or more of four functions; explanatory, prognostic, therapeutic, descriptive. They examine each in turn in relation to psychopathy and conclude: 'as a description the diagnosis tells one nothing . . . prognostically it exaggerates the difference between psychopaths and ordinary recidivists on the one hand, or on the other hand schizophrenics and subnormals . . .; it cannot be an explanatory label; and . . . as a method of indicating suitable forms of treatment it tells us only that none have been found very profitable. What cannot be argued away, however, is the fact that psychiatrists seem to feel a need to use it.'

The reasons for this need are not at all clear. Lewis indicated the long-held belief that some individuals have a warped or defective moral sense which makes them non-conforming and antisocial. However, moral sense is an extremely nebulous concept, and it is probably largely culturally determined. During the 150 years in which the concept of psychopathic disorder has been evolving, the moral scene has changed a great deal and it varies between nations. No doubt an intact and efficient central nervous system is required to develop moral sense, but if most of us were to try to devise a model for the biological development of morals we would probably use a learning model. If psychopathic disorder is a defect state then it is surely better viewed as a failure of learning rather than as a disease.

Perhaps this concept of a failure of learning is behind the fact that almost every attempt to define the condition or delineate a sample of subjects relies on social parameters. In this respect American psychiatrists are more candid that European ones because their term for the disorder is 'sociopathic personality'. All kinds of lists of social ineptitudes have been drawn up as typifying the psychopath, one of the best known being that by Lee Robins in her book *Deviant Children Grown Up* (1966). Quite recently Dr Graham Robertson and I had the opportunity to see if we could find a psychopathic factor in a group of prisoners all sent to Grendon prison for treatment with the diagnosis of psychopathic personality (Gunn and Robertson, 1976). We tried to measure a number of social indicators, such as occupational stability, personal relationships, marriage, and so on, and a number of psychological indicators like conscientiousness, anxiety, lying, impulsiveness, together with habit problems like heavy drinking, gambling. Immediately we ran into difficulties, because the ratings we were attempting, in spite of a standardized interview and joint training, proved so subjective that our inter-rater reliability was low for many of the scales. Of our original 19 scales we had to drop 9. From the remaining scales we could not extract an important single factor and it became clear to us that while the 107 prisoners had several characteristics in common, e.g. they had all broken the law, and most had neurotic symptoms of one sort or another, if we wanted to utilize any of the four diagnostic functions set out by Walker and McCabe we had to resort to a diagnostic formulation or description using a number of different parameters. All the men had neurotic problems which required treatment, some had sexual problems, others were deficient in basic social skills and had interpersonal difficulties, occupational instability and so on. In short the term psychopath was unhelpful and had to be amplified. An accurate description of the problems confronting any particular 'psychopath' is essential for effective diagnosis and treatment.

We can perhaps learn from the non-medical team of Walker and McCabe who conclude 'It seems highly likely that current and future research will identify subgroups of "psychopaths" . . . Progress of this kind, however, is not assistant by the assumption that all "psychopaths" have something in common—apart from the label. To categorize someone as psychopathic is all too often to exclude him from the hospitals where research is being most actively carried out; and sometimes it ensures that he is refused *any* hospital vacancy.' This last point is all too true, and if the term 'moral defective', later to become 'psychopath' was introduced to try to explain persistent criminality in medical terms, the hypothesis has not only failed, it has been counterproductive.

Epilepsy

The last condition I will use to illustrate the

nature of the relationship between crime and mental illness is epilepsy. Some years ago I had the opportunity to conduct a total census of epilepsy within the prisons of England and Wales (Gunn, in press). The results indicated a prevalence of at least 7·2 epileptics per 1,000 prisoners, which is considerably above the best estimates of the prevalence of epilepsy in the general population. At first sight this could have been taken as evidence for the traditional belief that epilepsy is in some way related to crime. Such a belief dates back to Lombroso, if not further. However, the institutional nature of the sample has to be remembered, and epileptics have always suffered high levels of institutionalization; there are epileptic colonies still flourishing. When the epileptic prisoners were matched with another sample from the same prison serving the same types of sentences very little difference between the two groups could be discerned. Dr Fenton and I examined the epileptics' records to see if any of the prisoners could have been convicted for committing an offence during a period of disturbed consciousness. One possible case of theft during an episode of post-ictal confusion was found and a survey of the three Special Hospitals, Broadmoor, Rampton and Moss Side, revealed three cases of automatic or unconscious violence (Gunn and Fenton, 1971). Automatism, then, is a very small factor in any association between epilepsy and crime.

There seemed to be four ways in which epilepsy could be related to antisocial behaviour (Gunn, 1974c). In some cases it seemed that brain dysfunction was responsible for both the ictal phenomena and the antisocial behaviour. In others it seemed that the epilepsy had generated social and psychological problems such as rejection, and feelings of inferiority which in their turn led to antisocial reactions. A third type of association seemed to occur in cases where harmful social factors such as overcrowding, parental neglect and the like lead to an excess prevalence of both epilepsy and antisocial behaviour—the battered child is an extreme example of this kind of relationship. Finally, there were cases where a tendency to recklessness and antisocial behaviour not only led to conflict with the law but also to accident and illness proneness which in their turn produced traumatic disorders such as epilepsy. Of course it was possible to find cases in which two or three of these various relationships between epilepsy and crime were mixed together, and others in which the association seemed purely fortuitous.

The aspect of this study which stood out most prominently was that any general statements about the relationship of the epilepsies and all epileptic patients on the one hand and criminality on the other were bound to fail because they did not take into account the wide degree of variation possible within these universes. I suspect that similar models could be constructed for the relationships between other types of disorder, both physical and psychiatric, and antisocial behaviour.

Conclusion

Although there is an increasing interest in forensic psychiatry, crime and mental disorder are difficult to relate together. Both concepts are difficult to define, both are heterogeneous, and crime is clearly a culturally determined phenomenon. Because crimes are committed very frequently, many psychiatric patients will commit them. If prison populations are studied they apparently contain a large number of mentally-disordered individuals, but this may be more closely related to their function as institutions than to any special relationship between crime and mental disorder. The best data on the relationship, if any, should come from court cohort studies, but this information is largely missing. Similarly, very few data are available about the criminality of psychiatric populations. What information exists strongly suggests that mental handicap services are more likely to have offenders referred to them than are mental illness services.

Attempts to discover overall relationships between two heterogeneous populations may be mistaken. There seems to be some support for the view that offending is most likely to be associated with personality problems, with social problems, with addictions (especially alcoholism) and, of course, with mental handicap. These problems constitute a large slice of general psychiatric work, and even on a chance basis a general psychiatric service will deal with a large number of offenders. It would be ludicrous and retrograde if all this work were to be pushed in the direction of the small (admittedly growing) number of so-called forensic psychiatrists.

Specific problems such as alcoholism, psychopathic disorder and epilepsy illustrate many of the difficulties faced by psychiatry in the overlap area with criminology. Sometimes there is doubt as to whether the patients categorized are patients at all. It follows from this that it is particularly difficult to decide whether an individual should receive compulsory treatment for a disputed disorder which has only come to light because of an offence. If disabilities such as 'psychopathic disorder' can be recognized at all they are best understood as defects of learning and socialization rather than as illnesses in the discrete sense. Epilepsy leads to social and sometimes to criminal problems. It illustrates the way in which it is possible for a biological disability either to generate special social and psychological difficulties which can lead to conflict with the law, or to result from the same disadvantages that lead to a criminal life, or indeed to result directly from criminal behaviour.

All in all, it is probably better to concentrate upon specific behavioural problems caused by specific disorders and to avoid too many generalizations about the mentally disordered and the criminally convicted. If forensic psychiatry is to have an enlarged role in psychiatry then surely it should be concerned with specialized research and teaching, and assistance with especially difficult or unusual problems.

ACKNOWLEDGEMENTS

I would like to thank the Department of Health and Social Security, both the Statistical Division and the MHC branch, and Mrs Elizabeth Parker, who directs the Special Hospitals Research Unit case register, for data kindly supplied. I would also like to thank the librarian at the Department of Health in London for carrying out a MEDLARS computer search of the literature for this review.

REFERENCES

BLUGLASS, R. S. (1966) A Psychiatric Study of Scottish Prisoners. M.D. Thesis (unpublished).

CLARE, A. (1976) *Psychiatry in Dissent*. London: Tavistock.

DHSS (1973) *Report on Security in NHS Hospitals*. (Unpublished.)

—— (1976) *A Review of the Mental Health Act 1959*. HMSO: London.

EDWARDS, G., HENSMAN, C. & PETO, J. (1971) Drinking problems among recidivist prisoners. *Psychological Medicine*, **1**, 388–99.

EDWARDS, J. L. J. (1961) Diminished responsibility. In *Essays in Criminal Science* (ed. G. O. W. Mueller). London: Sweet and Maxwell.

GIBBENS, T. C. N. (1963) *Psychiatric Studies of Borstal Lads*. London: OUP.

—— (1968) The task of forensic psychiatry. *Medicine, Science and the Law*, **8**, 3–10.

—— & SILBERMAN, M. (1970) Alcoholism among prisoners. *Psychological Medicine*, **1**, 73–8.

GOLDBERG, D. P. (1972) *The Detection of Psychiatric Illness by Questionnaire*. London: OUP.

—— COOPER, B., EASTWOOD, M. R., KEDWARD, H. B. & SHEPHERD, M. (1970) A standardized psychiatric interview for use in community surveys. *British Journal of Preventive and Social Medicine*, **24**, 18–23.

GUNN, J. (1974a) Prisons, shelters and homeless men. *Psychiatric Quarterly*, **48**, 505–12.

—— (1974b) Disasters, asylums and plans: forensic psychiatry today. *British Medical Journal*, *iii*, 611–13.

—— (1974c) Social factors and epileptics in prison. *British Journal of Psychiatry*, **24**, 509–17.

—— *Epileptic Prisoners*. London: Academic Press. In press.

—— & FENTON, G. (1971) Epilepsy, automatism and crime. *Lancet*, *i*, 1173–6.

—— NICOL, R., GRISTWOOD, J. & FOGGITT, R. (1973) Long-term prisoners. *British Journal of Criminology*, **13**, 331–40.

—— & ROBERTSON, G. (1976) Psychopathic personality: a conceptual problem. *Psychological Medicine*. **6**, 631–4.

—— —— DELL, S. & WAY, S. *Psychiatric Aspects of Imprisonment*. London: Academic Press. (To be published.)

GUZE, S. B. (1976) *Criminality and Psychiatric Disorders*. New York: Oxford University Press.

—— WOODRUFF, R. A. & CLAYTON, P. J. (1974) Psychiatric disorders and criminality. *Journal of the American Medical Association*, **227**, 641–2.

HOME OFFICE (1971) *Habitual Drunken Offenders*. London: HMSO.

—— (1975) *Criminal Statistics: England and Wales 1974*. London: HMSO. Cmnd 6168.

—— & DHSS (1975) *Report of the Committee on Mentally Abnormal Offenders*. London: HMSO. Cmnd 6244.

LEWIS, A. J. (1953) Health as a social concept. *British Journal of Sociology*, **4**, 109–24.

—— (1974) Psychopathic personality: a most elusive category. *Psychological Medicine*, **4**, 133–40.

MCCLINTOCK, F. H. & AVISON, N. H. (1968) *Crime in England and Wales*. London: Heinemann.

PENROSE, L. S. (1939) Mental disease and crime: outline of a comparative study of European statistics. *British Journal of Medical Psychology*, **18**, 1–15.

ROBINS, L. (1966) *Deviant Children Grown Up*. Baltimore: Williams & Wilkins.

ROLLIN, H. R. (1969) *The Mentally Abnormal Offender and the Law*. Oxford: Pergamon.

SHEPHERD, M., COOPER, B., BROWN, A. C. & KALTON, G. W. (1966) *Psychiatric Illness in General Practice*. Oxford: OUP.

SZASZ, T. S. (1962) *The Myth of Mental Illness*. London: Paladin.

TIDMARSH, D. & WOOD, S. (1972) Psychiatric aspects of destitution. In *Evaluating a Community Psychiatric Service* (eds J. K. Wing and A. Hailey). London: OUP.

TIDMARSH, D. & WOODS S. (1973) Psychiatric illness, destitution and crime. (Unpublished.)

WALKER, N. (1968) *Crime and Insanity in England: Vol 1. The Historical Perspective*. Edinburgh: University Press.

—— & MCCABE, S. (1973) *Crime and Insanity in England: Vol 2. New Solutions and New Problems*. Edinburgh: University Press.

WEST, D. J. (1963) *The Habitual Prisoner*. London: Macmillan.

WHITLOCK, F. A. (1963) *Criminal Responsibility and Mental Illness*. London: Butterworth.

WOOTON, B. (1959) *Social Science and Social Pathology*. London: Allen and Unwin.

John Gunn, M.D., M.R.C.Psych., *Director, Special Hospitals Research Unit, Honorary Senior Lecturer in Forensic Psychiatry, Institute of Psychiatry, De Crespigny Park, London SE5*

(*Received 13 October 1976*)

[4]

Med. Sci. Law (1990) Vol. 30, No. 3 *Printed in Great Britain* 247

Mental Abnormality and Criminality — an Uncertain Relationship

HERSCHEL PRINS, MPhil
Lecturer and writer on clinical criminology and social aspects of forensic psychiatry, 1 Home Close Road, Houghton on the Hill, Leicester, LE7 9GT

'How sad and bad and mad it was . . .'
Robert Browning
Confessions

ABSTRACT
Some aspects of the uncertain relationship between mental abnormality and criminality are considered. Comments are offered on the contextual framework for such a relationship, studies of penal and other populations and the relationship between some specific mental abnormalities and criminal behaviour. Some implications for management are identified.

CONTEXTUAL FRAMEWORK

The term 'mental abnormality' is used here to include mental disorder as defined in the Mental Health Act, England and Wales, 1983. This includes mental illness (which in the Act is not further defined), mental impairment, severe mental impairment, psychopathic disorder and any other disorder or disability of mind. It also enables us to consider a wide range of other disorders and abnormalities, some of which would not satisfy the criteria for compulsory hospitalization under the mental health legislation.

Admittedly the term 'mental abnormality' is a somewhat vague one and it has certainly led to difficulties for the courts, for example, in trying to determine what constitutes an abnormality of mind within the meaning of the Homicide Act, 1957. It is used here merely to encompass a range of disordered mental states, but its imperfections are recognized. In many respects it is easier to define mental illnesses, particularly those with clear-cut aetiology; it is less easy to define mental retardation, particularly the more mild forms, and we know that measured intelligence (IQ) alone is not a good indicator. As a first step we are faced with the difficult problem of trying to establish any relationship between mental abnormality and criminality. This is because we are trying to make connections between very different phenomena, and these phenomena are the subject of much debate concerning both substance and definition. It is as though the goal-posts for the 'game' are constantly being shifted.

Let us take mental disorder first. There are arguments as to whether some forms of mental disorder even exist. A major proponent of this view is the redoubtable critic of psychiatry Thomas Szasz. In his most recent book (Szasz, 1987) he summarizes most of what he has said on this subject during several decades. However, the seductiveness of his arguments and a good deal of apparent rhetoric have been criticized cogently by Roth and Kroll (1986). Other psychiatrists, for example Laing and Esterson (1964), have suggested that much of mental illness may have its origins in 'conspiracies' and 'mixed messages' within families.

At the other end of the spectrum we have the so-called biological psychiatric view as set out, for example, in some of the standard textbooks such as that of Slater and Roth (1969) and others. For most of us, Gunn's views would be acceptable. He says that 'somewhere in the confusion there is a biological reality of mental disorder . . . this reality is a complex mixture of diverse conditions, some organic, some functional, some inherited, some learned, some acquired, some curable, others unremitting' (Gunn, 1977a). It is also relevant

248 Med. Sci. Law (1990) Vol. 30, No. 3

to note that the prevalence and presentation of mental disorders appear to change over time. Hard facts concerning the epidemiology and substance of mental disorders, even for periods as recent as the nineteenth century, are not easy to come by. Researchers such as Hare (1983) and Scull (1984) have concluded, tentatively, that the schizophrenias as we know them today possibly did not exist in earlier times. However, anecdotal and some clinical evidence would seem to indicate that this assertion needs to be viewed with some caution (Bark, 1985; Prins, 1987). It is also worth while stressing that in earlier times there may well have been persons presenting with psychiatric symptoms in whom, these days, we would recognize a physical or 'organic' origin. For example, in the middle ages, malnutrition produced pellagric states with their psychological and psychiatric sequels; the use of bad flour probably produced ergot poisoning which in turn could and did produce psychiatric symptoms (Camporesi, 1989). Lead was in common use for cooking utensils and for water pipes; lead poisoning may also produce confused and disturbed behaviour.

When we come to consider criminal behaviour we are faced with similar problems. At its simplest, crime is merely that form of behaviour defined as illegal and punishable by the criminal law. At various times in our history, acts judged as criminal have been redefined, or even removed from the statute books — as instanced in the cases of attempted suicide and adult consenting homosexual acts committed in private. New offences are also created, particularly in times of war or of serious crisis; moreover, our increasingly complex technological society has necessitated the introduction of all manner of laws and regulations governing aspects of our conduct (see also Croft, 1978). Since much criminal behaviour is somewhat arbitrarily defined and there are arguments about the existence and definition of mental abnormality, it is hardly surprising that we find difficulties in trying to establish connections between these two somewhat ill-defined and complex forms of behaviour. Nevertheless, despite these difficulties, it still seems important to try to examine some of their possible relationships, acknowledging at the outset that any conclusions must be tentative and seen against the foregoing background. To do this it is usual to consider penal, correctional and other data. Before doing so, one final introductory point needs to be made. It concerns public attitudes. It is very difficult to judge public attitudes to mental abnormality and crime since hardly any surveys of substance have been carried out. (For a recent and helpful contribution see Appleby and Wesseley, 1988.) As Hill has suggested, such attitudes are bound up inextricably with part 'of a general social process involving economic, philosophical and moral factors' (Hill, 1982; see also Rosen, 1968 and Prins, 1983).

STUDIES OF PENAL AND CRIMINAL POPULATIONS

For many years considerable efforts have been made to study the prevalence of mental disorder in penal and criminal populations; these studies have been conducted on inmates of penal and correctional establishments and attenders at specialist court clinics. The populations are therefore highly selected. This fact has important implications. For example, it is quite likely that the act of incarceration may well exacerbate certain underlying psychiatric conditions; or the effects of such incarceration may be so severe as to precipitate mental abnormality in vulnerable individuals (see for example Schorer, 1965; Gunn et al., 1978; Coid, 1984, 1988a and b). Feldman (1977) has also suggested that those who are, in fact, mentally abnormal may be less skilful in crime and thus caught more easily. He also suggests that the police may tend to charge some of these offenders more readily. In addition, pleas of guilty may be more frequent; a point confirmed in a recent paper by Robertson (1988). Scott (1969) once suggested that even if we allowed for the high degree of selectivity in penal and remand populations, the proportion of clearly identifiable psychiatric diagnoses was only somewhere in the order of 15%. Gunn et al. (1978) have estimated that about one-third of a sample of 629 prisoners that they studied could have been regarded as requiring psychiatric attention at the time of interview.

More recent figures appear to indicate that the number of English prisoners assessed as formally mentally disordered within the meaning of the mental health legislation has shown a decline in recent years: from about 800 in 1977 to about 350 in 1986 (NACRO, 1987) and 235 in 1988 (House of Commons, written reply, 22.12.88). However, in addition to prisoners formally classified as mentally disordered, there are, of course, an unknown number of mentally abnormal prisoners who are not classified under the mental health legislation. These will range from a very small number of people who have committed notorious crimes, to a not inconsiderable number of socially inadequate people, many of whom are continually in and out of prisons and other institutions. The latter constitute the 'stage army' described so graphically by Rollin (1969). During the year ending 31 March 1986, 14,228 prisoners were referred to prison psychiatrists; the Principal Medical Officer for the Prison Department has estimated that on any one day there could be about 1,500 male prisoners who were formally mentally disordered. Of these, some 250 would be mentally ill, (NACRO, 1987). Although the remit of the Mental Health Act Commission does not extend to persons detained in penal institutions, the Commission has been able to make some assessment of the problems of mentally disordered persons in prison and has passed on its concern to the Home Office. It has also published the results of a survey on how the provisions of the Mental Health Act, 1983, which relate directly to mentally disordered offenders, have been working (MHAC, 1987). It concluded that the provisions were not being implemented as well as they might be, and that some modification of the legislation might be needed to bring about improvement.

About ten years ago, I examined some twenty studies that had been undertaken on penal and court clinic populations during a 50-year period. The results are described in detail elsewhere (Prins, 1980a and b). In 1982, Howells, as part of a study of the relationship between mental disorder and violent behaviour, summarized my findings in roughly the following fashion. The studies showed substantial disparities. The percentage of offenders found to be suffering from psychoses (affective disorders and the schizophrenias) ranged from 0.5%–26%; from mental subnormality from 2.4%–28%; from psychopathy from 5.6%–70% and from alcoholism/excessive drinking from 11%–80%. As Howells says: 'such variation is likely to be in part a function of the different populations surveyed', ranging as they did from homicides to approved school boys. However, 'in spite of these disparities, these studies do suggest a high level of mental disturbance in criminal groups' (Howells, 1982, p. 165). The point has also been made by Taylor (1986) in a recent study of life-sentenced prisoners in custody and in the community. It is also relevant to note here that some observers have suggested that suicide in prisons (a matter of much recent concern) is roughly three times more frequent than in the general population (Topp, 1979). After having made allowances for methodological weaknesses, the overall impression from most of these studies is that severe psychiatric illness (psychosis), organic disorders and severe mental impairment of a type to bring the person within the remit of the mental health legislation are comparatively uncommon in criminal populations. However, personality disorders (which may, of course, be accompanied by various forms of formal mental illness or mental impairment), alcohol and other drug- related and sexual problems figure quite prominently. Such findings should come as no great surprise.

Criminality in psychiatric hospital and similar populations

To provide firm evidence of a reasonably clear association between mental disorder and criminality, it would be desirable to demonstrate the prevalence of criminality in psychiatric hospital patients and similar groups. To date, little work of substance has been carried out in this area, largely, as Gunn (1977a) suggests, because of the considerable ethical problems involved in investigating the possible criminal backgrounds of hospitalized psychiatric patients. However, a few workers have attempted to explore certain aspects of this field. Walker (1968) estimated, on the basis

250 Med. Sci. Law (1990) Vol. 30, No. 3

of various epidemiological studies, that about twelve persons in every thousand would suffer from some kind of identifiable psychiatric disorder. Gunn (1977a), on the basis of calculations made by McClintock and Avison (1968), suggests that approximately one in three of the male population and one in twelve of the female population would be convicted in their lifetime of a 'standard list' (indictable or fairly serious) offence, such as a major assault or breaking and entering. Thus, as Gunn suggests, in the light of these figures, it would be surprising if psychiatric hospitals and clinics did not contain an appreciable number of persons with criminal records. In the USA, a number of workers have examined mental hospital populations and the records of persons attending psychiatric clinics. Guze (1976), who surveyed a population of some 500 such patients, found that 4% had committed a serious offence. Other studies have been made by Brill and Malzberg (1962) and Rappeport and Lassen (1967); and Rabkin (1979) has reviewed all the relevant literature critically. All of these studies tend to show that the relationship between mental disorder and crime in such populations is not straightforward; however, one thing is clear, namely, support for Rollin's 'stage army' of persons drifting between hospital and penal containment (Rollin, 1969). A more recent, and somwhat unusual, study was carried out by Cook (1983). This was a retrospective survey in Bristol of 78 men without previous convictions, who had at least one psychiatric hospital admission of not less than three months before the age of 30. The subsequent conviction rate of these men was determined and found to be comparable with that of men of the same age in the general population. However, as Cook suggests, some caution is necessary in drawing too many general conclusions from these results as his sample was a small one and may not be typical of the country as a whole.

This, and the other studies referred to, demonstrate the need for wider and more detailed surveys in this field (for useful comments on possible ways forward see Wardlaw, 1983; Mulvey et al., 1986). From our more general survey we may now proceed to examine, in a little more detail, some positive relationships between some specific mental abnormalities and criminality.

SOME SPECIFIC DISORDERS

Somewhat arbitrary choices have been made in the following examination of the possible relationship between certain categories of mental abnormality and criminality. Certain disorders have been chosen because their importance is sometimes overlooked. Alcohol and other drug abuse have not been included because these are not now intrinsically regarded in law, or in clinical practice, as mental disorders, although they may of course be associated with them. (However, I have dealt elsewhere with their relationship to crime generally and to violent crime in particular. See Prins, 1980a and 1986; see also Collins (ed), 1982).

Psychosis and crime

Affective disorder and crime

The relationship between severe depressive illness and serious offending has been well documented (see for example West, 1965; Schipkowensky, 1969; Hafner and Boker, 1982). However, the task of estimating the extent and duration of a depressive illness from a forensic point of view is very difficult. As Gunn et al. (1978) suggest: 'It is very difficult to establish, unless several helpful informants are available, whether a depressed murderer is depressed because he has been imprisoned for life, depressed by the enormity of his crime, or whether he committed murder because he was depressed in the first place . . .'. From a prognostic and management point of view, three kinds of case situations can usefully be recognized:

1. Cases in which the depressive state had not been recognized because its possibility had not been considered — a very important point.
2. A very small number of cases in which the clinical signs of depression disappeared as though the explosive nature of the criminal act had had a cathartic effect.
3. A few cases in which a tendency to repeated offences had been 'cured' by treating a depressive illness (Woddis, 1957).

In connection with severe depressive disorder, it is worth noting that the specific crime of infanticide[1] was originally introduced some 65 years ago, partly on the assumption that a post-puerperal state might, at least in part, be a cause of the offence. At the other end of the spectrum, milder depression may play its part in criminality (some cases of shoplifting would fall within this category) and these have been described by a number of researchers (Neustatter, 1953; Woddis, 1957; Gibbens et al., 1971; Lawson, 1984). Generally speaking, it is probably fair to suggest that severe depression is fairly rarely associated with offending, the exceptions being certain crimes of violence such as homicide and arson; milder forms may occasionally contribute to property offences such as shoplifting.

Manic episodes

Persons suffering from mania in varying degree sometimes come to the attention of the courts and associated authorities because of their frenetic, outrageous, disruptive and potentially dangerous behaviour. Such persons think themselves to be omnipotent and that their wild and grandiose ideas are entirely practical. For this reason they may overspend and get into serious debt or similar difficulties. Moreover, they are capable of giving rationalized arguments and explanations to support their proposed actions. They are almost always entirely without insight and usually require urgent compulsory care (Prins, 1980a and b).

Schizophrenic illnesses and criminality

The schizophrenic illnesses do not feature significantly from a numerical point of view in the causation or explanation of crime. Although Woddis (1957) found 9 out of 91 such cases referred to him from the courts, Kloek (1969) found only 1 case out of 500 referred to a Dutch court clinic. In 30 other cases the diagnosis of schizophrenia was considered to be a possibility, but doubtful. West (1965), in a highly selected 'morbid' sample, found only 4 out of 78 cases that could be classified as schizophrenic; 2 others were found to be suffering from morbid jealousy. Faulk (1976), in his rigorously selected sample of 72 men in Winchester Prison, assigned a diagnosis of schizophrenia in only 2 cases. The relationship between active, florid schizophrenic illness and violent crime has been surveyed extensively by Taylor (1982 and 1985), Taylor and Gunn (1985), Weller (1984 and 1986) and Bluglass (1988). It would appear to be not insignificant in some cases of homicide. In schizophrenia of more insidious onset and milder presentation, there is often an accompanying decline in social functioning and competence. In such cases, the individual may be tempted into, or drift into, crimes such as shoplifting, vagrancy type offences, breach of the peace or minor forms of arson (see for example Virkunnen, 1974 for a discussion of arson committed by schizophrenics). MacKay and Wight (1984), using a postal questionnaire, found that the involvement of schizophrenics in crime was trivial, for the most part, and that the police usually removed sufferers from the illness to hospital rather than subjecting them to prosecution.

Paranoid and allied states

Jealousy in varying degree is a fairly common phenomenon, and a degree of almost morbid suspiciousness is not uncommon amongst many offenders. In rather more severe form, the condition may be the result of alcoholic psychosis, dementia or manic-depressive illness and its presence in the elderly may be exacerbated by deafness (a point sometimes forgotten by the ill-informed). Its severest presentation may be seen in the abnormal condition of morbid or delusional jealousy. The consequence of this disorder may be very serious indeed for those who are the object of the paranoid individual's irrational ideas. One of the most serious problems is the degree to which such individuals appear to be perfectly sane and rational in every respect until their

1 The offence was originally created by the Infanticide Act 1922, and subsequently amended by the current statute — the Infanticide Act 1938.

252 Med. Sci. Law (1990) Vol. 30, No. 3

delusional ideas are touched upon. The condition has been graphically reviewed and described by Mowatt (1966), Planansky and Johnston (1977), Enoch and Trethowan (1979), Mullen and Maack (1985); see also Prins (1986, Chapter 4).

Hysteria, malingering, pseudo-dementia and amnesia

A few observations are in order concerning the role of hysterical states and their differentiation from both organic conditions and from malingering. (Hysterical states are those conditions in which motives, of which the patient seems unaware, produce a variety of disturbances of functioning which seems to provide some advantage or gain to the patient. Organic conditions differ in that it is usually possible to find some clear-cut physical explanation. Malingering is not an easy phenomenon to distinguish from hysteria, but the activities of the malingerer seem to be more consciously determined.) One or two useful generalizations may be stated briefly (for more detailed accounts see Prins, 1980a and b).

1. In malingering, the motivation is more or less at a conscious level; the symptoms are usually of sudden onset and have some connection with situations the malingerer wishes to avoid.
2. The symptoms are exaggerated. A good forensic example is the case of Haigh — the 'acid bath' murderer — who feigned insanity unsuccessfully.
3. Symptoms may be present only when the malingerer is being observed, and they may be made to order.
4. In cases of feigned illness, many of the usual signs and symptoms associated with the real illness may be missing.

Two associated conditions deserve brief mention: pseudo-dementia and the Ganser Syndrome. In these cases, the offender may give approximate answers, talk past the point and distort factual replies. Both conditions are comparatively rare; Ganser states are more commonly found in prison populations or comparable settings (see Schorer, 1965; Prins, 1980a, b and 1990 for more detailed discussion).

From time to time, offenders may claim an amnesic episode for their crime and/or the events leading up to or immediately following it. It is obviously important for courts to be able to satisfy themselves as to the genuineness of such a claim and to discern whether it be feigned, genuinely hysterical or of an organic origin. In the 1960s, O'Connell (1960) and Hays (1961) both addressed this problem. They concluded that it was extremely difficult to distinguish hysterical amnesia from apparent memory-loss due to conscious deception. Both conditions might co-exist in the same individual and serve a common purpose, namely loss of memory of an alleged crime. The problem has been discussed more recently by Taylor and Kopelman (1984). They found a variety of mechanisms that seem important in accounting for the amnesia — for example, repression, dissociation, and alcoholic 'blackouts'.

'Organic' conditions (the role of infections, disease, metabolic and hormonal disturbances and trauma)

A range of conditions that may conduce to criminality are now considered briefly. Some of them, the epilepsies for example, are not, of course, mental abnormalities as such, but they may produce psychiatric and psychological symptoms and sequelae. For brevity, they are discussed generically as 'organic'. It is important to stress that such states are only rarely associated with crime (see for example, Woddis, 1957; Faulk, 1976; Prins, 1986). However, because of their very rarity their importance may be overlooked by the less qualified and experienced.

Infections

Meningitis, encephalitis and a number of other conditions (such as herpes simplex) may produce severe or minimal brain damage followed by marked behavioural changes (Stott, 1963; Cleobury et al., 1971).

Huntington's Chorea

In this comparatively rare, but directly transmitted, hereditary and terminal condition there may be unpredictability of behaviour and occasional anti-social conduct, particularly in the early stages of the disease.

General Paralysis of the Insane (GPI)

This disorder, now rarely seen, is of syphilitic origin. It may produce lack of judgement or impropriety which may take a delinquent turn. On occasion it has been mistaken for a hypomanic state, but the differential diagnosis is quite easy on simple testing, such as the Wasserman Reaction. It is worth noting here that any outrageous, 'out of the blue' behaviour (particularly if it is recently repetitive) on the part of a person of previously impeccable behaviour and character, should alert us to the possible presence of this or other forms of 'organicity'.

Endocrine and hormonal disturbances

Hypoglycaemia may occur in certain predisposed individuals who have gone without food for long periods. Judgement may become impaired and there may be extreme irritability; individuals in such a state (as in untreated diabetes) may occasionally come into conflict with the legal and allied authorities. Thyroid imbalances may also have a part to play in anti-social behaviour, as may disturbances associated with various phases of the menstrual cycle (Dalton, 1982; D'Orban, 1983).

Brain trauma, tumour and the epilepsies

Brain injury, however caused, may have serious short- and long-term behavioural consequences. Minor brain injury or trauma may not always be easily detected and all professionals should be aware of the need for careful history taking. Children subject to abuse by parents may be particularly susceptible as may the children born to mothers who have been violently abused by their spouses or partners. Modern computerized radiographical techniques have provided much useful help in this complex area (Ward, 1978). It is also pertinent to note, as Buikhuisen (1982) has observed, that persistent offenders as a group appear to have more central nervous system dysfunction than control groups of non-offenders. The relationship between the epilepsies and crime (particularly violent crime) has been the subject of considerable study, notably by Gunn (see for example, Gunn, 1977b; Pincus, 1981). It would appear that epileptics are over-represented in prison populations, but this seems due as much to adverse social conditions such as overcrowded homes, where health care may be poor, and parental rejection, as to the epilepsy itself. Fenton (1984) tends to support this view: 'Though epilepsy is more common in prison populations than might be expected, anti-social behaviour as a direct result of . . . (for example) . . . epileptic automatism is rare' (p. 209). Gunn's original hypothesis gains support from a fairly recent study by Channon (1982). She examined an epileptic population drawn from an after-care hostel, a reception centre and a prison. The group appeared to be highly disadvantaged socially and the lack of adquate provision for their after-care seemed to have contributed to their continuing criminality.

Mental retardation,[2] genetic factors and crime

This section is concluded with some comments on the relationship between mental retardation and genetic (chromosomal) abnormalities and crime. There are several ways in which mental retardation may be associated with criminality. First, the retardation may be severe enough to prevent the person from understanding that their act was wrong in law, or they may be unfit to be tried. Second, the mild or moderately retarded offender may be more easily caught 'in the act'. Third, such offenders may be used very easily by others in the furtherance of delinquent activity; they may thus find themselves as unwitting accomplices. Fourth, if the retardation is associated with some kind of 'organic' disorder, the individual may be particularly impulsive and unpredictable. Fifth, a number of retarded persons have difficulties in making their often quite

2 The term 'mental retardation' is used in a generic sense to cover terms with a similar meaning such as handicap, subnormality or deficiency. It is not to be confused with mental *impairment*, which has a specific legal meaning within the mental health legislation.

254 Med. Sci. Law (1990) Vol. 30, No. 3

harmless intentions understood. Misunderstandings and subsequent rebuffs on the part of all parties may result perhaps in a criminal act, particularly a violent or sexual one. Sixth, public attitudes towards legitimate expressions of behaviour (such as sexuality) may be negative; this may make it difficult for the retarded individual to compete on equal terms with those more happily endowed. Finally, mentally retarded persons may be particularly vulnerable to changes in their social environment and may thus lapse quite easily into crime (see Prins, 1980a and Craft, 1984a for fuller discussion).

For nearly three decades there has been a considerable degree of interest in the possible relationship between chromosomal abnormalities, anomalies and crime (particularly violent crime) particularly, but not exclusively, the presence of the extra 'Y' chromosome. The research has been reviewed by Theilgaard (1983) and by Craft (1984b). In brief, little conclusive evidence for a causal link has been established. More than thirty years ago the distinguished geneticist Penrose stated that the disposition towards criminality was unlikely to be directly genetically determined (Penrose, 1955).

IMPLICATIONS FOR MANAGEMENT

The law has always made some allowance for mental abnormality in determining capacity and culpability for crime. However, at the risk of considerable over-simplification, it would seem that such allowance has often appeared to be capricious and, in some instances, idiosyncratic. Briefly put, the following are the main forms of psychiatric exculpation from responsibility for crime:

1. Severe insanity of the McNaghten variety may result in the 'special verdict' of not guilty by reason of insanity. That this is pleaded very rarely today is largely due to the severity of the test of insanity that is applied, to the extent that its use in murder cases has become virtually redundant since the passing of the Homicide Act, 1957, and because capital punishment has been abolished.
2. Inability to follow the proceedings, to challenge jurors and instruct counsel may permit a plea of 'unfitness to plead' (or being 'under disability' as it is now called). If successful, such a plea will also result in the 'special verdict'. One of the main problems with both these defences is that indefinite detention in hospital, usually under conditions of maximum security, is the automatic outcome. In addition, in the case of unfitness to plead, the facts of the case may never be heard unless the patient recovers sufficiently to be remitted for trial. This seems to occur only rarely.
3. Since 1957 (but only in murder cases) the accused may plead diminished responsibility on the grounds of an 'abnormality of mind'. If successful, such a plea will result in a verdict, or finding, of manslaughter, leaving the court unrestricted in its choice of disposal. If such a plea fails, the sentence is, of course, a mandatory one of life imprisonment, with or without a recommendation from the trial judge as to its length. The implementation of the Homicide Act has proved to be highly contentious and an area in which psychiatry and law have often proved to be incompatible; such public demonstrations of incompatibility have, on occasion, been far from edifying, as in the Sutcliffe and other well-known cases (Prins, 1983). The problem is that psychiatry does not lend itself well to the precise answers required by lawyers and judges. Various useful proposals for reform have been put forward, but have not as yet been acted upon (for summaries see: Home Office and DHSS, 1975; Prins 1980a and 1986).
4. In other cases, psychiatric evidence may be called in order to mitigate penalty. Generally speaking, courts do not request psychiatric reports very often. When they do, it is in cases where there would appear to be an important element of suspected mental abnormality. Examples are: homicide; serious repeated assault, sexual and non-sexual; cases in which the offence seems 'out of the blue'; repetitive crimes committed over a short period of time without obvious reason; or where the accused has a past or current history of mental disorder. (See Prins, 1980a and

Campbell, 1981 for reviews of some of the research.) Where courts do find, on the evidence, that mental disorder has played a significant part in the offending, or the offender is obviously ill at the time of the hearing, they may make orders under the relevant mental health legislation (Criminal Procedure (Insanity) Act, 1964 and Mental Health Act, 1983). They may also make probation orders with requirements for in- or out-patient treatment if the offender appears to require it, and is susceptible to informal, as distinct from compulsory, treatment. They may, of course, also deal with the case in such a manner that permits the offender to continue with treatment without any sanction for it being imposed. This is often the case when a defendant has been under medical care prior to the offence and/or the hearing. It is worth noting that even if mental disorder is present courts are not obliged to follow psychiatric advice, though they usually do (Prins, 1980a). It is also worth observing that cases do not always come to court; the police will sometimes exercise their discretion in the case of a mentally abnormal offender, perhaps by implementing the relevant section of the Mental Health Act, 1983 (s 136); or they may merely caution the person concerned in order to allow informal psychiatric care.

From the foregoing brief account one might think that both the legislation and the provisions were adquate for the disposal and treatment of mentally abnormal offenders. Both history and the contemporary scene inform us that this is not the case (see for example Parker, 1980 and 1985; Griew, 1988). There are many reasons for this, but the following seem to be the most important.

1. There are the arguments as to what kind of mental disorder or abnormality of mind is acceptable either in exculpation of criminal responsibility or in mitigation of penalty. A good example of the former is the current psychiatric and legal debate concerning epilepsy and its relationship to a finding of sane or insane automatism (see, for example, Duffield, 1987 for a short account of the main issues).
2. There are considerations of equity. A successful psychiatric defence or plea in mitigation may result in an offender spending far longer in hospital than if awarded a determinate sentence of imprisonment. Once in the system, considerations of possible dangerousness, quite apart from the presence of mental abnormality, may well mean a long period of incarceration (see, for example, Sadoff, 1978).

(3) During the last two decades, we have witnessed an increasing reluctance on the part of mental hospitals to receive or deal with offenders. This has come about for a number of reasons, one of the most important being the lack of secure facilities in ordinary mental hospitals. The slow gestation, birth and development of the secure units, first advocated in the Interim Report of the Butler Committee (Home Office and DHSS, 1974) have not provided an entirely satisfactory answer, partly because of divergencies of view as to the type of offender-patients they should receive.

4. The actual and impending closure of many large mental hospitals and the absence of adequate community support alternatives means that patients who require 'asylum' in the original meaning of the word are unlikely to receive it (MHAC, 1987). This, coupled with the more stringent criteria under the 1983 Mental Health Act for the detention in hospital of the mentally impaired and psychopathic, may well see these patients becoming increasingly marginalized and dealt with by the criminal justice and penal systems instead (see Lee-Evans, 1986; Adler, 1986). We could well see a reversion to the days before the passing of the Mental Deficiency Act, 1913 — an act which was passed in order to remove many such persons from our penal institutions.
5. The nihilistic, anti-therapeutic ideology that has been gaining ground in penal policy for some years has meant that prisons have not been willing or able to offer the therapeutic milieu that might have been a viable alternative to hospital

care (Orr, 1978; West, 1980 and 1985; Adams, 1985). In the light of our lack of knowledge about certain conditions, but particularly psychopathy, it would seem unwise to place all our therapeutic 'eggs' in one 'basket'. The Butler Committee unsuccessfully advocated treatment units in prisons for the more dangerous anti-social psychopaths (Home Office and DHSS, 1975); and more recently, Grounds (1987) has presented cogent arguments for not treating the seriously psychopathically disordered in the special hospitals. A much more flexible approach to the management and containment of mentally disordered offenders seems to be required. It is relevant to recall that nearly fifty years ago Penrose (1939) suggested, among other things, that there is an inverse relationship between the population of prisons and mental hospitals. This seems no less true today, for currently we have a situation where offender-patients are tossed back and forth like frail barks between hospital and correctional care. Menzies has expressed the problem graphically. We see 'a new kind of deviant — a medico-legal subject who drifts within and among systems, according to the peculiar currents of increasingly complex and interdependent institutional ecologies' (Menzies, 1987). Our need is for more rational and effective policies in order to encompass informed and flexible choice and equitable and compassionate containment (see also Beran and Toomey, 1979; Wardlaw, 1983).

CONCLUSIONS

In this article, an attempt has been made to show some of the difficulties involved in establishing clear causal connections between a broad range of mental abnormalities and crime, and the problems associated with sentencing and managing those who suffer from them. Most psychiatric disorders are only very occasionally associated with criminality; perhaps, because of this very rare association it is all the more important to be alert to it so that the importance of correct diagnosis in such rare cases is not overlooked. There is, of course, a much clearer connection between disorders of personality and criminality, but it has not been possible to discuss these controversial disorders within the confines of this particular presentation. At a time when notions of 'treatment' for criminality are not particularly popular it is hoped that this presentation has served as a reminder of the possibilities for clinical intervention for some kind of offenders.

REFERENCES

Adams K. (1985) Addressing inmate mental health problems: a new direction for prison therapeutic services. *Fed. Prob.* **XLIX**, 27–33.

Adler F. (1986) Jails as a repository for former mental patients. *Int. J. Off. Ther. and Comp. Crimin.* **30**, 225–36.

Appleby L and Wesseley S. (1988) Public attitudes to mental illness: the Influence of the Hungerford Massacre. *Med. Sci. Law*, **28**, 291–5.

Bark N. M. (1985) Did Shakespeare know schizophrenia? The case of poor mad Tom in *King Lear*. *Brit. J. Psychiat.* **146**, 436–8.

Beran N. J. and Toomey B. G. (1979) *Mentally Ill Offenders and the Criminal Justice System: Issues in Forensic Services*. New York, Praeger.

Bluglass R. (1988) Psychiatric approaches to aggression and violence, In: *Clinical Approaches to Aggression and Violence* (eds., Howells K. and Hollin C.), Leicester, British Psychological Society (Division of Criminological and Legal Psychology: Issues in Criminological and Legal Psychology, No. 12).

Brill H. and Malzberg B. (1962) Statistical report of the arre record of male patients released from New York State mental hospitals during the period 1946–1948. In: *Criminal Acts of Ex-Mental Hospital Patients.* (Supplement No. 153). Washington D. C. American Psychiatric Association Mental Hospital Service.

Buikhuisen W. (1982) Aggressive behaviour and cognitive disorders. *Int. J. Law & Psychiat.* **5**, 205–17.

Campbell I. G. (1981) The influence of psychiatric pre-sentence reports. *Int. J. Law and Psychiat.*, **4**, 89–106.

Camporesi P. (1989) *Bread of Dreams: Food and Fantasy in Early Modern Europe*. London, Polity Press.

Channon S. (1982) The Resettlement of Epileptic Offenders. In: Gunn J. and Farrington D. P. (eds.). *Abnormal Offenders, Delinquency and the Criminal Justice System*. Chichester, John Wiley.

Cleobury J. R., Skinner G. R. B., Thouless M. E. and Wildy P. (1971) Association between psychopathic disorder and serum anti-body to herpes simplex virus (Type 1). *Brit. Med. J.* **1**, 438–9.

Coid J. (1984) How many psychiatric patients in prison? *Brit. J. Psychiat.* **145**, 78–86.

Coid J. (1988a) Mentally abnormal prisoners on remand: (I) accepted or rejected by the NHS. *Brit. Med. J.* **296** 1779–82.

Coid J. (1988b) Mentally abnormal prisoners on remand: (II) - comparison of services provided by Oxford and Wessex Regions. *Brit. Med. J.*, **296**, 1783–4.

Collins J. J. (Ed) (1982) *Drinking and Crime: Perspectives on the Relationship Between Alcohol Consumption and Criminal Behaviour*. London, Tavistock.

Cook D. A. G.(1983) A study of criminal behaviour in discharged male psychiatric patients. *Med. Sci. Law* **23**, 279–82.

Craft M. (1984a) Low intelligence, mental handicap and criminality. In: Craft M. and Craft A. (eds.). *Mentally Abnormal Offenders*. London, Bailliere.

Craft M. (1984b) Genetic endowment and the XYY syndrome. In: Craft M. and Craft A. (eds.). *Mentally Abnormal Offenders*. London, Bailliere.

Croft J. (1978) *Research in Criminal Justice*. Home Office Research Study No. 44. HORU. London: HMSO.

Dalton K. (1982) Legal implications of P.M.S. *World Med.* **17**, 93–4.

D'Orban P. T. (1983) Medico-legal aspects of premenstrual syndrome. *Brit. J. Hosp. Med.* **30**, 404–9.

Duffied B. (1987) The impossible choice facing epileptics. *The Listener*, 10.12.87 (p.16).

Enoch M. D. and Trethowan W. (1979) *Uncommon Psychiatric Syndromes*. (Second ed.). Bristol, John Wright.

Faulk M. (1976) A psychiatric study of men serving a sentence in Winchester prison. *Med. Sci. Law*, **16**, 244–51.

Feldman M. (1977) *Criminal Behaviour: A Psychological Analysis*. London, John Wiley.

Fenton G. (1984) Epilepsy, mental abnormality and criminal behaviour. In: Craft M. and Craft A. (eds). *Mentally Abnormal Offenders*. London, Bailliere.

Gibbens T. C. N., Palmer C. and Prince J. (1971) Mental health aspects of shoplifting. *Brit. Med. J.* **3**, 612–15.

Griew E. (1988) Mental Disorder and the criminal code. In: *Psychiatric Disorders and the Criminal Process*. MacKay R. and Russell K. (eds). Leicester Polytechnic School of Law Monograph, Leicester.

Grounds A. T. (1987) 'Psychopathic disorder' patients in special hospitals: critical issues. *Brit. J. Psychiat.* **151**, 474–8.

Gunn J. (1977a) Criminal Behaviour and mental disorder. *Brit. J. Psychiat.* **130**, 317–29.

Gunn J. (1977b) *Epileptics in Prison*. London, Academic Press.

Gunn J., Robertson G., Dell S. and Way C. (1978) *Psychiatric Aspects of Imprisonment*. London, Academic Press.

Guze S. B. (1976) *Criminality and Psychiatric Disorders*. Oxford, Oxford University Press.

Häfner H. and Böker W. (1982) *Crimes of Violence by Mentally Abnormal Offenders*. Cambridge, Cambridge University Press.

Hare E. (1983) Was insanity on the increase? *Brit. J. Psychiat.* **142**, 439–55.

Hays P. (1961) Hysterical amnesia and the Podola trial. *Medico-Legal J.* **29**, 27–32.

Hill D. (1982) Public attitudes to mentally abnormal offenders. In: Gunn J. and Farrington D. P. (eds). *Abnormal Offenders Delinquency and the Criminal Justic System*. Chichester, John Wiley.

Home Office and DHSS (1974) *Interim Report of the Committee on Mentally Abnormal Offenders* Cmnd. 5698. London, HMSO.

Home Office and DHSS (1975) *Report of the Committee on Mentally Abnormal Offenders*. Cmnd. 6244. London, HMSO.

House of Commons (1988) Written reply by Douglas Hogg, 22.12.88.

Howells K. (1982) Mental disorder and violent behaviour. In: Feldman P. (ed). *Developments in the Study of Criminal Behaviour*. Volume 2: *Violence*. Chichester, John Wiley.

Kloek J. (1969) Schizophrenia and delinquency: the inadequacies of our conceptual framework. In: de Rueck A. V. S. and Porter R. (eds). *The Mentally Abnormal Offender*. London, J. and A. Churchill.

Laing R. D. and Esterson A. (1964) *Sanity, Madness and the Family*. London, Tavistock.

Lawson W. K. (1984) Depression and crime: a discursive approach. In: Craft M. and Craft A. (eds). *Mentally Abnormal Offenders*. London, Bailliere.

Lee-Evans M. (1986) The Mental Health Act and the treatment of abnormal offenders. In: Hollin C. and Howells K. (eds). *Clinical Approaches to Criminal Behaviour. Issues in Criminological and Legal Psychology*. No. 9 Leicester, British Psychological Society.

Mackay R. D. and Wight R. E. (1984) Schizophrenia and anti-social criminal behaviour — some responses from sufferers and relatives. *Med. Sci. Law*, **24**, 192–8.

McClintock F. H. and Avison N. H. (1968) *Crime in England and Wales*. London, Heinemann.

Mental Health Act Commission (1987) *Second Biennial Report, 1985–1987* October, London, HMSO.

Menzies R. J. (1987) Cycles of control: the transcarceral careers of forensic patients. *Int. J. Law and Psychiat.* **10**, 223–49.

Mowatt R. R. (1966) *Morbid Jealousy and Murder*. London, Tavistock.

Mullen P. E. and Maack L. H (1985) Jealousy, pathological jealousy and aggression. In: Gunn J. and Farrington D. P. (eds). *Aggression and Dangerousness*. Chichester, John Wiley.

Mulvey E. P., Blumstein A. and Cohen J. (1986) Reframing the research question of male patient criminality. *Int. J. Law and Psychiat.* **9**, 57–65.

NACRO (1987) NACRO Briefing. *Mentally Disordered Offenders*. Clapham, London.

258 Med. Sci. Law (1990) Vol. 30, No. 3

Neustatter W. L. (1953) *Psychological Disorder and Crime*. London, Christopher Johnson.

O'Connell B. A. (1960) Amnesia and homicide: a study of 50 murderers. *Brit. J. Delinq.* **X,** 262–76.

Orr J. H. (1978) The imprisonment of mentally disordered offenders. *Brit. J. Psychiat.* **133,** 194–9.

Parker E. (1980) Mentally disordered offenders and their protection from punitive sanctions: the English experience. *Int. J. Law and Psychiat.* **3,** 461–9.

Parker E. (1985) The development of secure provision. In: Gostin L. (ed.) *Secure Provision: A Review of Special Services for the Mentally Ill and Mentally Handicapped in England and Wales*. London, Tavistock.

Penrose L. S. (1939) Mental disorder and crime: outcome of a comparative study of European statistics. *Brit. J. Med. Psychol.* **18,** 1–15.

Penrose L. S. (1955) Genetics and the criminal. *Brit. J. Delinq.* **VII,** 15–25.

Pincus J. H. (1981) Violence and epilepsy. *New England J. Med.* **305,** 696–8.

Planansky K. and Johnston R. (1977) Homicidal aggression in schizophrenic men. *Acta Psychiat. Scandinav.* **55,** 65–73.

Prins H. (1980a) *Offenders, Deviants or Patients: An Introduction to the Study of Socio-Forensic Problems*. London, Tavistock.

Prins H. (1980b) Mad or bad: thoughts on the equivocal relationship between mental disorder and criminality. *Int. J. Law and Psychiat.* **3,** 421–33.

Prins H. (1983) Diminished responsibility and the Sutcliffe case: legal, psychiatric and social aspects. *Med. Sci. Law,* **23,** 17–24.

Prins H. (1986) *Dangerous Behaviour, The Law and Mental Disorder*. London, Tavistock.

Prins H. (1987) Understanding and managing insanity: some glimpses into historical fact and fiction. *Brit. J. Soc. Wk.* **17,** 91–8.

Prins H. (1990) Ganser and allied states. In: *Bizarre Behaviours*, London, Routledge.

Rabkin J. G. (1979) Criminal behaviour and discharged mental patients: a critical appraisal of the research. *Psychol. Bull.* **86,** 1–27.

Rappeport J. R. and Lassen G. (1967) Dangerousness — arrest rate comparisons of discharged patients and the general population. In: Rappeport J. R. (ed.) *Evaluation of the Dangerousness of the Mentally Ill*. Springfield, Illinois, Charles C. Thomas.

Robertson G. (1988) Arrest patterns among mentally disordered offenders. *Brit. J. Psychiat.* **153,** 313–16.

Rollin H. (1969) *The Mentally Abnormal Offender and the Law*. Oxford, Pergamon.

Rosen G. (1968) *Madness in Society*. London, Routledge and Kegan Paul.

Roth M. and Kroll J. (1986) *The Reality of Mental Illness*. Cambridge, Cambridge University Press.

Sadoff R. L. (1978) Developing community mental health centre — criminal justice system interactions. *Int. J. Law and Psychiat.* **1,** 427–37.

Schipkowensky N. (1969) Affective disorders: cyclophrenia and murder. In: Rueck A. V. S. and Porter R. (eds.). *The Mentally Abnormal Offender*. London, J. and A. Churchill.

Schorer C. E. (1965) The Ganser Syndrome. *Brit. J. Criminol.* **5,** 120–31.

Scott P. D. (1969) Crime and delinquency. *Brit. Med. J.* **1,** 424–6.

Scull A. (1984) Was insanity on the increase? A response to Edward Hare. *Brit. J. Psychiat.* **144,** 432–6.

Slater E. and Roth M. (1969) *Clinical Psychiatry* (third ed.). London, Bailliere Tindall and Cassell.

Stott D. H. (1963) New possibilities in the aetiology of delinquency. *Int. Annals Criminol.* **2,** 1–11.

Szasz T. (1987) *Insanity: The Idea and its Consequences*. New York, John Wiley.

Taylor P. J. (1982) Schizophrenia and violence. In: Gunn J. and Farrington D. P. (eds.). *Abnormal Offenders, Delinquency and the Criminal Justice System*. Chichester, John Wiley.

Taylor P. J. (1985) Motives for offending among violent and psychotic men. *Brit. J. Psychiat.* **147,** 491–8.

Taylor P. J. (1986) Psychiatric disorder in London's life-sentenced offenders. *Brit. J. Criminol.* **26,** 63–78.

Taylor P. J. and Kopelman M. D. (1984) Amnesia for criminal offences. *Psychol. Med.* **14,** 581–8.

Taylor P. J. and Gunn J. (1985) Violence and psychosis: 1: risk of violence among psychotic men. *Brit. Med. J.* **288,** 1945–9.

Theilgaard A. (1983) Aggression and the XYY personality. *Int. J. Law and Psychiat.* **6,** 413–21.

Topp D. O. (1979) Suicide in prison. *Brit. J. Psychiat.* **134,** 24–7.

Virkunnen M. (1974) On arson committed by schizophrenics. *Acta Psychiat. Scandinav.* **50,** 152–4.

Walker N. (1968) *Crime and Insanity in England*. (Volume 1) Edinburgh University Press.

Ward P. (1978) Head injury and the C.T. scanner. *Med. Sci. Law,* **18,** 263–90.

Wardlaw G. (1983) Models for the custody of mentally disordered offenders. *Int. J. Law and Psychiat.* **6,** 159–76.

Weller M. (1984) Violence and mental illness. *Brit. Med. J.* **289,** 2–3.

Weller M. (1986) Medical concepts in psychopathy and violence. *Med. Sci. Law,* **26,** 131–43.

West D. J. (1965) *Murder Followed by Suicide*. London, MacMillan.

West D. J. (1980) The Clinical Approach to Criminology. *Psychol. Med.* **10,** 619–31.

West D. J. (1985) Clinical criminology under attack. In: Ben-Aron M. H., Hucker S. J. and Webster C. D. (eds.). *Clinical Criminology: The Assessment and Treatment of Criminal Behaviour*, Clarke Institute of Psychiatry, Toronto.

Woddis G. (1957) Depression and crime. *Brit. J. Delinq.* **VIII,** 85–94.

ADDENDUM

Since this work was publised in 1990, one or two important volumes have appeared that supplement and up-date the information provided above. They are as follows:-

Bluglass, R. and Bowden, P. (eds.), *Principles and Practice of Forensic Psychiatry*. London: Churchill Livingstone.

Chiswick, D. and Cope, R. (eds.), (1995), *Seminars in Practical Forensic Psychiatry*. London: Glaskell Books.

Gunn, J. and Taylor, P.J. (eds.) (1993), *Forensic Psychiatry: Clinical Legal and Ethical Issues. London: Butterworth-Heinemann.*

Hodgins, S. (ed.) (1993), *Mental Disorder and Crime*. London: Sage.

* All the above have extensive material on the complex relationship between mental disorders and crime.

February 1998 Herschel Prins

[5]

Original Article

Mental Disorder, Intellectual Deficiency, and Crime

Evidence From a Birth Cohort

Sheilagh Hodgins, PhD

• Studies of criminality among patients in psychiatric hospitals and of mental disorder among incarcerated offenders have suggested an association between the major mental disorders (schizophrenia and major affective disorders) and crime. However, these investigations are characterized by notable methodological weaknesses, and, consequently, this conclusion has remained tentative. Little is known about the criminality of intellectually handicapped people. The present study examined the relationship between crime and mental disorder and crime and intellectual deficiency in an unselected Swedish birth cohort followed up to age 30 years. It was found that men with major mental disorders were 2½ times more likely than men with no disorder or handicap to be registered for a criminal offense and four times more likely to be registered for a violent offense. Women with major disorders were five times more likely than women with no disorder or handicap to be registered for an offense and 27 times more likely to be registered for a violent offense. These subjects committed many serious offenses throughout their lives. The criminal behavior in over half these cases appeared before the age of 18 years. Intellectually handicapped men were three times more likely to offend than men with no disorder or handicap and five times more likely to commit a violent offense. Intellectually handicapped women were almost four times more likely to offend than women with no disorder or handicap and 25 times more likely to commit a violent offense. The results of this investigation confirm and extend previous findings indicating that individuals with major mental disorders and those with intellectual handicaps are at increased risk for offending and for violent offending. However, in the United States, where rates of crime overall and crime by substance abusers are very high, the mentally disordered and intellectually handicapped would account for only a small proportion of these offenses.

(*Arch Gen Psychiatry*. 1992;49:476-483)

It has long been presumed by the general public that there is an association between mental disorder and violence and between intellectual handicap and violence. This belief has been reflected in literature and art and in both the civil and criminal laws of most countries around the world. Scientists, however, have only recently carried out investigations designed to address these issues.

Accepted for publication March 19, 1992.

From the Department of Psychology, Université de Montréal, Québec.

Reprint requests to Department of Psychology, Université de Montréal, CP 6128, Suc. "A," Montréal, Québec, Canada H1C 1H1 (Dr Hodgins).

Studies of Mentally Disordered Persons

Investigations of patients in the hospital and in the days preceding admission have revealed that many behave aggressively.[1-7] However, since aggressive individuals are more likely to be admitted than persons with symptoms of equal severity who are threatening, the observed association between mental disorder and aggressive behavior may result from sampling bias.

Follow-up studies of patients discharged from psychiatric wards[8-17] have suggested that more of these persons commit crimes than the general population of the community where they are released. The differences between the rates of conviction for the ex-patients and the general population are usually found to be greater for violent than nonviolent crimes.[9,12,13,16] There is a suggestion that men with substance abuse problems, men with schizophrenia, and those with both are at increased risk for criminality.[9,11,18,19] However, follow-up periods in these investigations were short, and samples of ex-patients rarely remained intact throughout. Consequently, patients who committed crimes would be more likely to be counted at the end of the follow-up period than patients who left treatment and had no contacts with the police. Data on criminal convictions were in many studies limited to one state or jurisdiction. Diagnoses were taken from hospital files and not validated in any way. In addition, it is difficult to compare the results from these various studies, as there is no way of knowing whether the distributions of diagnoses in the samples are similar. At the time the studies were conducted, some hospitals admitted large numbers of alcoholics, drug abusers, and patients with personality disorders, while others restricted inpatient care to psychotics.

A recent investigation,[20] which has none of these methodological weaknesses, included all inpatients in Stockholm County, Sweden, with a diagnosis of schizophrenia who were born between 1920 and 1959 and discharged in 1971. Patients underwent rediagnosis by an independent clinician, using *DSM-III* criteria, and 85% (644 patients) met the criteria for schizophrenia. These 644 patients were then followed up for 14 years. The relative risk of a criminal offense among these schizophrenics compared with the general Swedish population was 1.2 for the men and 2.2 for the women. However, the schizophrenics "committed four times as many violent offenses as the general population."[20(pp346-347)] Fifty-five percent of the schizophrenic subjects who were convicted of a crime also had a history of substance abuse.[21]

A number of investigations suggest that schizophrenics and their biological relatives are at increased risk for criminality. In a study of a cohort of 9182 consecutive live births, it was found that the offspring of schizophrenics had higher rates of registration for criminal offenses than those of parents with no disorder.[22] In the Danish high-risk schizophrenia project,[23] more of the high-risk mothers and children were registered for criminality than the low-risk mothers and children. The children's criminality was verified when they were between 21 and 31 years of age. Studies of children at increased genetic risk for schizophrenia identify an aggressive subgroup.[24] One study[22] of a cohort of 6770 male adoptees found that schizophrenia in the biological parents increased the risk of criminal behavior in the children. Furthermore, Kay[25] reports that the biological relatives of schizophrenics with positive symptoms frequently display antisocial behavior.

Studies of Offenders

Rather than looking at the criminality of identified patients, some investigators have focused on the mental disorders of criminals. Recent studies of representative samples of US prison inmates[26-29] and Canadian penitentiary inmates[30] have revealed higher prevalences of major mental disorders within these facilities than in the general population. Furthermore, two of these studies demonstrate that large numbers of the male inmates with major disorders are also substance abusers.[31,32] These five investigations all employed the same diagnostic criteria[33] and used standardized, reliable, and valid diagnostic instruments. These same instruments have been used to examine the prevalence of mental disorders in the general population,[34] and, consequently, comparisons between the prevalence of disorders among inmates and in the general population can be made with some confidence.

In addition to these studies showing that major mental disorders are more prevalent among incarcerated offenders than in the general population, three investigations suggest that the prevalence of major disorders is even higher among homicide offenders. Most investigations of homicide offenders include only compilations of assessments conducted at the request of the court. Such samples are biased and represent only a small proportion of homicide offenders.[35] In Scandinavia, all persons accused of homicide are evaluated by at least one psychiatrist, and these assessments are reviewed by panels composed of a number of other psychiatrists. A study of all homicide offenders in Copenhagen, Denmark, over a 25-year period revealed that 20% of the men and 44% of the women had a diagnosis of psychosis.[36] Among those who received a diagnoses of psychosis, 13% of the women and 41% of the men were found to be substance abusers. Lindqvist[37] studied every person who committed a homicide in Northern Sweden between 1970 and 1981. Thirty-four (53%) of 64 subjects were found to suffer from a major mental disorder, and slightly more than one third of them also received a diagnosis of substance abuse and/or dependence. Similarly, Côté and Hodgins,[38] working in Canada, have reported elevated prevalences (35%) of major mental disorders among homicide offenders.

A Population Study

To examine the relationship between mental disorder and crime, the research design with the least weaknesses is that of a longitudinal prospective study of an unselected birth cohort. This design limits any sampling bias, particularly if the cohort remains intact throughout the study. The use of central registers ensures that all convictions are compiled. Such an investigation is limited, however, by the use of hospitalization as an indicator of mental disorder. To our knowledge, only one study, a Danish thesis, has employed this design.

Ortmann[39] examined the criminal records of an entire birth cohort composed of 11 540 men born in Copenhagen in 1953 and still alive in Denmark in 1975. Data on admissions to psychiatric wards were collected from the central Danish psychiatric register in 1978 when the subjects were 25 years old. Data on offenses were collected from the central police register in 1976 when the subjects were 23 years old. While 34.8% of all the men with no disorder had been registered for at least one offense (comparable to the registration rate found in the Scandinavian countries for men[40]), 43.5% of those admitted with a major disorder, 83.2% of those admitted with substance abuse and/or dependence, and 50.9% of those with other diagnoses had been registered for an offense. Significantly more of those with psychiatric admissions had been convicted in every category of offense. While there were not many subjects within each diagnostic group, Ortmann's results suggested that the registration rates varied considerably by diagnosis.

Conclusion

The findings of studies of mentally disordered persons and of incarcerated offenders and one investigation of an unselected birth cohort suggest a relationship between major mental disorder and criminality. This relationship appears to be stronger among men, in the presence of a secondary diagnosis of substance abuse/dependence, and for violent rather than nonviolent crime.

Intellectual Capacity and Crime

Many studies have shown that offenders have lower IQ test scores than nonoffenders.[41,42] The difference in global IQ is about half an SD.[43] Prospective longitudinal investigations have demonstrated that children with lower IQ test scores are at increased risk for official delinquency and for self-reported delinquency.[44,45] This relationship has been shown to be independent of social class, race, and detection by the police.[46] Intellectual capacity is a factor that appears to protect otherwise high-risk boys from criminal involvement.[45,46]

While many studies have documented this relationship between intellectual capacity and official criminality, we were able to find only one investigation of the criminality of a population of intellectually deficient persons. Høgh and Wolf[47] investigated all 12 270 boys born in 1953 in the major urban areas of Denmark. In 1976, when the boys were 23 years of age, criminality was examined for all those still alive (94% of the original birth cohort). The IQ was assessed using a Danish adaptation of the Swedish test developed by Härnqvist. (Each subtest has scores ranging from zero to 40. The three subtest scores are summed to give a global score.) Half the sample, 7868 boys, were tested at age 12 years. One in five of the boys with an IQ score of 68 or lower had been registered for an offense by age 23 years as opposed to 8% of those with IQ scores of 90 to 120. This difference is greater for violent crimes than for nonviolent crimes. In fact, the boys who would most certainly be considered intellectually handicapped (IQ score of 1 to 44) were 13 times more likely than boys whose IQ score fell in the normal range to have been registered for a violent offense.

The Present Investigation

The present study was conducted to confirm and extend the reported findings about the relationship between mental disorder and crime and intellectual deficiency and crime. An unselected birth cohort was followed up to age 30 years. Data were collected from national psychiatric and police registers.

SUBJECTS AND METHODS

Subjects

The cohort is composed of all 15 117 persons born in Stockholm in 1953 and residing there in 1963.[48] Only subjects living in Sweden at the end of the 30-year follow-up period were included in the analyses.

Subjects who had been admitted to a psychiatric ward were divided into three groups based on the most serious discharge diagnosis: major mental disorder (schizophrenia, major affective disorders, paranoid states, and other psychoses), alcohol and/or drug abuse and/or dependence, and all other mental disorders. Among the 7362 men, 1.1% (82 subjects) were classified as having a major mental disorder, 2.1% (156 subjects) as being alcohol and/or drug abusers or dependent on alcohol and/or drugs, and 0.9% (64 subjects) as suffering from other mental disorders. Of the 7039 women, 1.1% (79 subjects) were classified as having a major mental disorder, 1.4% (98 subjects) as having alcohol and/or drug abuse or dependence, and 1.8% (124 subjects) as having another mental disorder. Studies of the schizophrenia diagnoses in this register[49] and in other Swedish registers[50] have suggested that these diagnoses are valid and closely resemble *DSM-III* diagnoses.

Intellectually handicapped subjects were defined as those who were placed in special classes for intellectually deficient children in high school and were never admitted to a psychiatric ward. Thus, 1.5% of the men (113 subjects) and 1.1% of the women (79 subjects) were considered intellectually handicapped. The comparison group was composed of all subjects who had never been admitted to a psychiatric ward or to an institution or class for the intellectually handicapped.

Procedure

In 1983, criminal records were collected from the Swedish National Police Register, and mental health records were collected from the Stockholm County register. Pregnancy and birth records, family data, school records, social welfare agency records, and military records were collected for all subjects.

RESULTS

Prevalence of Criminality

As can be seen in Fig 1, significantly more of the men with a major mental disorder, an intellectual handicap, or diagnosed substance abuse had been convicted of at least one criminal offense than men with other mental disorders or those with no disorder and no handicap. Men with major mental disorders were 2.56 (95% confidence interval [CI], 1.66 to 3.97) times more likely to have been convicted of a criminal offense than men with no disorder or handicap. The comparable odds ratio for men with other disorders was 1.15 (95% CI, 0.69 to 1.93); for intellectually handicapped men, 3.12 (95% CI, 2.17 to 4.49); and, for men

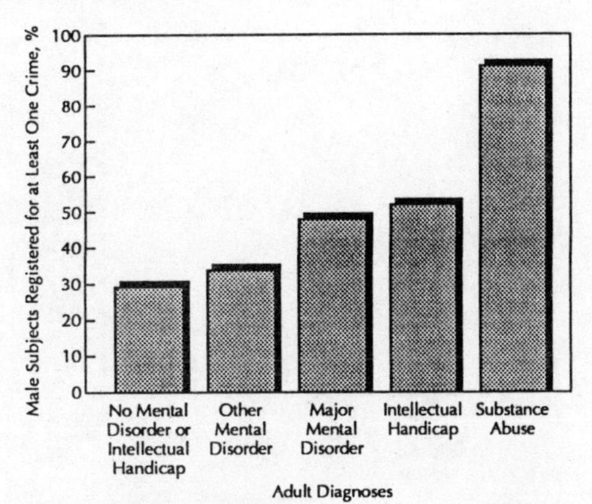

Fig 1.—*Male subjects registered for at least one crime by age 30 years by adult diagnosis status ($\chi^2[4, N=7362]=290.23$, P=.00000). Compared with subjects with no mental disorder or intellectual handicap, for subjects with other mental disorder, $\chi^2(1, N=7011)=0.74$ (not significant); for subjects with major mental disorder, $\chi^2(1, N=7029)=12.74$ (P=.01 corrected for type I error by the Bonferroni formula, P=.0025); for subjects with intellectual handicap, $\chi^2(1, N=7060)=25.44$ (P=.00000); and for substance abusers, $\chi^2(1, N=7103)=260.34$ (P=.00000).*

with diagnoses of substance abuse/dependence, 20.37 (95% CI, 12.12 to 34.26).

Figure 2 presents these results for the female subjects. Proportionately more subjects with major mental disorders and substance abuse problems were convicted of crimes than women with no disorder and no handicap. Women with major mental disorders were 5.02 (95% CI, 2.78 to 9.06) times more likely to have been convicted for a criminal offense than women with no disorder or handicap. The comparable odds ratio for women with other disorders was 1.67 (95% CI, 0.91 to 3.05); for intellectually handicapped subjects, 3.73 (95% CI, 2.00 to 6.94); and, for women with diagnoses of substance abuse/dependence, 32.34 (95% CI, 21.11 to 49.53).

Age Patterns

The patterns of proportions of subjects within each diagnostic group who had been convicted of a criminal offense are relatively stable over time for both the men and the women. In fact, χ^2 values calculated separately for gender and on group differences for convictions before age 15 years, from age 15 to 18 years, 18 to 21 years, and 21 to 30 years were all highly significant. In all age groups, the percentages of subjects with a major mental disorder, intellectual handicap, or substance abuse who had been convicted of a crime exceeded those of the subjects with no disorder and no handicap.

As can be observed in Fig 3, official criminal activity appears to begin at different ages for the different groups of male subjects. Among the men with no disorder and no handicap and those with an adult substance abuse diagnosis, the proportion of subjects beginning their criminal careers decreased with age. This pattern also describes the intellectually handicapped subjects, but the decrease begins only after age 18 years. However, among the men who develop major mental disorders, the proportions who begin their criminal careers at each age are more erratic—12%, 18%, 7%, and 9% at less than 15 years, 15 to 18 years, 18 to 21 years, and 21 to 30 years, respectively.

As can be observed in Fig 4, the proportion of women with no disorder and no handicap who begin their criminal careers remains stable over time. Among the substance abusers, the proportion of subjects beginning their criminal careers increases

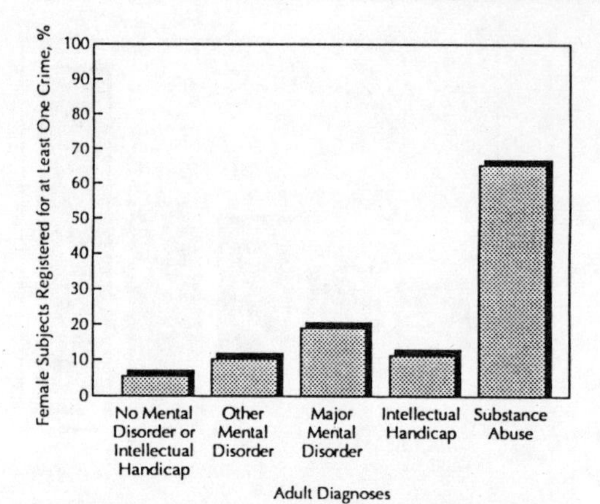

Fig 2.—*Female subjects registered for at least one crime by age 30 years by adult diagnosis status ($\chi^2[4, N=7039]=617.82$, P=.00000). Compared with subjects with no mental disorder or intellectual handicap, for subjects with other mental disorder, $\chi^2(1, N=6783)=5.57$ (not significant); for subjects with major mental disorder, $\chi^2(1, N=6738)=25.96$ (P=.00000); for subjects with intellectual handicap, $\chi^2(1, N=6738)=4.31$ (not significant); and for substance abusers, $\chi^2(1, N=6757)=617.03$ (P=.00000).*

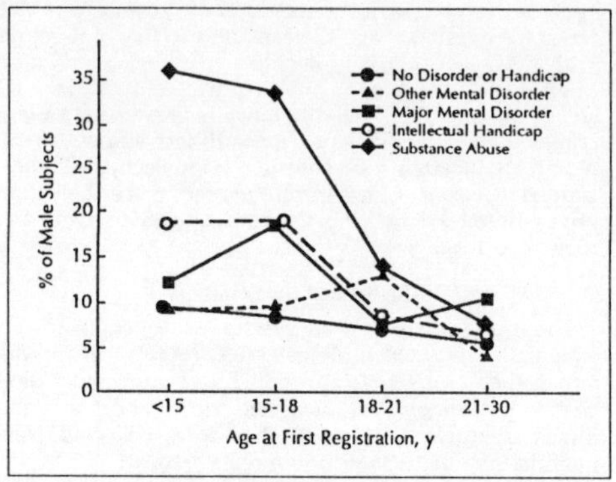

Fig 3.—*Male subjects by age at first registration. For first registration at less than age 15 years, compared with subjects with no mental disorder or intellectual handicap (NOMD), for subjects with other mental disorder (OMD), $\chi^2(1, N=7011)=0.00$ (not significant [NS]); for subjects with major mental disorder (MMD), $\chi^2(1, N=7029)=0.71$; for subjects with intellectual handicap (IH), $\chi^2(1, N=7060)=10.67$ (P=.001); and for substance abusers (SA), $\chi^2(1, N=7101)=120.75$ (P=.00000). For first registration at age 15 to 18 years, compared with NOMD, for OMD, $\chi^2(1, N=7011)=0.075$ (NS); for MMD, $\chi^2(1, N=7029)=10.12$ (P=.002); for IH, $\chi^2(1, N=7060)=14.64$ (P=.0001); and for SA, $\chi^2(1, N=7101)=118.52$ (P=.00000). For first registration at age 18 to 21 years, compared with NOMD, for OMD, $\chi^2(1, N=7011)=3.49$ (NS); for MMD, $\chi^2(1, N=7029)=0.06$ (NS); for IH, $\chi^2(1, N=7060)=0.32$ (NS); and for SA, $\chi^2(1, N=7101)=7.77$ (P=.005). For first registration at age 21 to 30 years, compared with NOMD, for OMD, $\chi^2(1, N=7011)=0.445$ (NS); for MMD, $\chi^2(1, N=7029)=3.97$ (NS); for IH, $\chi^2(1, N=7060)=0.37$ (NS); and for SA, $\chi^2(1, N=7101)=1.55$ (NS).*

up to age 21 years, then levels off. Among the intellectually handicapped, there is a burst of activity between the ages of 18 and 21 years. Among the women with major disorders, the proportions beginning their criminal careers at each age appear to be more stable, with an increase after age 21 years.

While 10.8% of the men with no disorder and no handicap were convicted in two or more age groups, 18.7% of the men with other disorders, 25.6% of those with major disorders, 32.7% of those with an intellectual handicap, and 72.4% of the substance abusers were convicted in at least two different age groups. Given the small number of female subjects in each group, patterns of convictions across age groups are difficult to verify.

Number of Convictions

Among the male offenders with no disorders and no handicap, the mean number of convictions was 7.3 (SD, 19.6); among offenders with other mental disorders, 12.0 (SD, 16.4) ($t[2066]=1.13$, $P=.261$); among offenders with a major mental disorder, 13.2 (SD, 16.4) ($t[2083]=1.87$, $P=.062$); among offenders with an intellectual handicap, 10.0 (SD, 17.2) ($t[2102]=1.03$, $P=.304$); and among substance abusers, 29.5 (SD, 39.3) ($t[143.78]=6.64$, $P=.000$). Similarly, among the female offenders, those with no disorder and no handicap had a mean number of convictions of 3.3 (SD, 7.0); among those with other mental disorders, 3.8 (SD, 3.6) ($t[14.09]=.41$, $P=.691$); among those with a major disorder, 3.8 (SD, 4.8) ($t[344]=.26$, $P=.795$); among those with an intellectual handicap, 7.9 (SD, 7.8) ($t[338]=1.83$, $P=.068$); and among substance abusers, 10.8 (SD, 19.3) ($t[65.11]=3.06$, $P=.003$). While the within-group variances are large, it appears that male and female offenders with a major disorder and those with an intellectual handicap commit as many offenses as offenders with no disorder, or even more.

Types of Offenses

Offenses were divided into seven categories by the Swedish criminologist Wikström.[51] The category "violent crimes" includes all offenses involving the use or threat of physical violence (for example, assault, rape, robbery, unlawful threat, and molestation). "Theft" includes all forms of stealing other than robbery as well as receiving stolen goods. "Fraud" includes embezzlement, crimes related to debts, and crimes of falsification. The category of "traffic crimes" does not include minor offenses, such as speeding. Drunken driving and driving without a license are the most frequent offenses in this category. The category "other" is very heterogeneous, including offenses such as defamation, sexual crimes other than rape, sexual coercion, perjury, gambling, bribery, absence without leave from the military, smuggling, and tax evasion.

As can be observed in Table 1, the various diagnoses are associated with all seven categories of crimes, as indicated by significant across-group χ^2 comparisons. Two-by-two comparisons (the percentage of subjects with no disorder or handicap compared with the percentage of subjects in each group who are convicted of a crime in each category) demonstrate that, compared with men with no disorder and no handicap, more men with other mental disorders committed fraud and vandalism, and more men with an intellectual handicap committed violent offenses, thefts, traffic offenses, and offenses classified as other. Male subjects with diagnoses of major mental disorders and substance abusers were registered for more crimes of every type than subjects with no disorder and no handicap.

The magnitude of the group differences for violent offenses was examined more closely. Men with major mental disorders were 4.16 times (95% CI, 2.23 to 7.78) more likely to have been convicted of a violent offense than men with no disorder or handicap. The comparable odds ratio for men with other disorders is 0.90 (95% CI, .33 to 2.50); for men with intellectual handicaps, 5.45 (95% CI, 3.38 to 8.80) ; and for men with diagnoses of substance abuse/dependence, 15.44 (95% CI, 11.11 to 21.44).

As can be observed in Table 2, the various diagnoses are associated with all seven categories of crimes for women, as indicated by the significant across-group χ^2 comparisons. More of the female subjects with a diagnosis of substance abuse were convicted of all types of crimes than the women with no disorder or handicap. The women with major mental disorders were 27.45 times (95% CI, 9.80 to 76.88) more likely to have been convicted of a violent offense than women with no disorder or handicap. The comparable odds ratio for the women with other mental disorders was 1.78 (95% CI, 0.43 to 7.37); for intellectually handicapped women, 24.77 (95% CI, 8.86 to 69.2); and for women with diagnoses of substance abuse/dependence, 54.58 (95% CI, 31.38 to 94.92).

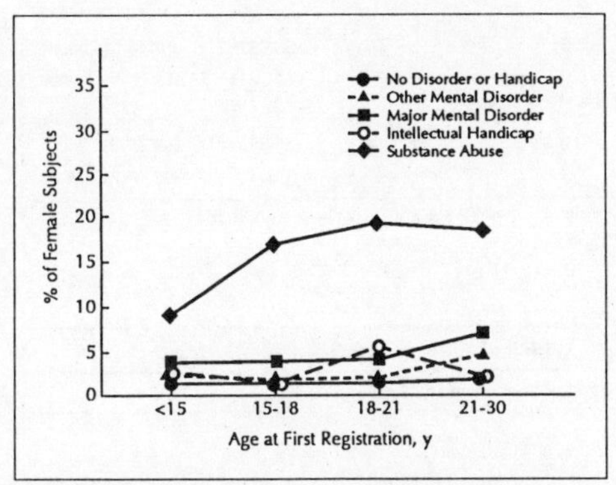

Fig 4.—*Female subjects by age at first registration. For first registration at less than age 15 years, compared with subjects with no mental disorder or intellectual handicap (NOMD), for subjects with other mental disorder (OMD), $\chi^2(1,N=6783)=0.715$ (not significant [NS]); for subjects with major mental disorder (MMD), $\chi^2(1,N=6738)=2.80$ (NS); for subjects with intellectual handicap (IH), $\chi^2(1,N=6738)=0.58$ (NS); and for substance abusers (SA), $\chi^2(1,N=6751)=30.23$ (P=.000). For first registration at age 15 to 18 years, compared NOMD, for OMD, $\chi^2(1,N=6783)=0.158$ (NS); for MMD, $\chi^2(1,N=6738)=4.22$ (P=.04); for IH, $\chi^2(1,N=6738)=0.00$ (NS); and for SA, $\chi^2(1,N=6751)=167.65$ (P=.00000). For first registration at age 18 to 21 years, compared with NOMD, for OMD, $\chi^2(1,N=6783)=0.391$ (NS); for MMD, $\chi^2(1,N=6738)=5.63$ (P=.02); for IH, $\chi^2(1,N=6738)=11.81$ (P=.0006); and for SA, $\chi^2(1,N=6751)=244.92$ (P=.00000). For first registration at age 21 to 30 years, compared with NOMD, for OMD, $\chi^2(1,N=6783)=7.38$ (P=.007); for MMD, $\chi^2(1,N=6738)=15.65$ (P=.008); for IH, $\chi^2(1,N=6738)=0.00$ (NS); and for SA, $\chi^2(1,N=6751)=206.64$ (P=.00000).*

Correlates of Criminality

The relationship between socioeconomic status and criminality within the different groups was examined. Socioeconomic status was indexed by father's occupation or, in the case of a single mother, mother's occupation. Social class was measured at the time of birth and when the subject was 10 years old. An indicator of poverty was the number of years the subject's family received social assistance. Among both the men and women with no disorder and no handicap, there are highly statistically significant relationships between socioeconomic status of the family of origin and criminality of the subject. These relationships are evident for measures at the time of subjects' births (for men, $\chi^2[4,N=6715]=123.51$, $P=.0000$; for women, $\chi^2[4,N=6648]=18.97$, $P=.002$) and when they were 10 years old (for men, $\chi^2[4,N=6947]=148.54$, $P=.0000$; for women, $\chi^2[4,N=6659]=27.31$, $P=.0001$). Also, among subjects with no disorder or handicap, significantly more offenders than nonoffenders were raised in families that received social welfare payments (for men, $\chi^2[1,N=6947]=132.77$, $P=.0000$; for women, $\chi^2[1,N=6659]=32.40$, $P=.0000$).

However, among the other groups of subjects, with one exception, there was no relationship between socioeconomic status and criminality. The exception is women with major mental disorders. At the time of these subjects' births, 43% of the families of women with a major disorder and a criminal record were upper middle class ($\chi^2[4,N=79]=11.62$, $P=.04$). When the subjects were aged 10 years, 36% of the families were upper middle class and another 36% were lower middle class ($\chi^2[4,N=79]=10.88$, $P=.05$). However, equivalent proportions of the families of those with and without a criminal record received welfare payments.

The relationship of substance abuse to criminality, both in childhood and adulthood, was examined within each group. The Child Welfare Committee records were used to index childhood substance abuse. As can be seen in Table 3, among the male subjects with no disorder or handicap, with major mental disorders, and with adult substance abuse, significantly more of those who had been convicted of a crime had a history of substance abuse in childhood. Among the women, an association between crime and childhood substance abuse is evident for subjects with adult substance abuse and for those with neither a mental disorder nor a handicap.

As adults, 48.7% of the offenders with a major mental disorder had a secondary diagnosis of alcohol and/or drug abuse and/or dependence. Among the women offenders with a major mental disorder, 42.9% had an additional diagnosis of substance abuse/dependence. No intellectually handicapped subject and,

Table 1.—Male Subjects in Each Group Convicted by Offense Type

	Male Subjects, %									All Disorders		
Type of Offense	No Mental Disorder or Handicap	Other Mental Disorder	χ^2(1,N =7011)*	Major Mental Disorder	χ^2(1,N =7029)*	Intellectual Handicap	χ^2(1,N =7060)*	Substance Abuse	χ^2(1,N =7103)*	χ^2(4,N =7362)*	P	Corrected P†
Violent	5.7	6.3		14.6	12.03§	16.8	25.19‡	49.4	471.58‡	482.06	.001	.0001
Theft	16.6	25.0		34.1	17.86‡	34.5	25.43‡	75.0	354.44‡	383.18	.001	.0001
Fraud	4.0	14.1	16.35‡	14.6	23.17‡	7.1		42.3	485.80‡	493.52	.001	.0001
Vandalism	4.1	10.9	7.31§	12.2	13.02‖	8.8		37.2	360.60‡	364.63	.001	.0001
Traffic	13.1	14.1		22.0		25.7	15.32‡	53.2	204.71‡	218.03	.001	.0001
Narcotics	2.4	1.6		8.5	12.89‖	4.4		42.3	773.26‡	767.35	.001	.0001
Other	11.1	12.5		25.6	17.23‡	23.0	15.92‡	54.5	272.37‡	292.15	.001	.0001

*Comparisons with the group with no mental disorder or handicap; only statistically significant values are given.
†Corrected for type I error by Bonferroni's formula.
‡$P=.001$; corrected for type I error by Bonferroni's formula, $P=.0001$.
§$P=.05$; corrected for type I error by Bonferroni's formula, $P=.007$.
‖$P=.01$; corrected for type I error by Bonferroni's formula, $P=.002$.

Table 2.—Female Subjects in Each Group Convicted by Offense Type

Type of Offense	Female Subjects, %									All Disorders	
	No Mental Disorder or Handicap	Other Mental Disorder	χ^2(1,N =6783)*	Major Mental Disorder	χ^2(1,N =6738)*	Intellectual Handicap	χ^2(1,N =6738)*	Substance Abuse	χ^2(1,N =6757)*	χ^2(4,N =7039)*	*P*
Violent	0.5	1.6		6.3	50.51†	3.8	17.26†	24.5	690.43‡	643.16	.00000
Theft	3.2	5.6		12.7		6.3		46.9	501.27‡	500.04	.00000
Fraud	1.0	4.0	10.87†	3.8		2.5		27.6	501.91‡	482.15	.00000
Vandalism	0.2	0.0		1.3		0.0		15.3	601.83‡	605.30	.00000
Traffic	0.9	0.8		1.3		2.5		7.1	40.69‡	42.06	.00000
Narcotics	0.5	0.8		0.0		0.0		22.4	554.95‡	569.38	.00000
Other	0.5	0.8		1.3		1.3		23.5	597.42‡	592.10	.00000

*Comparisons with the group with no mental disorder or handicap; only statistically significant values are given.
†$P=.001$; corrected for type I error by Bonferroni's formula, $P=.0001$.
‡$P=.00000$.

Table 3.—Childhood Substance Abuse in Subjects With and Without Criminal Histories

Adult Diagnosis Status	Childhood Substance Abuse, %							
	Men				Women			
	Crime	No Crime	χ^2	Corrected *P**	Crime	No Crime	χ^2	Corrected *P**
No mental disorder or handicap	17.5	2.7	482.54 (1,N=6947)	.002	19.0	1.2	491.95 (1,N=6659)	.002
Other mental disorder	9.1	4.8	0.46 (1,N=64)	NS	0.0	5.4	0.01 (1,N=124)	NS
Major mental disorder	38.5	7.0	11.83 (1,N=82)	.002	28.6	4.6	5.49 (1,N=79)	NS
Intellectual handicap	22.4	9.1	3.74 (1,N=113)	NS	12.5	4.2	0.03 (1,N=79)	NS
Substance abuse	53.6	18.8	6.96 (1,N=156)	.01	54.0	11.4	15.41 (1,N=98)	.002

*Corrected for type I error by Bonferroni's formula. NS indicates not significant.

by definition, no subject in the group with any other mental disorder had an adult diagnosis of substance abuse/dependence.

COMMENT

An investigation of an unselected birth cohort followed up prospectively from pregnancy to age 30 years has demonstrated that, among both men and women, the proportions of subjects with at least one criminal offense vary significantly by adult mental status. Men with a major mental disorder were 2½ times more likely than men with no disorder or handicap to be registered for a criminal offense. Among women, the risk for those with a major mental disorder was five times higher than for women with no disorder or handicap. The risks of violent crime for both men and women with major mental disorders were even higher than for crime in general. The criminal behavior of subjects who eventually developed major disorders often appeared in early adolescence, well before the mental disorder would have been diagnosed. Intellectually handicapped men were three times more likely to be registered for a criminal offense than men with no disorder or handicap. Intellectually handicapped women were almost four times more likely to have been registered for an offense than women with no disorder or handicap. The risks of committing violent crime for both men and women with intellectual handicaps were even more elevated than those of committing crime generally.

While criminality among the men with no disorder and no handicap decreased with age, this was not the case for those with major mental disorders. Significant numbers of these subjects began their criminal careers at all ages. The offenders with major mental disorders and those with intellectual handicaps committed multiple offenses of all types. Among both men and women, more of those with a major mental disorder and those with an intellectual handicap committed violent offenses and thefts.

These results are surprising, given that the subjects were only 30 years old when criminal offenses were documented. Investigations of persons responsible for violent crimes who were judged mentally disordered[52-57] and of inmates with major mental disorders[30] suggest that the mentally disordered commit crimes later in life than those with no mental disorder. The subjects in this cohort had not passed through the risk period for criminal behavior and had not passed through the risk period for the major mental disorders.[34] Thus, the age of the subjects would be expected to lessen the possibility of finding a difference in the proportions of mentally disordered and non–mentally disordered subjects convicted of crimes. In both the present investigation and Ortmann's study,[39] however, such differences were observed.

The association between major mental disorder and crime was weakened by excluding all subjects who died before the end of the follow-up period. A group of Swedish investigators[58] has shown increased mortality rates among mentally disordered offenders under age 30 years. Janson[59] has noted other factors that mitigated against finding such a difference in the present study. Persons sent to hospitals by the court were not counted. All had a diagnosis of psychosis, and "they would increase that male category's total offender rate by some 6% and the specific rates accordingly."[59(p49)] Men with psychoses also had less opportunity than other subjects to commit crimes because they were hospitalized, on average, for 552 days. Another factor that would also lessen the likelihood of finding higher rates of offending for those suffering from major mental disorders is the way in which admissions were documented. Patients still in the hospital at the time the data were collected were not included in the mentally disordered category.

Can we generalize from the results of this study? The specific crime rates cannot be generalized to other jurisdictions. The between-group comparisons can probably only be generalized to other countries with mental health systems, criminal justice systems, and social welfare systems similar to those in Sweden. To illustrate, the present results are similar to those of Ortmann[39] and Høgh and Wolf,[47] working in Denmark. However, consider extrapolating these results to the United States. In the United States, there is more crime and substance abuse than in Sweden but similar prevalence rates for the major mental disorders and for intellectual deficiency. Studies of mentally disordered persons would be expected to show that disproportionately more of the disordered commit crimes and violence. A sample of US offenders would be expected to include only a small proportion of subjects with major mental disorders and intellectual handicaps. Generally, that is what is reported. In other words, in the United States, given the large amount of crime and crime by substance abusers, the crimes of those with major psychiatric disorders and intellectual handicaps seem insignificant in comparison.

The within-group rates from the present investigation may be generalizable. The external validity of these findings may depend on the similarity of the ratio of crimes leading to prosecution compared with crimes committed and the similarity of the attitudes of the police and prosecuters toward the mentally disordered and intellectually handicapped.

The present findings correspond with results of studies in which significantly more subjects with major mental disorders, compared with those with no disorder, reported behaving aggressively.[60-62] The findings raise fundamental questions about these disorders, their etiology, and their treatment. A replication with a larger cohort, now under way, will allow us to examine the risk of criminality and violence by type of disorder.

This study was made possible by a grant for the author from the Enskilden Banken of Sweden to Leif Ojesjö. It was completed in collaboration with Carl-Gunnar Janson, PhD. Our thanks to Lennart Wetterberg, MD.

References

1. Convit A, Isay D, Gadioma R, Volavka J. Under-reporting of physical assaults in schizophrenic inpatients. *J Nerv Ment Dis*. 1988;176:507-509.
2. Lagos JM, Perlmutter K, Saexinger H. Fear of the mentally ill: empirical support for the common man's response. *Am J Psychiatry*. 1977;134:1134-1137.
3. Lion JR, Snyder W, Merrill GL. Under-reporting of assaults on staff in a state hospital. *Hosp Community Psychiatry*. 1981;32:497-498.
4. MacMillan JF, Johnson AL. Contact with the police in early schizophrenia: its nature, frequency and relevance to the outcome of treatment. *Med Sci Law*. 1987;27:191-200.
5. Incidence of violent patient admissions apparently stabilized at 37 percent. *Psychiatr News*. June 15, 1984.
6. Skodol AE, Karasu TB. Emergency psychiatry and the assaultive patient. *Am J Psychiatry*. 1978;135:202-205.
7. Tardiff K, Sweillam A. Assaultive behavior among chronic inpatients. *Am J Psychiatry*. 1982;139:212-215.
8. Durbin JR, Pasewark RA, Albers D. Criminality and mental illness: a study of current arrest rates in a rural state. *Am J Psychiatry*. 1977;134:80-83.
9. Giovanni JM, Gurel L. Socially disruptive behaviour of ex-mental patients. *Arch Gen Psychiatry*. 1967;17:146-153.
10. Rappeport JR, Lassen G. Dangerousness arrest rate comparisons of discharged patients and the general population. *Am J Psychiatry*. 1965;121:776-783.
11. Rappeport JR, Lassen G. The dangerousness of female patients: a comparison of the arrest rate of discharged psychiatric patients and the general population. *Am J Psychiatry*.1966;123:413-419.
12. Sosowsky L. Violence and the mentally ill. In: *Putting State Mental Hospitals out of Business: The Community Approach to Treating Mental Illness in San Mateo County*. Berkeley, Calif: University of California Graduate School of Public Policy; 1974:17-33.
13. Sosowsky L. Crime and violence among mental patients reconsidered in view of the new legal relationship between the state and the mentally ill. *Am J Psychiatry*.1978;135:33-42.
14. Sosowsky L. Explaining the increased arrest rate among mental patients: a cautionary note. *Am J Psychiatry*. 1980;137:1602-1605.
15. Steadman HJ, Cocozza JJ, Melick ME. Explaining the increased arrest rate among mental patients: the changing clientele of state hospitals. *Am J Psychiatry*. 1978;135:816-820.
16. Zitrin A, Hardesty AS, Burdock ET, Drossman AK. Crime and violence among mental patients. *Am J Psychiatry*. 1976;133:142-149.
17. Steadman HJ, Monahan J, Clark Robbins P, Appelbaum P, Grisso T, Klassen D, Mulvey E, Roth L. From dangerousness to risk assessment: implications for appropriate research strategies. In: Hodgins S, ed. *Mental Disorder and Crime*. Newbury Park, Calif: Sage Publications Inc. In press.
18. Cohen Cl. Crime among mental patients: a critical analysis. *Psychiatr Q*. 1980;52:100-107.
19. Mesnikoff AM, Lauterbach CG. The association of violent dangerous behavior with psychiatric disorders: a review of the research literature. *J Psychiatr Law*. 1975;3:415-445.
20. Lindqvist P, Allebeck P. Schizophrenia and crime: a longitudinal follow-up of 644 schizophrenics in Stockholm. *Br J Psychiatry*. 1990; 157:345-350.
21. Lindqvist P, Allebeck P. Schizophrenia and assaultive behaviour: the role of alcohol and drug abuse. *Acta Psychiatr Scand*. 1989;82:191-195.
22. Silverton L. *Crime and the Schizophrenia Spectrum: A Study of Two Danish Cohorts*. Los Angeles, Calif: University of Southern California; 1985. Thesis.
23. Mednick SA, Parnas J, Schulsinger F. The Copenhagen high-risk project, 1962-1986. *Schizophr Bull*. 1987;13:485-496.
24. Asnarow JR. Children at risk for schizophrenia: converging lines of evidence. *Schizophr Bull*. 1988;14:613-631.
25. Kay SR. Significance of the positive-negative distinction in schizophrenia. *Schizophr Bull*. 1990;16:635-652.
26. Collins JJ, Schlenger WE. The prevalence of psychiatric disorder among admissions to prison. Presented at the 35th Annual Meeting of the American Society of Criminology; 1983; Denver, Colo.
27. Daniel AE, Robins AJ, Reid JC, Wilfley DE. Lifetime and 6-month prevalence of psychiatric disorders among sentenced female offenders. *Bull Am Acad Psychiatry Law*. 1988;16:333-342.
28. Hyde PS, Seiter RP. *The Prevalence of Mental Illness Among Inmates in the Ohio Prison System*. Columbus, Ohio: Dept of Mental Health and the Ohio Dept of Rehabilitation and Correction Interdepartmental Planning and Oversight Committee for Psychiatric Services to Corrections; 1987.
29. Neighbors HW, Williams DH, Gunnings TS, Lipscomb WD, Broman C, Lepkowski J. *The Prevalence of Mental Disorder in Michigan Prisons*. Ann Arbor, Mich: Michigan Dept of Corrections; 1987.
30. Hodgins S, Côté G. The prevalence of mental disorders among penitentiary inmates. *Can Ment Health*. 1990;38:1-5.
31. Abram KM. The effect of co-occurring disorders on criminal careers: interaction of antisocial personality, alcoholism, and drug disorders. *Int J Law Psychiatry*. 1989;12:133-148.
32. Côté G, Hodgins S. Co-occurring mental disorder among criminal offenders. *Bull Am Acad Psychiatry Law*. 1990;18:271-281.
33. American Psychiatric Association, Committee on Nomenclature and Statistics. *Diagnostic and Statistical Manual of Mental Disorders, Third Edition*. Washington, DC: American Psychiatric Association; 1980.
34. Robins LN, Helzer JE, Weissman MM, Orvaschel H, Gruenberg E,

Burke JD, Regier DA Jr. Lifetime prevalence of specific psychiatric disorders in three sites. *Arch Gen Psychiatry*. 1984;41:949-958.

35. Côté G. L'homicide et la recherche quantitative: aspects méthodologiques. *Rev Int Crimin Police Tech*. In press.

36. Gottlieb P, Gabrielsen G, Kramp P. Psychotic homicides in Copenhagen from 1959 to 1983. *Acta Psychiatr Scand*. 1987;76:285-292.

37. Lindqvist P. Criminal homicide in Northern Sweden, 1970. *Int J Law Psychiatry*. 1986;8:19-37.

38. Côté G, Hodgins S. The prevalence of major mental disorders among homicide offenders. *Int J Law Psychiatry*. 1992;15:89-99.

39. Ortmann J. *Psykisk ofvigelse og kriminel adfaerd en undersogelse af 11533 mąend fodt i 1953 i det metropolitane omrade kobenhaun*. Copenhagen, Denmark: Rapport til Justitsministeriet, Direktoratet for kriminal forsorgen, Forksningsrapport; 1981. No. 17.

40. Reichel H. The intelligence-criminality relationship. In: Janson C-G, Janson A-M, eds. *Crime and Delinquency in a Metropolitan Cohort*. Stockholm, Sweden: Universitet Stockholms; 1989:7-29. Project Metropolitan Research Report 26.

41. Hirschi T, Hindelang MJ. Intelligence and deliquency: a revisionist review. *Am Sociol Rev*. 1977;42:571-587.

42. Wilson JQ, Hernstein RJ. *Crime and Human Nature*. New York, NY: Simon & Schuster; 1985.

43. Moffitt TE. The neuropsychology of juvenile delinquency: a critical review. In: Tonry M, Morris N, eds. *Crime and Justice: A Review of Research*. Chicago, Ill: University of Chicago Press; 1990:99-169.

44. West DJ, Farrington DP. *Who Becomes Delinquent?* London, England: Heinemann Educational Books Ltd; 1973.

45. Moffitt TE, Gabrielli WF, Mednick SA, Schulsinger F. Socioeconomic status, IQ, and delinquency. *J Abnorm Psychol*. 1981;90:152-156.

46. White JL, Moffitt TE, Silva PA. A prospective replication of the protective effects of IQ in subjects at high risk for juvenile delinquency. *J Consult Clin Psychol*. 1989;57:719-724.

47. Høgh E, Wolf P. Violent crime in a birth cohort: Copenhagen 1953-1977: Project Metropolitan: Denmark. Presented at the Symposium on Life History Research in Aggression and Antisocial Behavior; 1981; Monterey, Calif.

48. Janson C-G. *Project Metropolitan 21: A Longitudinal Study of a Stockholm Cohort*. Stockholm, Sweden: University of Stockholm; 1984.

49. Kristjansson E, Allebeck P, Wistedt B. Validity of the diagnosis schizophrenia in a psychiatric inpatient register. *Nord Psykiatr Tidsskr*. 1987;41:229-234.

50. Wetteberg L, Farmer AE. Clinical polydiagnostic studies in a large Swedish pedigree with schizophrenia. *Eur Arch Psychiatry Clin Neurosci*. 1990;240:188-190.

51. Wikström POH. Age and crime in a Stockholm cohort. In: Janson C-G, Janson A-M, eds. *Crime and Human Nature*. New York, NY: Simon & Schuster; 1989.

52. Häfner H, Böker W. *Crimes of Violence by Mentally Abnormal Offenders*. Cambridge, England: Cambridge University Press; 1982.

53. Walker N, McCabe S. *Crime and Insanity in England, II*. Edinburgh, Scotland: Edinburgh University Press; 1973.

54. Hodgins S, Webster C, Paquet J, Zellerer E. *Annual Report Year-1 Canadian Database: Patients Held on Lieutenant-Governor's Warrants*. Ottawa, Ontario; Ministère de la Justice; 1989.

55. Hodgins S, Webster C, Paquet J. *Annual Report Year-2 Canadian Database: Patients Held on Lieutenant-Governor's Warrants*. Ottawa, Ontario: Ministère de la Justice; 1990.

56. Hodgins S, Webster C, Paquet J. *Annual Report Year-3 Canadian Database: Patients Held on Lieutenant-Governor's Warrants*. Ottawa, Ontario: Ministère de la Justice; 1991.

57. Pasewark RA. Insanity plea: a review of the research literature. *J Psychiatry Law*. 1982;9:357-402.

58. Lidberg L, Wiklund N, Jakobsson SW. Mortality among criminals with suspected mental disturbance. *Scand J Soc Med*. 1988;17:59-65.

59. Janson C-G. Psychiatric diagnoses and recorded crimes. In: Janson C-G, Janson A-M, eds. *Crime and Delinquency in a Metropolitan Cohort*. Stockholm: University of Stockholm. 1989:31-55.

60. Swanson JW, Hozer CE, Ganju VK, Jono RT. Violence and psychiatric disorder in the community: evidence from the epidemiologic catchment area surveys. *Hosp Community Psychiatry*. 1990; 41:761-770.

61. Link BG, Andrews H, Cullen FT. Reconsidering the dangerousness of mental patients: violent and illegal behavior of current and former patients compared to controls. *Am Sociol Rev*. In press.

62. Steadman HJ, Felson RB. Self-reports of violence: ex-mental patients, ex-offenders, and the general population. *Criminology*. 1984; 22:321-342.

[6]

THE MENTALLY DISORDERED OFFENDER

A Call for Thought†

LORD MUSTILL*

Introduction

For most of the past thirty five years I have walked to work along the paths which connect the Temple underground station with the Temple itself and the Law Courts. Stomping along, virtually on auto pilot, I see changes as one would expect. The last scars of war have completely gone. The legal profession, which still dominates this little corner of London, and which was small and poorly paid when I began, is now numerous and rich, as one can see from the long lists of barristers outside chambers, and the profusion of electronic devices visible through their windows. The streets are dirtier and the passers-by more glum and surly. Even so, the scene has remained essentially the same. There is one exception, a sight which I remember from my childhood, but never thought to see again. The beggars

Of course the sturdy beggar, who chooses the mendicant life, has been with us through the centuries, and disappeared only for a few years when it became less trouble to wait for money to be thrust upon him by the state, than to hold out his hand in the street. He will always be with us, and so also will be the dossers and the meths drinkers. But they have been few in number and recognisably a race apart. They can be seen as beings whose dislocation from society is of their own choosing, a choice which we have, for motives good or indifferent, decided to tolerate by letting them live out their own lives in the way which they prefer. Whether this is due to a laudable reticence or simple laziness, we need not stay to consider. At all events, we manage to co-exist without too much strain. Last winter's beggars[1] are a different matter. I was a child of the Beveridge Report, an adolescent during the dawn of the Welfare State and a young man in the mid-fifties. When I began work I might, if challenged, have dimly foreseen the word-processor. I could not have imagined the sights which we have seen during the past few winters. The sodden

---

† This is an expanded version of a paper given at King's College London on May 2, 1991. The writer is greatly indebted to the Mental Health Foundation for secretarial assistance in producing the text.

* Lord of Appeal in Ordinary.

[1] The speaker was referring to the winter of 1991–92.

bundles of humanity in doorways and upon gratings; minds and bodies numbed not by drink but by cold and fatigue. Few of us can have escaped the impulse to cross to the other pavement: like the Levite to pass by on the other side. How many of us have always successfully resisted it? This is not the occasion to analyse the reasons for this impulse. Amongst them must, I believe, be a reluctance, almost physical, to confront the inward feeling that like Cowper's castaway "they perish each alone", whilst we their shipmates are free to sail away, warm and comparatively safe.[2]

What do we know about these castaways, whom one writer has aptly described as living like feral children in the forests of the city; and why are they there? Accurate statistics are unlikely to be obtainable, but I think it certain that a high proportion were offenders, either presently or in the past, albeit usually not of a really serious type, and that many were suffering from psychiatric illness.[3] Thus, there have been propelled into public view, in dramatically adverse conditions, some members of the large but hitherto mainly invisible population of mentally disordered offenders. Unless something effective is done, this population is destined to come before the courts again and again, continually recycled through a succession of ill-matched and uncoordinated[4] agencies.

Why are these people now so prominent, stepping (one is tempted to say) out of the pages of Dickens? In fact their life is not Dickensian, for the Cheeryble brothers are little to be seen in the modern world, any more than the non-fictional Lord Shaftesbury and Dr. Barnardo. Private benevolence is a shadow of its old self, and corporate philanthropy is withering on the vine, now that the lean years are upon us. In truth the primary responsibility for the welfare of the mentally disordered offender is and will remain that of the state, albeit the size and technique of its provision may vary according to shifts in political and economic attitudes. This

---

[2] Of course, only *comparatively* safe. Mental illness is no respecter of persons. Nor, indeed, is homelessness, as recent trends in domestic housing have forcefully shown. Are we perhaps frightened of even the most timid of them; and if we are, is this because we are different, or because we are potentially the same?

[3] According to "Homelessness in England", published by Shelter, there are 2–3,000 people sleeping rough in London. Of the 145,790 households accepted by local authorities as homeless, over 4,000 were accepted because of mental illness.

[4] It has been pointed out by Dr. Bill McWilliams, to whom I am indebted for a number of thoughtful comments on this essay, that coordination is not always beneficial. This is true. A hierarchical command structure, capably run, is an effective means of coordination, and yet it may not be psychologically apt for the task in hand. And of course a coordinated effort towards the wrong aim, or a coordinated deployment of unsound methods, will do more harm than good. nevertheless, I remain convinced that the poverty of the provision for the mentally disordered offender is to a great extent a consequence of organisational as well as conceptual failures.

responsibility the state has conspicuously failed to discharge. The reasons why are far too complex to analyse in a single evening, quite aside from raising political considerations which are rightly out of bounds for judges. The one thing I can say with confidence to this audience is that it is the professionals, we ourselves, who are in a large measure to blame.

This may seem a harsh judgment and I must at once explain what I mean. Every professional ought to possess the power to think and the will to do so; and this includes the will to be dispassionate in identifying the target, and recognising that thought must precede the drawing of the bow. Amongst all those who concern themselves, or who ought to concern themselves, with the unfortunates who are our subject tonight there is no shortage of brain-power. I do not suggest any lack of zeal, any failure to recognise the plight of these unfortunates and resolve to do something about it, any backwardness in applying the fruits of training and experience to the solution of each problem as it arises. Quite the reverse, for paradoxically I believe that some of our present difficulties are the result of a terrier-like eagerness to tackle each practical problem on the ground. It is this piecemeal attack which has created the world which the mentally disordered offender now inhabits; the world, not of Dickens, but of Franz Kafka. Although of course the comparisons are psychological and spiritual rather than physical I believe that for once this most overworked and misused of all literary allusions is justified. If a mentally disordered offender were to complain that he is in the grasp of a system which he cannot understand, operated according to rules partly hidden and partly incomprehensible; with responsibilities for his welfare switched from organisation to organisation; with no clear questions asked, and no unambiguous answers given; with those who care for him speaking in different voices and looking at him through different eyes—if he were able to express himself in these terms the offender would not, I believe, be very far from the truth. If he were to suspect that those entrusted with the task of operating the system had themselves no clear idea of what its aims might be, or of the reason why those aims rather than others had been chosen; or of how, why and by whom the methods employed were decided upon as the best way of achieving whatever aims there might be—again he would not be far from the truth. The fact is that provision for the mentally disordered offender is unsystematic, unfocused and short-winded.

How can this be, given all the anxious and devoted care expended by those concerned? I fear that the answer lies with those of us assembled here tonight, our colleagues and our teachers. We are guilty of the *trahison des clercs*. The learned ones have let the side down. We have failed to ask the awkward questions, and to hang on until we have received the unwelcome answers. We have failed to open our minds to ideas drawn from disciplines other than those which we individually practise; unfamiliar ideas, with which we are ill at ease. We have failed to look beyond immediate solutions to the reasons why the problems exist.

No doubt this sounds too sombre. Although the problems have recently become so conspicuous, real strides are now being taken to improve the lot of these unhappy people. Whether by coincidence or not, some deeply encouraging initiatives are under way. I need not list them now. The Home Office and the Department of Health; individual Members of Parliament; NACRO; informal inter-professional groups; and all sorts of others have projects in contemplation or already launched. All this is splendid, but there is a hidden danger. One of the prime defects of our regime for the mentally disordered offender lies in its incoherence. It is built up piecemeal over the years with only very rare attempts to think strategically—the Butler Committee was, of course, a shining exception. This is where the professionals come in, or ought to come in. The foundation of a sound strategy must be a survey of the intellectual ground. This is a painful task, for which nobody will thank us. We must ask questions which have not previously been asked, at the risk of accusations that we have made something complicated of what is essentially simple: that, like the opponent of John Locke, we have raised a cloud of dust and now complain that we cannot see through it. We shall then be required to suggest answers which may displease our fellow-professionals, who may see them as subversive, as devaluing the disciplines to which they have given so much skill and devotion.

Nevertheless, we must make the effort. I believe that our subject is very hard. We should not flinch from that, for after all we are gathered together here tonight in a university. But it is also very complex, far too much so to be engaged in depth within the space of a single discourse. What I shall attempt is therefore to sketch the outlines of two or three of the problems in the hope of showing what kind they are, and why they must be solved if we are to do our part in helping these people to a better life.

The Professionals

Since I have indicted the professionals for failure, the least I can do is to identify those who are said to be at fault. It seems obvious that since we are here concerned with persons who are mentally disordered and persons who are offenders, the professional populations under review must at least include:

—those concerned with health, in the broadest sense
—those concerned with the criminal justice system.

As I have suggested elsewhere,[5] the professional aims, training and philosophies of the persons in these two groups have nothing in common, and are in some respects antithetical. This being so, it is not surprising that where their fields of activity overlap there is a confusion of purpose; a degree of mutual incomprehension; and friction. Most doctors and judges would, I believe, be willing to acknowledge, ruefully, that when psychiatric medicine comes into the judicial forum neither profession shows itself at its best. They would at least agree on this, that the imprecision and indeed unworkability of the statutory language with which they have to grapple is much to blame. But there are deeper reasons, springing from the gulf between the training, inclination and professional aims of those who practise within the two systems.

These are not however the only professional groups involved. We have also those who think and work in the field of the social sciences. These professionals have some common ground with the other two groups. Thus, the social welfare system, like the criminal justice system, is concerned with the relationship between the individual and society. But this is almost the only point of similarity between the two. Social welfare is essentially permissive and supportive, and is aimed at the protection of the individual. Social workers deal with those who, through lack of skills, lack of will or simple bad luck, are unable to keep afloat in the modern world. The social services provide a life raft, which enables the client to maintain a place however precarious and austere in society at large.

The criminal justice system by contrast subordinates the interests of the individual to those of society, whilst acknowledging that society will benefit if the offender is able to reintegrate himself into the community sufficiently well to have the power of conforming with the prescribed norms of behaviour. Ultimately, the criminal justice system is coercive in nature. The social welfare system is not.[6]

This diversity of aim persists throughout the professional lives of those involved. The student enters a sphere of training which has the prescribed aim as a moral as well as a practical imperative, and the skills which he learns are selected with the idea of enabling him to achieve that aim. When he has finished his training, and is

[5] The Mentally Disordered Offender, *eds.* K. R. Herbst and J. Gunn, Butterworth-Heinemann, (1991) pp.225 *et seq.*

[6] At least, in theory. Speaking practically, one must acknowledge that all institutionalised social welfare has at least some coercive element, although it may not always be overt.

at work, he is surrounded by those who have invested energy and goodwill in pursuing the same ends. The idea that the aims might be ill-chosen becomes harder and harder to accept, or even to contemplate; and skills directed towards the achievement of that aim rather than some other become part of an intellectual tool-kit to which the professional will instinctively turn whenever a task presents itself.

The relationship between the probation service and other institutions affords a ready example of how the aims of those concerned with offenders may differ. Whilst it would be a mistake to say that the probation service was ever integrated into the criminal justice system, at least its practitioners had a sufficient community of aim with those who operated in that system to enable their methods to co-exist. More recently the two seem to have drifted apart, perhaps in part because entry to the probation service is preceded by a training which is permeated by the ethos of the social services. Consequently, too many social enquiry reports give the impression that the writer treats the fact of the offence as almost adventitious, as a part of the offender's personal history, in a real sense no more important than other aspects of that history, such as his childhood, education, economic circumstances and circle of friends. The judge by contrast is obliged to focus on the offence, and hence on the individual as an offender, rather than as a person who for one reason or another is out of tune with society and needs the help and support of the state in order to ensure his survival. Of course a judge will look for a disposal which, so far as consistent with the gravity of the offence, will conduce to the rehabilitation of the offender as a properly functioning member of society. Nevertheless, his objective is fundamentally different from that of the social worker. These distinctive perspectives of the sentencing process can lead to mutual incomprehension and (one must say) occasional exasperation. The problems which can arise may of course very often be avoided by common sense and tact on both sides, but that they do potentially exist is a direct product of a collision between two professional cultures. How much the more complex their problems become when the case is overlaid by the special social and ethical issues arising from the fact that the offender is mentally unwell.

Just as real, although less obvious, are the problems which arise when the medical and the social welfare systems overlap. The doctor and the social worker have this much in common, that their functions both embrace the care of the individual. But the doctor's primary concern is to cure the disease which underlies the symptoms, and care is a fallback remedy which fills the gap when a cure is either impossible or has not yet been achieved. By contrast, a social worker would I believe be disconcerted and perhaps repelled by the suggestion that her or his task involves the "cure" of the client whose relationship with the existing social order the worker is trying to improve. Essentially, the doctor seeks to adjust the patient so as to restore his characteristics which constitute normality (*i.e.* health), whereas the social worker, although of course hoping to improve the client's performance, will often concentrate on adjusting the social environment in which the client finds himself, so as to create a situation in which the client can be kept afloat, notwithstanding the lack of buoyancy created by his personal disadvantages.[7]

I do not want to make too much of this. In their dealings with the mentally disordered offender both the psychiatrist and the social worker set out to normalise the relationship between his behaviour and his surroundings, but it would be a mistake to assume that because of this the aims and the ethos of the two professional groups are necessarily the same.

There remains one other category of professionals. They are presently hidden from view: the philosophers, whose only duty is to think. The sub-group with whom we are concerned consists of those whose duty it is to think about ethics, about the meaning of right and wrong, and about the place which these notions play in the lives of individuals and of societies. There is more than one reason why the ethicist has scarcely featured in the discussions of the mentally disordered offender.

In the first place, ethicists have been a rather submerged group in the past sixty years, at least in the English-speaking world. The hostility of logical positivism to the notion that the philosophy of ethics is by nature capable of having anything useful or indeed meaningful to say has tended to discourage all but the boldest from even trying to say it.

Again, since the study of ethics is an activity which involves abstract thought, it is unlikely to find a warm welcome amongst the practitioners of law and medicine. By disposition and discipline, lawyers and doctors tend to be profoundly uninterested in abstract thought, and indeed suspicious of it. Although, as I have suggested, their methods and aims are very different, these two groups share a predilection for concentrating on individual cases, in the light of established goals to be achieved by existing methods. It is quite rare for a doctor or lawyer to stand back from day-to-day activity focused on a particular case, so as to ask himself whether he is

[7] This is of course an over-simplification, since the social worker will not infrequently (although very often unconsciously) try to "adjust" the client as well as his environment. All the same, I believe that the contrast is real.

trying to do quite the wrong thing, or setting about it in quite the wrong way. Any theoretician coming in from outside to suggest that all their hard work—and the doctors and lawyers do work hard—is misplaced and possibly even harmful, may well encounter incomprehension and resentment.

This does not of course mean that ethics is wholly dissociated from medicine; the presence in this building of a centre devoted to the study of medical ethics shows that this is not so. The importance of this topic is coming to be widely acknowledged.

Nevertheless, attention, has thus far tended to be concentrated on two areas. First, on the ethics of the doctor's conduct towards the patient—for example in the giving or withholding of information about his medical condition. Secondly, on the conduct of society towards the patient—for example in the denying or facilitation of abortion. But medical ethics has not so far had much to say about the conduct of the patient himself. This is not surprising. Many medical ethicists have a medical background. A doctor is concerned to cure the patient's illness. The question whether the illness is the result of the patient's own conduct may be important to the doctor as a means of enabling him to identify the illness with accuracy, and hence to work towards an effective cure. But I believe that most people involved in the field of health would regard it as quite irrelevant, and indeed impermissible, to have regard to the moral implications of that conduct. Thus, psychiatrists are much more interested in the aetiology of aberrant behaviour than with the qustions whether the norm from which it departs has a moral worth of its own, or whether the departure reflects what may be called fault on the part of the actor. Admirable as it may be in many contexts, this professional stance surely needs modification where the doctor is dealing with a mentally disordered offender—who, being an offender, has done something generally believed to be wrong.

When one comes to the criminal justice system the ethicist is once again little in evidence; and once again this is not surprising. For many years, orthodox doctrine has embraced a mechanistic explanation of offending, and a utilitarian penal policy. We have been encouraged to think that the offender offends because of his upbringing, or the conditions in which he is forced to live, or the bad company with which hc has been brought into contact. That he is "an engine that moves in determinate grooves, . . . not even a bus . . . [but] a tram". If this is really so, then we cannot blame him for what he has done, and the ethcist must remain silent. So also have we been taught to assume that the object of penal measures should be to deter the offender or others from further offences; or to make further offences impossible for a time by locking up the offender; or to adjust and improve the offender's social skills so as to make reoffending seem less attractive or more easy to resist. If these are the aims of criminal justice, the moral status of the act which has made the individual an offender is of secondary importance, and the ethicist can have little useful to say. I doubt whether in reality these austere intellectual positions were ever widely accepted by the public at large. The refrain of Flanders and Swan's song—"You don't eat people, eating people is wrong"—would not seem empty of content to the average citizen. Practically everybody thinks that *something* is wrong, although there may be sharp disagreement about what it is. This viewpoint has I believe found covert expression in the application of penal sanctions, day in and day out, although the Courts have often been cautious about its articulation.

There are now signs that this way of thinking is becoming respectable: but what Rabbi Jonathan Sacks in his Reith Lectures[8] called "the demoralisation of discourse" is on the wane. Philosophers are only human—to a degree at least—and perhaps it has come to be felt that the Martian landscapes of logical positivism are stimulating to visit but impossible to inhabit. Perhaps the public perception that a crime is something to do with wrongdoing is not so absurd after all.

Equally it is coming to be recognised that the notion of offenders being in the grip of circumstances beyond their control leaves something important out: namely the conscious and willed choice of a harmful act, in circumstances where the actor knows (but does not care) that the choice is one that he ought not to make. If these ideas are regaining currency, and if they are coming to be seen as legitimate elements in formulating a penal policy and applying it to the individual case—and I shall suggest in a moment that they are—then there will have to be some marked changes in attitude throughout the criminal justice system. These changes are likely to prove painful in the areas where penal and social welfare methods intersect.

Of more particular importance however for our purposes tonight, is the impact which such changes will have on the way we think about the mentally disordered offender; for here the doctors (in the widest sense) are engaged, and they are professionally dissociated from any judgment on the moral qualities of the patient's act.

Unfortunately it happens that these far-reaching intellectual adjustments are going to be required at just the time when new practical initiatives are being impelled by a sensation that something

[8] "The persistence of Faith", Weidenfeld and Nicolson, (1990).

must be done at once about the mentally disordered offender. It is right that this impulsion should be exploited, and that energy, resources and goodwill should be mobilised whilst the problem is in the public eye. But the conceptual problems associated with the mentally disordered offender are more difficult than is generally realised, and will become more difficult still if the principles of penal policy are in a state of flux. It would be foolish of course to say that the new practical measures will make the position worse. They will not. We need psychiatric bail hostels. Let us have them. We need more Regional Secure Units. Let us have them. We need more trained psychiatric support for offenders within the community. But there is a very real risk that unless thinking at least keeps pace with acting, the host of new practical ideas will increase the fragmentation, ill-directed goodwill and lack of interdisciplinary consensus which is the curse of our provision for the mentally disordered offender, and thus will paradoxically stunt the growth of the new initiatives.

Where should this thinking start? I believe that it must begin with penal policy, and that we must have a policy which is clear and self-consistent, upon which all those who deal with the mentally disordered offender are agreed. Not necessarily agreed that the policy is right, but agreed as to what it is, and agreed that it must be conscientiously put into effect.

Penal Policies

A regime for the mentally disordered offender might take several forms. One could leave all such offenders in the penal system, giving them whatever treatment they might need within it. Or one could extract them entirely and place them in the medical system, treating the fact that they are offenders as entirely irrelevant. Or they could be in a part of one and a part of the other at the same time. Or there could be created for them—if only it could be so!—an entirely new and specially tailored regime.

In practice the disposal of the mentally disordered offender does not take any of these shapes. The present ramshackle structure is widely regarded as unsatisfactory.

Undoubtedly, the best course would be to get rid of it and start entirely afresh. Realistically, we must accept that this is not going to happen. The planning and execution would cost too much, and would take too long at a time when remedies are being urgently demanded. The most we can hope for is to patch-up the estate which we have inherited by improving the relationships between the various agencies and making available more human, physical and financial resources. But a decision on how to do this should not be taken without an explicit formulation of what the system aims to do with mentally disordered offenders, and why: so that those who are responsible for refurbishing the system can ensure that its design accurately reflects those aims, and so that the professionals and the disciplines concerned can work together harmoniously towards goals which they all understand. I think it clear that there is no chance of achieving this unless we know what our society wants to do with mentally disordered people and what it wants to do with those who commit crimes.

The aims of the medical side of the equation are straightforward enough: to diagnose disease, to cure it if possible and to care for the person afflicted. When one turns to the criminal justice system one could hope to find there also a basic objective or set of objectives, clearly articulated and with methods specifically designed to achieve them. Unfortunately this is not so. The design of a penal policy depends on the answers to the following questions—

1. When we deal with offenders do we have a moral or a practical purpose?
2. Should the offender be regarded as a free agent in his choice to engage in crime?

Opinions on these questions have changed and changed again over the years, but not in phase. Moreover, the people who hold opinions about them, and have the power to make their opinions count—namely the public enunciators of morals such as clergymen and writers for The Guardian, legislators and the deep constituencies of the political parties—do not have the same opinions at the same time and do not alter them synchronously.

This constant shifting of assumptions speaks against any idea of a legal policy widely and consistently applied. Instead one finds a kind of stew of policies whose flavour varies from time to time. This is an uneconomical and inefficient way of organising a penal system. The people who run it become inwardly confused about what they are trying to do, and outwardly fall into disagreement with other workers in the system. Moreover the system easily becomes out of date. It takes substantial time to erect it and put it into effect; and those who operate it tend to have moral, emotional and intellectual commitments drawn from the period, often quite distant, when they were learning their skills and from the long and often discouraging years of trying to put them into practice. Too often it happens that just when a system is up and running and the participants are thoroughly imbued with its ethos, current opinions have shifted to such an extent that it has become obsolete.

Moreover, even if the general shape of the penal system remains broadly the same for a substantial period of time this may disguise shifts in the relative importance attached to the objectives which keep it in being. Thus the utilitarian principles which have ruled during the working lifetimes of most of those who operate the system today have yielded a variety of ambitions. Amongst these—deterrence of the offenders; deterrence of others; the prevention of further offences; rehabilitation of the offender; forestalling unlicensed revenge by the indignant; helping the offender not to reoffend; and so on. English penal theory has never had much in the way of a formal ranking of these utilitarian aims although most sentencers probably have their own tacit hierarchies which, since they are tacit, cannot be relied upon to correspond with those of others. But even if one could write down a weighted list of objectives, valid for a particular time, almost certainly the weightings will have changed within a decade.

Nevertheless, although one cannot expect and does not get a high degree of consistency from a system with such shallow intellectual foundations, it manages to limp along without too much dislocation, because those who take part in it have through experience developed enough common ground to make it work. But when one tries to fit the mentally disordered offender into this essentially utilitarian regime the results are unhappy, for more than one reason. In the first place, it seems to be universally assumed that the mentally disordered offender ought, by the very fact of his disorder, to be dealt with more humanely than the average offender: and since it is also assumed that doctors are by definition humane it is taken for granted that the disposal should be in the medical system. The validity of these assumptions is rarely if ever questioned, although it ought to be. What is there about mental illness which entitles the mentally disordered offender to be extracted from the penal system whereas, except in extreme cases, the physically ill person remains within it? And is medical disposal necessarily more humane than a penal disposal? I believe that many sentencers feel, when they make a hospital order or attach a condition of treatment to a probation order, that for once they have had the chance to do something pleasant and helpful to a fellow human being. I am far from sure that all of those in the dock would concur: but then they do not shape penal policies. Be that as it may, there does seem to be a presumption that mentally disordered offenders do not belong in the penal system. This is plainly inconsistent with a wholly utilitarian attitude towards sentencing.

Another reason why the mentally disordered offender and utilitarian principles are at odds is that the offender does not fit neatly into the peanl system. He is a nuisance in prison, and if curing his disorder has a utilitarian purpose (as seems to be assumed) this cannot be achieved in prison, at least in the kind of prison which we have today.

Finally, it is obvious that some utilitarian objectives are inapposite for some mentally disordered offenders. Personal deterrents will not work with those whose reasoning powers are seriously out of joint. Nor, if the offender is conspicuously off-centre, can the imposition of a penal sanction be relied upon to deter those who regard themselves as normal. Similarly, although sanctions may have to be applied to a mentally disordered offender in order to forestall unlicensed revenge, the steps which are necessary and sufficient to assuage public indignation will not necessarily be the same for the mentally disordered as they are for normal offenders. These examples can readily be multiplied. Quite plainly, the range of disposals which are available for the offender who is mentally sound must be modified to cope with the disordered. But unless there is some consensus on what the utilitarian targets are, what types of measure are thought appropriate for each of these targets, and what is their relative importance, one cannot tell which of the orthodox penal methods need to be displaced or changed when dealing with the mentally disordered offender. That the provision for such offenders has proved so inadequate is in no small degree due to the fact that these questions have not even been asked, let alone answered.

It seems however that we are not going to maintain a strictly utilitarian policy: by no means. Let me give some extracts from the very important White Paper on Crime, Justice and Protecting the Public[9]:

> "The aim of the Government's proposals is better justice through a more consistent approach to sentencing, so that convicted criminals get their 'just deserts'. The severity of the sentence of the court should be directly related to the seriousness of the offence.
>
> . . .
>
> The Government proposes a new legislative framework for sentencing, based on the seriousness of the offence or just deserts.
>
> . . .
>
> Punishment can effectively denounce criminal behaviour and exact retribution for it. The sentence of the court expresses public repugnance of criminal behaviour and determines the punishment for it. If the punishment is just, and in proportion to the seriousness of the offence, then the victim, the victim's family and friends, and the public will be satisfied that the law has been upheld and there will be no desire for further retaliation or private revenge.
>
> . . .
>
> For most offenders, imprisonment has to be justified in terms of public protection, denunciation and retribution. Otherwise it can be an expensive way of making bad people worse. The prospects of

[9] Cm 965.

reforming offenders are usually much better if they stay in the community, provided the public is properly protected.

. . .

Deterrence is a principle with much immediate appeal. Most law abiding citizens understand the reasons why some behaviour is made a criminal offence, and would be deterred by the shame of a criminal conviction or the possibility of a severe penalty. There are doubtless some criminals who carefully calculate the possible gains and risks. But much crime is committed on impulse, given the opportunity presented by an open window or unlocked door, and it is committed by offenders who live from moment to moment; their crimes are as impulsive as the rest of their feckless, sad or pathetic lives. It is unrealistic to construct sentencing arrangements on the assumption that most offenders will weigh up the possibilities in advance and base their conduct off-centre on rational calculation. Often they do not."

Of course we see here a number of familiar utilitarian concepts. But there is a very significant addition: namely an explicit ethical aim which treats considerations such as punishment, retribution and denunciation not only as legitimate but as necessary components of penal practice. After a long period of eclipse this old idea has been freshly minted under the title of "just deserts", and has joined the list of buzz-words which includes "tough", "condign" and "community". It is a telling turn of phrase because it suggests that any disposal in accordance with its precept must automatically be just; and "deserts" has a gritty and purposeful ring. In fact there is nothing new about the concept, which has been a feature of theoretical writings here and abroad for several years, but this is the first occasion in the United Kingdom when it has been officially and publicly espoused. Interestingly, we also see it acknowledged as a legitimate element in the battery of sentencing in "The Real Alternative",[10] a publication of NACRO, a body not hitherto seen as sympathetic to ideas of this kind.

I have also been struck by statements which appeared within a few days of each other last September in two newspapers. I will quote from them. The first was in the context of treatment for mentally disordered offenders in the community, in the absence of which the writer foresaw—

". . . we risk seeing men continuing to repeat offences (statistically sex offenders have one of the highest recidivism rates) but with their problems remaining essentially untreated until such time as they have committed either so many or so serious an offence *that they deserve to go to prison for a long time*" (my emphasis).

The other extract reads as follows:

[10] 1989 ISBN 0 85069 0684. See especially pp.5–6.

"A prison sentence matters, because it clearly relays society's disapproval. Treatment (which has yet to prove successful in the long-term) should come during or after sentence, not instead of it. At least it keeps an offender away from children for a little longer."

These quotations come, first from a letter to *The Times* by a probation officer and the other from an article in *The Observer*—not quite the provenance we might expect. It is not I believe accidental that both writers were concerned with offences against women and children, which tend to engender thoughts of retribution and punishment in the minds even of those to whom they would ordinarily be distasteful. This has produced a marked shift in the opinions of those who are articulate enough to influence social policies, and has helped to provide backing for the notion of just deserts.

Now if this doctrine is to become firmly established somebody ought to be thinking how it can be applied to the mentally disordered offenders: for in one of its manifestations it has a strong ethical content. I say "one of its manifestations" for there are two, which are constantly being confused, although they are very different. This important difference can be detected in the words of the sentencer. Version 1—"This crime merits five years' imprisonment". Version 2—"You deserve five years' imprisonment for having committed this crime". These are not the same.

The practical and theoretical problems of version 1 are well known and we need not spend long with them. It posits a one-to-one correspondence between offence and penalty, and seems to work something like this. Those with authority to do so establish a hierarchy of sentences—starting at the top with, say, public disembowelment and ending at the bottom with an absolute discharge. Those penalties which seem to be out of tune with the time are eliminated: decapitation, transportation for life, branding, flogging and so on. Next, the authorities establish a hierarchy of crimes in order of perceived badness, and set the two hierarchies alongside, so that the sentencer can read across from the crime to the penalty. From time to time one hierarchy or the other is revised. In the hierarchy of sentences, penalties may be added or subtracted and the existing assumptions about whether one particular penalty is more severe than another may be reformulated. Equally, as regards the hierarchy of crimes the assessments of relative gravity may undergo a change.

Plainly, this method serves little utilitarian purpose. Not long ago the correspondence between rape and the sentence deemed to be appropriate was changed. This cannot have been done for utilitarian reasons. The deterrent effect of an increase in the starting-point sentence for a contested charge of rape from (say) four years to five years imprisonment must surely be very small. What has happened is that rape has moved some rungs up the ladder of perceived gravity.

Manifestly the establishment of these hierarchies, and hence of the relationship between them, is not based on logic, although it is given a semblance of intellectual respectability by calling it the "principle of proportionality". In reality, there is no reason why a sentence of (say) three years imprisonment is more "proportional" to a baddish public-house "glassing" on a plea of guilty than sentences of six months or six years. It is a simple value judgment incapable of being rationalised—although not necessarily the worse for that.

Now if a system of direct correspondence between crime and sentence has no intellectual rigour it will be impossible to enforce it consistently, unless the criminal justice system is so arranged that there is a unique sentence for every crime. Such correspondences are very rare in current sentencing practice, the only important ones being the mandatory life sentence for murder and certain mandatory periods of disqualification in serious driving offences. Apart from these, the coupling between crime and sentence is very loose. For obvious practical reasons nobody even tries to apply the idea of just deserts according to version 1. For example, very few would consider that an offence by a youth of blameless character should carry the same penalty as if it had been committed by a hardened adult who had done the same thing twenty-five times before. Even the enthusiasts for proportionality do not say this: as witness to the fact that the American sentencing grids are grids, not linear scales. But if the idea is to be taken seriously, as the White Paper seems to suggest, the proponents should tell us how it can be applied to the mentally disordered offender. Surely it is simple nonsense to say that the standard penalty is appropriate where the offence was committed by someone who was floridly schizophrenic at the time: although I can just see that the standard penalty might perhaps provide a ceiling for any element of deprivation of liberty involved in the medical disposal of the offender. But if there are at least some mentally disordered offenders to whom the doctrine of just deserts, according to version 1, does not apply we must find out why not, for until we do that we shall have no way to tell which mentally disordered offender is extracted from the just deserts system and which is not.

Much more realistic however is the assumption that what is really being aimed at in the new policy documents is version 2—"You deserve five years for committing that offence". This approach to sentencing is concerned with personal responsibility and it focuses on the individual offender, and not simply on the offence.

It seems from the literature to have two practical functions. First to recall to the offender a sense of the subordination of his own interests to those of a higher order. Second, to give a sharp reminder to others that their interests also are so subordinated.[11]

These are not by any means ignoble aims. But if a system is to be based on ethics somebody must prescribe the norms. Are they religious, or the Kantian imperative or something else? The norms must then be promulgated so that people know what they are and how to work them in practice by applying them to the particular offender and offence. I have seen no indication so far that these questions are being tackled. If they are not, then the existing methods will simply roll on unchanged, save for some cosmetic new vocabulary.

If however the White Paper is intended to convey a real shift in policy, then thought and action are urgently needed about the way in which its principles are meant to bear on the mentally disordered offender. It is obvious, is it not, that what society can fairly expect of the mentally disordered person in his relation to the moral order, and what steps society may and should take to restore him to what is seen as a proper relationship with that order, cannot fairly be the same as in the case of a person who is mentally sound. Furthermore, a legion of professionals will have to think in entirely new terms: for the medical people and those in the social sciences will now be compelled, if not to apply, at least to acknowledge, the relevance and validity of ethical considerations which hitherto have been quite outside their sphere.

The matter may go further than this. It may be that the just deserts doctrine is founded not on the twin objectives of reminding the offender and of reminding potential offenders that the individual's egotistical desires are not paramount, but of an altogether less intellectual notion that the very concept of a moral order implies a punitive reaction to deviant conduct. William Temple warned[12] against re-working Bacon's epigram so as to regard Justice as "a tame or civilised kind of Revenge". It is possible that this peril is being overlooked? Or perhaps even that it is regarded as not a peril at all but as a legitimate response of authority on behalf of society to the corrosive effects of crime. If so, we should be told this clearly, for it will entail that a large proportion of those currently involved in dealing with mentally

[11] A full treatment of this important and difficult topic, an understanding of which is essential to any attempt to put a doctrine of just deserts into practice could not be undertaken within the compass of the present lecture. A brief but compelling account is to be found in Archbishop William Temple's masterly Clarke Hall lecture of 1934.

[12] *Ibid*, at p.18.

disordered offenders are going to have to learn fundamentally new modes of thought. There is no sign that they are being invited to do so.

Who are the mentally disordered?

The issues just raised in relation to the criminal justice system are concerned primarily with policies: what is the state trying to achieve when establishing the system; what kinds of conduct are to be stigmatised as criminal; what penal methods should be available, and how should they be applied to various types of crime? The problems to which I shall now briefly turn are, or at first sight appear to be, of a very different nature. Once the penal system is set in order, one knows who is an offender. But how does one know whether he is a mentally disordered offender? If we are to create a special regime, or sub-regime, for the mentally disordered offender, we must know who he is, who qualifies for the regime. Even a moment's thought will show that the boundary between those who do qualify and those who do not is in a state of constant flux.

Let me illustrate the problem by reference to five individuals, each of whose behaviour deviates from the statistical norm.

1. The person who kills in the grip of emotional stress
2. The habitual robber
3. The alcoholic who commits arson whilst drunk
4. The practising adult male homosexual
5. The paederast

In classical times none of these people would have been classed as mentally disordered offenders. The fourth and fifth because homosexual behaviour with adult and young boys was neither criminal nor regarded as aberrant. The remainder, because although they were certainly offenders they would not have been regarded as mad, and it would have made no difference if they had been.

In mediaeval times the outcome would have been the same but for different reasons. By now, all five forms of behaviour were criminal, although in certain cases the offences were against the canon rather than the secular law. None of the offenders would have been regarded as mentally disordered, apart possibly from the anguished murderer. They would have been seen as bad, not mad. All would be firmly within the penal system; although, within it, the murderer might conceivably be dealt with in a special way.

Now let us look at the position, say, thirty years ago. The robber presented no problem. He was just a villian. So also was the alcoholic. But the position of the other three was different. By now the anguished murderer had acquired the so-called defence of diminished responsibility, and although he remained a criminal—having committed manslaughter—he would in quite a number of cases be extracted from the penal system and treated specially as a mentally disordered offender. As for the arsonist, the homosexual and the paederast they had come to be recognised as mentally disordered. Their conduct remained criminal, but their behavioural traits were seen as pathological in origin. As late as 1970 we find the Encyclopedia Britannica[13] asserting—"medically, inversion must be considered an illness", and then going on to deal briefly with methods of "cure". So also had alcoholism been firmly established as a disease. Yet although these three individuals qualified as mentally disordered offenders they remained within the penal system and were not, unless they were very lucky, remitted to a special regime outside it.

Finally there is the picture that we see today, which shows our individuals distributed between four populations. The robber and the alcoholic are still retained within the penal system. The anguished murderer is still in the regime for the mentally disordered offender. The position of the homosexual is totally different, for he is no longer a candidate for either regime. His conduct has been de-criminalised, and his behaviour is no longer regarded as symptomatic of disorder. He is just an ordinary citizen, like his ancestor in ancient Greece. The paederast by contrast is at least a possible qualifier for mental disorder, since some doctors still try to persuade sentencers that he can be cured. Even so he remains firmly in the penal system; probably even more firmly now than he was thirty years ago. Here he differ profoundly from his Greek forebear.

Even a glance at these examples will show that something odd is going on. I believe that at least two processes are involved, neither of them concerned with science or logic. The first process takes offenders who are regarded in medical terms as mentally disordered and who *prima facie* are "mentally disordered offenders", and subtracts them from the category of those who would normally qualify for a special regime within or outside the penal system. By modern thinking, an alcoholic and (possibly) the paederast are mentally disordered, and yet unlike the schizophrenic they are left to the ordinary penal processes.

The criteria for identifying the members of this sub-set of offenders who, though mentally disordered are not treated as such, are not static, and indeed it is hard to find them candidly articulated. Still less do they have any semblance of logic. As it seems to me there is no choice but to admit that these criteria are

[13] Vol. 11, p.649.

purely arbitrary, and reflect contemporary value judgments. The offender may be ill, but he is not seen to have the kind of illness which entitles him to be "let off". Seen by whom? The answer must be, I believe, by those who lay down penal policy, with behind them the massive but amorphous bulk of general public opinion: *i.e.* primarily Parliament, and to a lesser degree the churches. Undoubtedly one element in the value-judgment thus involved is a sensation that offenders cannot too readily rely on the sympathy which energises the "humane" treatment of the mentally disordered, if the disorder can be regarded as in one sense of another the offender's own fault. The schizophrenic cannot be blamed for being schizophrenic. But the alcoholic is viewed as the author of his own misfortune. So also the paedophile or the violent man, who may not be responsible for his impulses but is responsible for not resisting them. This may not be sound thinking, or indeed any kind of thinking, but I am sure that it is part of the decision-making process. Whether other factors are in play is too complex a topic to be addressed here tonight.

Still, since the entire penal system is based on a set of value-judgments there is nothing very surprising about the discovery that such judgments are at work when decisions are taken about the categorisation of mentally disordered offenders and the way in which persons falling within various categories are dispersed within and outside that system.

More disturbing however is the problem raised by the question why persons allocated to a particular category are (or are not) to be regarded as mentally disordered. Twenty years ago he was regarded as mentally disordered: as suffering from a "disease". Now he is not. His personality, predilections and behaviour are unchanged. If he remains the same, and yet was diseased one day and not diseased the next, something must have happened to the "disease". What is it?

In order to set about this question we must pause for a few commonplace observations on the nature of disease. Essentially a disease is a matter of labelling, resulting from a combination of statistics and choice. The researcher first identifies a series of norms for physical conditions which he believes to be potentially interesting. He then investigates the deviations from the norms displayed by a group of subjects. Amongst these deviations will be some which the researcher regards as harmful. He examines these deviations to see whether there is a statistical connection between them: whether they go together (*i.e.* literally, are a "syndrome"). If he finds that the deviations, whether individually harmful or not, do constitute a syndrome he gives it a name, often his own. We may take an example. It is known that most humans do not simultaneously display an elevated body temperature, spots in the mouth, a body rash and a runny nose. Since these deviations group together in a statistically significant degree, it is thought legitimate to concatenate them and call them "measles". Once the concatenation is established and found interesting the researcher sets out to find means by which he can reduce either all the deviations, or at least the ones which he regards as deleterious, to zero. When he has done this he announces that he has found a "cure". Thereafter, physicians look for the concatenation, and apply the same means with the aim of curing their own patients.

The success of this method depends upon the researcher's technical skill in identifying concatenations which really are statistically significant, rather than adventitious, a task made difficult by the small size of the samples generally available to researchers in human medicine. The skill of the researcher is also involved in his selection of those deviations which he regards as interesting enough to merit investigation.

Against this background we must now consider in what way, to repeat the turn of phrase used a few moments ago, something can "happen to" a disease. In relation to physical disorders there seem to be two possibilities. The first is that the cures are so successful, in identifying and attacking the causes of the syndrome, that the concatenation of symptoms ceases on any interesting scale to be found, so that there is no longer anything to which the label can be attached. In this sense, the group of symptoms constituting "pulmonary tuberculosis" has in north-western Europe almost ceased to be found, so that the disease no longer "exists" there.

Quite plainly, this cannot be an explanation why the adult male homosexual has been subtracted from the roll of mentally disordered offenders. I believe that to find a more convincing explanation one must look at the power of those who define diseases to select the deviations from the norm which they regard as sufficiently important to form an element in a group of symptoms which is given the label of a disease. A statistician would be just as interested in the concatenation of (say) red hair, left-handedness and musical ability, if it was shown to exist, as with the group of deviations from the physical norm which is called measles. The doctor does not work like this. He is interested in syndromes only because they are pointers to disease, because some element of the group of symptoms have harmful aspects, or perhaps because they are signposts to a covert condition which has such an aspect. The doctor is interested in the grouping because it enables him to identify the consistent presence of deleterious factors which, once identified, can be the more easily eradicated.

What seems to me to have happened, in the cases we are now considering, is that the doctors have decided, or someone has decided for them, that the symptoms of homosexuality, or the underlying condition which the symptoms display, are no longer to be regarded as deleterious. Once this decision has been made the condition ceases to be of medical significance and it is crossed out of the list of diseases.

If this explanation is anything like correct, a series of questions with direct practical bearing on the future of the mentally disordered offender will be raised and must be answered: not in relation to homosexuality, which has been de-criminalised, but in relation to those persons who commit offences which are not very serious, for reasons which may or may not be classed as symptomatic of mental disorder. It is essential for important constitutional, and not simply theoretical, reasons that those who determine whether or not a syndrome is characteristic of mental disorder, and hence a motive for transferring people in and out of the sub-set of mentally disordered offenders, should be clearly identified. We should know by what authority these persons bring about these changes. We should know who has the right and duty to scrutinise the process by which the boundaries of the class of the mentally disordered offender are redefined.

These are important constitutional questions,[14] for there is a risk that the rights and responsibilities of individuals and groups, and the rights and responsibilities of the state towards them, are being modified in important respects, by concensus among professionals, without proper accountability to the public at large and the public's elected representatives. Whether this risk is in fact materialising does not seem to be discussed, at least in any forum accessible to the non-specialist.

At this stage I must pause to give one example—and there are many others—of the way in which these intellectual problems bear directly on the futures of the unhappy people whose interests we all wish to serve. I will give the example a pompous title.

"The Paradox of Degree"

Imagine three men with bad habits which get them into trouble.

A's habit is to burgle unoccupied commercial premises. He recognises—just about—that this causes inconvenience, upset and

[14] There are a number of other questions, more fundamental than those sketched in the text, which bear upon this problem. As examples only, one may cite—A. Why should not all repetitious criminal conduct, be treated as symptomatic of a disease? (The immediate answer, that the deleterious effects of criminal conduct are felt by society, whereas a disease afflicts the patient himself cannot be right, for the psychotic who may cause great harm to others is nevertheless regarded as ill.) B. Do social workers try to "cure" their clients? If not, what do they try to do?

loss to the proprietors. He does not care. He likes burglary: it is a quicker and more interesting way of getting money than honest work or being unemployed. He breaks into a shop and is caught. He is brought before the magistrates and put on probation. He pays no attention. He burgles another five shops and is caught again. Now he is a candidate for community service, or possibly even a custodial sentence. Later, he burgles another fifty shops. Custody for a substantial time is a certainty. On the horizon is the prospect that if he goes on offending he will ultimately receive an extended sentence of imprisonment, designed to keep him in a place where further burglaries are impossible.

B's habit is to steal bicycles. He steals one and is caught. He is told off by the constable. He steals another five. This time he is charged and put on probation. He steals another fifty and finds himself sent up to the Crown Court for sentencing. The judge gives him a long hard stare and put him back for reports. The psychiatrist and the social worker convince the Court that B is not doing this for easy money. He does not even particularly care about riding cycles. He simply gets an impulse to take one, and yields. Nobody can tell why he does this, and nobody can suggest a way of stopping him. The judge does not know what to do, but with the connivance of the doctors, probation officers and social workers cobbles up a way of not sending him to prison: for the moment. Everyone in Court has the uneasy feeling that a custodial disposal within the penal system is in sight—even if, as they all hope, it may be some distance away.

C's habit is to take women's underwear from clothes lines. He has probably been doing it for some time before anyone takes official notice. His offending is concealed within the community. If there are sanctions, they are applied physically by his neighbours. He goes on, and is reported. A good police officer has a word with his mother and with his social worker to try and get him to desist. This does no good. Eventually C appears in court, and everyone strains, probably with success, to keep him out of the penal system and arrange for medical treatment.

Now there is something strange here. Each of these men is behaving in a deviant way. Most people do not burgle houses any more than they steal cycles or underwear. Whereas the repetition of A's deviant behaviour digs him deeper and deeper into the penal system, without any doctor exerting himself to present A as the sufferer from a syndrome with a fancy Greek name, the repetition by C and possibly also by B of aberrant acts may well point the offender towards an exit from that system. For C, in sharp contrast to A, the more he misbehaves the more sympathy he gets, and the kindlier his fate. Why should this be so?

The only explanation which I can suggest is that a tacit moral judgement is at work. The kind of professionals, such as ourselves, who are called on to deal with A, B and C are not by temperament and upbringing disposed to commit acts of dishonesty, and if they are then they believe that the temptation should be resisted. In most cases it is resisted. The burglar is therefore seen as doing something wrong which he would not do if he had more moral fibre. He inhabits a different world from the professionals. The acts of C (the underwear man) are of course just as unlikely to be done by the average professional as are those of A. Nevertheless, they spring from an underlying sexual drive which most professionals share, even though with C it manifests itself in a bizarre and unacceptable fashion. It is therefore much easier than in the case of A for the professional to say that C's offending is the result of an essentially legitimate or at least neutral shared human experience. What has gone wrong with C is that the mainspring is simply driving the wrong wheels.

On this view, C (unlike A) is not choosing to do something which is morally wrong, but is simply malfunctioning, and can therefore be given appropriately sympathetic treatment.

This is no more than speculation, and may be fanciful, but I make no apology for introducing the topic, for any properly thought-out regime which caters specifically for the mentally disordered offender must necessarily have a mechanism for determining who is and who is not to fall within it. In cases such as those which we have examined the persons responsible for making this determination must understand:

1. The basis on which eccentric behaviour is or is not to be categorised as mental disorder, and
2. The basis on which a mental disorder which undeniably does exist is to be treated as if it did not.

I believe that this need will soon arise in practice. There is a movement afoot, which I fervently endorse, to secure through local inter-professional co-operation that the low-level offender who is mentally disordered is diverted directly into the medical regime without ever entering the criminal justice system. This is splendid, but there are some dangers. If A, B and C are to be treated differently, and it seems plain that they will be, all concerned (and that includes the offenders themselves) must have a clear idea of why this is so, and of the basis on which those who have the responsibility for diversion from custody can deal with situations more difficult than those which we have taken as examples.

Constitutionality

The issue just discussed has another aspect. Currently, three initiatives have political and institutional backing. The diversion of criminal offenders from custody; diversion of psychiatric patients from long-term in-patient care; and diversion of the mentally disordered offender from the criminal justice system. The fact that these movements are going on at the same time, and produce broadly the same result—*viz.* that someone who would have been inside is now outside—make them easy to regard simply as different practical manifestations of the same general principle. This apparent common advance on a broad front lends mutual encouragement to the participants, and a more prominent place in the public eye.

So far so good; but less good if those whose task it is to create the necessary administrative structures forget that the three movements are in reality quite distinct, as to their history, their intellectual and ethical foundations, and practical purposes which they are intending to secure. The reasons for extruding long-stay patients into the community are different from those which will motivate the local groups who undertake the deflection of the mentally disordered offender from the criminal justice system. It is essential that we start asking now, before it is too late, by what right, according to what principles, and subject to what accountability the latter process is to take place.

I take as the starting point the proposition that if the state creates a criminal justice system it ought to apply equally to all, and that if persons are capriciously withdrawn from it this is just as corrosive a source of injustice as where persons are wrongly brought within it. So caprice must be avoided. We therefore need a formal definition, rigorously applied, for determining who are to form the exceptions to the general applicability of the system; and, to make sure that the application is indeed rigorous, a formal system of accountability. In practice this vision has never quite been realised. In the past, minor juvenile offenders were dealt with informally by the village constable, employing forms of sanction which are now out of fashion. There have also been long-standing and ill-defined discretions assumed by local prosecuting authorities in relation to the decision whether to prosecute. These discretions have been inherited by the Crown Prosecution Service, and are applied in a more methodical and supervised way. Their exercise involves value-judgments, either ethical or economic, about whether the case is one in which it would be right to prosecute, and whether proceedings are worth the trouble and expense.

When we add the ingredient of mental disorder the ethical element of the discretion becomes much more complex, for the reasons already touched upon. This will leave more room for legitimate difference of opinion on the moral weight of factors pointing towards or away from a disposal within the general system of criminal justice. As soon as such differences arise there will be injustice, for it is not right that (say) offender C in the example we have considered should be exposed to the risk of penal sanctions in one part of the country whilst in another part a precisely similar offender should be spared from any involvement in the public mechanisms of the criminal law. These are important decisions—important for the victim as well as the offender—and if they are to be taken informally and in private the public is entitled to be assured that the same principles hold good throughout. This calls for scrupulous adherence to precise and published norms, which in my view can only be achieved by legislation, and by the creation of a system of review.

This suggestion may be greeted by dismay—the thought of introducing more legislation into a field where what already exists has been such a conspicuous failure is bound to be unwelcome. Why inhibit the zeal and initiative of those who perceive a need and who want to do something about it? This reaction is understandable, but unsound, for experience is constantly reminding us that energy and well-wishing may from time to time create imbalances just as serious as those which they set out to remedy. Moreover it is precisely that combination of professional skills and experience, which it is hoped will be the strength of the proposed local bodies, which may prove a source of divisiveness and erratic decision-making. For the intellectual cultures of those reared in the various disciplines may make it hard to achieve a consensus in borderline cases; and it is the borderline cases with which the new system will be designed to deal. If each local body has to address for itself the difficult combination of penal, medical and moral issues which I have partially sketched this evening, the result will at best be a wasteful duplication of effort, and more probably a patchy and unpredictable system of para-justice which may well do more harm than good. How much better if the thinking is done in advance and the results embodied in a systematic code, so that the energies of those who are eager to take part can be harnessed at once to effective use.

Further thoughts

The purpose of this evening's remarks has been to suggest that serious intellectual, as well as ethical, practical and humanitarian problems are raised by the mentally disordered offender. It has not been practical to do more than open up a few of them, in the hope that professionals with the necessary resources and skills will be encouraged not only to explore them in more depth, but also to pose some more. In conclusion, I offer for consideration two further areas for exploration.

1. Risk assessment. "Just deserts" looks to the offence rather than the risk of repetition. But where there is seen to be a risk that the offender will commit serious violence in the future—where he is regarded as "dangerous"—a different principle is involved. The element of proportionality is subordinated to the interests of the community. We need to think about this matter of dangerousness. Is the court given sufficient data to enable a proper judgment to be made? What level of probability as regards the commission of serious violence in the future is required before this new sentencing principle comes into play? If the judge describes the armed robber as "a very dangerous man", on what does he base this assessment? Is he not implicitly saying that the robber is mentally disordered? And if he is, why does he go to prison, not to hospital?
2. Causation and timing. It is very often taken for granted, when an offender is diagnosed as mentally disordered, that he has offended because he is disordered, or at any rate that his disorder is all that matters. Why are these assumptions not more widely questioned? Cannot a disordered offender, in the commission of the offence, occasionally be bad, as well as mad: and, if so, why is not the badness of his conduct to be marked in some way?

   Again, what is the correct approach when by a process of catharsis the offender cures his mental disorder by committing the crime. He was disordered then, but is not disordered now. To which regime does he belong? Conversely if he was mentally sound when he committed the offence, and would (according to the doctrine of just deserts be in line for punishment), what happens if he becomes disordered by the time he is sentenced? Is the fact that he will almost inevitably attract a medical disposal simply a recognition that he does not fit into the penal system, or has his culpability somehow become subordinated to his later illness: and if so, why?

All practitioners concerned with the mentally disordered offender could, if they set themselves to the task, greatly enlarge this sample list of queries. Yet they never seem to do so, still less examine what the answers might be. Perhaps this is somewhere to start.

This is a time of enthusiasm for improving the fate of the mentally disordered offender, and it may seem particularly inopportune to spend an evening in uttering that most unpopular of phrases—"Yes, but wait a minute . . . !". We are only a few hundred metres from the refuges of the wretched people whom we called to mind an hour ago. Have we not lost sight of them in a theoretical empyrean?

No. We have everything that they have not. A settled life. Enough money to live and have some fun. The security which comes from success: and we would not be in the lecture hall of a university if we did not enjoy a measure of success. So we owe them something. Certainly we should agitate, plan, manoeuvre and work on their behalf: all the activities at which the great benefactors of the past have excelled. Most of all however we should think, and make others do so, whether it is congenial or not. Fellow-feeling is good. Thought is hard. Let us give them our best.

[7]

THE HUMANITARIAN THEORY OF PUNISHMENT [1]

By C. S. LEWIS
Fellow of Magdalen College

IN ENGLAND we have lately had a controversy about Capital Punishment. I do not know whether a murderer is more likely to repent and make a good end on the gallows a few weeks after his trial or in the prison infirmary thirty years later. I do not know whether the fear of death is an indispensable deterrent. I need not, for the purpose of this article, decide whether it is a morally permissible deterrent. Those are questions which I propose to leave untouched. My subject is not Capital Punishment in particular, but that theory of punishment in general which the controversy showed to be almost universal among my fellow-countrymen. It may be called the Humanitarian theory. Those who hold it think that it is mild and merciful. In this I believe that they are seriously mistaken. I believe that the "Humanity" which it claims is a dangerous illusion and disguises the possibility of cruelty and injustice without end. I urge a return to the traditional or Retributive theory not solely, not even primarily, in the interests of society, but in the interests of the criminal.

According to the Humanitarian theory, to punish a man because he deserves it, and as much as he deserves, is mere revenge, and, therefore, barbarous and immoral. It is maintained that the only legitimate motives for punishing are the desire to deter others by example or to mend the criminal. When this theory is combined, as frequently happens, with the belief that all crime is more or less pathological, the idea of mending tails off into that of healing or curing and punishment becomes therapeutic. Thus it appears at first sight that we have passed from the harsh and self-righteous notion of giving the wicked their deserts to the charitable and enlightened one of tending the psychologically sick. What could be more amiable? One little point which is taken for granted in this theory needs, however, to be made explicit. The things done to the criminal, even if they are called cures, will be just as compulsory as they were in the old days when we called them punishments. If a tendency to steal can be cured by psychotherapy, the thief will no doubt be forced to undergo the treatment. Otherwise, society cannot continue.

[1]This article first appeared in *Twentieth Century* and is now republished without alteration. It is printed again because it seems important that it should reach as wide a legal audience as possible. The succeeding article appeared in the same magazine, as a reply to this. We express our gratitude to the editor of *Twentieth Century* for his ready help in making both these articles available.

My contention is that this doctrine, merciful though it appears, really means that each one of us, from the moment he breaks the law, is deprived of the rights of a human being.

The reason is this. The Humanitarian theory removes from Punishment the concept of Desert. But the concept of Desert is the only connecting link between punishment and justice. It is only as deserved or undeserved that a sentence can be just or unjust. I do not here contend that the question "Is it deserved?" is the only one we can reasonably ask about a punishment. We may very properly ask whether it is likely to deter others and to reform the criminal. But neither of these two last questions is a question about justice. There is no sense in talking about a "just deterrent" or a "just cure". We demand of a deterrent not whether it is just but whether it will deter. We demand of a cure not whether it is just but whether it succeeds. Thus when we cease to consider what the criminal deserves and consider only what will cure him or deter others, we have tacitly removed him from the sphere of justice altogether; instead of a person, a subject of rights, we now have a mere object, a patient, a "case".

The distinction will become clearer if we ask who will be qualified to determine sentences when sentences are no longer held to derive their propriety from the criminal's deservings. On the old view the problem of fixing the right sentence was a moral problem. Accordingly, the judge who did it was a person trained in jurisprudence; trained, that is, in a science which deals with rights and duties, and which, in origin at least, was consciously accepting guidance from the Law of Nature, and from Scripture. We must admit that in the actual penal code of most countries at most times these high originals were so much modified by local custom, class interests, and utilitarian concessions, as to be very imperfectly recognizable. But the code was never in principle, and not always in fact, beyond the control of the conscience of the society. And when (say, in eighteenth-century England) actual punishments conflicted too violently with the moral sense of the community, juries refused to convict and reform was finally brought about. This was possible because, so long as we are thinking in terms of Desert, the propriety of the penal code, being a moral question, is a question on which every man has the right to an opinion, not because he follows this or that profession, but because he is simply a man, a rational animal enjoying the Natural Light. But all this is changed when we drop the concept of Desert. The only two questions we may now ask about a punishment are whether it deters and whether it cures. But these are not questions on which anyone is entitled to have an opinion simply because he is a man.

He is not entitled to an opinion even if, in addition to being a man, he should happen also to be a jurist, a Christian, and a moral theologian. For they are not questions about principle but about matter of fact; and for such *cuiquam in sua arte credendum*. Only the expert "penologist" (let barbarous things have barbarous names), in the light of previous experiment, can tell us what is likely to deter: only the psychotherapist can tell us what is likely to cure. It will be in vain for the rest of us, speaking simply as men, to say, "but this punishment is hideously unjust, hideously disproportionate to the criminal's deserts". The experts with perfect logic will reply, "but nobody was talking about deserts. No one was talking about *punishment* in your archaic vindictive sense of the word. Here are the statistics proving that this treatment deters. Here are the statistics proving that this other treatment cures. What is your trouble?"

The Humanitarian theory, then, removes sentences from the hands of jurists whom the public conscience is entitled to criticize and places them in the hands of technical experts whose special sciences do not even employ such categories as rights or justice. It might be argued that since this transference results from an abandonment of the old idea of punishment, and, therefore, of all vindictive motives, it will be safe to leave our criminals in such hands. I will not pause to comment on the simple-minded view of fallen human nature which such a belief implies. Let us rather remember that the "cure" of criminals is to be compulsory; and let us then watch how the theory actually works in the mind of the Humanitarian. The immediate starting point of this article was a letter I read in one of our Leftist weeklies. The author was pleading that a certain sin, now treated by our laws as a crime, should henceforward be treated as a disease. And he complained that under the present system the offender, after a term in gaol, was simply let out to return to his original environment where he would probably relapse. What he complained of was not the shutting up but the letting out. On his remedial view of punishment the offender should, of course, be detained until he was cured. And of course the official straighteners are the only people who can say when that is. The first result of the Humanitarian theory is, therefore, to substitute for a definite sentence (reflecting to some extent the community's moral judgment on the degree of ill-desert involved) an indefinite sentence terminable only by the word of those experts—and they are not experts in moral thology nor even in the Law of Nature—who inflict it. Which of us, if he stood in the dock, would not prefer to be tried by the old system?

It may be said that by the continued use of the word punishment and the use of the verb "inflict" I am misrepresenting Humanitarians. They are not punishing, not inflicting, only healing. But do not let us be deceived by a name. To be taken without consent from my home and friends; to lose my liberty; to undergo all those assaults on my personality which modern psychotherapy knows how to deliver; to be re-made after some pattern of "normality" hatched in a Viennese laboratory to which I never professed allegiance; to know that this process will never end until either my captors have succeeded or I grown wise enough to cheat them with apparent success—who cares whether this is called Punishment or not? That it includes most of the elements for which any punishment is feared —shame, exile, bondage, and years eaten by the locust—is obvious. Only enormous ill-desert could justify it; but ill-desert is the very conception which the Humitarian theory has thrown overboard.

If we turn from the curative to the deterrent justification of punishment we shall find the new theory even more alarming. When you punish a man *in terrorem*, make of him an "example" to others, you are admittedly using him as a means to an end; someone else's end. This, in itself, would be a very wicked thing to do. On the classical theory of Punishment it was of course justified on the ground that the man deserved it. That was assumed to be established before any question of "making him an example" arose. You then, as the saying is, killed two birds with one stone; in the process of giving him what he deserved you set an example to others. But take away desert and the whole morality of the punishment disappears. Why, in Heaven's name, am I to be sacrificed to the good of society in this way?—unless, of course, I deserve it.

But that is not the worst. If the justification of exemplary punishment is not to be based on desert but solely on its efficacy as a deterrent, it is not absolutely necessary that the man we punish should even have committed the crime. The deterrent effect demands that the public should draw the moral, "If we do such an act we shall suffer like that man." The punishment of a man actually guilty whom the public think innocent will not have the desired effect; the punishment of a man actually innocent will, provided the public think him guilty. But every modern State has powers which make it easy to fake a trial. When a victim is urgently needed for exemplary purposes and a guilty victim cannot be found, all the purposes of deterrence will be equally served by the punishment (call it "cure" if you prefer) of an innocent victim, provided that the public can be cheated into thinking him guilty. It is no use to ask me why I assume that our rulers will be so wicked. The punishment of an innocent, that is, an undeserving, man is wicked only if we grant the traditional view that righteous punishment means deserved punishment. Once we have abandoned that criterion, all punishments have to be justified, if at all, on other grounds that have nothing to do with desert. Where the punishment of the innocent can be justified on those grounds (and it could in some cases be justified as a deterrent) it will be no less moral than any other punishment. Any distaste for it on the part of a Humanitarian will be merely a hang-over from the Retributive theory.

It is, indeed, important to notice that my argument so far supposes no evil intentions on the part of the Humanitarian and considers only what is involved in the logic of his position. My contention is that good men (not bad men) consistently acting upon that position would act as cruelly and unjustly as the greatest tyrants. They might in some respects act even worse. Of all tyrannies a tyranny sincerely exercised for the good of its victims may be the most oppressive. It may be better to live under robber barons than under omnipotent moral busybodies. The robber baron's cruelty may sometimes sleep, his cupidity may at some point be satiated; but those who torment us for our own good will torment us without end for they do so with the approval of their own conscience. They may be more likely to go to Heaven yet at the same time likelier to make a Hell of earth. Their very kindness stings with intolerable insult. To be "cured" against one's will and cured of states which we may not regard as disease is to be put on a level with those who have not yet reached the age of reason or those who never will; to be classed with infants, imbeciles, and domestic animals. But to be punished, however severely, because we have deserved it, because we "ought to have known better", is to be treated as a human person made in God's image.

In reality, however, we must face the possibility of bad rulers armed with a Humanitarian theory of punishment. A great many popular blue prints for a Christian society are merely what the Elizabethans called "eggs in moonshine" because they assume that the whole society is Christian or that the Christians are in control. This is not so in most contemporary States. Even if it were, our rulers would still be fallen men, and, therefore, neither very wise nor very good. As it is, they will usually be unbelievers. And since wisdom and virtue are not the only or the commonest qualifications for a place in the government, they will not often be even the best unbelievers. The practical problem of Christian politics is not that of drawing up schemes for a Christian society, but that of living as innocently as we can with unbelieving fellow-subjects under unbelieving rulers who will never be perfectly wise and good and who will sometimes be very wicked and very foolish. And when they are wicked the Humanitarian theory of punishment will put in their hands a finer instrument of tyranny than wickedness ever had before. For if crime and disease are to be regarded as the same thing, it follows that any state of mind which our masters choose to call "disease" can be treated as crime; and compulsorily cured. It will be vain to plead that states of mind which displease government need not always involve moral turpitude and do not therefore always deserve forfeiture of liberty. For our masters will not be using the concepts of Desert and Punishment but those of disease and cure. We know that one school of psychology already regards religion as a neurosis. When this particular neurosis becomes inconvenient to government, what is to hinder government from proceeding to "cure" it? Such "cure" will, of course, be compulsory; but under the Humanitarian theory it will not be called by the shocking name of Persecution. No one will blame us for being Christian, no one will hate us, no one will revile us. The new Nero will approach us with the silky manners of a doctor, and though all will be in fact as compulsory as the *tunica molesta* or Smithfield or Tyburn, all will go on within the unemotional therapeutic sphere where words like "right" and "wrong" or "freedom" and "slavery" are never heard. And thus when the command is given, every prominent Christian in the land may vanish overnight into Institutions for the Treatment of the Ideologically Unsound, and it will rest with the expert gaolers to say when (if ever) they are to re-emerge. But it will not be persecution. Even if the treatment is painful, even if it is life-long, even if it is fatal, that will be only a regrettable accident; the intention was purely therapeutic. Even in ordinary medicine there were painful operations and fatal operations; so in this. But because they are "treatment", not punishment, they can be criticized only by fellow-experts and on technical grounds, never by men as men and on grounds of justice.

This is why I think it essential to oppose the Humanitarian theory of punishment, root and branch, wherever we encounter it. It carries on its front a semblance of mercy which is wholly false. That is how it can deceive men of good will. The error began, perhaps, with Shelley's statement that the distinction between mercy and justice was invented in the courts of tyrants. It sounds noble, and was indeed the error of a noble mind. But the distinction is essential. The older view was that mercy "tempered" justice, or (on the highest level of all) that mercy and justice had met and kissed. The essential act of mercy was to pardon; and pardon in its very essence involves the recognition of guilt and ill-desert in the recipient.

If crime is only a disease which needs cure, not sin which deserves punishment, it cannot be pardoned. How can you pardon a man for having a gumboil or a club foot? But the Humanitarian theory wants simply to abolish Justice and substitute Mercy for it. This means that you start being "kind" to people before you have considered their rights, and then force upon them supposed kindnesses which they in fact had a right to refuse, and finally kindnesses which no one but you will recognize as kindnesses and which the recipient will feel as abominable cruelties. You have overshot the mark. Mercy, detached from Justice, grows unmerciful. That is the important paradox. As there are plants which will flourish only in mountain soil, so it appears that Mercy will flower only when it grows in the crannies of the rock of Justice: transplanted to the marshlands of mere Humanitarianism, it becomes a man-eating weed, all the more dangerous because it is still called by the same name as the mountain variety. But we ought long ago to have learned our lesson. We should be too old now to be deceived by those humane pretensions which have served to usher in every cruelty of the revolutionary period in which we live. These are the "precious balms" which will "break our heads".

There is a fine sentence in Bunyan: "It came burning hot into my mind, whatever he said, and however he flattered, when he got me home to his house, he would sell me for a slave." There is a fine couplet, too, in John Ball:

> Be ware ere ye be woe
> Know your friend from your foe.

One last word. You may ask why I send this to an Australian periodical. The reason is simple and perhaps worth recording: I can get no hearing for it in England.

[8]

Law and Human Behavior, Vol. 16, No. 1, 1992

Putting Mental Health into Mental Health Law*

Therapeutic Jurisprudence

David B. Wexler

This article critiques the traditional doctrinal approach to mental health law and compares the traditional approach with a new, interdisciplinary approach known as therapeutic jurisprudence. Therapeutic jurisprudence views the law itself as a potential therapeutic agent. Examples are given of how legal rules, procedures, and the roles of legal actors may produce therapeutic or antitherapeutic results and of how the law may improve therapeutic outcomes without sacrificing the interests of justice.

This article seeks to explain how and why mental health law developed outside of a truly interdisciplinary tradition and claims that mental health law's nearly exclusive doctrinal focus has resulted in the field having largely lost its academic appeal. But the article further claims that the time is ripe to create a truly interdisciplinary field of therapeutic jurisprudence with a creative/analytical approach and stylistic *genre* quite different from the analogical reasoning approach that characterizes traditional mental health law.

Traditional Mental Health Law

Although scholars and professionals from many disciplines are involved in mental health law and scholarship, the field is by and large not interdisciplinary in approach and content. Legally trained writers typically write about legal doctrine; mental health professionals often translate that doctrine so that it will be intelligible to mental health audiences. Mental health professionals also suggest how

* Reprint requests should be sent to David B. Wexler, College of Law, University of Arizona, Tucson, AZ 85721.

0147-7307/92/0200-0027$06.50/0

mental health practitioners might cope with the doctrine, how they might write proper reports, how they might handle themselves in court and under cross-examination, and so forth.

Basically, then, mental health law has been doctrinal, constitutional, and rights oriented. Recently, with respect to the teaching of mental health law in law schools, I wrote that

> What is striking about typical Mental Health Law courses is the *absence* of a truly interdisciplinary law and behavioral science approach. To the extent such courses substantially rely on another discipline at all, that discipline is likely to be philosophy (What is coercion? When is it justified? What is the proper place of paternalism?), rather than psychology or psychiatry. Besides providing information on pedestrian matters such as the difference between psychologists and psychiatrists, and, more substantively, on the possible adverse side-effects of antipsychotic medication and electroconvulsive therapy, the typical course seems to be a traditional law course with a constitutional bent, relying heavily, if not exclusively, on judicial opinions in an effort to extract and critique doctrinal development.[1]

The reason for the doctrinal and constitutional emphasis is presumably because modern mental health law was conceived during the civil liberties revolution, during which litigation and scholarship served to expand the rights of criminal suspects, defendants, prisoners, and ultimately mental patients and respondents in civil commitment proceedings.[2]

Typically, the creative and analytical work in traditional mental health law scholarship has been to determine whether a right recognized elsewhere in the law—usually in the area of constitutional criminal procedure (or perhaps in disability law)—should be stretched to cover the mental health system. The approach was well advocated by Ennis in a 1971 article[3] in which he argued that "if persons are involuntarily to be confined because of mental illness, the standards and procedures for confinement should guarantee no fewer rights than those afforded criminal defendants."[4] Here are some examples of traditional doctrinal development:

- The Supreme Court has said indigent criminal defendants[5] and juveniles alleged to be delinquent[6] have a right to appointed counsel. Since civil commitment can also lead to a deprivation of liberty, shouldn't proposed patients have a similar right to counsel?[7]

---

[1] Wexler, *Training in Law and Behavioral Sciences: Issues from a Legal Educator's Perspective,* 8 Behav. Sci. & the Law 197, 199 (1990).

[2] Ennis, *Civil Liberties and Mental Illness,* 7 Crim. L. Bull. 101 (1971). See also Brooks & Winick, *Foreword,* 39 Rutgers L. Rev. 235 (1987).

[3] *Id.*

[4] *Id.* at 108. The article's publication in the *Criminal Law Bulletin* is a significant statement in itself of mental health law's relationship to the criminal law area. Many of the law professors attracted to the field at that time were "crossovers" from criminal law and procedure.

[5] Argersinger v. Hamlin, 407 U.S. 25 (1972).

[6] In re Gault, 387 U.S. 1 (1967).

[7] R. Reisner & C. Slobogin, Law and the Mental Health System: Civil and Criminal Aspects 723 (2d ed. 1990).

- What about the right to jury trial? Criminal defendants have a right to jury trial.[8] But the Supreme Court has held that the right to jury trial does not extend to juvenile delinquency proceedings.[9] Since civil commitment is closer to juvenile delinquency proceedings than to criminal proceedings, perhaps no right to jury trial should attach in commitment proceedings.[10]
- What standard of proof is appropriate in civil commitment cases? Criminal cases of course require proof beyond a reasonable doubt. Traditional civil cases, on the other hand, require only a mere preponderance of the evidence. Is civil commitment "truly" criminal or is it civil? Or is it perhaps a hybrid? And if it is a hybrid, should a compromise standard of "clear and convincing" evidence suffice?[11]
- The Supreme Court has held a probable cause hearing to be required in the criminal context.[12] Should such a right apply as well to civil commitment?[13]
- Should prisoners have a right to refuse psychiatric treatment?[14] Don't ordinary medical patients have a right to refuse treatment?[15] What's the difference? But don't prison administrators have a big say regarding much of prison life? Shouldn't they have a say with respect to this matter as well? Should the right to refuse treatment question be resolved differently for prisoners and for institutionalized mental patients?[16]

This sort of legal development and scholarship surely has its place. It certainly was important in the early years of modern mental health law. But a nearly exclusive emphasis on this approach is both risky and, after 20 years, sterile.

The Decline of Traditional Mental Health Law

The sterility seems self-evident. Why do I also say risky? Because if scholarship is exclusively dependent upon the recognition or the pursuit of certain rights, then as society and the composition of the Supreme Court change, making the viability or the attainment of those rights less likely, the entire branch of scholarship is likely to die on the vine.[17]

Perhaps the best example is provided by the field of constitutional criminal procedure. With the Warren Court and the criminal procedure revolution, con-

---

[8] Duncan v. Louisiana, 391 U.S. 145 (1968).
[9] McKeiver v. Pennsylvania, 403 U.S. 528 (1971).
[10] R. Reisner & C. Slobogin, *supra* note 7, at 712.
[11] Addington v. Texas, 441 U.S. 418 (1979).
[12] Gerstein v. Pugh, 420 U.S. 103 (1975).
[13] R. Reisner & C. Slobogin, *supra* note 7, at 702.
[14] Washington v. Harper, 111 S. Ct. 1028 (1990).
[15] R. Reisner & C. Slobogin, *supra* note 7, at 848.
[16] *Id.* at 865.
[17] In mental health law, for example, consider the current lack of persuasiveness of the argument that insanity acquittees should be committed only according to the standards and procedures used to commit ordinary civil patients. Before the *Hinckley* verdict, however, the argument was very much in vogue. Wexler, *Insanity Issues after Hinckley: Time for a Change*, 35 Cont. Psychology 1068 (1990) (review).

stitutional criminal procedure and its scholarship had its heyday—*Miranda,* the line-up cases, expansive Fourth Amendment protections, and so forth. But as society got more conservative and as the composition of the Court changed, criminal procedure scholarship—which was based on constitutional doctrine and nothing more—ran out of steam if it did not actually die.

Those attempting to salvage the area made a last gasp effort to pin new, liberal, far-reaching constitutional rights on *state* constitutional provisions.[18] But when times change, they change, and constitutional criminal procedure activity and scholarship basically fizzled. Articles advocating reliance on state constitutional provisions seem symptomatic of the impending demise of a field of legal scholarship.

And so it has been for traditional mental health law, a body of law and scholarship that was itself highly dependent upon constitutional law and especially constitutional criminal procedure. In 1982, Meisel noted that the 1970s witnessed real growth in mental health law and rights.[19] Then, the United States Supreme Court entered the picture, construing constitutional rights and disabled person federal statutes rather narrowly. Thus, his suggestion that we keep this field of law alive and moving by invoking state constitutional provisions—provisions that, he hoped, would continue the march of rights.

Five years later, in 1987, Perlin presented a similar thesis.[20] Sure enough, traditional mental health law was dying. What, one might ask, kept mental health law and scholarship alive even during the 5-year period between the Meisel and Perlin pieces?

Don't look to the academy for the answer. In the summer of 1982, Meisel was published in *Law and Contemporary Problems.* And in the summer of 1982—on June 21, 1982, to be precise—John Hinckley was acquitted in the District of Columbia.[21]

In fact, the considerable mental health law activity in the 1980s dealt mainly with mental health issues in the *criminal justice system,* and much of that had to do with the insanity defense and with a public, professional, judicial, and legislative reaction against the *Hinckley* verdict: the decline of the ALI (American Law Institute) Test of insanity and the reascendance of the narrower *McNaughtan* rule[22]; the *Jones*[23] case and the automatic and indefinite commitment of insanity acquittees; efforts to abolish the insanity defense[24]; the flourishing of GBMI (guilty but mentally ill) statutes,[25] together with the empirical examination of them

[18] Brennan, *State Constitutions and the Protection of Individual Rights,* 90 Harv. L. Rev. 489 (1977).
[19] Meisel, *The Rights of the Mentally Ill under State Constitutions,* 45 Law & Contemp. Prob. 7 (1982).
[20] Perlin, *State Constitutions and Statutes as Sources of Rights for the Mentally Disabled: The Last Frontier?,* 20 Loyola-L.A. L. Rev. 1249 (1987).
[21] United States v. Hinckley, Crim. No. 81-306 (D.D.C. June 21, 1982).
[22] Wexler, *Redefining the Insanity Problem,* 53 Geo. Wash. L. Rev. 528, 532 (1985).
[23] Jones v. United States, 463 U.S. 354 (1983).
[24] Wexler, *Redefining the Insanity Problem, supra* note 22, at 530.
[25] I. Keilitz & J. Fulton, The Insanity Defense and its Alternatives: A Guide for Policymakers 42 (1984); McGraw, Farthing-Capowich, & Keilitz, *The "Guilty But Mentally Ill" Plea and Verdict: Current State of Knowledge,* 30 Vill. L. Rev. 117 (1984).

by the National Center for State Courts[26] and the academic assault on them by Slobogin[27]; the ABA, AMA, and American Psychiatric Association position statements regarding the insanity defense[28]; and the ABA Criminal Justice Mental Health Standards,[29] which got a boost from the excitement over *Hinckley* and the ABA's position statement on the insanity defense.[30]

But that activity and interest has run its course. We again face the danger of a decline of interest in mental health law. If alternative routes are not taken, mental health law may fade, or at best fold into and become a mere subcomponent of disability law,[31] health law, or law and medicine.[32]

Therapeutic Jurisprudence as an Antidote

In my view, the most effective antidote to the current mental health law malaise would be to put some mental health into mental health law—much in the way that economic principles have informed the development of antitrust law. My best guess on why such a movement did not occur earlier is that modern mental health law, as part of the civil liberties revolution, was conceived to correct the abusive exercise of state psychiatric power.[33] Accordingly, mental health law has in large measure been part of the antipsychiatry movement, mistrustful of the mental health disciplines and of their practitioners.[34]

The lesson—learning to be skeptical of supposed scientific expertise—is an important one, and I doubt the law will ever again simply *defer* to psychiatry and the related disciplines, as it once did in the area of the civil commitment of the mentally ill. But to the extent that the legal system—and even legal academics—now *ignore* developments in the mental health disciplines, the lesson of healthy skepticism has been overlearned.

Indeed, as work by Monahan and Walker,[35] Melton,[36] and others give us a

---

[26] National Center for State Courts, The "Guilty But Mentally Ill" Plea and Verdict: An Empirical Study: Final Report Submitted to the National Institute of Justice, U.S. Department of Justice (working draft Nov. 15, 1984).

[27] Slobogin, *The Guilty But Mentally Ill Verdict: An Idea Whose Time Should Not Have Come*, 53 Geo. Wash. L. Rev. 494 (1985).

[28] Wexler, *Redefining the Insanity Problem, supra* note 22, at 529.

[29] ABA Criminal Justice Mental Health Standards (1984).

[30] Wexler, *Redefining the Insanity Problem, supra* note 22, at 529, 538–40.

[31] Significantly, in 1984, the Mental Disability Law Reporter, which began publishing in 1976, expanded its scope and changed its title to the Mental and Physical Disability Law Reporter. See 8 Mental & Phys. Dis. L. Rep. 2 (1984) (calling the change to the attention of readers).

[32] Interestingly, during the early 1970s, the Association of American Law Schools' (AALS) Section on Law and Psychiatry (known since 1990 as the Section on Law and Mental Disability) was formed as an offshoot of the AALS Law and Medicine Section (which is itself now known as the Section on Law, Medicine, and Health Care).

[33] B. Ennis, Prisoners of Psychiatry (1972).

[34] *See, e.g.*, Ennis & Litwack, *Psychiatry and the Presumption of Expertise: Flipping Coins in the Courtroom*, 62 Calif. L. Rev. 693 (1974); Plotkin, *Limiting the Therapeutic Orgy: Mental Patients' Rights to Refuse Treatment*, 72 Nw. U.L. Rev. 461 (1978).

[35] J. Monahan & L. Walker, Social Science in Law: Cases and Materials (2d ed. 1990).

[36] Perry & Melton, *Precedential Value of Judicial Notice of Social Facts: Parham as an Example*, 22 J. Fam. L. 633 (1983–84).

methodology by which the law may better *evaluate* behavioral science contributions, ignorance *by* the law becomes less and less excusable. Remaining mindful of our recent history, we nonetheless ought to develop a familiarity with mental health materials and explore ways in which, *consistent with principles of justice*, the knowledge, theories, and insights of the mental health disciplines can help *shape* the development of the law. That exploration is the job of therapeutic jurisprudence.

The Task and Scope of Therapeutic Jurisprudence

Therapeutic jurisprudence is the study of the role of the law as a therapeutic agent.[37] It looks at the law as a social force that, like it or not, may produce therapeutic or antitherapeutic consequences. Such consequences may flow from substantive rules, legal procedures, or from the behavior of legal actors (lawyers and judges). In other words, one may look at the law *itself* as being a therapist—or at least a therapeutic agent or tool. Likewise, like iatrogenic disease in medicine, the law may itself produce psychological suffering ("law-related psychological dysfunction" or "juridical psychopathology").

The task of therapeutic jurisprudence is to identify—and ultimately to examine empirically—relationships between legal arrangements and therapeutic outcomes. The research task is a cooperative and thoroughly interdisciplinary one (potentially involving law, philosophy, psychiatry, psychology, social work, criminal justice, public health, and other fields). Such research should then usefully inform policy determinations regarding law reform.

It is crucial to emphasize, however, that therapeutic jurisprudence asks us to be clear about the therapeutic consequences of legal arrangements, but it does not suggest that therapeutic consequences should trump other considerations. Therapeutic jurisprudence is not paternalism and it does not call for increased coercion and state intervention. Indeed, if studies of coerced treatment yield results of therapeutic inefficacy, the case for coercion will be far more difficult to sustain. And even if the results indicate therapeutic efficacy, we must still ask and answer the separate social and normative question of whether coercion should be resorted to.

Whether therapeutic ends should prevail is a normative question that calls for a weighing of other potentially relevant normative values as well, such as patient autonomy, liberty, and so forth. Therapeutic jurisprudence assumes that, *other things being equal*, the law should be restructured to better accomplish therapeutic values. But whether other things are equal in a given context is often a matter of dispute. Therapeutic jurisprudence, although it seeks to illuminate the therapeutic implications of legal practices, does not resolve *this* dispute, which requires analysis of the impact of alternative practices on other relevant values. Thus, to take an obvious example, there seems little doubt that the offensiveness and dignitary affront of executing the mentally incompetent should call for a rule prohibiting such executions, even though the legal prohibition might be antither-

[37] D. Wexler, Therapeutic Jurisprudence: The Law as a Therapeutic Agent (1990).

apeutic by encouraging death row inmates to become mentally incompetent. Further, therapeutic considerations themselves will often mandate civil libertarian results, as often illustrated in later parts of the essay.

The relevance of looking at therapeutic consequences is not wholly unfamiliar to the Supreme Court. In the *Parham*[38] case involving juvenile hospital admission procedures, for example, the Court explicitly stated that "it is appropriate to inquire into how such a hearing would contribute to the long-range successful treatment of the patient."[39] Regardless of what one thinks of the balance actually struck by the *Parham* Court, the case makes it clear that a therapeutic analysis can be important not only to scholarship but to advocacy as well.

My interest in therapeutic jurisprudence jelled during 1987—the same year Perlin sounded his warning in his "Last Frontier" paper. That summer, I prepared a paper on law and therapy for an NIMH (National Institute of Mental Health) workshop. The paper ultimately became the introduction to my anthology *Therapeutic Jurisprudence: The Law as a Therapeutic Agent.*[40] Preparing the paper gave me an opportunity to do many things, among them to think in retrospect about my own work in mental health law, which began in 1971. I soon realized that I had a much stronger attachment to a handful of my publications[41] than to the remainder. They were not necessarily my best-known publications. Instead, what those pieces had in common was their use of mental health material and their perspective of looking at the law as a therapeutic agent.

While the pickings were somewhat slim, I realized that other writers had also published pieces that held particular interest for me and that could be categorized as implicitly embracing the therapeutic jurisprudence perspective.[42] Those pieces

---

[38] Parham v. J.R., 442 U.S. 584 (1979).

[39] *Id.* at 610. Indeed, even in an area far removed from mental health law, the Supreme Court has indicated a willingness to consider therapeutic values. United Steelworkers v. Am. Manuf. Co., 363 U.S. 564, 568 (1960) (arbitration). The Supreme Court has even been described as itself having a therapeutic function, often serving as a nondirective psychotherapist. W. Bishin & C. Stone, Law, Language, and Ethics 399–402 (1972). Professor Weckstein has asserted that the concept of justice embraces much more than truth, and that therapy might itself be a component of justice. Weckstein, *The Purposes of Dispute Resolution: Comparative Concepts of Justice*, 26 Am. Bus. L.J. 605, 608, 624 (1988). Although therapeutic jurisprudence probably ought to cut its teeth on mental health law, it can obviously have implications and applications far beyond the mental health law area.

[40] D. Wexler, Therapeutic Jurisprudence: The Law as a Therapeutic Agent (1990) (hereafter referred to as Therapeutic Jurisprudence).

[41] Wexler, *Grave Disability and Family Therapy: The Therapeutic Potential of Civil Libertarian Commitment Codes*, 9 Int'l J.L. & Psychiatry 39 (1986); Wexler, *Inappropriate Patient Confinement and Appropriate State Advocacy*, 45 Law & Contemp. Prob. 193 (1983); Wexler, *Doctor–Patient Dialogue: A Second Opinion on Talk Therapy through Law*, 90 Yale L.J. 458 (1980) (review); Wexler, *Patients, Therapists, and Third Parties: The Victimological Virtues of Tarasoff*, 2 Int'l J.L. & Psychiatry 1 (1979); Wexler, *Criminal Commitment Contingency Structures*, in B. Sales (ed.), Perspectives in Law and Psychology: The Criminal Justice System 121 (1977).

[42] Many of those "implicit" therapeutic jurisprudence pieces are included in Therapeutic Jurisprudence, *supra* note 40. For *explicit* applications of the therapeutic jurisprudence perspective, see Wexler, *Health Care Compliance Principles and the Insanity Acquittee Conditional Release Process*, 27 Crim. L. Bull. 18 (1991); Wexler, *Insanity Issues after Hinckley: Time for a Change*, 35 Cont. Psychology 1068 (1990) (review); Wexler, *Training in Law and Behavioral Sciences: Issues*

dealt with the therapeutic or antitherapeutic aspects of substantive rules, legal processes, and legal and judicial roles. An example of a substantive *rule* possibly yielding an antitherapeutic result is provided by Fein.[43] With regard to therapeutic aspects of the legal *process,* pertinent writings include Ensminger and Liguori[44] and Perlin's critique of *Parham,*[45] both of which are at once illustrative of the therapeutic jurisprudence approach and highly civil libertarian in flavor. Examples of therapeutic aspects of lawyer *roles* include an article by Applebaum[46] and one by Miller and Maier suggesting that prosecution for criminal behavior may help aggressive mental patients accept responsibility for their behavior.[47]

Illustrations of Therapeutic Jurisprudence

Therapeutic jurisprudence encourages us to mine interesting mental health literature and to suggest how that literature may bear on the formulation of legal arrangements. Mental health law scholarship, teaching, and law reform efforts can be enriched and invigorated by the infusion of such materials. Consider the following inquiries:

- What does the literature say about those who make homicidal threats, about those against whom they are made, about the role of the victim in contributing to the violence, and about the best therapeutic approaches to take when violence is threatened against a specified other? What do those

from a Legal Educator's Perspective, 8 Behav. Sci. & the Law 197 (1990); Wexler, *Inducing Therapeutic Compliance through the Criminal Law,* 14 Law and Psychology Rev. 43 (1990); Wexler & Schopp, *How and When to Correct for Juror Hindsight Bias in Mental Health Malpractice Litigation: Some Preliminary Observations,* 7 Behav. Sci. & the Law 485 (1989); Wexler & Schopp, *Therapeutic Jurisprudence: A New Approach to Mental Health Law,* in D. Kagehiro & W. Laufer (eds.), Handbook of Psychology and Law (in press); Schopp & Wexler, *Shooting Yourself in the Foot with Due Care: Psychotherapists and Crystallized Standards of Tort Liability,* 17 J. Psychiatry & L. 163 (1989); Schopp, *The Psychotherapist's Duty to Protect the Public: The Appropriate Standard and the Foundation in Legal Theory and Empirical Premises,* 70 Neb. L. Rev. 327 (1991); Winick, *Competency to Consent to Treatment: The Distinction between Assent and Objection,* 28 Hous. L. Rev. 15 (1991); Winick, *Harnessing the Power of the Bet: Wagering with the Government as a Mechanism for Social and Individual Change,* 45 U. Miami L. Rev. 737 (1991); Winick, *Competency to Consent to Voluntary Hospitalization: A Therapeutic Jurisprudence Analysis of Zinermon v. Burch,* 14 Int'l J.L. & Psychiatry 169 (1991); Klotz, *Limiting the Psychotherapist-Patient Privilege: The Therapeutic Potential,* 27 Crim. L. Bull. 416 (1991). Many of these pieces appear in D. Wexler & B. Winick, Essays in Therapeutic Jurisprudence (Carolina Academic Press) (1991).

[43] Fein, *How the Insanity Acquittal Retards Treatment,* 8 Law & Hum. Beh. 283 (1984).

[44] Ensminger & Liguori, *The Therapeutic Significance of the Civil Commitment Hearing: An Unexplored Potential,* 6 J. Psychiatry & L. 5 (1978).

[45] Perlin, *An Invitation to the Dance: An Empirical Response to Chief Justice Warren Burger's "Time-Consuming Procedural Minuets" Theory in Parham v. J.R.,* 9 Bull. Am. Acad. Psychiatry & L. 149 (1976).

[46] Appelbaum, *Paternalism and the Role of the Mental Health Lawyer,* 34 Hosp. & Comm. Psychiatry 211 (1983).

[47] Miller & Maier, *Factors Affecting the Decision to Prosecute Mental Patients for Criminal Behavior,* 38 Hosp. & Comm. Psychiatry 50 (1987).

findings tell us about whether the *Tarasoff*[48] requirement of warning or protecting potential victims is a good or bad rule in its likely aggregate impact? Apparently, homicidal threats are overwhelmingly made against intimates who themselves play a substantial role in contributing to the violence. It can be argued, therefore, that *Tarasoff* may have an overall beneficial impact, for it will encourage therapists to make contact with potential victims—persons who might well be brought into some sort of "couple" or "conjoint" therapy.[49]

- What is Jay Haley's theory and therapy regarding the treatment of disturbed young persons?[50] How much support is there for his theory? Haley's theory suggests that disturbed young persons should be forced, step-by-step, to begin leading a normal life in the world of work—such as taking buses, looking for jobs, and so forth. If his theory is accurate, wouldn't it suggest that, even therapeutically speaking, civil libertarian commitment laws are preferable to so-called paternalistic ones? The reasoning is as follows: Civil libertarian laws disallow commitment absent proof of one's *actual* inability (not *presumed* or *predicted* ability) to provide for food, clothing, or shelter. Such laws should encourage parents to force their adult children to do things like take a bus and look for a job—if only as a way for the parents to build a case for commitment. If Haley is correct, however, that type of parental action may be therapeutic and may render commitment unnecessary[51]—another civil libertarian (and antipaternalistic) application of therapeutic jurisprudence.
- When authorities are sued for negligently releasing a patient, the jury knows that the released patient actually injured or killed an innocent third party. In theory, of course, the reasonableness of the behavior of the releasing authorities should not depend upon whether the released patient did or did not commit a violent act after release. But the jury will be armed with hindsight. Does the fear of being judged by hindsight[52] in the event a released patient commits an act of violence lead releasing authorities to *delay* release—and hence to provide unnecessary and inappropriate institutional treatment for—mental patients who have been violent in the past? If so, can the antitherapeutic aspects be ameliorated by Poythress's suggestion of *bifurcating* trials in negligent release cases, having jurors first decide the question of negligence, without being told of the violent outcome?[53] Will other, less radical, "debiasing" techniques suffice, such as

---

[48] Tarasoff v. Regents of the Univ. of Calif. 131 Cal. Rptr. 14 (1976).

[49] Wexler, *Patients, Therapists, and Third Parties: The Victimological Virtues of Tarasoff*, 2 Int'l J.L. & Psychiatry 1 (1979).

[50] J. Haley, Leaving Home: The Therapy of Disturbed Young People (1980).

[51] Wexler, *Grave Disability and Family Therapy: The Therapeutic Potential of Civil Libertarian Commitment Codes*, 9 Int'l J.L. & Psychiatry 39 (1986).

[52] Fischhoff, *Hindsight ≠ Foresight: The Effect of Outcome Knowledge on Judgment under Uncertainty*, 1 J. Exper. Psychology: Human Perception & Performance 288 (1975).

[53] Poythress, *Negligent Release Litigation: A Proposal for Procedural Reform*, 17 J. Psychiatry & L. 595 (1989).

having experts (or jury instructions) inform the jury of the hindsight bias, its potency, and techniques for avoiding it in decision making?[54] Here we have another example of therapeutic jurisprudence seeking to limit, rather than prolong, deprivations of liberty.

- If psychotherapy is successful largely because of therapeutic relationships in which patients perceive therapists to be fiduciaries interested in the *patient's* well-being, then doesn't tort regulation of psychotherapy run the risk of being self-defeating?[55] That is, if tort rules encourage psychotherapists to practice their profession with a wary eye toward their *own self-interest,* that factor may be sufficient to dilute the patient's trust in the relationship and thus to undermine therapeutic effectiveness. Arguably, however, certain types of tort rules tend dramatically to focus practitioner attention on their own self-interest, whereas other types of tort rules do not have such a profound effect.[56] That observation may tell us about the wisdom of promulgating certain types of tort rules.
- Can principles of cognitive behavior modification be tapped to marshall treatment motivation through systems of government "wagers" with persons exhibiting troublesome behaviors, as Winick has suggested?[57] Winick suggests that government programs be established to invite persons with problematic behaviors to "wager" on their ability to overcome the behavioral problem. The wagerer would put up something of value that would be sacrificed if change did not occur, but would stand to win substantial benefits from the government if desired behavior change did result. Might this radical approach be worth an experimental try even with traditionally intractable populations such as drug addicts?
- Can health care compliance principles, recently synthesized by Meichenbaum and Turk,[58] be brought into play in the insanity acquittee conditional release process? One such principle is that compliance is greater among those who enter into behavioral contracts; another is that compliance is greater among those who make a public commitment to comply. If the use of behavioral contracts and public commitments increase patient compliance, can the conditional release and furlough system incorporate these

[54] Wexler & Schopp, *How and When to Correct for Juror Hindsight Bias in Mental Health Malpractice Litigation: Some Preliminary Observations,* 7 Behav. Sci. & the Law 485 (1989).

[55] Schopp & Wexler, *Shooting Yourself in the Foot with Due Care: Psychotherapists and Crystallized Standards of Tort Liability,* 17 J. Psychiatry & L. 183–84 (1989).

[56] Apparently, those rules which are "crystallized" or black letter (e.g., duty to warn, patient labor requires consent, electroconvulsive therapy cannot be performed on minors) tend to lead practitioners to consider their own self-interest more so than does the flexible "ordinary care and competence" standard. *Id.* at 187–88. Professor Schopp has embellished the theory in Schopp, *The Psychotherapist's Duty to Protect the Public: The Appropriate Standard and the Foundation in Legal Theory and Empirical Premises,* 70 Neb. L. Rev. 327 (1991).

[57] Winick, *Harnessing the Power of the Bet: Wagering with the Government as a Mechanism for Social and Individual Change,* 45 U. Miami L. Rev. 737 (1991).

[58] D. Meichenbaum & D. Turk, Facilitating Treatment Adherence: A Practitioner's Guidebook (1987).

devices?[59] If so, courts might be able to structure conditional release proceedings so as not simply to *predict* whether a patient will continue to take medication if released, but also to actually *influence* and *facilitate* that compliance. Here, therapeutic compliance and public safety may presumably be enhanced without any sacrifice to liberty/justice principles.

As should be evident from the above examples, therapeutic jurisprudence scholarship utilizes source material different from that traditionally employed in mental health law. Likewise, the creative and analytical process is different.

In traditional doctrinal analysis, the creative/analytical process typically revolves around analogical reasoning: Why has the Supreme Court held there is a right to a jury trial in criminal cases but not in juvenile cases? Is a civil commitment hearing more similar to a criminal case or to a juvenile case? In therapeutic jurisprudence, by contrast, the process revolves around relating a body of therapeutically relevant psychology to a body of law and exploring the fit between the two.

In fact, the "format" of a paradigmatic therapeutic jurisprudence piece written by an academic lawyer is likely to be quite predictable: Apart from the obligatory introduction and conclusion, there is likely to be a section on the pertinent law, a section on the pertinent psychology, and an integrative section—the guts of the project—relating the psychology to the law.[60]

CONCLUSION

Therapeutic jurisprudence, then, is not particularly hard to do. It has the advantage of expanding our horizons and has the potential of allowing the law to develop as psychology develops. And while social context will obviously remain important in determining the acceptability of certain suggested legal schemes, therapeutic jurisprudence is not as dependent upon ideological concerns and the precise composition of the U.S. Supreme Court as is the traditional doctrinal/constitutional approach to mental health law. Although therapeutic jurisprudence is not overwhelmingly dependent upon the doctrinal/constitutional approach, it is surely not ideologically grounded in paternalism and coercion. In addition to the

---

[59] Wexler, *Health Care Compliance Principles and the Insanity Acquittee Conditional Release Process*, 27 Crim. L. Bull. 18 (1991).

[60] See *id.* for an example that clearly fits the mold. While the present essay focuses on the format explicitly and emphasizes its appropriateness to the therapeutic jurisprudence mission, it is evident that the format has been in use for some time, especially in articles implicitly embracing the therapeutic jurisprudence approach. See the format of Wexler, *Grave Disability and Family Therapy: The Therapeutic Potential of Civil Libertarian Commitment Codes*, 9 Int'l J.L. & Psychiatry 39 (1986). See also Wexler, *Patients, Therapists, and Third Parties: The Victimological Virtues of Tarasoff*, 2 Int'l J.L. & Psychiatry 1 (1979). For a collection of essays all explicitly employing a therapeutic jurisprudence format, see D. Wexler & B. Winick, Essays in Therapeutic Jurisprudence (Carolina Academic Press) (1991).

many examples already given, it is probably worth noting that a powerful argument can be made from a therapeutic jurisprudence perspective to sustain a mental patient's right to refuse treatment and to oppose the forcible treatment of mentally incompetent death row inmates.[61]

Incidentally, one of the major consequences of disentangling mental health law from its overwhelming dependence on American constitutional law is that the field may become far more international and comparative in its perspective. After all, if a major emphasis is placed on ascertaining the relationship between legal arrangements and therapeutic outcomes, our laboratory should surely be international as well as interdisciplinary.[62]

Many of those working in mental health law now seem interested in new approaches—therapeutic jurisprudence as well as others[63]—that may revivify the field in terms of scholarship, teaching,[64] and practice. For example, the 1991 program of the Law and Mental Disability Section of the Association of American Law Schools had as its theme "Approaching the Twenty-First Century: 'Therapeutic Jurisprudence,' Cognitive Psychology, and the Future of Mental Disability Law." With some hard work, some new approaches, and a little luck, mental disability law just might make it into the twenty-first century as a viable and exciting field of scholarship.

---

[61] D. Wexler & B. Winick, Essays in Therapeutic Jurisprudence (Carolina Academic Press) (1991).

[62] U.S. mental health law scholars and practitioners will be humbled to learn how few pages of a recent 1,500 page forensic psychiatry treatise, written by 141 contributors worldwide, is devoted to the law and practice of the United States. R. Bluglass & P. Bowden (eds.), Principles and Practice of Forensic Psychiatry (1990).

[63] For a new and important approach to the insanity defense area, see Perlin, *Unpacking the Myths: The Symbolism Mythology of Insanity Defense Jurisprudence,* 40 Case West. Res. L. Rev. 599 (1989–90).

[64] In terms of teaching, a therapeutic jurisprudence approach to mental health law enables an instructor to expose students to the fundamentals of mental health law and also to the most pressing questions of "law and social science" generally. Wexler, *Training in Law and Behavioral Sciences: Issues from a Legal Educator's Perspective,* 8 Behav. Sci. & the Law 197 (1990).

Part II
Methodological and Conceptual Problems: Conflicting Legal and Historical Models

[9]

International Journal of Law and Psychiatry, Vol. 15, pp. 157–169, 1992
0160-2527/92 $5.00 + .00

Psychiatric, Psychological, and Legal Models of Man

Nigel Eastman*

Introduction

Models of man are rarely defined in such practical disciplines as law and medicine, but are implicit and frequently covert. They gain their character and variation, one with another, through the pursuit of specific purposes and through the methods of thought and procedure applied to those purposes. Hence, the very different general traditions of law and medicine (specifically here psychiatry) combine with their varying purposes to determine essential disjunctions when the two disciplines are drawn into an apparently common purpose. Such disjunctions are commonly misperceived according to their superficial and case-specific appearance rather than correctly viewed as deriving ultimately from incongruous models of man variously implied by each discipline and coincidentally applied one "discipline type" against the other.

This paper attempts to explore the characteristics both of the variety of implied models originating in both law and psychiatry and of the potential and real model disjunctions. It will argue that the *degree* of disjunction operating will vary according to the model characteristics arising from law and from psychiatry in any particular case. Finally, it will suggest that incongruence will be minimised both by encouraging legal rules which put the two disciplines into inherently "least disjunctive" model interactions and by encouraging law and psychiatry (and their practitioners) coincidentally to recognise the implicit varying purposes and models which they apply and the character of case-specific "model boundaries" and incongruities. The argument is presented in terms of English law but has applicability to other common law traditions and jusidictions and perhaps even beyond.

Psychiatric and Psychological Purposes and Models

Diagnosis is the core of the traditional "medical model," not being restricted to (clinical and research) psychiatry. However, an apparently unifunctional and simple concept is, in reality, both multifunctional and complex. Specifically, the practice of "diagnosing" varies according to specific, sometimes undefined purposes, varying notions of disease, and varying "levels" of disease definition and understanding. Further, there is an (often) complex and covert interrelation between such purposes, disease notions, and the level of disease understanding.

---

*Barrister at Law, Senior Lecturer in Forensic Psychiatry, St. George's Hospital Medical School, Jenner Wing, Cranmer Terrace, Tooting, London, SW17 0RE, U.K.

Purposes

The idea that diagnosis operates to cure is simplistic and incomplete. Specifically, diagnosis may function towards the various purposes of (1) *description, classification*, and *taxonomy* (2) *predicting prognosis* (3) *determining therapy* and finally, and infrequently in reality, (4) *pathological understanding*. In psychiatry (Becker, 1963; Scheff, 1966; Szasz, 1960, 1972, 1974), as well as in other branches of medicine (Illich, 1974; Kennedy, 1981), some argue there are "unscientific" and value-laden social purposes. This suggestion has particular relevance where diagnosis is applied to the overtly social purpose of legal process. Even within each purpose there may be "subpurposes" that operate. A simple example will illustrate the general point concerning multiple purposes. Pain of a particular character in the chest was, at first, recognised as a *syndrome* and given the *diagnosis* of "*angina pectoris*" (*classificatory*). It was recognised to be a precursor of sudden unexpected death (*prognosis*) but also to be relieved by glyceryl trinitrate (*therapeutic*). The *origin* of the condition came to be recognised as atheroma of the coronary arteries (*pathological understanding*), although long after the condition's original classification. The *diagnosis* called angina pectoris operated, therefore, towards different realistic purposes in a hierarchy of sophistication, in this case at different historical stages.

Although the paradigm case is that of historical development of a specific diagnosis up through a hierarchy towards the ultimate goal of detailed pathological understanding, the historical sequence can vary or pathological understanding can itself be split (e.g., with AIDS the infectious agent is recognised but the full story of its interaction with the body is unknown). A conscious decision may be made to pursue one particular purpose in recognition that the view of a disease it offers is one of many (as in the distinction between a photograph of a bridge and a detailed engineering description thereof).

Psychiatry is, using the historical paradigm, at an early stage; that is, it has failed to uncover (validated) *psychopathology* to any significant degree (other than in relation to recognised "neuropsychiatric" conditions). It pursues the diagnostic purpose through *classification* (American Psychiatric Association, 1980; Shepherd, 1976; WHO, 1978), in an attempt to distinguish one condition of madness from another, *prognosis* (e.g., schizophrenia is defined as an entity because it has a worse outcome than affective psychoses), and *therapy* (e.g., psychotic phenomena specifically respond to neuroleptics).

All such psychiatric activities are firmly rooted in the tradition of the medical model, which, in turn, is embedded in a (particular approach to) the concept of *disease*. Implied models of man vary according to the varying purposes already identified but also according to the specific model of disease which is adopted in pursuit of those purposes. Although there is a highly entangled relationship between purposes and disease concepts (largely in terms of a particular disease concept providing the *assumptions* lying behind classificatory, prognostic, therapeutic, and psychopathological purposes) any attempt to characterise varying implied psychiatric models of man must specifically address the variety of disease concepts applied. It will become apparent later that varying concepts of disease have specific relevance in determining specific psycho-legal disjunctions and their degree.

Disease Concepts[1]

Most medical classificatory systems, especially uniaxial ones (notably ICD9 and DSMIII), presume a disease entity already there, or waiting to be identified. They often also presume the concept of "*disease as a lesion*" (Szasz, 1960; Virchow, 1958). Close cousins of the latter concept are "*disease as disturbance of part function*" (Lewis, 1953), "*disease based in reductionism*" (with or without "*exclusionism*") (Engel, 1977), and "*phenomenological disease*" (Jaspers, 1963), itself essentially described as *categorical disease* (as distinguished from *dimensional disease*) and evinced by notions of "interrater reliability" and various forms of "validity". These aspects of the disease concept are, in simple and non rigorously philosophical terms, clustered together as a family which might be nicknamed "*the psychiatric or phenomenological approach*", and it *is* a family by virtue of the distinction of its members from other families.

The **psychiatric phenomenological approach** recognises its theoretical limitations characteristically by resorting to a variety of simple "dichotomies"; most notably those of organic/functional, psychotic/neurotic, (neurotic) mental illness/personality disorder, acute/chronic, and endogenous/exogenous. The history of the understanding of depressive illness illustrates the failure of the individual dichotomy as a solution as well as the attempted rehabilitation of a dichotomy approach, through defining apparent correlations between specific poles from differing dichotomies. Perhaps the major psychiatry training textbook in the United Kingdom (Gelder, Gath, & Mayou, 1983) finally rejects all attempted dichotomies and resorts to three types of depressive illness, (1) mild (2) moderate, and (3) severe. Doubt is cast on the validity of all the common psychiatric dichotomies and, as we shall see, models of man presented by psychiatry in the courts frequently resort to such dichotomisation to "force" psycho-legal congruence. It may be the case that the "higher order" dichotomies (specifically, organic/functional and, perhaps, psychotic/neurotic) are of real psycho-legal value; however, even here, the "class membership" is historically fluid, especially in relation to organic/functional.

An "alternative family" is best termed the **psycho-understanding approach**. It most clearly has its representation in the psychodynamic tradition but is by no means limited to it (in the sense I shall use the term). It includes a cluster of models of human psychological dysfunction which have, at their core, the rejection of the medical model and the lesion based, categorical, scientific, reductionist, and phenomenological aspects thereof. The approach varies not only in its assumptions about the nature of psychopathology per se, but in its basis of validation. It rejects the notion that truth is defined according to the population hypothesis testing methodology defined by science (classically represented in the "controlled clinical trial" model), but accepts, rather, that

[1] An excellent review of this field is offered by Clare (1985).

hypothesis testing can be conducted with one patient and that detailed explanations of psychological cause and effect are valid in spite of their lack of availability to "scientific" invalidation through attempted replication. Further, it admits "*psychological content*" as valid and enlightening, in contrast to "*abnormality of form*" being seen as solely valid in the phenomenological approach.

There are a number of other attitudes to psychopathology which, although not at all related to the psychodynamic tradition and the psycho-understanding family, nevertheless give rise to models of man which have something in common with the psycho-understanding approach in terms of the potential psycho-legal disjunctions to which they give rise (particularly in contrast to those originating from models in the phenomenological tradition). The most prominent attitude in this group is the "dimensional approach," that is, the presumption that "disease entities" do not exist and that the pursuit of the categorical classification of psychopathology is both hopeless and spurious. According to this view, disorder exists on multiaxial (not uniaxial) and dimensional (not categorical) bases. It will become clear that such a model of man produces greater psycho-legal disjunction than do models of man deriving from the disease model, phenomenological approach. According to this **psychometric approach**, man is on a continuum and disorder is defined not according to "abnormality from a previous or ideal state," but rather only according to "statistical abnormality against a population of others." Such an approach argues that it avoids forcing dimensional reality into categorical fiction.

Eclecticism as an Escape

The eclectic tradition in Western psychiatry is an "escape" from the failure to identify wished-for disease entities, implying specific cures. It functions as an approach to pragmatic solutions to real clinical problems. As such it *variously* applies *psychopathological explanatory* and *therapeutic* approaches, based on the recognition that no "disease cure" model has been identified. Such practised eclecticism operates often in stark contrast to the "theoretical psychiatry" which purports to be its foundations. Eclecticism, by definition, *has no* single model of man, even for any individual situation. It will become clear that the involvement of practical (eclectic) psychiatrists in legal proceedings forces them to *pretend* a belief in the models of man originating in theoretical psychiatry.

In summary, psychological models of man vary according to theoretical approach (*psychiatric phenomenological, psycho-understanding*, and *psychometric*) and according to the practical abandonment of single model theories.

Legal Purposes and Models

In direct contrast to the (stated) purposes and methods of medicine and psychiatry, law is moral, value laden, and balancing (of one individual against another or against the mass of others) in its purposes; it is binary, unifactorial, "fictional" and adversarial in its substance and process. Further, it allows of the possibility of *several* conceptual fictions as potentially applicable to a *single* real event; for example, a particular homicide defendant *might* have a defence in all three categories of insanity, automatism and diminished responsibility, as well as coincidentally being able to argue liability only to the lesser charge of infanticide. Hence, implied legal models of man have both general and specific characteristics, the general being derived from the nature of legal epistemology and the specific arising additionally from particular legal definitions, rules (for example, of evidence) and processes.

The law sometimes appears to purport explicitly and overtly to *define* a specific model of man, always in relation to a specific legal purpose. But, additionally, it makes a single distinction between lay and expert models; that is between models of human behaviour that are (presumed) available to ordinary human identification and understanding (by a member of a jury) and models that are available only to an expert (by virtue of their inherent abnormality). The famous man on the Clapham omnibus is available to lay and expert alike. The notion is developed towards the presumption of an infinite set of predictable behaviours, described in terms of the *reasonable man*. The test of the reasonable man is used (amongst other functions) directly to pursue the determination of culpability.

The law applies not only different *specific* models in different legal situations but different *general* models as well. Hence, where the law is binary, unifactorial, "fictional," and adversarial in its method towards issues of verdict, it all but abandons such strictures in relation to issues of disposal. The model shift which is implied as occurring between trial and sentencing has particular relevance to the degree of psycho-legal disjunction.

Taken as a whole, the law most obviously defines models of man in relation to mental capacity and responsibility (civil and criminal, respectively). Considering only criminal law, the heart of the definition of most crimes (*actus reus* plus *mens rea*) incorporates the requirement of (varying degrees of) intention, that is, it invents *intentional man*. It implies a model of human behaviour which is clearly exclusively cognitive in nature, unitary (in relation to each defined crime), and based on a presumption of free will rather than (scientific) determinism. Further, it appears to pursue a dualistic body/mind philosophy, most obviously in the defence of "automatism" through distinguishing the absence of *mens*.

The law sometimes apparently, and sometimes consciously purports to incorporate "terms of art" from the sciences, including psychiatry. For example, it includes scientific "psychopathic disorder" in Section 1 of the English Mental Health Act (1983). Less obviously solely scientific notions are "disease of the mind" (*R. v. McNaughten*, 1843), 'abnormality of mind' (Homicide Act, 1957; *R. v. Byrne* [1960]) and "disturbed balance of mind" (Infanticide Act. 1938). However, even where the concept can clearly be seen to originate in psychiatry, the law either immediately redefines it or distorts it through interpretation such that it rapidly drifts away from its original scientific meaning and its parentage becomes unrecognisable. A notable example is the judgement of Lord Denning (in *Bratty v. Attorney General for Northern Ireland*, 1963), which states that "any mental disorder which has manifested itself in violence and is prone to recur is a disease of the mind. At any rate it is the sort of disease for which a person should be detained in hospital rather than be given an unqualified acquittal." This definition clearly incorporates elements that are constructurally totally unrelated to it.

Psychiatric, Psychological, and Legal Model Disjunctions and Incongruities

The disjunctions and incongruities between legally and medically implied models of man are greatest in relation to verdict issues and are conveniently explored in relation to specific (English legal) psychiatric defences, so as to narrow down the number of potential model mixes. Given the great variety of psychological models implicit in the forgoing discussion, it will be helpful to consider each defence in relation to each of the psychological model approaches; that is, (1) *psychiatric phenomenological*, (2) *psycho-understanding*, and (3) *psychometric*, even though this blurs real model distinctions between variants within each category.

The law allows the mental element of a crime to be negated by evidence that the (normal) rational reasonable man model is inappropriate to the defendant and that a deterministic, expertly available abnormal man model is the appropriate standard. However, although it admits the latter *as if* it derived from psychiatric reality it does so by defining not *psychological* abnormal men but (of course) *legal* ones. It is several of these (legal) abnormal men that I shall consider, as well as juxtaposing the (normal) reasonable man which is explicit in the different (though in psychological reality often related) defence of provocation.

Automatic Man

A defendant who was in an automatism at the time of the offence had no *mens rea* because his "mind" was not operating, although some jurists say there is not even a (willed) *actus*. The paradigm case describes actions deriving from a complex partial seizure arising not from the mind but from the brain. Hence, *automatic man* has the ultimate psychiatric defence." The law here operates a "dualistic" and necessarily binary model of man in that there is no intention (because of insufficient consciousness). However, the English courts have included "*somnambulistic man*" and the "*night terrorist*," as well as the "*(fugue) dissociated man*," the "*hypnotised man*," and the "*(involuntarily) intoxicated man*" also amongst automatons. Although the English courts are continually narrowing down the circumference of "*non-insane automatic man*" (McKay, 1987) the core notion of automatic man is still inherent.

Psychiatry views medical automatic man variously but many argue that *only* a condition and action based upon abnormal cerebral electrical activity is truly automatic (Fenton, 1972). Even with such a tight definition it is not clear that *only* the brain is operating (to adopt dualistic terminology). *Somnambulistic man* is variously understood as organically and hysterically neurotically determined, as is the *night terrorist* (see Howard & D'Orban, 1987; Oswold & Evans, 1985). Hence, the *psychiatrist* may say *somnambulistic man* solely has a brain (sleep) disorder or perhaps that he has a neurotic basis for his activity, whilst the *psycho-understanding expert* will (by definition) tend to postulate the latter; similar positions would apply in relation to the *night terrorist*. "*Dissociated man*" is even more likely to be the subject of dispute since (some) psychiatrists would not accept that his consciousness and intention is *qualitatively* abnormal (in relation to malingering) but only *quantitatively* different (again in relation to malingering). Hence, the disjunction between legal and medical automatic man will depend, in this case, on *which* psychiatric model of man is offered. Even where a qualitative definition is offered, there is the immediate potential for medico-legal confusion and incongruence, arising out of differing legal and psychological notions of "unconscious," "preconscious," and "subconscious."

Although expert evidence is not, in law, permitted to address the "ultimate issue," one particular psychological model of man may (in contrast with some other psychological model) automatically imply a particular legal result. Hence, if the view of *night terrorist* is that he commits an offence in Stage III or IV sleep, then he is necessarily legally "automatic." If the *actus* is thought to occur as the sleeper moves into wakefulness, as one expert believes (Crisp, personal communications, 1988), then sub-/pre-/unconscious motivation may (at least partly) determine his actions. Again, if the psychopathological theory of *dissociated man* is a *qualitative* one then a different (automatic) legal result may occur than if the theory is a *quantitative* one.

Legal automatic man, as classically perceived in epilepsy or post-head injury concussion, is of course, most congruent with a "disease as lesion" model of abnormal man and, therefore, with the *medical psychiatric* approach. Other "possibly neurotic" automations give risk to greater potential model disjunctions. Intermediate cases perhaps exist in relation to conditions thought by some to be on a continuum between the two poles of complex partial epilepsy and personality disorder (for example explosive personality disorder, pathological drunkenness and episodic dyscontrol syndrome).

Irrational Man

Responsible man is variedly intelligent but rational. The primary root of "McNaughten man" (*R. v. McNaughten*, 1843) is irrationality and, although further and restrictively qualified, his insanity *amounts to* his "defect of reason." Further, his culpability is not merely diminished by such irrationality but abolished thereby. In psychological terms only, cognition is recognised as determining of nonculpability and the final "two limbs" of the McNaughten Rules ("not *knowing* the nature or quality of the act or not *knowing* it was wrong") reinforce the sole relevance of cognition.

Such a legal model does not even admit the possibility of introduction of *psycho-understanding* or *psychometric* approaches (except by definition of the "level" of intellectual functioning in the latter case) and even the *phenomenological psychiatrist* is permitted to address only cognition related phenomena. The McNaughten Rules are, thus, exemplary of direct legal limitation of the "admissibility," by form, of psychological evidence. It was the recognition of the psychological incompleteness of McNaughten man which was a major spur towards the introduction into English law of a model (abnormal man) which, through its ill definition, is exemplary of limitless "admissibility" of psychological evidence; not being restricted to other *elements* of phenomenology but allowing also of both *psycho-understanding* and *psychometric* models.

Mentally Diseased Man

The restriction of the insanity defence to defects of reason arising from a "*disease of the mind*" would suggest, through its semantics, psycho-legal congruence. Conversely, however, the disjunction between legal and psychological epistemologies is well illustrated by viewing legal precedent defining "disease of the mind" through medical and psychological spectacles.

The case precedents bear little relation to any but the *psychiatric-phenomenological* approach, and further, the primary "test" of disease of the mind appears to be defined almost exclusively in terms of a "disease as lesion" model. In *Quick*'s case (*R. v. Quick*, 1973) man is only *non*-diseased if the cause of his disorder was "external" to him; specifically, in that case, caused by injected insulin. Hence, *diseased* man has an "internal" abnormality. This apparently simple and sensible test appears to derive from medical reality but falls when it is *viewed* medically; the internal/external distinction is ill defined in medical and psychological reality. Hence, where a seizure (disorder) is defined in law as being a disease of the mind, immediate confusion arises if an externally (e.g., insulin) induced (internal) seizure occurs, particularly if an abnormally low seizure threshold can be demonstrated in the defendant. Further, a defendant with a profound personality disorder, which results in his/her "using" insulin overdoses towards manipulative personal interaction may be variously viewed as suffering or not from a disease of the mind, according to whether the cause or the route of his/her behaviour is taken as definitive. In any event, where excess insulin can also be produced *inherently* (by an insulinoma) the internal/external test might cause "disease of the mind" and "disease of the pancreas" to coincide (Eastman, 1986).

Additionally, a number of other "accepted" non-insane automatisms have been accepted as "non-mind diseases" in spite of obvious inherency, most notably somnambulism and night terrors (although the *Quick* test is being applied increasingly restrictively now in the English courts).

The alternative "disease of the mind" test, the *Bratty* test, is clearly constructurally unrelated to any psychological or medical notion of disease and, in light of the verdict implications, overtly incorporates criteria of social implication towards the expressed purpose of public protection. Social policy is thus pursued through distortion of a "model of man" via the introduction of constructs not necessarily related to *diseased* man.

Mentally Abnormal Man

Whereas "irrational man" and "mentally diseased man" are tightly and restrictively defined, in terms of the implied limitation on the "admissibility" of psychological approaches, "mentally abnormal" man is so broadly defined, moreover, in lay terms, as to admit potentially *any* form of psychological evidence. The defence to murder of "diminished responsibility" defined by

Section 2 of the English Homicide Act 1957, and elaborated in *Byrne* (*R. v. Byrne*, 1960), requires only that there be an "abnormality of mind (whether arising from a condition of arrested or retarded development of mind or any inherent causes or induced by disease or injury) as substantially impaired his mental responsibility." The definition, and its elaboration, imply a number of aspects and classes of models. Only the parenthetic clause is inherently psychological in character (*R. v. Matheson*, 1958). "Abnormality of mind" is elaborated (*R. v. Byrne*, 1960) as "a state of mind so different from that of ordinary human beings that the reasonable man would term it abnormal." Hence, the model is a "lay" model and is qualitatively undefined.

Impairment of mental responsibility is not directly related to abnormal psychology; however, the attempt to limit the boundaries of psychological expertise to description of *only* the parenthetic clause (perhaps with inclusion of the determining of the presence of an "abnormality of mind") is often, in legal practice, difficult. English courts not uncommonly misapply the law and invite the expert to make a "diagnosis of diminished responsibility." The, admittedly intimate, relationship between the definition and determining of an "abnormality of mind" *and* the "impairment of mental responsibility" commonly gives rise to definitional "circularity," thus, "he is mad because he was not responsible, he is not responsible because he is mad" (Wooton, 1959). More generally, mental responsibility is seen not as a binary construct (as in relation to "irrational man"), but as a graded construct.

The coincidence of a lay definition of abnormality, the ill definition of that abnormality (impliedly also in psychological terms) and the consequent "admissibility" of (almost) any psychological approach to abnormality gives rise to inter-case inconsistency. Hence, juries can decide what psychological model they will allow as being indicative of "abnormal man" with little judicial restraint in terms of definition *in law* of what may constitute the notion. The only restraint on the jury is the requirement of an expert to define that the defendant falls into one of the elements of the parenthetic clause.

In spite of the potential flexibility of the defence, it is "diminished responsibility" that, in practice, gives rise most frequently to psycho-legal incongruence (because of the frequency with which it is pleaded). The degree of incongruence varies, commonly, with the particular psychological approach being offered to the court. Most simply, where the approach presents apparent (or forced) "dichotomisation" there is, in the necessarily "binary" legal context, least disjunction. Hence, the *psychiatric-phenomenologist* is most easily incorporated into the legal process since he/she purports to define the presence of objective mental signs and to derive a categorical diagnostic conclusion therefrom. His categorical diagnostic structure commonly implies, or overtly describes, dichotomies which the court readily accepts as legally definitive. Hence, "organic" contrasts nicely with "functional" and the former is more readily accepted by the courts as "mental abnormality" (the law thus being demonstrated as most congruent with "disease as a lesion"). Similarly, "psychotic" and "neurotic" (within "functional" illness) are moderately easily legally distinguished and incorporated, again the former being seen as more obviously congruent with legal notions of mental abnormality. Further down the hierarchy still, even the distinction between (neurotic) mental illness and personality disorder *appears* to offer a basis for determining the presence or absence of an "abnormality of mind."

The *psychometric approach* (by definition) would eschew any such dichotomisation. False psycho-legal congruence, it would be argued, arises out of the spurious attempt to define qualitative "disease entities" where reality is merely "quantitative." It can also be argued more generally that, even if "dichotomisation" is a realistic clinical psychiatric practice, psychiatry falsely incorporates into legal proceedings (because it is forced so to do *by* those proceedings) *one* of many *possible* dichotomies as definitive whereas, in its own terms, it would use a *number* of dichotomies *together*, where any of these might conflict with the legal result implied by using a single dichotomy. Practical psychiatry uses eclecticism as an escape and eclecticism, by definition, is incongruous with dichotomisation.

Illustration of the foregoing argument may illuminate it. Psychiatrists are commonly forced into a false distinction between "personality type" and "personality disorder"; commonly, opposing experts agree as to the defendant's psychological patchwork but, when forced to dichotomise, disagree as to whether the patchwork amounts to a disorder, which can be an abnormality of mind and thus found a defence. Similarly, the coincidence of personality disorder and intoxication requires the expert spuriously to attribute causation between the two factors. Even where dichotomisation appears to the expert to be operating at such a gross level as to be "obvious" (e.g., organic/functional, psychotic/neurotic) it may operate *alongside* an accepted simple "spectrum" classification, as in the case of depressive illness (Gelder et al., 1983), and the mere admission of a quantitative notion immediately casts doubt on the apparently legally convenient dichotomy.

Even ignoring "false dichotomisation" as a problem, the very foundation of the psychiatric-phenomenological approach, that is value free objectivity, may be in question in such a fashion that expert evidence veers towards moral philosophy. Hence, it *could* be expertly argued that because "alcohol dependence syndrome" (as a recognised psychiatric "disease") incorporates psychological, physiological and histopathological changes, which directly influence the threshold for ingestion, then intoxication in a defendant suffering from that disorder should not be adjudged as voluntary intoxication. Voluntariness is, of course, a moral and not a medical concept.

Relatedly, where delirium tremens can be a defence (even an insanity defence), it might be argued that psychological reality is such that the potential defendant is reckless as to foresight by *not* taking alcohol, where he might injure another in such an abnormal mental state. Apparent medical reality is not reflected in any English legal exception to the rule that (self) "intoxicated man" is responsible; neither is medical reality reflected in any legal rule that *not* drinking might make the defendant guilty in spite of being in a delirium, which could even amount to insanity. Again relatedly, where (self) *intoxication* is no defence, but a substance-induced *psychosis* (e.g., from amphetamines) *is* a defence, it might be cogently argued that the psychological distinction between the two states is less than definite, such that forced spurious dichotomisation again arises.

The *psycho-understanding approach* is not naturally "dichotomous." However, it is inherently explanatory (as compared with the phenomenological-descriptive approach) and may, through its presumption that *all* men have psychopathology, purport to "over-identify" abnormality. Hence, it is not uncommon for contested personality disorder cases to juxtapose a psychoanalyst for the defence and a phenomenologist for the prosecution. Even in the context of "psychosis" there is a clear distinction between expert evidence that describes the coincidence of instructional auditory hallucinations and the *actus* on the one hand, and evidence that *explains* the *actus* by way of those hallucinations on the other.

Unbalanced Woman

There is a long and international tradition of recognising puerperal mental illness as a legal excuse for infanticide. This is perhaps the only clear example of intentional legal incorporation of a specific psychiatric diagnosis (Infanticide Act, 1938). Even here, however, psychiatry has "moved on" so as to blur the picture, since it appears now that an experienced puerperal illness is illness to which that woman is, in any event, predisposed and the puerperium represents only a (perhaps hormone-specific) stressor towards illness.

Reasonable Man

In contrast to cause being seen in the abnormal defendant, the defence of provocation defines a normal ("reasonable man") defendant who reacts to the abnormal (unreasonable) provocation of the victim. Such a binary system is in itself unlikely to accord with psychological reality, which is likely to be defined both in graded terms, and in interactive terms, with respect to both defendant and victim.

However, even taking the model of the "reasonable man" in isolation, psycho-legal incongruence is obvious. The test of whether the "reasonable man" would have reacted as did the defendant appears to imply a notion of "normality," and perhaps even "statistical normality." Even taken in the latter sense this must certainly be a legal fiction, since it is not the case that most respond even to substantial provocation by homicide; taken in the more general sense of normality, again it cannot be seen as "normal" to kill. It is clear that these falsehoods arise out of the law's need to find a route to its purpose of recognising that provoked homicide is not morally equivalent to the unprovoked variety.

A further difficulty concerns the law's recognition that the reasonable man's susceptibility is not that of the *perfect* man but of the man with the characteristics of the defendant. Little difficulty arises in relation to physical characteristics (classically, the "hunch-back") but logically a defendant should be no more culpable for being susceptible to taunts as to his mental characteristics than as to his physical ones. The law's reluctance to admit mental characteristics is understandable in psychological terms, since it must surely then be impossible to distinguish between the operation of those characteristics in relation to his *susceptibility* and their operation in relation to his *reaction*, which latter only the jury can legally address. However, distinction between the physical and the mental may itself, at times, be impossible. Hence, a man may be impotent because of a diabetic neuropathy (which would be allowed as a "characteristic"), yet alternatively be impotent through character trait anxiety, clearly a mental characteristic (which might not be so allowed).

More generally, the law's model of "reasonable man" *appears* to use statistical normality to derive moral normality, in contrast to legal models of abnormality, which are inconsistent with a spectrum approach (notably the *psychometric approach*).

Conclusions

Convicted man is subjected to a very different legal model from that which he faced during his trial. A binary approach gives way to a graded one and the general potential for psycho-legal incongruence greatly diminishes. The need, specifically, for the *psychiatric-phenomenological approach* to force itself into its non-eclectic, uni-theoretical framework largely disappears, and the other two approaches may similarly be more "at home." Psychiatric evidence, particularly phenomenological psychiatry, can therefore avoid confronting its own model uncertainty or avoid pressing itself into greater protestations of dichotomous and general categorical certainty than is warranted. In recognition that not even the general disputes between the three approaches are validly settled, it can embrace its customary, and perhaps solely "valid," eclecticism in the court room. A generally applicable solution to most (inherent) psycho-legal disjunction lies, therefore, in the removal of psychiatric evidence uniquely to the "disposal stage." Resistance to such a move lies in the legally perceived unfairness of conviction on the basis of an "*automatic*," "*irrational*," "*mentally diseased*," "*mentally abnormal*," or "*mentally unbalanced*" *mens*.

Where psychiatry and psychology remain pressed into evidence towards issues of verdict, the impact of incongruence with their legal host is minimised through clarity of definition of psychiatric and psychological models and through allowing courts to take verdict decisions in full knowledge of the real constructural uncertainty that such expertise harbours. Perhaps the very least that must be required of psychiatric and psychological expertise, therefore, is that it applies the same "diagnostic" procedures and uncertainties to defendants as it does to patients and that, in particular, it avoids legally derived distortions of its constructs, their reliability, and the probability of their validity. Hence, such expertise should continue at least to *pursue* non-value-ladeness even in the highly value-laden legal context. Finally, psychiatric and psychological evidence should incorporate the concepts of "*reliability*" and "*validity*" so as to limit the scope of its presentation and its potential legal impact. Even if it is not possible to be sure of the validity of constructs offered to the courts, at least the lower order objective of inter-rater reliability should be pursued. It may be that these various objectives are more easily pursued through *psychiatric-phenomenology* and *psychometry* than through attempts at *psycho-understanding*.

References

American Psychiatric Association. (1980). *Diagnostic and statistical manual of mental disorders* (3rd ed.). Washington, D.C.: Author.

Becker, H. (1963). *Outsider: Studies in the sociology of deviance*. New York: The Free Press.

Bratty v. Attorney General for Northern Ireland, AC at 413–417 (1963).

Clare, A. (1985). The disease concept in psychiatry. In P. Hill, R. Murray, & A. Thorley (Eds.), *Essentials of postgraduate psychiatry*. London: Gunne and Stratton.

Eastman, N. L. G. (1986). *Defending the mentally ill, psychiatric aspects of insanity and automatism*. R. Mackay & K. Russell (Eds.), Leicester: Leicester Polytechnic School of Law Monographs.

Engel, G. L. (1977). The need of a new medical model: A challenge for biomedicine. *Science, 196, 4286*, 129–136.

Fenton, G. (1972). Epilepsy and automatism. *British Journal of Hospital Medicine, 7*, 57–66.

Gelder, M., Gath, D., & Mayou, R. (1983). *Oxford textbook of psychiatry*. Oxford: Oxford University Press.

Howard, C., & D'Orban, P. T. (1987). Violence in sleep: Medico-legal issues and two case reports. *Psychological Medicine, 17*, 915–925.

Illich, I. (1974). Medical nemeses. *Lancet, I*, 918–921.

Infanticide Act. (1938). Section 1.

Jaspers, K. (1963). *General psychopathology* (J. Hoenig & M. W. Hamilton, Trans.). Manchester: Manchester University Press. (Original work published 1913)

Kennedy, I. (1981). *The unmasking of medicine*. Allen and Unwin.

Lewis, A. (1953). Health as a social concept. *British Journal of Sociology, 4*, 109–24.

McKay, R. (1987). Craziness and codification: Refining the automatism and insanity defences. In I. H. Dennis (Ed.), *Criminal law and justice*. Sweet and Maxwell.

Oswold, I., & Evans, J. (1985). On serious violence during sleepwalking. *British Journal of Psychiatry, 14*, 688–691.

R. v. Byrne, 2. QB. 396 (1960).

R. v. McNaughten, 10 Cl & F200, 8ER 718 (1843).

R. v. Matheson, 1 WLR 474, 2 ALL ER 87, 42 CAR 145 (1958).

R. v. Quick, QB. 910 (1973).

Scheff (1966). *Being mentally ill*. Chicago: Aldine.

Shepherd, M. (1976). Definition classification and nomenclature: A clinical overview. In D. Kemali, G. Bartholin, & D. Richter (Eds.), *Schizophrenia today*. Oxford: Pergamon Press.

Szasz, T. S. (1960). The myth of mental illness. *American Psychologist, 15*, 113–118.

Szasz, T. S. (1972). Bad habits are not diseases. *Lancet, ii*, 83–84.

Szasz, T. S. (1974). *The second sin*. London: Routledge and Kegan Paul.

Virchow, R. (1958). Standpoints in scientific medicine. In *Disease, life and man. Selected Essays* (L. J. Rather, Trans.). Palo Alto: Stanford University Press. (Original work published 1847)

World Health Organisation. (1978). *Mental disorders: Glossary and guide to their classification in accordance with the ninth revision of the International Classification of Diseases*. Geneva: Author.

Wooton, B. (1959). *Social science and social pathology*. George Allen and Unwin.

[10]

Coexistence **28**: 23–43, 1991.

REASON, EMOTION AND CRIMINAL RESPONSIBILITY

L. H. LEIGH

Few English lawyers would deny that English law responds unevenly to problems raised by emotional stress. Whether an actor is given benefit for the fact that his response was stress-related will largely depend upon whether it can be brought within a defence category which gives value to such a circumstance. As will be seen, the insanity defence is based on rationalistic principles. So too are duress and necessity. English law has moved away from this emphasis in the case of diminished responsibility. Mistake, self-defence, provocation, and superior orders make some accomodation to stress-induced errors of judgment.

It would be wrong to start from the premise that all these defences should attract the same response. The social purposes which each serves may well be different, though some are conceptually related. Duress, necessity, and self-defence are all particular expressions of an underlying necessity principle.[1] It would be wrong simply to deduce from that proposition that the same rules should apply fully to each. Before reaching a conclusion on that point, we must examine both the social justifications for the defences and the dangers which each may present.

One major issue concerns the purposes of punishment and the extent to which they can be vindicated in any given set of circumstances.[2] It would not be unfair to say that, in respect of deterrence, courts and scholars have adopted a curiously deliberative model of the actor weighing up his felicific calculus; of others consciously adverting to the pains of punishment before acting. It is questionable whether this, as distinct from reception by social osmosis, affords the truer reality of the working of deterrence which, after all, probably represents no more than a crude insight into learning theory.

Punishment is, however, in utilitarian theory at least, merely instrumental. One must pose, as a prior question, what social obligations we are conceived to owe, whether to each other, to the State, or to both. This question raises large issues in political and ethical philosophy. Nonetheless, one cannot for example impose a rule which implicates the response of the reasonable man without having some idea of the standard of social duties we expect of this exemplar. Whether a person is to be blamed for an inappropriate response depends upon the light in which we view his explanation for it. Blame will be a construct which involves our conception of a person's social duties and the extent to which he could reasonably be expected to perform them given the circumstances in issue, and any assumptions which we may make concerning normal human powers of self-control in this context.

There will, of course, be cases in which we will allocate no blame to acts. If blame is to be allocated in any given case it may, nonetheless, be mitigated by reference to such circumstances as the presence of stress, conceivably over a long period. Mitigation may be expressed in moral terms, as was the case when capital punishment applied of an announcement that the Judge would join the jury in a recommendation to mercy. It may be expressed in terms of a reduced sentence. It may be expressed as reducing a crime to a less serious category. The relevant issues are not simply of mercy but of stigma. It is tempting, but wrong, to conclude that the problems posed by stress can be resolved satisfactorily simply by bringing them under a flexible sentencing regime. Such a solution would ignore questions of stigma, and it might also, in the relatively unformed state of English sentencing law and practice, involve assigning issues which need to be structured in terms of principle, to the unsystematic preferences of a judiciary which has neither the time nor the inclination to work out the principles of a philosophy of sentencing.

I

A few words are in order about stress, for that term is doubtless as imprecise as any other.[3] This paper essentially refers to complex emotional states such as anxiety or anger which are brought about by a particular situation of stimulus.[4] The stimulus which moves a person to anger or more broadly excitation may not consist of anything wrongful done by one person to another. A victim may have suffered from reactive depression. So too may a mother who kills. This disorder of mood is characterized by abnormal feelings of grief, despair, worthlessness, and the like and carries a distinct risk of suicide.[5] The stress of living with a person who is severely depressed, whether because that person suffers from a terminal illness or from a psychotic episode, can be intense.[6] Love can turn, tragically, to an outburst of fatal anger. Where there is continuing strain, a condition of nervous tension may become chronic.[7] Lack of sleep may, as recent cases show, lead to aggression.[8]

On the other hand, an inappropriate response may not necessarily arise from any such circumstances or conditioning.[9] The actor may be an hysteric whose response to a threatening situation is affected by that neurotic disorder.[10] On the other hand, his response may be the response of a normal person thrust into a situation where emotion and reason conflict, a situation of invidious choice. The fact that such a personality is normal does not mean that the effect of stress upon action must be disallowed for legal purposes. The extent to which and the manner in which allowance may be made for such a response will necessarily reflect the flux of social values involved in the situation, and this may differ from one situation or group of situations to another. A consideration which affects the entire question of what response the legal system ought to adopt in these various situations is that the law of defences has grown up piecemeal, that the tradition of the law is strongly intellectualistic and moralistic, and that judicial moralism sometimes reflects a simplistic response to social problems couched, occasionally, in offensive language.[11] Neither Parliamentarians nor judges are moral philosophers. Defences to crime, which are still largely creatures of the common law, albeit affected by statutes, reflect the want of any over-arching philosophy which might assimilate them to a coherent structure.

The effect of stress upon defences

The existing English law in relation to the effect of stress upon defences, as in relation to the classic defence of insanity, is strongly marked by an intellectualist bias. Without discussing the defence of insanity at length, it is well-known that the *McNaghten* rules which govern the defence specify that a person is to be adjudged not guilty by reason of insanity if either he did not know the nature and quality of his act, by which is meant that he lacked the barest appreciation of its physical characteristics, or that he did not know that it was wrong by the Laws of England.[12] English courts have consistently rejected the notion of "irresistible impulse" which has attracted the "hangman at the elbow" philosophy, according to which the appropriate judicial response, where a person is aware of what he is doing but has difficulty in controlling his actions, is to reinforce his deliberative powers by stressing the deterrent threat of punishment.[13]

The late Lady Wootton summed up the reasons why the *McNaghten* rules appeal so strongly to English lawyers. The intellectualist conception which it embodies is deep-rooted within the legal system. The formula is both narrow and precise. It presumes a general rationality of behaviour and seeks to prove or disprove normal intellectual capacity by the degree with which such rationality is maintained. Furthermore, a defence of intellectual insufficiency can be tested by criteria external to the actions which it is invoked to excuse. This, in turn, avoids the problem of circularity which arises when the behaviour complained of is itself used as the principal criterion for classifying the actor's condition. But this emphasis on intellectualism, a dominant theme in much of English criminal law, is also a matter of criticism, for it is a commonplace of modern psychiatric thought that insanity and irresponsibility are as much a matter of emotional disorder as of intellectual disorder.[14]

Rather than discuss the insanity defence, it is proposed, first, to examine the flux of intellectualism and emotionalism, and the influence of a third factor related to emotionalism, the desire to exclude bad excuses, in relation to diminished responsibility which does involve mental disorder and where intellectualism has to some extent ceded to a wider appreciation of irresponsibility than is implied by the *McNaghten* rules.

Whereas the *McNaghten* rules represent a rigid standard of responsibility, the statutory provision relating to diminished responsibility, which reduces murder to manslaughter and thus gives the Judge complete discretion in sentencing, virtually represents an abdication of rules of responsibility. Section 2(1) of the Homicide Act 1957 provides:

> Where a person kills or is a party to the killing of another, he shall not be convicted of murder if he was suffering from such abnormality of mind (whether arising from a condition of arrested or retarded development of mind or any inherent causes or induced by disease or injury) as substantially impaired his mental responsibility for his acts and omissions in doing or being a party to the killing.

This provision is said to cover the mind's activities in all its aspects, including the ability to control one's acts in accordance with rational judgment.[15] It represents the continued dominance of an intellectual tradition mitigated where the admittedly loose and imprecise aetiology specified by the section is made out.

Diminished responsibility is not infrequently raised in cases of stress-related killing and, in particular, where as the result of a long period of anguish by a suffering spouse coupled with requests to end his or her life, the surviving spouse does in fact kill his partner.[16] Some, but not all of these killings, will have occurred when the actor was in a state of fugue. They represent what Lady Wootton has referred to as cases of anguished rationality.[17] Most are cases where at the very least one would expect executive leniency to be manifested were the offender convicted of murder and sentenced, as he must be, to life imprisonment. Many of these cases should not be treated as murder at all.

The section presents certain inelasticities which limit its utility in such cases. First, it is the mind which must be abnormal and not the response to the stimulus. In theory, therefore, agonised rationality falls outside diminished responsibility. Second, even were a fugue state deemed to be an abnormality of the mind, it could not, without more, readily be brought within the aetiology prescribed by the bracketed words in the section. That aetiology is insisted upon in other contexts, and notably where actors seek, uniformly unsuccessfully, to pass off the toxic effect of alcohol as an injury.[18] The materials for a restrictive interpretation of diminished responsibility are present in the law and surely mark stress killings as ones to which diminished responsibility is not, and was not intended to be, applicable.[19]

This emphasis on the integrity of the categories of defence which in the case of diminished responsibility excludes the toxic effect of drink unless it amounts to a distinct disease of the mind, and excludes stress killings as well, can be seen in other contexts. One such is infanticide, statutorily defined as the killing by a woman of her infant child at a time when the balance of her mind was disturbed by reason of her not having fully recovered from the effects of giving birth, or by reason of the effect of lactation consequent upon the birth of the child.[20] This singular provision was first introduced into the law to mitigate the fixed penalty of death pertaining to murder. Whilst few child deaths are today attributable to abandonment, that was certainly not the case at the turn of the century and before.[21]

Equally, this does not exclude the influence of economic factors in provoking reactive depression. But whilst the stress arising from economic deprivation may result in a case being dealt with as infanticide rather than murder, the statute makes no allowance for the stress which the situation may cause in the father, nor does it help a mother who, distraught by the arrival of an infant, kills a child over the age of twelve months. In such cases there may be an imbalance of mind, but that imbalance is excluded from consideration as a case of infanticide and may be excluded as a case of diminished responsibility by the construction put upon the relevant statute.[22] In short, the retreat from intellectualism as a guiding principle is in part covered by a smokescreen of psychiatric terms. It is perhaps worth noting that in respect of suicide pacts, which may result from mutual anguish or from a settled and rational desire, for example, on the part of spouses, to terminate lives no longer thought to be worth living, English law, responding however imperfectly to the dictates of humanity, plainly and directly reduces the crime in a survivor to manslaughter only.[23]

A further defence which is explicitly directed towards stress-related killings is provocation, the effect of which is to reduce murder to manslaughter. In the light of its history, the modern law of provocation is paradoxically both broad and narrow. Originally conceived in terms of a wrongful act by the deceased towards the actor, the law in 1957 was altered in order to comprehend words as well as deeds.[24] Section 3 of the Homicide Act, 1957 now provides:

> Where on a charge of murder there is evidence on which the jury can find that the person charged was provoked (whether by things done or by things said or by both together) to lose his self — control, the question whether the provocation was enough to make a reasonable man do as he did shall be left to be determined by the jury; and in determining that question the jury shall take into account everything both done and said according to the effect which, in their opinion, it would have on a reasonable man.

The section thus contains both objective and subjective components. The accused must have been provoked in fact. The provocation must have been enough not only to cause the reasonable man to react, but to react as he did. This question is for the jury which, because its verdict is opaque, leaves us with no knowledge of why it reached the decision which it did.

In terms of stress-related killings, certain features of this scheme stand out. First, the section assumes that provocation is compatible with an intent to kill. Indeed, it is provocation which partially mitigates the formation of that intention.[25] A Canadian court has held that even where provocation produces a state of blind rage so that the accused is perhaps not consciously thinking when he kills, the appropriate defence is not insanity, but provocation.[26] The denial of the insanity defence in this context surely evidences a tacit judicial assumption that reaction to provocation involves fault.[27] Second, both the statute and the common law before it, assume that there must be a certain proportionality between the stimulus and the response. This principle is obviously intended to ensure against bad excuses on the part of someone who was not provoked in fact and to ensure that an actor, whose conduct passes beyond that of excusable to intolerable, shall not be even partially excused. Fists may be answered with fists, but not with knives.[28] In short, an accused may not take advantage of inexcusable aspects of his emotional make-up. He must conduct himself according to the mores of society as these are conceived by the jury. In assessing the reasonable man, the jury may take into account his age, for that will affect his self-control, and other definite and enduring characteristics which he has, but not excitability of temperament.[29–33] In short, the reasonable man is a reagent whose presence serves to guard both against bad excuses and against an undue weakening of social control.

In theory, the law should work satisfactorily in cases at either extreme. In most cases the maximum intent which can be inferred will be to do serious bodily harm.[34] In some cases intent to kill will be proven. Where the stimulus is gross, a jury may feel justified in saying that a reasonable man might have been provoked to use lethal force; where it is trifling one would expect the opposite conclusion to be reached. Cases in the middle could go either way and the reasons for decision in any given case will remain concealed from view.

If it be conceded that the Homicide Act can be understood without reference to the roots of provocation in wrongful act, any stimulus which has produced a violent response must be left to the jury's consideration of its effect upon a reasonable man. English law has indeed taken this step and, in *Doughty*, has held that the effect of a persistently crying baby upon an exhausted father as a result of which he killed may go to the jury on the issue of provocation.[35] The jury will thus have to determine whether the father was provoked to kill and whether such a response could have been expected of a reasonable man. In terms of bad excuses, it will have to decide whether this was not simply a case of gratuitous baby-battering. Yet provocation in this respect is inelastic. It is premised not simply upon a response to a stimulus which conduced to anger, however irrational, but upon a stimulus which led to a want of self-control, and in this respect intellectualism again prevails. In *Cocker*[36] a husband killed his wife who had long pleaded with him to do so and on the relevant occasion was particularly emotional and exigent. His defence was baulked because he stopped in mid-career to ask her whether she wanted to die. Of this two observations may be made. First, although Cocker retained some powers of self-control, it is surely naive to suppose that at any point of the transaction he acted in a state of calm tranquillity. The historic intellectualism of the common law tradition prevailed. Second, his moral fault, if such there was, was surely less than that of many persons who kill in circumstances which permit them to take advantage of provocation.

Here, then, we have a situation in which most people would agree that some amelioration of the actor's punishment should be permitted, and in which some at least would concede that the label of murderer is inappropriate.[37] The problem is that this case is akin to diminished responsibility and to provocation without quite falling within either. Are we really to say that the presence of some awareness of what is happening and some self — control should disentitle the actor to the benefit of a sympathetic rule of law whilst a person who is aware of his actions but suffers from a severe mental disorder, or who reacts consciously, but savagely, to a continuing stimulus, benefits from an ameliorative rule? At the very least, some philosophical justification is needed to support the conclusion.

Problems concerning the flux of intellectual and emotional factors can also be seen in self-defence, duress, necessity and superior orders. Once again, the relationship between these considerations in the various defences illustrates that there are issues of basic policy, in terms of accommodating reactions which are the conjoint product of these factors, which have never fully been resolved. It is not, indeed, clear that they have ever been fully recognised.

Under the rules relating to self-defence, or more properly, private defence a person who uses reasonable force in self-defence, or in the prevention of crime, has a complete defence in respect of injuries inflicted upon his assailant.[38] English law is reasonably accommodating to the person who uses reasonable force. He need not necessarily retreat from an attack, though he would be expected to do so were this possible, and he may even, where necessary, launch a pre-emptive strike.[39]

It is clear that in self-defence the Courts face difficulties in dealing with a case where a person misapprehends the force required in any given situation and where, in strictness, it may be said that the force which he used was excessive. The problem is that the actor intended only to defend himself. His overreaction must therefore have been caused by a defective appreciation of the situation which may well be attributable to his emotional make-up. He may be unusually excitable, or timorous. This will affect his response to situations of stress. It does not follow that he was necessarily wholly innocent in the situation: the attack which he faces may be the result of his own provocative or unlawful actions.[40] Nonetheless, courts obviously wish to give value to the actor's defensive purpose in what may have been a genuinely difficult situation. At the same time, English courts show no desire entirely to abandon an intellectualist position which insists that the actor must measure his response by what is reasonable in the circumstances.

A possible response would have been to give some credit to the accused's defensive purpose by reducing murder to manslaughter where the actor used undue force in defending himself, and to take that purpose into account in sentencing in respect of other crimes where there is no fixed penalty. Such a rule for long represented Australian law and has been recommended for adoption in England in the proposed Criminal Code.[41] A different response would have been to give full credit to the actor's purpose and to use evidence of overreaction simply as a possible indicium that the actor's purpose was not truly defensive.[42] English courts instead adopt a position according to which evidence of what the actor did on the spur of the moment is the best evidence of what was reasonable in the circumstances. In the words of Lord Morris in *Palmer v. The Queen*:[43]

If there has been an attack so that defence is reasonably necessary it

> will be recognised that a person defending himself cannot weigh to a nicety the exact measure of his necessary defensive action. If a jury thought that in a moment of unexpected anguish a person attacked had only done what he honestly and instinctively thought was necessary that would be most potent evidence that only reasonable defensive action had been taken.

In so stating the rule, the Privy Council plainly desired to give a wide latitude to honest action. It did not, however, abandon objective considerations, the justification for which must lie in the extent to which an actor is presumed to be able to control his responses and the value which the law places upon such control. In according honest and instinctual reaction evidentiary status on the question of reasonableness, the Privy Council was not entirely logical. Such a reaction could only have evidentiary value in the case of a person whose qualities of temperament fell within those premised of the reasonable man; the rule could not logically apply to an hysteric whose reaction cannot be evidence of what is objectively reasonable.

Where, thus, there is an actual situation of self-defence, the courts insist that the actor's response be measured, but that that response be evaluated in the light of the circumstances including the danger which the situation presented and the opportunities for reflection open to the actor. The courts give considerable, but not absolute weight, to the actor's defensive purpose. Singularly enough, where the actor labours under a mistake concerning whether a situation is one of self-defence, the courts appear to give absolute value to his mistake, yet that mistake may be as much due to the actor's deficiencies of temperament as was the use of undue force in the circumstances. There are elements of incoherence in the law which require exploration.

Prima facie, one would have expected the law to insist, particularly where force is used in the prevention of crime, that the actor's appreciation of the situation be reasonably grounded. This is especially so when one recalls that English law has never allowed police officers, for example, to use whatever force was necessary to prevent crime or to arrest a suspect, whatever may have been the crime which he committed. English law does not permit a constable to shoot a fleeing petty thief. Even in terrorism situations, a police officer or a soldier must weigh up, however rapidly, the harm to be expected from allowing a terrorist suspect to escape against the harm, very often death, that will be done to such a suspect.[44] In this context a strong element of control over executive actions has historically been asserted.

It is the more paradoxical, therefore, that an actor is permitted to take advantage of his honest mistake concerning whether a situation really required self-defence.[45] The law looks positively schizophrenic. An actor who honestly but unreasonably believes that he faces a self-defence situation may take advantage of the mistake, but only to the extent that the force which he uses would have been reasonable had the facts been as he supposed them to be. These rules do not appear to relate to any coherent theory of the interaction of moral fault and social control, or of the relative weight to be given to intellectualist and emotional factors in ascribing blame, or indeed to a coherent theory of how criminal law controls individual and social responses.

This state of affairs is attibutable to an assumption which courts dealing with self-defence cases have adopted from the general law concerning mistake, namely that outside offences of inadvertence or strict liability, mistake as to a definitional element of the offence need only be honest, since to insist that it be reasonable would, to the extent that it was applied, render the offence *pro tanto* one of negligence. As Lord Hailsham put it in *D.P.P.v. Morgan*:[46]

> Once one has accepted . . . that the prohibited act in rape is non — consensual sexual intercourse, and that the guilty state of mind is an intention to commit it, it seems to me to follow as a matter of inexorable logic that there is no room either for a "defence" of honest belief or mistake, or of a defence of honest and reasonable belief and mistake. Either the prosecution proves that the accused had the requisite intent or it does not.

Lord Hailsham's assertion in its context is unobjectionable. The result of carrying it forward into cases of mistake as to a defence like self-defence which stands outside the *mens rea — actus reus* dichotomy is, however, to make the conditions of an affirmative defence to which courts should be able to attach restrictive conditions in the interests of social policy, the mathematical product of an equation which is valid in a different context.[47] Incongruity of the sort noted above appears to be dictated by "inexorable logic," but only if the premise be applicable.[48]

Similar problems beset duress and necessity; the latter, extending to the threat of death or serious bodily harm, are recognised in English law as duress by circumstances.[49] Here, the rules differ from self-defence in certain particulars. Not only must the actor's reaction be reasonable, but so also must be his appreciation of the factual situation.[50] Stress, as such, appears to be but little regarded though it may affect what intention should be inferred from conduct.[51] Elliott rightly criticises the Courts for confusing reasonable fortitude with reasonable belief. What is less clear is whether a defensible policy would not insist on the same rule for each.

One's belief in the existence of a threat may well be conditioned by one's emotional makeup and if reasonable fortitude is to be insisted on, presumably to emphasize a need for deliberation before taking action which may produce serious harm to another, so also should a reasonable appreciation of the situation be insisted upon.[52] In short, one may accept Elliott's premise that duress, necessity, and self-defence are sufficiently alike conceptually, and sufficiently attract the same policy considerations as to dictate that the same rules apply to them, and yet arrive at a different conclusion which would uphold objective criteria of reasonableness as necessary to public policy.[53] In any event the policy issues may be somewhat different when one considers what duties ought to be imposed upon police and soldiers acting in the prevention of crime, but consideration of that issue can be dealt with later in this paper.

A further problem concerning both duress and necessity concerns the balancing of harms. English law is categorical in denying a defence whether of duress or necessity to one who kills, and perhaps to one who attempts to kill.[54] In such a case there can be no question of a balance of harms. But what of cases where a threat of death or serious bodily harm, either as a result of human action or the operation of natural forces, is in issue?[55] Is there scope for a balancing of threat and harm? Would there be scope for such a balancing if the threat were to property?

English law is unsettled on these points. Some common law, and indeed civil law jurisdictions, actually insist upon a balancing formula. Such a requirement, if imposed as an inflexible rule of law, would again raise issues of response to stress of the sort which we have been considering. Ignoring the context of homicide, in what has been taken to be the paradigm case, that of the slow starvation by mariners whose decision it ultimately was to kill the cabin boy that they might live, *Dudley and Stephens*, there was obviously time for reflection and assessment.[56] There will, however, be cases in which the actor will have little if any time for reflection. In some, there will be little possiblity of weighing matters in the balance; for example, an actor may well have to respond to a fast — moving situation on the basis of imperfect knowledge. He may, indeed, be emotionally engaged for others, for example where he acts to avoid a collision which may injure his wife and family and produces a tragedy for others.[57] To insist upon proportionality in all cases would be to require a calm and rational assessment in circumstances where the actor cannot be expected to act in so deliberative a fashion.[58] As yet, these matters are speculative in English law, for the courts have not gone beyond a narrowly expressed defence of duress by circumstances. It cannot be said that there is no room for a balancing of harms in such circumstances, but in few cases would this be possible. In perhaps fewer would it be desirable.

Paradoxically, perhaps, stress leading to mistake may be better catered for in the cognate defence of superior orders. The rule of English law appears to be that a soldier, or police officer, cannot plead superior orders to a criminal charge where the act done was manifestly illegal.[59] To the extent that reliance on superior orders produces a mistake of fact, and thus a defence, the same problems which beset the conjunction of mistake and self-defence should apply.[60]

The problem is somewhat different where the actor alleges that to him the order was not manifestly illegal. Here, the argument is one of error of law, and it is one which common law courts have always approached circumspectly. No court has as yet said that the plea may not apply to serious offences including homicide. Dicey, citing Sir FitzJames Stephen, was inclined to conclude that superior orders would excuse a soldier for using violence where the soldier might reasonably suppose that his officer had good reason so to order.[61] The error is not so much one concerning the rule of law, for example against homicide, as its application in the facts of the given case. May a soldier legitimately suppose that a rule of law against murder cannot apply to render illegal an order to shoot a person who his officer, and he too, may think to be a terrorist.?[62] Whether and to what extent the exigencies of the moment may be brought to bear upon reasonableness, in this case and in the case of mistake of fact, remains unclear, It is, perhaps, unclear whether courts would not today apply the simple mistake of fact rule. The draft Criminal Code after all adopts the reasonableness rule in the analogous cases of duress and necessity. It may well be argued, in any event, that the response of a member of a disciplined force acting in the course of duties for which he is trained ought to be more rigorously assessed than would be the response of a civilian.

Social policy considerations

It will be clear, from what has been said, that English law does indeed deal unevenly with stress, not only across topics which may not be thought to be analogous, one to another, as for example provocation and duress are not, but also within topics which may be thought to be analogous. It would be possible but, in the light of Elliott's illuminating survey unprofitable, to examine the discrepancies as between analogous defences. It seems better to examine the social policy considerations which underlie these disparate rules and to inquire in what way the criminal law may promote them. If any common thread unites the topics dealt with in this paper, it is the lawgiver's fidelity to a rationalistic model of human behaviour as a basis for a legal rule. Despite the extent to which this is departed from in mistake cases, there is a general assumption that a person who has rational capacity can in factual terms, and should in evaluative terms, conform his conduct to standards which society requires of him. In turn, this assumption is related to another, namely, that the actor's behaviour can be regulated by the coercive and deterrent force of the criminal law.

First addressing the second point, if an individual's behaviour cannot be regulated by the criminal sanction, or at any rate the existence of a criminal prohibition, the appropriate response ought either to be to seek another justification for the use of the criminal sanction, or to seek other means of social control. If, for example, a threat of immediate harm will either overbear the actor's critical faculties or lead him to choose to avoid an immediate peril at the price of ultimately incurring a legal sanction, the argument from deterrence and therefore from utilitarianism will not work.[63]

Arguments from deterrence usually assume a deliberative model. It is assumed that the offender will weigh up immediate gratification against the possible ultimate exaction of a criminal penalty. It would be foolish to deny, in the light of Andenaes' study of deterrence in wartime Norway, that that deterrence can work in this way. Where the actor has time for deliberation, there is point in Dr. Kenny's declaration that he would rather be shipwrecked in the company of men who believed themselves to be subject to the law, than with those who did not.[64]

It seems improbable to assume that this model describes how deterrence generally works. The constable is often remote from the scene. The threat will not be certain. Furthermore, as Dennis points out:[65]

> An appeal to the deterrent value of a law disallowing duress as a defence is thus an empty gesture: the deterrent is ineffective because it is not immediate and because it is subverted by admitting duress through the back door as evidence in mitigation.

Furthermore, in many cases emotional stress will preclude a calm and rational assessment of the situation. If deterrence depends upon such an assessment of benefits and detriments, it cannot be supposed to work in many of these cases.

The deliberative model of deterrence may not, however. describe the manner in which the criminal sanction works. Most people refrain from committing crimes not because they fear the constable at the elbow, but because they are socially conditioned not do commit crimes. Many who did commit crimes have slipped the bonds of social conditioning without much thought of deterrence. Viewed thus, the criminal law may be said to work as an agent of social conditioning, interacting with and reinforcing received social mores, by the fact of its existence, and by the stigma of publicity.[66]

This argument enables one to turn the argument that deterrence will not work in certain circumstances. A legal system which punishes an hysteric whose crime is attributable to an hysterical over — reaction at least affirms the message that a basic legal prohibition applies to the conduct complained of.[67] It does not follow from that, or from the possibility that other theories of punishment may be thought applicable, that conduct performed under conditions of stress ought to be punished, either at all, or with the full rigour of the law. One must further inquire what conduct ought fairly to be expected of human beings in any given circumstance and in what way lapses ought to be dealt with. In short, difficult issues of social policy and, indeed, moral philosophy, emerge.

The policies of English law

In provocation, the social value concerned is that of self-control. Gratuitous descents into violence should not lead to mitigation. The law accomodates human frailty only within narrow bounds. The precise mix of factors which now applies to provocation really reflects a tension between the desire to exclude bad excuses and a willingness to mitigate the guilt and punishment of a person who, although at fault in not maintaining self — control, genuinely was moved to anger by a stimulus which a jury is prepared to conclude would provoke a response on the part of ordinary people. The evidentiary significance attached to the presence of proportionality of stimulus and response evidences the former point. It seems to suggest that the reasonable man in anger will be a reasonably angry man though a want of proportion is not necessarily probative of anything except that the accused lost his temper and the jury may so treat it.[68] __Still, an accused who controls his response is most likely to benefit from provocation, so that here, as elsewhere, intellectualism in theory prevails. __It cannot surely be argued that a person's moral deserts ought necessarily to be assessed in terms of proportionality of stimulus and response since this truly would be to impose a model of calculation upon a response to stress.

An apparent showing of deliberation will defeat the defence, for this is taken as an infallible indicium that the intellect can control the emotions. This may not appear unfair in some classical provocation situations. One is uneasy about it when transposed to stress based killings like that in *Cocker.* Where there is stress over a long period, it may be naive to assume that the actor is fully in control of his emotions, even where he exhibits a degree of rationality. But it should be questioned whether existing law does justice in such situations. Without addressing the difficult question of euthanasia, it could be argued not only that such stress-based killings should benefit from a reduced sentence but also from a reduced classification of crime so as to avoid stigmatizing the actor as a murderer. They are, after all, usually readily identifiable by reference to history within the family.

These situations are such that individual deterrence, in its classic mode of operation, cannot touch. In many of them, social conditioning has operated; the killing has taken place after long pressure by the victim. The social conditioning force of the law will not be eroded by classifying the offence as less than murder. It could not be said that such a disposition would signal a diminution in the respect accorded to the value of life. Such cases are often more deserving than provocation cases, but, formally at least, are more harshly treated.

For similar reasons we should look again at infanticide, the restrictions on which do not really correspond to any rational social policy. A mother who, in a state of severe post-natal depression, kills a child of tender years, but of over twelve months of age, has not responded to deterrence and could hardly be supposed to have been likely to do so.[69] The same points noted above in relation to the stress-based killing of a spouse surely apply, as do the remarks concerning stigma. English law presents the absurdity that a mother or father who is provoked to violence by a stimulus which reacts on depression may plead provocation, whatever the age of the slain child. But depression alone will not do, at least not unless it is accompanied by some circumstance (other than poverty or misery), which would rouse a reasonable person to violence. To call killings which are the product of severe depression murder is surely not required either in the interests of social conditioning or by the respect to be given to the value of life. In short, the value of deterrence (assuming that one can identify and deal satisfactorily with cases of gratuitous violence) as an element of social conditioning, does not here require the severity which the law exhibits in case which fall outside the singular definition of infanticide. Neither does the theory of "just deserts." These cases together with infanticide as it is now understood should be formally classified as homicides less than murder.

The other group of stress-based acts dealt with revolve around duress, necessity, superior orders, and self-defence. These are; no doubt, conceptually distinct from the first group, but, as *Palmer v. The Queen* makes clear, defences from both groups can arise on the same facts. The basic distinction arises from the fact that these defences, which involve hard choices, apply to minds which are both normal, and expected to deliberate. A second distinction is that the actor is expected to reason in terms of social value. Here, distortions in reasoning are, in some but not all contexts, catered for, however imperfectly. A fundamental question must be whether the response of English law is simply imperfect in the sense that the rules ascribing guilt cannot cater perfectly for every situation, so that at best they merely approximate to an ideal solution, or whether they are flawed in some fundamental sense.

In assessing these matters the first step must be to examine the social justifications both for the particular rule in issue and for any purported exception. Here there is no unanimity. The rules which limit duress, necessity, superior orders, and self-defence clearly are founded on the value of life. They differ in gross and in detail, however, sometimes obviously defensibly, sometimes less so. It is clear that the courts, in considering mistake in self-defence and in particular the use of force in the prevention of crime and the arrest of offenders, give considerable latitude to misapprehension of the situation as one requiring action. This is surprising, at least in the context of the prevention of crime when once it is realised that such acts are usually performed by trained personnel, the police or the army, and in accordance with Standing Orders as well as the general law. Not every trained soldier is a model of absolute calm, but it does seem strange that a rule which permits defensive action should, in this context, abandon the control which could flow from a rule that the actor's assessment of the situation must be reasonable.

It seems singular that when the court passes to a consideration of the amount of force used, the appreciation involved must be reasonable. How can this rule work, save cynically, in the case of an assessment which was unbalanced in the first place. It seems clear that courts are working towards a compromise position which will balance two competing values. The first is that of accommodating a mental state where the actor honestly means to defend himself or herself. The second is to give value to the need for restraint in such situations. In English law this is done by adopting the flawed rule that instinctual reaction is evidence of reasonableness. The former Australian rule would make killing in self-defence, where the mistake or the use of force was unreasonable, manslaughter only.

It might be better to distinguish some of these situations by reference to the character of the actor. For example, and by analogy to superior orders, it might be thought preferable in the interests of social control, and not unjust, to require reasonableness in the case of a police officer's or soldier's assessment both of a situation as requiring defensive force and of the degree of force necessary. It may be that to do so promotes observance of rules by reinforcing conditioning in a specific context. It might, conversely, be thought just to give full value in respect of the great majority of persons to defensive purpose, leaving it to the jury to filter out bad excuses. One could argue in favour of such a rule that a deterrent is unlikely to work in cases of hysterical over-reaction, and that social conditioning will not be impaired by permitting acquittals on such grounds, especially as the rule would apply to civilians only.

But can there be a perfect rule? Much must depend on what the courts conceive the social duties of individuals to be in the use of force and how observance of these can best be ensured by law. One could argue in favour of conviction for a lesser offence, manslaughter instead of murder, as was formerly done in Australia, provided that the accused intended to act in self-defence and did not intend to go beyond what self-defence requires. This would give value to the accused's intent to act defensively so avoiding the stigma of conviction for murder whilst at the same time, in the interests of sustaining standards of conduct emphasizing the need for an individual to act deliberately, and it could apply both to appreciation of the situation of risk and the necessary degree of defensive force.

The problem of duress and of duress by circumstances (otherwise necessity) is particularly intractable in the present state of English law. At the level of the taking of life, duress and necessity do not permit balancing; the rule against any such defence is categorical. The courts do not draw any analogy between self-defence or superior orders. This is no doubt because in the case of self-defence the actor acts against the aggressor, so that the value in issue is not diluted by other considerations. In superior orders there is a clear, but not unlimited value to obeying orders, in circumstances where a police officer's or soldier's appreciation of a situation of danger may not coincide precisely with that of his superior, so that a compromise position of manifest illegality is adopted. The latter formula both sets a standard of social duty and ensures that the soldier or policemen who acts negligently is not excused. It is a rule which is punctiliously taught to both officers and other ranks. It is also the sort of rule which, in a group milieu, can altogether too readily be subverted by an antipathetic or hostile culture unless it be enforced according to its terms.

It is questionable whether, in duress and necessity generally, such severity is necessary. The House of Lords was influenced both by the need to reinforce the value of life and by the need to eliminate bad excuses of the sort which might otherwise be advanced by a member of a terrorist gang desirous of minimizing his responsibility for a killing.[70] This latter problem does not, alone, seem sufficient to justify so harsh a rule. We must ask ourselves whether, where the accused is faced with a peremptory threat of death, to himself or another, our conception of social duty is such as always to require him to withstand the threat on pain of criminal conviction if he does not? This question seems proper to ask quite apart from questions of the efficacy of punishment.

The range of factual situations and the responses which may be made to them are surely much more complex than the judgments in *Howe* would lead us to believe. Even if we require that the citizen be a hero, there may well be situations in which the threat is not directed towards him. If the threat to me is to kill A, lest my wife be killed, am I a hero, a repository of antique Roman virtue, or a coward, for sacrificing her? What of a threat to a person that unless he kills A, a multitude will be killed? Is he to be condemned for an utilitarian response, assuming as seems to be the case that utilitarianism is not to prevail in these circumstances? What of cases where the threat to me requires me to chance the death of others?

Of course any civilised society will wish to discourage an easy abandonment of standards in the face of threats. But both the justice and the necessity of an absolute should be questioned. Deterrence, in the sense of conscious calculation, will only operate in a few of these situations, perhaps conceivably when a person considers joining a terrorist gang, perhaps where facts, as in *Dudley and Stephens*, unfold slowly. Where the threat is immediate, leaving little time for assessment, the conscious model of deterrence doubtless will usually not operate; the calculating man will, unless his reactions be tempered by humanity, choose to avoid the immediate peril. On the level of social conditioning, the argument is no more compelling. A strong assertion of the right to life is surely compatible with acquittal or the recognition of a lesser offence, if it is felt that the law must do something, in what will be a few tragic cases. That, functionally, is what was done in *Dudley and Stephens* itself.[71] No reasonable person, were a verdict of manslaughter possible in such cases, could really conclude that English law, by not treating the case as murder, demonstrated an inadequate concern for the right to life. We need, in elaborating a set of rules, to take account of the possibilities for calm deliberation which the individual has, and the imperfect control of emotional reactions which characterises most of us. The hero may be our exemplar; he cannot readily be our daily standard.

Conclusion

Here, we come to an end; in the middle of moral quicksand. Reason, emotion, fault, liability. A plea has been made for fuller recognition of stress and emotion; of a somewhat less dominant role for intellectualism, though not certainly for its abandonment. But the context in which the problems arise are various and perhaps one can, in the event, do no more than indicate a starting point, which lies in the identification of those factors, which as social duties of fairness, the function of criminial law, and its characteristics as an instrument of social control, seem relevant to the solution of some exceedingly difficult issues.

Notes

1. This, in relation to duress and necessity, has been recognised: see per Viscount Hailsham LC and Lord Mackay in *Reg. v. Howe* [1987] 1 AC at 429C, and p. 459 respectively.
2. This observation is but the merest commonplace; its implications have been worked out in part by others, and notabley by I. H. Dennis, "Duress, Murder and Criminal Responsibility" (1980) 96 L.Q.R. 208.
3. Its effects are well — documented both in battlefield conditions and in respect of interrogations: see W. Sargant, *Battle For The Mind* (1957).
4. Studies of stress in relation to particular situations of stimulus are of some antiquity: see R. Thompson, *The Pelican History of Psychology* (1968).
5. See Hilary Allen, *Justice Unbalanced* (Open U.P. 1987), p. 95.
6. See further A. Crowcroft, *The Psychotic* (Pelican, 1967).
7. C. J. Adcock, *Fundamentals of Psychology* (Pelican, 1964), pp. 207—209.
8. *Doughty* (1986) 83 Cr.App.R. 319.
9. We deliberately refrain from labelling such conditions of sensitization as insanity. In the first place, there are those who deny that any insanity or abnormality of mind is involved: see e.g. H. A. Davidson, "Irresistible Impulse and Criminal Responsibility" in *Crime and Insanity* (ed. R. W. Nice, 1958). Second, the label is unimportant provided that the phenomenon be known and, where appropriate, proven. What the legal response to a phenomenon should be cannot ultimately depend upon its medical classification. See *Sullivan* [1983] 3 W.L.R. 123.
10. Neuroses it is said, do not in general lead to crime: J. K. Mason, *Forensic Medecine For Lawyers* (2d ed., 1983).
11. See e.g. remarks of Lord Hailsham in *Howe* [1987] AC at p. 432.
12. *Reg. v. McNaghten* (1843) 10 Cl. & F. 200. In addition, a person who suffers from delusion and who commits a criminal act is judged according to the rule which would apply had the facts been as he supposed them to have been.
13. *Reg. v. Haynes* (1859) 1 F. & F. 666.
14. B. Wootton, *Social Science and Social Pathology* (Allen and Unwin, 1959), at pp. 230—232.
15. *Byrne* [1960] 2 Q.B. 396.
16. A number of these are collected by R. Lęng, "Mercy Killing and the CLRC" (1982) N.L.J. 76; see also G. L. Williams, *Criminal Law, The General Part* (2d ed., 1961), pp. 557—558.
17. B. Wootton, *Crime and the Criminal Law* (2d ed., 1981), chapter 3.
18. *Fenton* (1975) 61 Cr.App.R. 261.
19. Courts do not always, however, interpret the words strictly: pre-menstrual tension sometimes is, but most often is not, considered to be a disease: See L. Luckhaus, "A Plea for PMT in the Criminal Law" in S. Edwards, (ed.) *Gender, Sex and the Law* (Croom Helm, 1985), pp. 159—182. See also British Medical Journal, 24 March 1973,

pp. 689—690; *Times*, 12 November 1981. The leading case which denies that PMT is a defence is *Reg. v. Smith (Sandie)* [1982] Crim. L. R. 531.

20. Infanticide Act 1938, s. 1.
21. J. K. Mason, *op. cit.* at p. 208. Before the passing of the Infanticide Act 1922 (the precursor of the present statute) the offence most often charged was concealment of birth which served because it did not present the same problems of proving a live birth as did murder: D. R. S. Davies, "Child Killing In English Law", *Modern Approach To Criminal Law* (ed. J. W. C. Turner, 1947), p. 301.
22. *Cf.* G. L. Williams, *Criminal Law, The General Part* (2d ed., 1961), p. 557 arguing that the Infanticide Act 1938 could now be repealed on the ground that it is but a particular expression of diminished reponsibility. This would be acceptable were both to be reviewed together.
23. Homicide Act, 1957 s. 4; for the background to this measure, see G. L. Williams, *The Sanctity Of Life And The Criminal Law* (1958), pp. 264—276.
24. The Report of the Commissioners who prepared the English Draft Code treated one clear case of provocation, that of a person who committed adultery with the actor's wife, within his sight (even though the deceased may have been unaware of ther husband's presence) as an outrage to him: see *Martin's Criminal Code* (1955), pp. 390—391.
25. The English authorities on this are usefully summed up by Stephen J. in *Viro v. The Queen*, 18 A.L.R. at p. 228.
26. *Parnerkar* [1974] S.C.R. 449.
27. *Lesbini*, (1914) 11 Cr. App. R. 7 at p. 9.
28. *Mancini*, [1942] A.C. 1; the contrast posed between a stereotype excitable and violent Italian and a supposedly controlled Englishman looks rather quaint in this post-Heysel Stadium age.

29.—33. *Camplin*, [1978] 2 All E.R. 168; *Newell*, (1980) 71 Cr. App. R. 331.

34. This suffices for murder in English law: *Reg. v. Cunningham* [1982] A.C. 566.
35. *Doughty* (1986) 83 Cr. App. R. 319.
36. [1989] Crim.L.R. 740.
37. The case is not one of euthanasia which raises fundamental and difficult problems.
38. Private defence is provided for by the common law; the use of reasonable force in the prevention of crime, etc., is provided for by s. 3 (1) of the Criminal Law Act, 1967.
39. *McInnes* [1971] 1 W.L.R. 1600 (retreat only a factor in determining reasonable force); *A. G.'s Reference (No. 2 of 1983)*, [1984] Q.B. 456 (pre-emptive strike).
40. *Edwards* [1973] 1 All E.R. 152, *Johnson*, [1989] 1 W.L.R. 740.
41. Law Commission Draft Code, cl. 59. For the change in Australian law, see *D.P.P. v. Zecevic* (1987) 61 A.L.J.R. 375.
42. See remarks of Murphy J. in *Viro v. the Queen*, 18 A.L.J.R. 375.
43. [1971] A.C. 814 at p. 832.
44. *A.G. of N. Ireland's Reference* [1977] A.C. 105.
45. *Gladstone Williams* (1984) 78 Cr.App.R. 276.
46. [1976] A.C. at p. 214.
47. This is not universally agreed: see S. M. H. Yeo, "The Element of Belief in Self-Defence" (1989) 12 Sydney L.Rev. 132.
48. See K. Campbell, "Offence and Defence" in I. Dennis (ed.), *Criminal Law and Justice* (1987).
49. On the details of this see D. W. Elliott, "Necessity, Duress and Self-Defence", [1989] Crim. L. R. 611.
50. *Graham* [1982] 1 All E.R. 801. The Law Commission, Draft Code cll. 42 and 43 appears to be consistent in allowing the actor both in duress and duress of circumstances to take advantage of his subjective appreciation of the situation as one in which

a threat has been made, provided always that the threat in all the circumstances is one which he cannot reasonably be expected to resist. It is, however, not clear whether the expectation is determined by the objective character of the threat or the actor's subjective assessment of it. The Law Commission (see Law Comm. No. 177, Vol. 2 at para. 12. 16) specifies that the former is meant. This, if so, perpetuates difficulties alluded to above. It is clear that the issue is not simply whether the actor intends to act reasonably.

51. *D.P.P. v. Lynch* [1975] A.C. 653 at p. 699 per Lord Simon; see further G. Orchard, "The Defence of Compulsion", (1980) 9 N.Z.U.L.Rev. 105.
52. *Cf.* D. W. Elliott, *loc. cit.* at p. 615.
53. It should, however, be noted that Elliott does not argue for an entire identity of rules, and further that is quite impossible in a paper of this scope to deal with the totality of matters which he raises.
54. *Howe* [1987] A.C. 417.
55. It is a doubtful question whether threats of lesser harm will do: D. W. Elliott, *loc. cit.* thinks not: J. C. Smith, *Justification and Excuse In the Criminal Law* (1989) at pp. 90—91 believes that the common law has not definitively excluded the possibility that threats to property may excuse certain crimes.
56. (1984) 14 Q.B.D. 873. For the background to this cause celebre, see A. W. B. Simpson, *Cannibalism and the Common Law* (1984).
57. Just such a problem is dealt with in the notes to the *Indian Penal Code*, s. 81 where it is assumed that a defence, albeit cast in terms of *mens rea*, would be available.
58. For an argument that balancing should be required, see M. Conde, "Necessity Defined: A New role In The Criminal Defense System", 29 U.C.L.A. L. Rev. 409 (1982). In *Reg. v. Howe* [1987] A.C. at p. 433 Lord Hailsham suggests that there is no room for a balancing formula.
59. See further I. D. Brownlee, "Superior Orders — Time For A New Realism", [1989] Crim. L. R. 396.
60. Brownlee, *loc. cit.* cites *McKee v. Chief Constable for N. I.* [1985] 1 All E. R. 1. Note that because the officer mistakenly believed that he had grounds for an arrest, it was not necessary to rely on superior orders, but such a suspicion could derive from instructions given by a superior.
61. A. V. Dicey, *Introduction To The Study Of The Law Of The Constitution* (10th ed., repr. 1962), pp. 302—304.
62. See e.g. *Reg. v. Smith* (1900) 17 Cape S.C. 561. The *A.G. of Northern Ireland's Reference*, supra n. 43 does not refer to superior orders as such, and relates primarily to levels of response.
63. G. Orchard, *loc. cit.* at n. 50 above.
64. A. Kenny, *Freewill and Responsibility* (1978), p. 38.
65. I. Dennis, *loc. cit.*
66. J. Gorecki, *A Theory Of Criminal Justice* (1979), chapter 1. See further G. B. Melton and M. J. Saks, "The Law As An Instrument Of Socialization and Social Structure" in G. B. Melton (ed.), *The Law As A Behavioral Instrument* (1986), pp. 235—278.
67. This was, indeed, pointed out by H. L. A. Hart many years ago; see *Punishment and Responsibility* (1968), pp. 19—20.
68. As a model of conduct it is more appropriate to Kissinger's geopolitical theories than to the sequence of events in a Saturday night pub crawl.
69. The relevant arguments are put with great clarity in a Canadian decision *Reg. v. Szola* (1977) 33 C.C.C. (2d) 572 (Ont.C.A.).
70. *Howe* [1987] A.C. 417 at p. 434 per Lord Hailsham.
71. A. W. B. Simpson, *Cannibalism and the Common Law* (1984).

[11]

British Journal of Psychiatry (1991), **158**, 593–601

Lecture

Jealousy: The Pathology of Passion

PAUL E. MULLEN

Emotions may be rooted in biology but the process of cultural construction gives those emotions form and a language for their expression. The changing construction of jealousy in Western societies has transformed a socially sanctioned response to infidelity into a form of personal pathology which is the mere outward expression of immaturity, possessiveness and insecurity. This is a history of the stripping away of social, ethical and finally interpersonal meanings from an experience, to leave it as a piece of individual psychopathology. Fidelity and jealousy are constructed as they are because of the nature of the social and economic realities which drive our culture. The erosion of the area of human experience which could be identified with normal jealousy leaves the boundary between the pathological jealousy of psychiatry and normal experience increasingly problematic.

Jealousy can confront the psychiatrist in a variety of guises. Convictions about the partner's infidelities may form the content of psychopathological phenomena such as delusions (Jaspers, 1910; Lagache, 1947; Shepherd, 1961; Mullen, 1990*a*). When jealousy arises not as a symptom of obvious underlying disorder, but as a reaction to some understandable threat to the relationship, then the distinction between the responses of those 'normally' and those 'pathologically' jealous can present formidable problems (Vaukhonen, 1968; Retterstol, 1967; Tiggelaar, 1956; White & Mullen, 1989). These problems are compounded by the absence of any clear notion of what constitutes normal jealousy and where the boundaries of that normality, in terms of both behaviour and experience, should be drawn. It is accepted that jealousy is a common, if not universal, experience, but despite this, its status as 'normal' is in increasing doubt.

Eliot Slater argued that psychiatrists could, and should, apply their particular perspective to issues of social and cultural importance to contribute to the common pool of understanding. This paper examines jealousy as a construct which is altering with the changing cultural contingencies of Western societies in the hope of shedding some light on why normal jealousy has become problematic.

The manner in which jealousy is regarded and experienced has changed repeatedly over the history of Western societies. The changing cultural construction of jealousy has gradually transformed it from a socially sanctioned response to infidelity into a personal pathology. In the 17th century jealousy was a passion, albeit one that could cause problems. Today jealousy is a problem which can stir up damaging and embarrassing emotion. Jealousy was once a passion which had a role in expressing and maintaining individual and social values which, admittedly, if uncontrolled could usher in pathology. Today jealousy is often regarded as a pathology which offends against the ethics of liberal individualism and its free market in goods, ideas and people. Jealousy is riven by contradictions. At one extreme it embodies a longing for an ideal in human relationships and a cry of protest at the loss of that dream of sustained commitment and fidelity. At the other, it has always been contaminated by the attempt to impose the desires and priorities of one person upon another. The changing balance between destructive possessiveness and disappointed hope is central to jealousy's history. The path that jealousy has travelled from the zealousness of the Renaissance to become a hallmark of personal immaturity is examined here in terms of the changing construction of emotion and the alterations in patterns of sexual behaviour.

There are a number of assumptions implicit in interpreting emotions as being in part cultural construction. One is that we are subject to a multiplicity of emotions and desires but we only have names for some of them and, by and large, only the grosser examples. Jealousy, as a self-description, covers a wide range of potential experiences, a range which alters according to the constructions of the individual and the wider culture. In speaking of emotions and desires we are limited by the language of our culture and perforce we fit our experiences as best we can into the available vocabulary. Over time this vocabulary changes. Finlay-Jones (1983)

This paper is based on the 1990 Eliot Slater Memorial Lecture.

described the disappearance of the emotion *accidie* from Western culture, but more importantly, claimed that a group of those who now call themselves depressed, would have found better expression for their state of mind within the lost language of *accidie*. The relationship between experience and the words used to express that experience is a two-way process and in our culture of prefabricated feelings, words and phrases increasingly give birth to reality (Adorno, 1973). To begin to know about a person's emotions and desires it is necessary to embark on an archaeology both of their own personal development and their culture's words.

The changing face of jealousy can be introduced by looking at some of the virtues and vices attributed to jealousy in different historical periods. The word 'jealousy' carried with it in the 14th century the connotation of eagerness, devotion and zealousness (*Oxford English Dictionary*, 1971). It implied a solicitousness to preserve something possessed or esteemed. The adage attributed to St Augustine that who is not jealous does not love ("Qui non zealat non amat") surely speaks more to the enthusiasm of love than to possessiveness or suspicion. The potential for any solicitousness and devotion in jealousy to give way to suspicion and distrust has long been recognised. Thus in *Othello* (1694) Shakespeare has Emilia tell Desdemona: "They are not ever jealous for the cause, but jealous for they're jealous. Tis a monster begot upon itself, born on itself".

Jealousy, despite its attendant darker side, was accorded a role in preserving social esteem in societies ruled principally by concepts of honour. Honour, at least as an ideal, involves an uncompromising pursuit of the good which puts aside individual advantage in preference to moral and social principle. Where monogamy is a moral and social imperative, jealousy is regarded as a protector of the integrity of the family. Gonzales-Crussi (1988), in an essay on male jealousy, which harks back nostalgically to a Spanish culture still ruled by codes of honour, claimed the modern era "turns a sanctimonious eye" on jealousy, seeing it as "but a sign of sociopathic or psychological maladjustment" and fails to credit that "jealousy is not without worthy elements" for it "stems at bottom from a concern for the inviolate perfection of others". The balance between the perceived virtues and vices of jealousy has shifted at different historical periods to culminate in the modern view of jealousy as compounded of vices mitigated by little, if any, virtue. Stearns (1989), in his pioneering work on the evolution of jealousy in America, put the position succinctly when he wrote, "for over 60 years all the evaluations of jealousy, scholarly and popular, supportive of, or hostile to, conventional monogamy condemn the emotion". Jealousy is now described as a disaster to be avoided whenever possible (Fisher, 1990). The 'official' view of jealousy does not necessarily reflect the attitudes and practices of those currently living in Western societies, let alone members of different cultures. In a recent survey of jealousy nearly half the respondents agreed with the proposition that jealousy is an inevitable part of love and only a tiny minority disclaimed any experience of the emotion in their sexual relationships (Mullen *et al*, in preparation).

Jealousy survives, if not thrives, in our societies. To understand how it is constructed and experienced at the end of the 20th century it is necessary to briefly examine the conceptualisations of emotions in general. There is a wide range of views on what constitutes an emotion. At one extreme, emotions are regarded as conditioned or unconditioned reactions to stimuli in which reason and judgement have no part. MacNaughton (1989), in his book on the biology of the emotions, coyly disclaimed any desire, or necessity, to define emotion, but finally stated emotions are "in essence any state, or set of states, of the organism which involve the co-occurrence of specific patterns of response of more than one of the skeletal, autonomic and hormonal systems". In such an interpretation the conscious mind is in absence. At the other extreme, the American philosopher Robert Solomon (1980) claimed "emotions are defined primarily by their constitutive judgements, given structure by judgements, distinguished as particular emotions (anger, love, envy etc.) by judgements". Here cognition is all, and biology together with instincts and automatic reactions are nowhere. I do not attempt to resolve the conflict between such formulations but give a passing glance at how two such very different constructions emerged and how they impact on our view of jealousy.

MacIntyre (1988) made elegant use of the Homeric poems and subsequent translations to illustrate the perceived relationship between practical reasoning and emotion at different historical periods. The translators of Homer's epic poems project the traditions and discourse of their own age back onto the Homeric template, thus providing an accessible record of the changing understanding of what constitutes emotion. If we take the example of the passage in the *Iliad* where Achilles is subjected to a public insult from Agamemnon, according to MacIntyre's rendering of Homer he suffers a momentary indecision as the passion of anger infects, or is inflicted on, his 'humus' (spirit, the force which propels the person toward action) before his 'arete' (virtue, duty to fulfil his proper role) reasserts itself. He is helped in this by the prompting of the goddess Athena.

Passion, for Homer, is external and infects the individual, bringing blind infatuation, or in this case, blind rage, but it also has a social and moral dimension. It brings with it the danger of being diverted from the lawful path, from the path of destiny. The concept of passion as external and penetrating is common in early Indo-European societies where emotions are often likened to illnesses which invade or insinuate themselves into us (Crespo, 1986). A surviving image from such emotionologies is that of Cupid firing his dart into the love-struck victim and we still speak of being infected by jealousy. What then of the jealousy of Menelaus confronted by Helen's infidelity. Homer tells us little of his immediate responses, but the whole Trojan War stems from the duty Menelaus accepted to avenge this public humiliation. The infidelity was an insult to his person, to his kingship and to the morality of the society. It placed upon him the duty to avenge the affront and gave him the right to call all Greeks to his assistance. Homer has Helen castigate herself for the adultery as "a whore and a nightmare of a woman" and she attributes the infidelity to "harlotry in me and madness [in Paris]" (Fitzgerald's translation, 1984). This is an infidelity with associated jealousy which can only be understood in terms of moral imperatives, honour and adherence to one's social role.

If we turn to Chapman's translation of Homer from the late 16th century, dominated intellectually as it was by the rediscovery of Aristotle, Achilles is transformed from Homer's publicly humiliated hero infected by anger into a prototype for an Aristotelian debating society, in which, for Chapman, Achilles "at this stood vexed", his heart

> "Bristled in his bosom and two ways did draw his discursive part
> If from his thigh his sharp sword drawn, he should make room about
> Atrides person slaughtering him, or sit his anger out
> And curb his spirit. While these thoughts strived in his blood and mind . . ."

There stands indecisive Achilles immersed in an internal debate about the correct course to follow. Anger is presented as an event separate from the rational mind which can be thoughtfully considered and then acted upon as reason dictates. Passion, emotion as we know it, has almost disappeared, buried under the discursive deliberations of an educated rationality. Cognitions are all and biology given no place. This however represents only one of the constructions of emotion current at that time, for a biological view of passion also had adherents through the penetration into the wider culture of Galenic humeral theory. Hobbes (1677) translated the same passage:

> "This swelled Achilles choler to the hight
> And made him study what to do were best
> To draw sword and Agememnon kill,
> Or take some time his anger to digest."

Here the model of passion is based in the physiology of the humours, although reason also plays a part in studying "what to do were best". Note the resolution of the anger appeals to a physical process of digesting the excess of anger. For Chapman reason is paramount, but for Hobbes it is secondary to the rise and flow of the humours.

Jealousy is, for Shakespeare both in *Othello* (1604) and *The Winter's Tale* (1610), a consuming passion driven onward by a sense of affronted honour, but in both instances based on error. By the simple expedient of making the jealousy unjustified, Shakespeare becomes subversive of the social and ethical imperatives associated with jealousy. He shifts the passion from its social role into the product of an individual's error which flourishes on the basis of personal vulnerabilities. There is little of Aristotle's educated rationality in the jealousy of Leontes or the Moor. Camillo likens the jealousy of Leontes to a sickness (I, ii, 380) and it certainly has a sudden onset based on a flash of false insight heralded by palpitations (I, ii, 110). Once in motion, these jealousies of Shakespeare are characterised by their imperviousness to reason, at least until after they reach their fatal conclusion. In the Sonnet (number 147) which deals with love and jealousy, Shakespeare also uses the image of emotion as infection which reason like a physician tries to treat, but without success. Shakespeare's jealousy does have something of Homer's infection diverting the sufferer from the path of destiny and duty, but it is a jealousy stripped of any morally or socially redeeming features. This can be contrasted with jealousy as portrayed in the work of Shakespeare's great Spanish contemporary Calderon (1630–81), where the passion is both justified and rational, being as morally admirable as it is murderous.

In Alexander Pope's 18th-century translation of Homer, a view of passion is articulated in which there are two entirely separate realms, that of passion and that of reason, both contending for attention:

> "Distracting thoughts by turns his bosom rule'd
> Now fired by wrath and now by reason cool'd:
> That prompts his hand to draw the deadly sword,
> Force through the Greeks to pierce their haughty lord;
> This whispers soft his vengeance to control".

Achilles now stands buffeted between the twin discourses of reason and passion. Passion prompts violent action, but reason counsels control. In 17-century and early-18th-century Europe, a common view of passion was of what we might now term a 'motivating force', which aroused by an event, drove the affected individual towards action. Passions could cause acts, but such actions were likely to be uncontrolled and inconsistent outbursts. In contrast, when reason governed the response it was likely to be measured and effective. Reason, for most Christians at this time, partook of the divine and had the advantage over passion of being modifiable by experience and open to the direction of education. Passion and reason occupy different realms of discourse and govern alternative modes of responding which lead to different and potentially opposing actions. This view of passion and reason as alternative and opposing still informs much of the commonsense folk psychology of emotion. Jealousy in this construction is entirely separated from reason.

Passion was, for an educated person in the 17th century, best avoided, and reason cultivated as an independent alternative. The view of passion changed during the 18th century: a change which was both influenced and articulated by European philosophers. Hume offers an example. He clearly stated his view of the relationship of reason to passion in *A Treatise on Human Nature* (1740): "Reason is, and ought only to be the slave of the passions and can never pretend to any other office than to serve and obey them . . . tis only in two senses that any [passion] can be called unreasonable . . . where it is founded on false suppositions or chooses means insufficient for the end". Hume's concept of the passions did not, like the previous emotionology, place reason into a separate discourse from passion. In terms of what we would call motivation he ceded primacy to passion, but reason was inserted into the chain connecting passions both to their objects and to their consequent actions. Passions were not mere reactions, but had their origin in pre-existing dispositions and arose in relationship to an object. To use the jargon of our age, Hume's passions were intentional. Reason could in this model influence the choice of object, one could reason about the suitability of someone as a love object or whether that was an event which really justified the emerging jealousy. Further, reason was inserted into the process connecting the passion once formed to any course of action. For Hume reason served the passion by deciding on how best to facilitate its expression.

Passion as understood by Hume does not translate directly into the modern term 'emotion'. It was more closely allied to desire and to the concept of a sentiment. It could influence actions and take part in reactions, but was not the elaboration of biologically determined conditioned or unconditioned reflexes. Hume's views of passion appear somewhat more complex when he articulates his model through specific examples. Love, for example, he views as compounded of three elements: the aesthetic appreciation of beauty, sexual appetite and benevolence. The mixture of these elements may vary, but without all three the passion is not for Hume one of love. The notion of passion as sentiment is illustrated by the 18th-century novelist Fielding in *Tom Jones* (1749) when he wrote: "but it is with jealousy as with the gout, when such distempers are in the blood there is never any security against their breaking out and that often on the slightest occasions". This supposes a passion to be a persisting potentiality, in the very blood of the person, a concept close to the current notion of a trait.

Emotions during the 19th century increasingly acquired the connotations of the transitory and the organic, at least in the literature of science, both scholarly and popular. They shifted from traits to states. They ceased to be compounded of abiding sentiments and desires and became involuntary reactions independent of morality and of those permanent values which characterise a person. Reason's only remaining roles were in helping the individual to avoid situations or attitudes which could trigger the less appetising of these emotional reactions and in mitigating the damaging impulses they engendered. Instinct and biology, reaction and reflex, these became the words appropriate to emotions.

The shift from sentiment to physiological response is only part of the story of how the cultural construction of emotions developed from the 19th century until today. While the scientists, for want of a better word, were exploring ideas of instinct and the biology of emotion, the novelists, quite independently, were redrawing the map of the emotions. Hume's pre-conceptual and pre-linguistic passionate drives were gradually transformed into a complex patterned regularity of dispositional and occurrent feelings, of judgements and actions, such that each element was a necessary part of the whole (MacIntyre, 1988). A recent attempt to deduce a phenomenological description of jealousy employing literary examples derived just such a pattern of dispositions and feelings (Mullen, 1990*b*). The analysis of this material suggested that the elements contributing to the experience of jealousy included judgements, desires, feelings, fantasies and predispositions to behave. The jealousy complex as constructed at the highest cultural level (Tolstoy's

Kreutzer Sonata (1889) and Proust's *Remembrance of Things Past* (1913–22) is far removed from an automatic reaction for it consists of an intentional state of mind in which judgement and fantasy occupy central positions.

Reason re-enters with such models into the very substance of emotions in general and jealousy in particular. Part of the current debate about emotions and the emergence of such trends as the judgementalist and social constructionist views of emotion is about reintroducing, reinjecting this tradition, carried forward until recently largely by novelists, back into the psychological and social sciences.

The evolution of today's jealousy also involved a shift from a passion rooted in socially and morally sanctioned values towards an emotion expressive only of personal desires and preferences. Jealousy in the 'honour' societies was a largely male prerogative connected to public retribution for the damage inflicted on social prestige. In the 18th century jealousy expressed distress at the loss of the person both as a source of gratification and as a possession, but jealousy continued to incorporate a protest against the infringement of ethical and moral values, albeit now more internalised values. The element of loss of property was amply illustrated by the proliferation in 18th-century England of law suits against adulterous wives and their paramours for monetary compensation. Property and marriage had long been intermingled; what was new was the concept of a contract open to renegotiation or a failure to fulfil. The association of jealousy with the treatment of the loved one as a possession has continued as a theme in both popular and scholarly writings. Davis (1936), in his often quoted account of jealousy, claimed "in every case [jealousy] is a fear or rage reaction to a threatened appropriation of one's own, or what is desired as one's own, property".

In Western societies at the end of the 18th century there occurred important changes in the attitude to love and marriage, at least among the more privileged social strata. Love received increasing emphasis as a basis for courtship and marriage. There was nothing new in romantic love; what was novel was viewing marriage as the appropriate and preferred playground for this passion. Love now preceded rather than followed marriage and there was a heightened valuation of heterosexual love and family affection (Gay, 1984, 1986). This is amply illustrated by the family advice manuals which became such a prominent part of middle-class life in the 19th century both in Britain and America (de Gasparin, 1865). In some ways this new emphasis with its idealising of fidelity, particularly female fidelity, would have tended to increase jealousy fears, but more importantly there developed an increasingly hostile attitude to jealousy which was seen as potentially eroding the love relationship and undermining the stability of the family.

Stearns (1989) points out in his history of jealousy in America that the 19th century was riven by conflicting influences on jealousy. On one hand urbanisation broke down the traditional small communities with their mutual enforcement of fidelity by public scrutiny. America gradually abandoned the institutional enforcement of sexual fidelity through its laws against adultery. At the same time the opportunities for romantic and sexual encounters increased and prostitution flourished. Equally, the rise of commercial codes of behaviour made concerns for honour seem anachronistic. Counterbalancing these various forces, which might have tended to heighten jealous anxieties, was the increasing emphasis on the dangers of jealousy. There was an insistence on true love being incompatible with jealousy. The emphasis on female fidelity, coupled with the acceptance of male infidelity, placed the burden for avoiding jealousy squarely on the woman.

Through the 19th century jealousy shifts from being the prerogative of the male to being the problem of the woman. The myth of the 'one great love' central to the 19th-century and early-20th-century emotionology was in practice gender specific. For women it meant what it said, one love, one partner. For men it was interpreted as meaning you, my wife or lover, are the one great love of my life, so all the little transgressions of monogamy are trivial and neither merit nor justify jealousy.

Women were increasingly portrayed as more emotional and less controlled than men and were encouraged to overcome this weakness, particularly to avoid possessiveness and jealousy in the interests of preserving the family. The split between reason and passion reappears embodied in the contrast between the rational male and the emotional female. Jealousy is no longer the expression of offended honour, but of weakness and lack of control stemming from inadequacies of character. Women were increasingly regarded as more prone to emotion, but less prone to carnal desire. Any qualms about double standards with regard to jealousy could be calmed by an appeal to the fortuitous freedom from undue sexual desire which made infidelity for women unnatural and the unfortunate insistence of male urges which made men's indulgence a matter of physical and mental hygiene. The 19th-century view of the bourgeois wife as virtually bereft of sexual desire contrasts with the early-18th-century view of women as more amorous than men and more likely to consume themselves with their passion (Bouce,

1982; Flynn, 1987). Advice manuals, usually written by women for women, in the 19th century regularly praised men who took the trouble to conceal affairs for showing due concern for their wives' feelings. Such manuals tended to urge wives not to make any effort to discover that which knowing could only bring them pain and distress (Stearns, 1989).

Although jealousy was under severe attack in the 19th century both from the forces of the self-declared progressives and the writers of advice manuals, it did not lack champions. The family, at least in theory, remained central. Marriages were about rearing children and infidelity presented a potential threat. A prominent forensic psychiatrist, Charles Mercier (1918), wrote: "the institution of marriage and the instinct of jealousy work for the same end and serve the same purpose. Love selects, jealousy mounts guard to repel third parties from entering the sacred fold". The 20th century saw even this justification for jealousy eroded as the emphasis in emotional and sexual relationships firmly shifted from the family and children to the quality of the couple's relationship. "Does the relationship satisfy my sexual and emotional needs?" became not just an acceptable question, but the central question for many. Jealousy has little place in satisfying anyone's sexual and emotional needs.

Jealousy came under further attack at the beginning of the 20th century from psychologists and psychiatrists who increasingly emphasised that romantic jealousy arose from personal immaturity and reflected a hangover from the sibling rivalries of childhood, with no place in mature adult relationships. Freud and his disciples added to jealousy's burdens with the concept of projection, which emphasises that jealous individuals often had only their own impulses to infidelity to blame which they were projecting onto the innocent partner (Freud, 1955, first published 1922; Jones, 1937).

The picture is further complicated by the version of romantic love promoted by 20th-century popular culture. This love emphasises passionate excitement and enthusiasm which is blind to mundane social constraints. Such love is sustained by novelty. Those in permanent relationships are thrown back into the realm of comparison, which is the realm of jealousy (de Rougemont, 1950), but at the same time, their own opportunities for a further chance at the imagined splendours of new love depends on negating their partner's potential jealousy.

Jealousy approaches the end of the 20th century as an outcast, a problem best avoided, if not avoided then suppressed, and if you fail to suppress it then you become a suitable case for treatment, well if not treatment, at least counselling. A study of 60 counsellors in America (White & Devine, 1991) revealed that their predominant views were that jealousy arose from low self-esteem and excessive dependence on the partner combined with feelings of inadequacy as a lover; in short, a character defect. It leads to excessive demands for attention and sexual exclusivity. Their opinions on the inadequacy of their jealous clients was despite the fact that the couples usually presented in the context of an actual, and acknowledged, rival relationship.

Jealousy has become a pathology of the person suffering it. Gone are its virtues and its justifications. That infidelity conjured it into existence simply allows the therapist, should they be of an old-fashioned bent, to empathise with its emergence before turning to the task of knocking the dependent wimp, who cannot satisfy their partner and is unreasonable enough to demand attention and fidelity, into a shape befitting the late-20th-century person.

What place does the zeal, once central to jealousy, hold for us today? Rawls (1971), a persuasive spokesmen for modern liberalism, wrote "human good is heterogenous because the aims of the self are heterogenous. Although to subordinate all our aims to one end does not strictly speaking violate the principles of rational choice, it still strikes us as irrational or more likely as mad". Rawls is referring in this passage to the subordination of all one's aims to ideological or theological systems, but presumably the same caveat would apply to the overweening enthusiasm of jealousy which from this viewpoint also disfigures the self. Jealousy is nothing if not a protest at a failure to subordinate all of your, and someone else's, aims within a relationship to one end. Zealousness and the pursuit of exclusivity are clearly anachronisms for the liberal individualist. Another philosopher, Heller (1985), expressed this idea about jealousy directly when she wrote "now that freedom has become a universal value idea, hatred felt because of the other's withdrawal of love is irrational indeed".

Current Western society reflects the influence of the market economy, of democratisation, and of the notion of freedom expressed through individual rights. Modernism leaves no place either for jealousy's claims for exclusivity, which offend against individual rights and liberal notions of freedom, or for the jealous person, who is an emotional bankrupt in the market-place of love. Equally, the acceptance of ideas about individual rights as the final arbiter of the good in our society marginalises any claims made on behalf of moral or ethical imperatives which infringe such notions. In the abortion debate, for example, those who oppose claims made on the basis of the rights of the woman to choose, increasingly make their appeal to public opinion in terms of another set of putative rights, those of the unborn child, rather than in terms of moral or divine imperatives. Debates on ethical or social values are replaced by assertion and counter-claim as rights are opposed to rights. Demands for fidelity and exclusivity, central to jealousy, are difficult to sustain on the basis of individual rights, particularly in a liberal society where mutual duties and obligations are dissolved into contracts, actual or implicit. The collective, the social, and even the interpersonal dimensions to which the individual is subject, are lost, to be replaced by the notion of the sovereignty of the individual consumer.

If sexual and emotional relationships are about two individuals entering into an implicit contract to augment their sexual and emotional returns, then jealousy brings with it all the vices and precious few virtues. If we accept the estimates derived from Lawson's (1987) research and review of the literature, up to 50% of women and some 65% of men become involved in extramarital affairs, and a good proportion have multiple affairs. Adultery is now a participation sport indulged in by the masses. Citizens increasingly assume the right to change and vary their erotic attachments. In such a context, and with an ethic in Western society emphasising the rights of fragmented, isolated individuals, how can jealousy be anything but pathology?

There is however a different view of liberal individualism. Hampshire (1989) writes: "A deadening encrustation of conventional classifications of human concerns prevents us looking inwards and from recognising the unnamed exultations and depressions of our inner life for what they are, the revelations of our real nature concealed by our social role". Building on this model of the individual trying to free their rich inner world from the impoverishing influences of tradition and social roles, he offers this construction of love. "Sexual love is associated with a desire to know an individual person with a peculiarly violent curiosity which becomes a desire to enter into another inner world, and to take possession for a time of another person's consciousness, through the body that expresses that consciousness". There could be no more individual and individualistic construction. As the pendulum swings from social and ethical imperatives towards individual freedom so jealousy moves closer to pathology. He is clear that love is no product of reason, "one does not love for a reason any more than one enjoys a joke for a reason, the particularity of the occasion excludes calculation and causal analysis". Does such a construction have a place for jealousy? It leaves plenty of room for envy of those fortunate enough to be the subjects, or objects, of such imaginative curiosity, but it appears to involve no actual claims on the other, to be only "for a time" and to be free of social or traditional encrustations or expectations. This leaves jealousy without a rational basis. Although there is curiosity about the other and their inner world, it is the inquisitiveness of the spectator which regards and explores the other in all their manifestations, physical and psychological. There is no obvious need in this model for reciprocity. It can have Hume's aesthetic and lustful appreciations, but what of benevolence with its desire to promote the happiness of the other? Such love is the love of subject for object, if neither demands nor requires love in return, it desires only "to take possession for a time". The loved one is presumably free to reciprocate the curiosity, or not, for such love would not need to intrude or ask, let alone demand, commitment. Jealousy with such a model would surely be a jarring irrelevance. On the other hand, if love is compounded of curiosity and imaginings its kinship to jealousy would be clear, for jealousy is nothing if not curious and nothing if not driven by a fevered imagination. As Proust (1913–22) wrote: "a little jealousy is not unpleasant . . . for it enables people who are not inquisitive to take an interest in the lives of others, or in one other at any rate".

If we enter sexual relationships not as free and independent contractors, but as members of a society whose values and traditions are not dominated solely by the ethic of the market place; if we enter not as isolated self-sufficient monads, however imaginative, but as dependents seeking some security and reassurance; in short, if we are the human, all too human, members of a tradition which still seeks to realise some of their potential through intimate relationships, then jealousy cannot yet be relegated entirely to a pathology of the passions. But then again perhaps it can and perhaps it should.

This paper could be read as an attempt to rehabilitate jealousy by recalling that it once had both social relevance and interpersonal meaning. Jealousy is about infidelity, and infidelity has a moral dimension. Some commentators claim jealousy is an inescapable part of our nature which can only be controlled by the habit of fidelity (Scruton, 1986). This paper has asserted that fidelity and jealousy are constructed differently at different historical periods and in different cultures, in part because of the changing nature of social and economic realities. The ideology of our age promoted a greater acceptance of polygamous erotic activity and the reputation of jealousy is in eclipse. Moral relativists claim that we can describe the influences of culture on ethical standards, but deny the existence of any transcendent values by which differences could be assessed. Conversely, some would judge this history of jealousy in terms either of ethical perspectives resurrected from the past, or of those dreamed of as future possibilities. The changes in sexual practices in Western culture reflect, in part, the influences of late capitalism's need for mobile atomised labour and the marketing of commodities through the medium of an anonymous eroticism. The deformations imposed on sexuality by the world of profit are often explained not in terms of social forces, but in terms of the victim's own licentious nature. This view sees man's nature as immutable with personal renunciation and strictness offering the only counterbalances to lasciviousness. There may well be biological givens relevant to the world of emotion, but because cultural construction plays a major role, it is change which is characteristic of the history of sexual behaviour and passions rather than the repeated expressions of unvarying nature.

What then of the distinction between normal and pathological jealousy? The problem is the erosion of any area of human experience corresponding to normal jealousy. In our culture jealousy is now regarded not just as problematic or undesirable, but increasingly as unhealthy, as a symptom of immaturity, possessiveness, neurosis or insecurity. To be jealous is to be showing signs of personal, or interpersonal, instability. The symptoms of the psychiatrist are carved out of the totality of human experience by the expedient of attributing them to the causal processes of madness and disorder. This creation of symptoms from phenomena can claim both theoretical and pragmatic justifications, but even the most subtle and sophisticated of clinicians strip much of the cultural and personal meaning from an experience in metamorphosing it into a symptom. What remains of the moral resonance and heroic achievement if the despair of Kierkegaard's (1849) *The Sickness Unto Death* is annexed to a major depression by the criteria of DSM-III-R or is regarded as a symptom of his personal insecurities and relationship problems? The language of symptom claims to understand what really lies behind the other's behaviour but in the process invalidates that behaviour. Our culture makes increasing use of such language to stigmatise the unacceptable. The morally reprehensible, the socially deviant, the personally disruptive, and what remains of old-fashioned evil is likely to be spoken of in the language of our age as a symptom, be it of character defect, social disintegration or developmental disorder. This process is nothing new: one only has to think of the influence of Galen's theory of the humours to realise that biological explanations of social and experiential phenomena are deeply rooted in Western culture. However, between the encroachments of the discourse of psychiatry and that of the wider culture, there now remains little room for jealousy as a valid human activity. With regard to jealousy, whether this is a loss is open to debate. More troubling perhaps, is the progress of a similar process in a range of human experiences such as despair, guilt, fear and nostalgia, whose painful ambiguities make them prime candidates for pathologies, psychiatrically and culturally defined.

References

Adorno, T. (1973) *The Jargon of Authenticity* (eds & trans. K. Tarnowski & F. Will). London: Routledge & Kegan Paul.

Bouce, P. G. (1982) *Sexuality in Eighteenth Century Britain*. Manchester: Manchester University Press.

Crespo, E. (1986) A regional variation: emotions in Spain. In *The Social Construction of Emotions* (ed. R. Harre). Oxford: Blackwell.

Davis, K. (1936) Jealousy and sexual property. *Social Forces*, **14**, 395–405.

de Rougemont, D. (1950) *Passion and Society* (trans. M. Belgion). London: Faber and Faber.

Fisher, M. (1990) *Personal Love*. London: Duckworth.

Fitzgerald, R. (1984) *The Iliad*. Oxford: Oxford University Press.

Finlay-Jones, R. (1983) Accidie and melancholy in a clinical context. *Australian and New Zealand Journal of Psychiatry*, **17**, 149–152.

Flynn, C. H. (1987) Defoe's idea of conduct: ideological fictions and fictional reality. In *Ideology of Conduct* (eds N. Armstrong & L. Tennehouse), pp. 73–95. London: Methuen.

Freud, S. (1955) Some neurotic mechanisms in jealousy, paranoia and homosexuality. In *Standard Edition, Vol. 18* (eds & trans. J. Strachey), pp. 221–232. London: Hogarth Press.

Gay, P. (1984) *The Bourgeois Experience: Victoria to Freud, Vol. I. The Education of the Senses*. New York: Oxford University Press.

—— (1986) *The Bourgeois Experience: Victoria to Freud, Vol. II. The Tender Passion*. New York: Oxford University Press.

Gonzalez-Crussi, F. (1988) *On the Nature of Things Erotic*. London: Picador Press.

Hampshire, S. (1989) *Innocence and Experience*. Boston: Harvard University Press.

Heller, A. (1985) *The Power of Shame: A Rational Perspective*. London: Routledge & Kegan Paul.

Jaspers, K. (1910) Eifersuchsqahn: Zeitschrift fur die gesamte. *Neurologie und Psychiatre*, **1**, 567–637.

Jones, E. (1937) Jealousy. In *Papers on Psychoanalysis*, pp. 469–485. London: Bailliere, Tindall.

Lagache, D. (1947) *La Jalousie Amoureuse*. Paris: Universitaires de France.

Lawson, A. (1987) *Adultery: An Analysis of Love and Betrayal*. New York: Basic Books.

MacIntyre, A. (1988) *Whose Justice? Which Rationality?* London: Duckworth.

MacNaughton, N. (1989) *The Biology of Emotion*. Oxford: Oxford University Press.

Mercier, C. (1918) *Crime and Criminals*. London: University of London Press.

Mullen, P. E. (1990*a*) Morbid jealousy and the delusion of infidelity. In *Principles and Practice of Forensic Psychiatry* (eds R. Bluglass & P. Bowden), pp. 823–834. London: Churchill Livingstone.

—— (1990*b*) A phenomenology of jealousy. *Australian and New Zealand Journal of Psychiatry*, **24**, 17–28.

Proust, M. (1980) *Remembrance of Things Past* (trans. F. Scott-Moncrieff & T. Kilmartin). New York: Random House (original 1913–1922).

Rawls, J. (1971) *A Theory of Justice*. Oxford: Clarendon Press.

Retterstol, N. (1967) Jealousy paranoic psychosis: A personal follow-up study. *Acta Psychiatrica Scandinavica*, **43**, 75–107.

Scruton, R. (1986) *Sexual Desire: A Philosophical Investigation*. London: Weidenfeld and Nicholson.

Shepherd, M. (1961) Morbid jealousy: Some clinical and social aspects of a psychiatric symptom. *Journal of Mental Science*, **107**, 607–753.

Solomon, R. C. (1980) Emotions and choice. In *Explaining Emotions* (ed. A. O. Rorty). California: University of California Press.

Stearns, P. N. (1989) *Jealousy: The Evolution of an Emotion in American History*. New York: New York University Press.

Tiggelaar, J. (1956) Pathological jealousy and jealous delusions. *Folia Psychiatrica, Neurologica et Neurochirurgica Netherlandia*, **59**, 522–541.

Tolstoy, L. (1985) *The Kreutzer Sonata and Other Stories* (ed. & trans. D. McDuff) (original 1892). London: Penguin Books.

Vaukhonen, K. (1968) On the pathogenesis of morbid jealousy. *Acta Psychiatrica Scandinavica* (suppl. 202).

White, G. L. & Mullen, P. E. (1989) *Jealousy: Theory, Research and Clinical Strategies*. New York: Guilford Press.

White, G. O. & Devine, K. (1991) Romantic jealousy: Therapists' perception of causes, consequences and treatment. *Family Relations*.

Paul Mullen, *Department of Psychological Medicine, University of Otago, PO Box 913, Dunedin, New Zealand*

[12]

Pergamon

International Journal of Law and Psychiatry, Vol. 18, No. 1, pp. 15–28, 1995

0160-2527/95 $9.50 + .00

0160-2527(94)00024-7

Assessing Mental Disorder in the Criminal Justice System:

Feasibility Versus Clinical Accuracy

Sheilagh Hodgins

A number of investigations have now shown that the rates of mental disorder among inmates in correctional facilities in North America far exceed the rates for these disorders in the general population (Collins & Schlenger, 1983; Daniel, Robins, Reid, & Wilfey, 1988; Hodgins & Côté, 1990; Hyde & Seiter, 1987; Motiuk & Porporino, 1991; Neighbors et al., 1987; Teplin, 1990a). The rates of major disorders (schizophrenia and major affective disorders) have been found to be up to four times greater than the general population rates matched for sex. These recent studies have further suggested that, in a large majority of cases, the major disorder had been present before the current period of incarceration.

Previous estimates of the prevalence of mental disorders among offenders had suggested that only about 5% of inmates suffered from psychosis. However, these estimates were obtained using various diagnostic criteria, reliabilities of the diagnoses were not examined and/or reported, samples were small and biased (usually those referred for treatment), and comparable prevalence rates for the general population were not available (for a review of these older investigations, see, for example, Roth, 1986; Wormith & Borzecki, 1985). The new studies succeeded in correcting many of the methodological weaknesses that characterized the older investigations. They examined representative samples of inmates, all used the DSM-III criteria, and all but one (Hyde & Seiter, 1987) used the same standardized, reliable, and valid diagnostic tool that had been used to obtain prevalence rates of mental disorder in the general population (the Diagnostic Interview Schedule, DIS, Robins, Helzer, Croughan, & Ratcliff, 1981). Interviewers were specifically trained to use the instrument and supervised during the course of the study to ensure that they adhered to the rules of the instrument, and these studies examined and reported inter-rater reliabilities for the diagnoses.

**Author's note*: Correspondence and requests for reprints should be sent to Sheilagh Hodgins, Université de Montréal, CP 6128, Suc. Centre Ville, Montréal, Québec, H3C 3J7.

Not only have these investigations identified a considerable challenge for those responsible for mental health care within correctional facilities, and clearly exposed a situation in which the constitutional rights to treatment of inmates are not being respected (Ferguson, 1988); they have provided valuable information in furthering our understanding of the relation between mental disorder and crime. The findings demonstrate that individuals with major mental disorders are far more prevalent within correctional facilities than had previously been assumed, that they often receive no treatment while in the correctional facility, that they have not received mental health treatment when they were in the community (despite the fact that the disorder was already present) (Hodgins & Côté, 1990; Teplin, 1990b), that they are often put in isolation cells (Hodgins & Côté, 1991), that they suffer from a number of co-occurring disorders (Abram, 1990; Côté & Hodgins, 1990), that they commit serious violent offenses at rates higher than do the other inmates (Côté & Hodgins, 1992; Teplin, McClelland, & Abram, 1993), and that their criminal careers relate to the combinations of disorders from which they suffer, rather than simply to the major disorder (Hodgins & Côté, 1993; Côté & Hodgins, 1990).

Consequently, the importance of this first group of studies that examined large, representative samples of inmates with standardized diagnostic tools cannot be underestimated, either for mental health policy and programs for offenders or for understanding the relation between mental disorders and crime. These studies were first and foremost applied studies, designed to provide information relevant to mental health policies and programs for the correctional, mental health, and criminal justice authorities in the jurisdictions where the studies were conducted. Given the high prevalence rates of mental disorder that were documented, the results of these studies might suggest the need for such investigations in other jurisdictions. The findings clearly indicate that in order to respect inmates' rights, intensive, long-term mental health care has to be provided within these correctional facilities and in the communities where the inmates return following release. Given the numbers of offenders requiring care, this is a daunting prospect for any correctional facility. To mental health agencies already unable to provide adequate community care for noncriminal patients, it is impossible to envisage treating these individuals unless significant new resources are made available. In order to set up effective treatment programs, the correctional facilities and mental health agencies will need to know why so many of the inmates surveyed had never had any treatment. Would they accept treatment if it was offered? To jurists, the high prevalence of mental disorder among inmates of correctional facilities might suggest the need for investigations of the court process. Were all of the inmates with major mental disorders in these studies ineligible for an acquittal or an altered judgment on the grounds of mental disorder? Were they all adequately assessed prior to trial? How do these convicted, incarcerated mentally disordered individuals differ from those acquitted because of mental disorder or found guilty but mentally ill? Not only are the results of these studies of use to the jurisdictions in question, they are consistent with a growing body of data showing that individuals who suffer from major mental disorders and alcohol and drugs use disorders are at increased risk for criminal behavior and for violence.

Given the importance of these findings not only to the jurisdictions where they were carried out, but also for other jurisdictions and for our understanding of mental disorder and crime, it is essential to examine them critically and to make proposals for future work in this area. The validity of the findings from the studies of inmates will first be examined. Next, the congruence of these findings with other recent, relevant investigations will be examined. If the evidence from different types of studies concurs, it increases confidence in the validity of the various investigations. Third, the accuracy of the diagnoses in the inmate studies is examined. To conclude, proposals for assessing inmates' needs for mental health care and for future research are developed.

Are the Findings from the Inmate Studies Valid?

An examination of the methodology of the inmate studies suggests that the results are valid. These studies were designed to document the prevalence of mental disorders among jail, prison, and penitentiary inmates using the same diagnostic procedure and instrument used to document the prevalence of mental disorders in the general population. Most of these studies used the instrument designed to obtain prevalence rates for mental disorders in a U.S. community sample of more than 11,000 subjects, and in large-scale epidemiological studies in Canada, Germany, Peru, and Puerto Rico (Robins, 1985). The DIS was developed in cooperation with the National Institute of Mental Health in Washington, in order to produce estimates of the prevalence of all mental disorders among a random, stratified sample of the U.S. population. Estimates of past and current symptoms are documented, and ages of onset of disorders can be estimated (Robins, Helzer, Croughan, & Ratcliff, 1981).

Like all research and diagnostic instruments, the DIS was the result of many compromises (Robins et al., 1981). It measures all mental disorders, it was designed for use with subjects who have diverse socio-demographic characteristics, it is not administered by clinicians (who are costly) but rather by lay interviewers trained in about two weeks, and it takes less time than a clinical interview, thereby increasing the subject compliance rate.

In designing the inmate studies, as in designing any study, feasibility was weighed against clinical accuracy. At the time, the best estimates suggested that the prevalence of mental disorders among inmates was low (see, for example, a review of the literature and a previous study we had conducted, Hodgins, Cyr, Paquet, & Lamy, 1988). In order to document the prevalence of the major disorders, which have a very low prevalence in the general population (schizophrenia 1%, bipolar disorder 1.2%, and major depression 3% among men and 7% among women; Robins et al., 1984), a relatively large sample was required. However, diagnosing many subjects is costly. To ensure that the diagnoses obtained were reliable, 20% of the interviews had to be done twice by independent interviewers. Given these methodological concerns and the objective to document the prevalence of disorders as had been done in the general population, the DIS was by far the best available diagnostic tool.

Although the results of these studies appear to be valid, they are not generalizable to other jurisdictions. The numbers of mentally disordered persons entering the criminal justice system are determined by a multitude of factors, which differ from one jurisdiction to another and from one time period to another. These include police practices in diverting suspects they judge to be mentally disordered to mental health facilities, the attitude of prosecutors in proceeding against mentally ill accused, the legal structure for dealing with mentally ill offenders, the ease with which acquittals for reasons of "insanity" are obtained, the possibility of a death penalty, the proportion of the mentally ill population living in the community, and the policy and practice of legalizing violent incidents that occur within hospitals.

Are the Findings from Studies of Inmates Consistent with Studies of Mental Disorder and Crime?

If it is true that a disproportionate number of incarcerated offenders suffer from mental disorders that were present before their incarceration, then we would expect to find that either more mentally disordered persons commit crimes, as compared to non-disordered persons, or that mentally disordered persons are more often arrested for crimes than are non-disordered persons. In fact, both of these have been found. Hodgins (1992; 1993b) examined an unselected Swedish birth cohort, composed of 15,110 subjects, followed to age 30. At the end of the follow-up period, mental health records were screened to document all admissions to psychiatric wards, and national police records were screened to document all registrations for criminal offenses. Whereas 29.4% of the men with no disorders were registered for a crime, 47.6% of those with a major mental disorder had been registered for at least one crime, as had 89.6% of those with alcohol and drug use disorders, and 34.4% of those with "other" diagnoses (not personality disorders). Among the women, 4.9% of those with no mental disorder were registered for a crime, as compared to 17.7% of those with a diagnosis of a major mental disorder, 65.3% of those with alcohol and/or drug use disorders, and 9.6% of those with other disorders. Whereas the "other" mental disorders appear to increase the risk of crime among women, this was not the case among the men. On average, both the men and women with major mental disorders were registered for as many or more crimes than the subjects with no disorders. The proportions of men and women with major mental disorders exceeded the proportions of non-disordered men and women having committed all types of offenses. The differences between the men and women with major disorders and the men and women with no disorders were even greater for violent than for nonviolent crimes. These findings are consistent with those of Ortmann (1981), who examined an unselected Danish birth cohort of over 12,000 males followed to age 23.

Studies of patients discharged from psychiatric wards also suggest that persons suffering from major mental disorders are at increased risk for crime. Lindqvist and Allebeck (1990) followed 644 schizophrenic patients who had been discharged from a psychiatric ward in Stockholm for 14 years. During this period, the discharged male patients were arrested for 1.2 times the average number of crimes of men in Stockholm. The female patients were arrested for 2.2 times the number of crimes by Stockholm women. However, the patients were arrested for four times more violent offenses than were non-disordered Stockholmers during the same period. In New York, Link, Andrews, and Cullens (1992) studied patients discharged to the community, and compared them to a control group of subjects from the same neighborhood. Again, the discharged patients were arrested for more crimes than the community control subjects, and again this difference was greater for violent than for non-violent crime. The pilot study for the MacArthur Risk Assessment Study (Steadman et al., 1993) found that 26.7% of three samples of patients reported at least one violent offense in the six months following discharge.

The findings of elevated rates of major disorders among incarcerated offender populations are also consistent with the findings that schizophrenics and their biological relatives are at increased risk for crime (Asnarow, 1988; Coid, Lewis, & Reveley, 1993; Kay, 1990; Mednick, Parnas, & Schulsinger, 1987; Silverton, 1985).

One study, conducted in Chicago, has shown that police may be biased in arresting subjects with major mental disorders (Teplin, 1984). Although a police bias was demonstrated in one jurisdiction at one period of time, such a bias does not necessarily exist elsewhere, or at other periods of time. Steadman and Felson (1984) showed a number of years ago that subjects with mental disorders were arrested less often than non-disordered subjects for weapon offenses. More recently, Link et al. (1992) obtained similar results. These authors suggest that mentally disordered persons are not arrested for trivial offenses; they are arrested more often than the non-disordered because more of them behave aggressively more often. It is hard to dismiss the findings from the birth cohort studies and from the follow-up studies of discharged patients on the grounds of police bias.

The findings from the studies of mental disorder among incarcerated offenders also are consistent with studies of homicide offenders. In a study of all homicide offenders in Northern Sweden over an 11-year period, Lindqvist (1986) found that 53% received a diagnosis of a major mental disorder. In a 25-year period in Copenhagen, it was found that 20% of male homicide offenders and 44% of female homicide offenders suffered from a major mental disorder (Gabrielsen, Gottlieb, & Kramp, 1987). In Canada, we found that 35% of a random sample of incarcerated homicide offenders received a lifetime diagnosis of a major mental disorder (Côté & Hodgins, 1992).

To conclude, findings from two unselected birth cohorts and from at least three recent, methodologically sound studies of patients discharged to the community, from a study of twins, from studies of schizophrenics and their biological relatives, and from investigations of unbiased samples and cohorts of homicide offenders concur with results from investigations showing that persons with major mental disorders are overrepresented in incarcerated offender populations. The rigor with which the studies of mental disorder among inmates were conducted, and the fact that the findings are consistent with the results from many other types of studies conducted in several different countries suggest that the conclusion is correct. At least in the jurisdictions studied, there are a disproportionate number of mentally disordered persons within correctional facilities.

Are the Diagnoses Obtained in the Inmate Studies Accurate?

Accurate for what? For providing estimates of the prevalence of mental disorder among incarcerated offenders as compared to the prevalence in the general population? Yes. Accurate for estimating the type and quantity of mental services required in the facilities studied? Yes. Accurate for questioning a legal process that allows so many severely ill persons to be convicted without a mental health assessment prior to trial? Yes. Accurate for individual diagnoses? No.

An inmate population is different in many ways from the general population. It is composed largely of men from lower socio-economic strata, who have a long history of aggressive behavior, drug and/or alcohol abuse and dependence, and who have probably suffered many brain insults (see, for example, Moffitt, 1990). Those studies that examined subjects shortly after arrest were confronted with additional difficulties. It is reasonable to assume that some proportion of the sample were intoxicated at the time of the interview, and that many were anxious and depressed in reaction to their recent arrest and incarceration. The DIS was designed to be used with subjects who cooperate fully with the interview and who have nothing to gain or to lose by completing the interview. The extent to which this was true in the inmate studies is unclear. For example, in our study (Hodgins & Côté, 1990), we examined a representative sample of male penitentiary inmates. These inmates had been in the penitentiary on average of 116 weeks before the interview, and therefore had presumably made some adjustment to their situation. We assumed that they were not intoxicated or using illegal drugs. Whether they were using prescribed medication was difficult to ascertain. We were able to guarantee the subjects absolute confidentiality unless they presented an immediate danger to themselves and/or to others. To our knowledge, we obtained the highest prevalence rates for the major disorders of all of the published studies. Is this because the inmates believed our guarantee of confidentiality? Of those diagnosed as suffering from a major disorder, 52% reported that they had never discussed their symptoms with a mental health professional or a physician.

The surprising finding of the inmate studies was the high rates of the major disorders. The DIS, as noted above, was designed to estimate the prevalence of all disorders in a random population sample. Even in the absence of co-occurring disorders, it is not a good tool for diagnosing major disorders. In many cases, lay interviewers using the DIS fail to detect a major disorder diagnosed by a clinician. For example, Folstein and colleagues (1985) have reported that 21% of clinically diagnosed schizophrenics are identified by the DIS, and 59% of patients with major depression receive a DIS diagnosis of major depression. In another investigation (Anthony et al., 1985), it was found that of 14 clinically diagnosed schizophrenics, three received corresponding DIS diagnoses. The other 16 subjects who received DIS diagnoses of schizophrenia all received other clinical diagnoses.

Given that the DIS fails to detect cases of major disorder identified by a clinician, it is not surprising that "lifetime" diagnoses have been shown to be unreliable. "Lifetime" refers to the presence of the disorder any time in the subject's life, even if he or she does not meet the criteria for the diagnosis at the time of testing. For example, only 67% of subjects given a lifetime diagnosis of schizophrenia by a clinician received a DIS lifetime diagnosis of schizophrenia. Similarly, 42% of those given a lifetime diagnosis of major depression by a clinician received a lifetime DIS diagnosis of major depression, and only 32% of those given a lifetime diagnosis of mania by a clinician received the same diagnosis from a lay interviewer using the DIS (Helzer et al., 1985). Similarly, subjects in the International Pilot Study on Schizophrenia were diagnosed by clinicians, and then 11 years later by lay interviewers using the DIS. Only two-thirds of those previously diagnosed as schizophrenic and manic were given corresponding DIS diagnoses (Pulver & Carpenter, 1983). The problem of establishing lifetime diagnoses may be more difficult for men than for women, at least in the case of depression (Angst & Dobler-Nikola, 1988, cited in McGrath, Keita, Strickland, & Russo, 1990).

The DIS was not designed to detect major mental disorder in persons suffering from a number of disorders. The correspondence in these cases between clinical diagnoses and DIS diagnoses is, not surprisingly, even lower than in the studies reviewed above (Griffen et al., 1987; Hasin & Grant, 1987a,b). Even experienced clinicians using structured diagnostic interview protocols fail to reliably diagnose major disorders and alcohol and drug disorders among substance abusers (Bryant, Rounsaville, Spitzer, & Williams, 1992).

To conclude, a first generation of studies of representative samples of inmates have shown that the prevalence rates of disorder among these inmates are higher than those among sex-matched samples of the general population. The results of these studies of inmates concur with studies of large, unselected birth cohorts, of follow-up studies of psychiatric patients discharged to the community, and with investigations of unbiased samples of homicide offenders clinically assessed before trial. The methodology and diagnostic procedures that are feasible, appropriate, and accurate for such large-scale epidemiological studies may not be appropriate for detecting mental disorder on an individual basis.

Future Studies of Mental Disorder Among Inmates of Correctional Facilities

How do we proceed? It depends on what we are attempting to accomplish. It may well be that policy-oriented research conducted for prison authorities may have to be distinct from more basic research on the links between the various disorders and criminality. In order to decide whether research on mental disorder among inmates can be conducted along with correctional authorities' efforts to assess inmates' needs for mental health services, small studies need to be conducted in the milieu in question. These studies would be designed to determine if the rates of mental disorders obtained when confidentiality is absolutely guaranteed are the same as rates obtained by mental health programs of the correctional facility. Inmates with different mental disorders would be expected to react differently to the two situations, and the answer may depend on the disorder to be studied.

Prison and mental health authorities have to clarify their objectives with this population and specify the quantity and intensity of care to be provided. Depending on these objectives, assessment procedures will differ. If prison authorities want to provide mental health care to all inmates who require such care, they would first have to screen inmates as they arrive in the institution. The inmate studies show that previous psychiatric treatment would be a poor indicator of which inmate would require care. Procedures designed to assess needs following arrest would differ from those designed to assess needs for long-term care once the accused is sentenced to a period of incarceration.

Assessing the need for mental health care in the period from arrest to court judgment is complicated by the inmates' justified fear that whatever is told to a mental health professional could be used against them during the impending trial. This is added to the inmates' reticence to admit to symptoms, even very severe ones, as was noted in the studies reported above. Further, during this period, the role of alcohol and drugs in determining behavior and symptoms cannot be underestimated, at least in large North American cities. Toxicological screens of urine that detect with good accuracy intake of alcohol and drugs in the previous days are now readily available (for alcohol screening see Borg, Beck, Helander, Voltaire & Stibler, 1992; kits for detecting most street drugs and many medications are now available from several of the large pharmaceutical companies). They could easily be incorporated into a screening procedure, and would significantly increase the accuracy of diagnoses at this stage. Assessments of needs at admission are further complicated by the severe anxiety and/or depressive reactions manifest in response to arrest and the possibility of long-term incarceration. Many of the needs assessed at admission might well disappear as the inmate adjusts to conviction and sentencing and becomes free of alcohol and drugs.

The assessment of needs for mental health care after conviction and sentencing is complicated by most, but not all, of the factors noted above. Although inmates should at this stage be free of alcohol and drugs, the role of prescription drugs in determining symptoms merits further investigation. The high rate of depression noted in the inmate studies invites speculation about the role of benzodiazepines and sleeping medications (Bukstein, Brent, & Kaminer, 1989; Regier et al., 1990; Rydberg, 1991) and brain insults resulting from alcohol and drug use, fighting, and accidents (Blumer & Zielinski, 1988; Hayes & Goldsmith, 1991; Larson & Richelson, 1988) in the production of at least some of these symptoms. As was suggested above, diagnostic tools appropriate for epidemiological studies are not necessarily appropriate for making individual diagnoses. The difficulty of accurately diagnosing individuals who present with several disorders cannot be underestimated. However, it has been demonstrated that reliable diagnoses of both the major disorders and the other disorders can be obtained in such cases with clinicians using the Structured Clinical Interview for DSM-IIIR (SCID) after subjects have been drug free and symptom free for a lengthy period (Bryant et al., 1992). All of the accumulated evidence strongly argues in favour of diagnoses being made by experienced clinicians using structured interview protocols such as the SCID. However, this procedure, too, depends on an inmate's willingness to cooperate. The findings from the inmate studies reviewed above suggest that at least in the cultures where the studies were conducted, the offender with mental health problems does not discuss them either while outside in the community or while inside, regardless of the severity of these problems.

The provision of long-term care to inmates suffering from major mental disorders may only be accomplished by instituting cooperation between correctional and mental health authorities. It has been demonstrated that continuity of care is of great importance to these cases (for a review, see Hodgins, 1988). One model that may have some merit for those with major disorders is in place in Norway (personal communication, Dr. Randi Rosenqvist, 1993). Here, mental health professionals who would provide care for this individual were he or she in the community, provide the care required while he or she is incarcerated. This model has several advantages: It ensures continuity of care; it is cost effective in that re-assessment is not needed as the individual moves from one setting to another; the mental health practitioner is free of any constraints from the correctional authorities. However, the disadvantages of this model is that the mental health professional must repeatedly travel to the facility where the inmate is housed. Despite this inconvenience, the idea of different agencies working together to provide services efficiently to multiproblem subjects suffering from major mental disorders must be seriously considered (see, for example, Corrado, Doherty, & Glackman, 1989). The resistance of community mental health agencies to provide care to such cases is a real obstacle in this area. It has been shown that these patients who suffer from major disorders as well as several other disorders are not particularly interested in continued, structured long-term care (Ridgely, Goldman, & Talbot, 1986). Mental health practitioners have not been trained to work with such cases—a major disorder, alcohol and drug use disorders, antisocial personality disorder (APD), and a long history of crime and interpersonal violence—and understandably, they can usually find a way to avoid it (Lewis & Appleby, 1988; Protter & Travin, 1983; Travin & Potter, 1982).

There is now some evidence to suggest that the long-term treatment programs for major mental disorders may be improved by making them specific to the inmate's history of criminal behavior. We have found that among inmates with major disorders there are two distinct groups: one in which the inmate has displayed a well established pattern of antisocial behavior before the age of 15, and a second group in which the inmate only begin offending later at about the time the symptoms of the major disorder would begin to appear (Hodgins & Côté, in press). The first group, the early starters, begin offending early and commit as many nonviolent and violent crimes as do the inmates with no major disorder but with APD. The late-start group, however, commit on average the same number of violent crimes in a shorter period of time. These two types of offenders with major mental disorders have again been identified in the Swedish cohort study (Hodgins, 1993b; 1992; Hodgins, in press) and in a study of psychiatric patients (Hodgins, Toupin, & Tremblay, 1994). Treatment for the early starters could be limited to treatment of the major disorder, which appears to have little to do with the longstanding pattern of antisocial behaviour. Treatment for the late starters, however, might involve investigation of the role of the symptoms of the major disorder in the perpetration of crimes.

Diagnoses are made to provide appropriate and adequate treatment. If diagnoses were made as suggested above (by a clinician using a structured interview protocol once the subject is alcohol and drug free), and inmates were assigned to treatment and rehabilitation programs based on these diagnoses, the effectiveness of these programs might increase. It has been repeatedly demonstrated that the effectiveness of a treatment program is determined in part by the homogeneity of the clientele being treated and the specificity of the treatment program for that clientele (Garfield & Bergin, 1986). For example, different alcohol and drug rehabilitation programs could be designed and offered to inmates with and without a history of major depression, to the schizophrenics, and to those with bipolar disorder. A further division based on the presence or absence of APD might be warranted. Similarly, the efficacy of social-skills training programs, cognitive-skills programs for preventing recidivism (Ross, Fabiano, & Diemer-Ewles, 1988), and programs for sex offenders may be improved if separate groups are run for inmates with and without APD. (At worse, this would no doubt please the staff who are assigned to lead the groups with non-APD inmates.)

A great deal remains to be learned about the relation between the various mental disorders and crime (Hodgins, 1993a). For example, are various combinations of major disorders and personality disorders occurring more often than would be expected if these disorders were independent? We have data from three samples in which we examined the prevalence of schizophrenia and APD. Among male penitentiary inmates diagnosed schizophrenic, we found that the prevalence of APD was 63.2% (Côté & Hodgins, 1990). Among a sample of male schizophrenics being discharged from forensic and psychiatric hospitals, the prevalence of APD was 27.0% (Hodgins, Toupin, & Tremblay, 1994). Among a sample of schizophrenics recruited from the outpatient clinics of two general hospitals, two of my graduate students have found that the prevalence of APD was 23.3% among the men, and 16.7% among the women. A control group composed of non-disordered subjects matched for socio-economic strata was also examined. The prevalence of APD was 3.3% among both the non-disordered men and women (Dube, 1992). Whereas the diagnoses in the penitentiary study were made with the DIS, the diagnoses in the two subsequent studies were made using the Schedule for Schizophrenia and Affective Disorders (SADS) (Endicott & Spitzer, 1979); good inter-rater reliability was obtained both for the SADS diagnoses and comparing the SADS to file diagnoses. Using the lowest of these estimates of the prevalence rate of APD among schizophrenics, these two disorders are co-occurring 13 times more frequently than would be expected if they were independent disorders. This is consistent with findings noted above that schizophrenics and their biological relatives have an excess of criminality as compared to non-disordered subjects.

What are the effects of the various combinations of disorders? In the three samples described above, we have shown that the combination of APD with a major disorder relates to nonviolent criminality, but not to violent criminality nor to self-reported aggressive behavior (Hodgins & Côté, in press; Hodgins, Toupin, & Tremblay, 1994; Dube, 1992). Further, we have carried out neuropsychological testing on a subsample of 30 of the schizophrenic men from the forensic and psychiatric hospitals and on a non-disordered control group matched for sex, age, and educational level. Whereas the schizophrenics as a group were found to be significantly impaired on all measures of frontal lobe functioning, those with a history of a drug use disorder had significantly better frontal lobe functioning than did the "pure" schizophrenics (Hodgins, Toupin, Braun, & Lapierre, 1994). These results suggest that combinations of disorders may not always be worse than one disorder. More importantly, they underline how little we know about combinations of major disorders and personality disorders.

Research of this kind will only succeed in elucidating the relations, or lack of relations, between mental disorders and crime to the extent that the diagnoses are accurate. The problem of reliability and validity of diagnoses is particularly acute if studies focus on the inmates with major disorders, many of whom also suffer from numerous other disorders, as the studies reviewed above have shown. In order to increase the likelihood of obtaining valid diagnoses, with this type of subject, it will be essential to have experienced clinicians making diagnoses with structured interview protocols. However, the challenge of obtaining acceptable levels of inter-clinician reliabilities for these diagnoses is considerable. As has been recently noted, it is difficult to obtain acceptable levels of inter-diagnostician reliability for diagnoses of personality disorders (Perry, 1992). Such studies would require even more acceptable inter-clinician reliabilities on combinations of disorders. For studies of the correlates of crime among the various diagnostic groups, strict diagnostic criteria are required to ensure that these groups are homogeneous. In other words, errors of exclusion from the study group are acceptable, but errors of inclusion in the study group are unacceptable.

Being able to make accurate diagnoses using procedures such as those outlined above will depend on the funding available. Good diagnoses are expensive! Wrong diagnoses, however, are even more expensive!

References

Abram, K. (1990). The problem of co-occurring disorders among jail detainees: Antisocial disorder, drug abuse, and depression. *Law and Human Behavior, 14*, 333–345.

Anthony, J. C., Folstein, M., Romanoski, A. J., Von Korff, M. R., Nestadt, G., Chahal, R., Merchant, A., Brown, C. H., Shapiro, S., Kramer, M., & Gruenberg, E. (1985). Comparison of the lay diagnostic interview schedule and a standardized psychiatric diagnosis. *Archives of General Psychiatry, 42*, 667–675.

Asnarow, J. R. (1988). Children at risk for schizophrenia: Converging lines of evidence. *Schizophrenia Bulletin, 14*, 613–631.

Blumer, D., & Zielinski, J. J. (1988). Pharmacologic treatment of psychiatric disorders associated with epilepsy. *Journal of Epilepsy, 1*, 135–150.

Borg, S., Beck, O., Helander, A., Voltaire, A., & Stibler, H. (1992). Carbohydrate-deficient transferrin and 5-hydroxytryptophol. In R. Litten, & J. Allen (Eds.), *Measuring alcohol consumption* (pp. 149–159). New York: Humana Press.

Bryant, K. J., Rounsaville, M. D., Spitzer, R. L., & Williams, J. B. (1992). Reliability of dual diagnoses: Substance dependence and psychiatric disorders. *The Journal of Nervous and Mental Disease, 180*, 251–257.

Bukstein, O. G., Brent, D. A., & Kaminer, Y. (1989). Comorbidity of substance abuse and other psychiatric disorders in adolescents. *American Journal of Psychiatry, 146*, 1131–1141.

Collins, J. J., & Schlenger, W. E. (1983, November). *The prevalence of psychiatric disorder among admissions to prison*. Paper presented at the 35th Annual Meeting of the American Society of Criminology, Denver, CO.

Coid, B., Lewis, S. W., & Reveley, A. M. (1993). A twin study of psychosis and criminality. *British Journal of Psychiatry, 162*, 87–92.

Corrado, R., Doherty, D., & Glackman, W. (1989). A demonstration program for chronic recidivists of criminal justice, health, and social service agencies. *International Journal of Law and Psychiatry, 12*, 211–229.

Côté, G., & Hodgins, S. (1990). Co-occurring mental disorder among criminal offenders. *Bulletin of the American Academy of Psychiatry and the Law, 18*(3), 271–281.

Côté, G., & Hodgins, S. (1992). The prevalence of major mental disorders among homicide offenders. *International Journal of Law and Psychiatry, 15*, 89-99.

Daniel, A. E., Robins, A. J., Reid, J. C., & Wilfley, D. E. (1988). Lifetime and six-month prevalence of psychiatric disorders among sentenced female offenders. *Bulletin of the American Academy of Psychiatry and the Law, 16*(4), 333-342.

Dubé, M. (1992). *Une comparison entre l'histoire des comportements d'agression des hommes et des femmes souffrant de schizophrenie et ceux et celles ne manifestant aucun trouble mental grave*. Unpublished master's thesis, University of Montreal.

Endicott, J., & Spitzer, R. (1979). A diagnostic interview: The Schedule for Affective Disorders and Schizophrenia. *Archives of General Psychiatry, 35*, 837-844.

Ferguson, G. (1988). Le droit aux soins de santé mentale en milieu carcéral. *Crimonologie, 21*(2), 13-26.

Folstein, F. F., Romanoski, A. J., Nestadt, G., Chahal, R., Merchant, A., Shapiro, S., Kramer, M., Anthony, J., & Gruenberg, E., McHugh, P. R. (1985). Brief report on the clinical reappraisal of the Diagnostic Interview Schedule carried out at the Johns Hopkins site of the Epidemiological Catchment Area Program of the NIMH. *Psychological Medicine, 15*, 809-814.

Gabrielsen, G., Gottlieb, P., & Kramp, P. (1987). *The increase in homicide in Copenhagen 1959-1963 statistical analysis*. Technical Report, Institute of Theoretical Statistics Copenhagen Business School, Denmark.

Garfield, S. L., & Bergin, A. E. (1986). *Handbook of psychotherapy and behavior change*. New York: Wiley.

Griffin, M. L., Weiss, R. D., Mirin, S. M., Wilson, H., et al. (1987). The use of the diagnostic interview schedule in drug dependent patients. *American Journal of Drug and Alcohol Abuse, 13*, 281-291.

Hasin, D. S., & Grant, B. F. (1987a). Psychiatric diagnosis of patients with substance abuse problems: A comparison of two procedures, the DIS and the SADS-L. *Journal of Psychiatric Research, 21*, 7-22.

Hasin, D. S., & Grant, B. F. (1987b). Diagnosing depressive disorders in patients with alcohol and drug problems: A Comparison of the DIS and the SADS-L. *Journal of Psychiatric Research, 21*, 301-311.

Hayes, S. G., & Goldsmith, B. K. (1991). Psychosensory symptomatology in anticonvulsant-responsive psychiatric illness. *Annals of Clinical Psychiatry, 3*, 27-35.

Helzer, J. E., Robins, L. N., McEvoy, L. T., Spitznagel, E. L., Stoltzman, R. K., Farmer, A., & Brockington, I. F. (1985). A comparison of clinical and Diagnostic Interview Schedule diagnoses: Physician reexamination of lay-interviewed cases in the general population. *Archives of General Psychiatry, 42*, 657-666.

Helzer, J. E., Spitznagel, E. L., & McEvoy, L. (1987). The predictive validity of lay Diagnostic Interview Schedule diagnoses in the general population: A comparison with physician examiners. *Archives of General Psychiatry, 44*, 1069-1077.

Hodgins, S. (1993a). *Mental disorder and crime*. Newbury Park, CA: Sage.

Hodgins, S. (1993b). The criminality of mentally disordered persons. In S. Hodgins (Ed.), *Mental disorder and crime*. Newbury Park, CA: Sage.

Hodgins, S. (1992). Mental disorder, intellectual deficiency and crime: Evidence from a birth cohort. *Archives of General Psychiatry, 49*, 476-483.

Hodgins, S. (1988). An aftercare programme for mentally disordered offenders. In F. Koenraadt & M. Zeegers (Eds.), *Trends in law and mental health* (pp. 223-235). Arnhem, The Netherlands: Gouda Quint BV.

Hodgins, S., & Côté, G. (1993). The criminality of mentally disordered offenders. *Criminal Justice and Behavior, 28*, 115-129.

Hodgins, S., & Côté, G. (1991). The mental health of penitentiary inmates in isolation. *Canadian Journal of Criminology, 33*, 175-182.

Hodgins, S., & Côté, G. (1990). The prevalence of mental disorders among penitentiary inmates. *Canada's Mental Health, 38*, 1-5.

Hodgins, S., Cyr, M., Paquet, J., & Lamy, P. (1988). Etude de relance auprès des détenus fédéraux traités en milieu psychiatrique: Description des antécédents du séjour, des rechutes et des récidives. *Criminologie, 21*, 27-62.

Hodgins, S. & Janson, C. G. (1994). A prospective longitudinal study of the early childhood correlates of offending among the mentally disordered. Manuscript in preparation.

Hodgins, S., Toupin, J., Braun, C., & Lapierre, D. (1994). Cognitive functioning of male schizophrenics with co-occurring disorders. Manuscript in preparation.

Hodgins, S., Toupin, J., & Tremblay, L. (1994). Schizophrenia and APD: A criminal combination. Manuscript submitted for publication.

Hodgins, S. (in press). Major mental disorder and crime: An overview. *Psychology, Crime and Law.*

Hyde, P. S., & Seiter, R. P. (1987). *The prevalence of mental illness among inmates in the Ohio prison system.* The Department of Mental Health and the Ohio Department of Rehabilitation and Correction Interdepartmental Planning and Oversight Committee for Psychiatric Services to Corrections.

Kay, S. R. (1990). Significance of the positive-negative distinction in schizophrenia. *Schizophrenia Bulletin, 16*, 635-652.

Larson, E. W. & Richelson, E. (1988). Organic causes of mania. *Mayo Clinic Proceedings, 63*, 906-912.

Lindqvist, P. (1986). Criminal homicide in Northern Sweden 1970-1981: Alcohol intoxication, alcohol abuse and mental disease. *International Journal of Law and Psychiatry, 8*, 19-37.

Lindqvist, P., & Allebeck, P. (1990). Schizophrenia and crime: A longitudinal follow-up of 644 schizophrenics in Stockholm. *British Journal of Psychiatry, 157*, 345-350.

Link, B. G., Andrews, H., & Cullen, F. T. (1992). The violent and illegal behaviour of mental patients reconsidered. *American Sociological Review, 57*, 275-292.

Lewis, G., & Appleby, L. (1988). Personality disorder: The patients psychiatrists dislike. *British Journal of Psychiatry, 153*, 44-49.

Mednick, S., Parnas, J., & Schulsinger, F. (1987). The Copenhagen high-risk project 1962-1986. *Schizophrenia Bulletin, 13*, 485-496.

McGrath, E., Keita, G. P., Stickland, B., & Russo, N. F. (1990). *Women and Depression*. Washington, DC: American Psychological Association.

Moffitt, T. E. (1990). The neuropsychology of juvenile delinquency: A critical review. In N. Morris & M. Tonry (Ed.), *Crime and justice: An annual review* (pp. 99-169). Chicago: University of Chicago Press.

Motiuk, L., & Poporino, F. (1991). *The prevalence, nature and severity of mental health problems among federal male inmates in Canadian Penitentiaries.* Correctional Services of Canada Research Report, *24*.

Neighbors, H. W., Williams, D. H., Gunnings, T. S., Lipscomb, W. D., Broman, C., & Lepkowski, J. (1987). *The prevalence of mental disorder in Michigan prisons.* Final report submitted to the Michigan Department of Corrections, MI.

Ortmann, J. (1981). Psykisk ofvigelse og kriminel adfaerd en under sogelse af 11533 maend fodt i 1953 i det metropolitane omrade kobenhaun. *Forksningsrapport* (vol. 17).

Perry, C. (1992). Problems and considerations in the valid assessment of personality disorders. *American Journal of Psychiatry, 149*, 1645-1653.

Protter, B., & Travin, S. (1983). The significance of counter-transference and related issues in a multiservice court clinic. *Bulletin of the American Academy of Psychiatry & Law, 11*, 223-230.

Pulver, A., & Carpenter, W. (1983). Lifetime psychotic symptoms assessed with the DIS. *Schizophrenia Bulletin, 9*, 377-382.

Regier, D. A., Farmer, M. E., Rae, D. S., Locke, B. Z., Keith, S. J., Judd, L. L., & Goodwin, F. K. (1990). Comorbidity of mental disorders with alcohol and other drug abuse. *Journal of the American Medical Association, 264*, 2511-2518.

Ridgely, M. S., Boldman, H. H., & Talbott, J. A. (1986). *Chronic mentally ill young adults with substance abuse problems: A review of relevant literature and creation of a research agenda.* Baltimore, MD: University of Maryland School of Medicine. Mental Health Policy Studies.

Robins, L. (1985). Epidemiology: Reflections on testing the validity of psychiatric interviews. *Archives of General Psychiatry, 42*, 918-924.

Robins, L. N., Helzer, J. E., Croughan, J., & Ratcliff, K. S. (1981). National Institute of Mental Health Diagnostic Interview Schedule: Its history, characteristics, and validity. *Archives of General Psychiatry, 38*, 381-389.

Robins, L. N., Helzer, J. E., Weissman, M. M., Orvaschel, H., Gruenberg, E., Burke, J. D., & Regier, D. A. Jr. (1984). Lifetime prevalence of specific psychiatric disorders in three sites. *Archives of General Psychiatry, 41*, 949-958.

Ross, R. R., Fabiano, L., & Diemer-Ewles, C. (1988). Reasoning and rehabilitation. *International Journal of Offender Therapy and comparative Criminology, 32*, 29-36.

Roth, L. H. (1986). Correctional psychiatry. In W. J. Curran, A. L., McGarry, & S. A. Shah (Eds.), *Forensic psychiatry and psychology* (pp. 429-468). Philadelphia: Davis.

Rydberg, U. (1991). Depression, alcohol dependence and drug dependence. In K. Strandberg & G. Lonnerholm (Ed.), *Treatment of depression* (pp. 233-241). Uppsala, Sweden: Medical Products Agency.

Silverton, L. (1985). *Crime and the schizophrenia spectrum: A study of two Danish cohorts.* Unpublished doctoral dissertation, University of Southern California, United States.

Steadman, H. J., Monahan, J., Robbins, P. A., Applebaum, P., Grisso, T., Klassen, D., Mulvey, E., &

Roth, L. (1993). From dangerousness to risk assessment: Implications for Appropriate research strategies. In S. Hodgins (Ed.), *Mental disorder and crime*. Newbury Park, CA: Sage.

Steadman, H. J., & Felson, R. B. (1984). Self-reports of violence. Ex-mental patients, ex-offenders, and the general population. *Criminology, 22*, 321–342.

Teplin, L. A. (1990a). The prevalence of severe mental disorder among urban jail detainees: Comparison with the Epidemiological Catchment Area program. *American Journal of Public Health, 80*, 663–669.

Teplin, L. A. (1990b). Detecting disorder: The treatment of mental illness among jail detainees. *Journal of Consulting and Clinical Psychology, 58*, 233–236.

Teplin, L. A. (1984). Criminalizing mental disorder: The comparative arrest rate of the mentally ill. *American Psychologist, 39*, 794–803.

Teplin, L. A., McClelland, G., & Abram, K. (1993). The role of mental disorder and substance abuse in predicting violent crime among released offenders. In S. Hodgins (Ed.), *Mental Disorder and Crime* (pp. 86–103). Newbury Park, CA: Sage.

Travin, S., & Protter, B. (1982). Mad or bad? Some clinical considerations in the misdiagnosis of schizophrenia as antisocial personality disorder. *American Journal of Psychiatry, 139*, 1335–1338.

Wormith, J. S., & Borzecki, M. (1985). *Mental disorder in the criminal justice system*. Programs Branch User Report, Ministry of the Solicitor General of Canada.

[13]

Criminal Behaviour and Mental Health, 1, 193–228, 1991

Madness and crime: Criminology versus psychiatry

S. Wessely and P. J. Taylor Department of Forensic Psychiatry, Institute of Psychiatry, London, UK

Abstract
In considering the relationship between criminal behaviour and severe mental illness two schools of thought can be identified. One, arbitrarily labelled the 'criminological', holds that criminality and mental illness are only weakly associated, if at all. The second, labelled the 'psychiatric' view, holds that there is a real and consistent relationship between mental illness, in particular psychosis, and violence. There are at least two explanations for these apparently conflicting views. Methodological difficulties, such as case definition, information bias, selection bias and confounding, have led to flawed results. The opposing conclusions are, however, not just the result of methodological shortcomings but reflect more fundamental differences in approach. The criminological emphasis on populations and offending, largely in quantitative terms, is contrasted with the psychiatric emphasis on individuals and violence. Longitudinal cohort studies, using the methodology of criminal careers, may allow the two approaches to be combined, and lead to conclusions of more practical value.

Introduction

The possible relationship between crime and mental illness has long been a source of interest. Each represents a deviation from normality, albeit in different ways. Each is also potentially destructive in its deviancy – whether to society or to the individual. The relationship between the two is thus of theoretical and practical interest, not least for those involved in the provision of health and custodial services.

Although there is a large literature on the relationship between crime and mental disorder, many conflicting conclusions have been reached. One explanation for this conflict lies in the difficulty of comparing one cluster of mixed concepts and constructs (mental illness) with another (crime). *Mental illness* is a concept that eludes precise medical definition, and is explicitly undefined in the UK Mental Health Acts. Serious mental illness probably represents a qualitative deviance from normality, but most other forms of mental disorder are more readily seen as quantitative deviations, representing the extreme ends of a normal spectrum. This is particularly true of mental impairment – superior intelligence is as statistically deviant as severe impairment, but is rarely seen as such. Thus psychiatric disorders are mixtures of the social and the medical. *Criminal behaviour* is defined purely in social and legal terms, with behaviour so designated varying markedly between societies and within societies according to circumstance. The difficulties in achieving precise definitions have obvious implications when the relationship between mental illness and criminal behaviour is considered.

One step towards resolving the confusion is to pay more attention to definitions and to give most credence to studies which contain clear definitions. Internationally accepted definitions now exist for mental disorder, and at least for the psychotic illnesses diagnoses are now reasonably reliable. Psychotic disorders are by general agreement the most serious forms of mental illness, and in order to facilitate further discussion we will focus on this subgroup.

Even if only those with the most serious and most rigorously defined mental illnesses are considered, two opposing schools of thought on the relationship between crime, violence and mental illness can be identified. These reflect ideological and methodological differences. For the sake of clarity we shall refer to one as the *criminological* and to the other as the *psychiatric* school of thought, although it must be emphasised that these two labels do not refer to an exclusivity of approach within the two disciplines, but are intended to symbolise two contrasting views.

There are areas of agreement between the two schools, although these tend to be more negative than positive. Both would concur that most crime committed has nothing to do with mental illness. The criminological school extends this argument to assert that there is no special association between criminality and mental illness. The psychiatric view is that there exists a small but important relationship between criminal behaviour, in particular violence, and serious mental illness. Violence and psychosis coexist more frequently than can be explained by chance, and the nature of this relationship suggests that in a certain proportion of cases this may have aetiological significance. This paper explores how these differences have arisen, and attempts to show that they can, at least partially, be reconciled. To do this we shall first assemble the evidence that supports the criminological view, and then present the arguments from a psychiatric viewpoint. We shall then follow the example of Monahan and Steadman (1983), and use an epidemiological framework to explain how apparently mutually opposing views have arisen and can be at least partially reconciled.

The Criminological View

Acquiring a Criminal Record

Possessing a criminal record is by no means unusual. Farrington (1981) has shown that the lifetime prevalence of convictions for standard list (non-traffic) offences is 39.3% by age 50 (males) and 12.2% (females) in England and Wales. These figures lie midway between the proportions found in Sweden (Stattin, Magnusson & Reichel, 1989) and the USA (Blumstein & Cohen, 1987), but all are comparable.

What factors may influence this? There is an overwhelming body of evidence on the social factors that influence the development of offending. For example, in one longitudinal study (West & Farrington, 1973; West, 1982) 400 randomly selected juveniles in a south London area were followed up from age 8 to 32 years. Six independent factors predicted offending at age 21 years (Farrington, 1990a):

1. Economic deprivation.
2. Family history of criminality.
3. Parental mishandling.
4. School failure.
5. Hyperactivity/attention deficit disorder.
6. Antisocial childhood behaviour.

Similar conclusions have been reached in the longitudinal studies of Robins and her colleagues (Robins, 1978) and many others. Normal criminal activity is related to levels of deprivation in the community (Reiss, 1986) and in individual families (Kolvin, Miller, Fleeting & Kolvin, 1988). None of this is disputed – the question relevant to the theme of this paper is whether different or additional factors influence offending in those with mental illness.

Common Ground between Criminal Behaviour in the 'Mentally Ill' and 'Normal'

There is evidence that the variables implicated in 'normal' offending are equally important in determining the risk of offending in the mentally abnormal. In the West and Farrington studies, for example (West & Farrington, 1973; West, 1982), once an offending career had commenced the best predictor of offending was previous offending. A similar association has been found in many studies of the mentally ill (Walker & McCabe, 1973; Steadman, Cocozza & Melick, 1978; Gibbens & Robertson, 1983). Several studies of the mentally ill give sufficient data to enable calculation of the effect of possessing a criminal record on subsequent offending. This is achieved by calculating odds ratios, which approximate to relative risk and indicate the magnitude of the increase in risk of subsequent offending associated with a pre-admission arrest record (Table 1). The wide confidence limits indicate the problem of small sample size, but the strength of the association is clear. As with so-called mentally normal offenders, there is evidence that the greater the number of previous convictions the greater the probability of reconviction (Steadman et al., 1978; Klassen & O'Connor, 1988b). In conventional epidemiology such a dose–response curve is

Table 1 Influence of arrest record on subsequent offending in samples of the mentally ill.

Author	*Odds ratios (95% CI)*
*Payne, McCabe & Walker, 1974	11.1 (4.8–25.8)
Durbin, Pasewark & Albers, 1977	9.02 (2.97–27.51)
Steadman et al., 1978	13.05 (9.06–18.81)
Soskowsky, 1980	4.04 (2.43–6.63)
*Shore, Filson, Johnson., Rae, Muehrer, Kelley, Davis, Waldman & Wyatt, 1989	3.57 (2.04–6.25)

*Restricted to those with schizophrenia only.

strong evidence for an aetiological relationship (Bradford Hill, 1965).

The clear relationship between past and current offending plays a further role in strengthening the criminological case. A well-known piece of literature demonstrates that the risk of criminal behaviour in patients discharged from state mental institutions in the USA has increased over the last 30 years (Rabkin, 1979). These rates now exceed the rates of criminal behaviour found either in control samples or derived from local statistics. On the surface such findings seem to contradict the criminological position because they suggest a strong association between illness and crime; Steadman and colleagues have, however, shown how this observation actually supports their position. Their explanation is that the observed increase results from a change in the input to the state mental health system, because the proportion of patients possessing an arrest record has increased during the period in question (Steadman et al., 1978). In 1947 15% of the men released from mental hospitals had an arrest record before hospitalisation; by 1968 this had risen to 32%, and to 40% in 1975. The data refer to those discharged in each year, but this is a reflection of a change in the characteristics of those being admitted. When the sample was stratified according to the presence or absence of a record, the rates of subsequent arrest remained stable over a 20-year period. Robertson and Gibbens noted a similar phenomenon in their studies of the criminal careers of those subject to restriction orders in the UK – the mean number of previous convictions had doubled between 1962 and 1975 (Robertson, G. & Gibbens, T., 1978, unpublished report to the Home Office). Since it is accepted that offending is strongly associated with subsequent offending, the apparently increased rates of criminality by discharged mental patients is explained by confounding, and the apparently high rate of criminal behaviour found in the mentally ill does not contradict the criminological argument.

Further support for the criminological position comes from the so-called Baxstrom studies (Steadman & Keveles, 1972). Johnny Baxstrom successfully challenged the legality of his continued detention, an action which led not only to his release, but also to the abrupt discharge of 967 other patients detained because of continuing alleged dangerousness. A sample of one in five were followed up. From these studies Cocozza and Steadman (1974) identified variables associated with further offending: previous violent convictions; juvenile convictions; number of previous offences; severity of initial offence; being under 50 years of age. The similarity of these to variables identified among 'normal' persistent criminals is clear.

These studies mean that the criminologist can point to several predominantly sociological reasons for an increasing over-representation of the mentally ill in studies of crime. First, a criminalisation of mental illness, in which increasing numbers of people who would previously have been dealt with by the mental health system are now appearing in the criminal justice system – due perhaps to increasing opinion that the mentally ill should be responsible for their actions, or to the poverty of resources within the mental health system. Others have argued the reverse; there is a medicalisation of criminal disorder, in that those who would previously have stayed within the criminal justice system are appearing more in psychiatric hospitals (Melick, Steadman & Cocozza, 1979). Recent studies have shown the interaction between both systems. In a sample chosen for violence potential Klassen & O'Connor (1988b) demonstrated an association not only between prior arrest and subsequent arrest, but also between prior hospital admission and subsequent admission. Furthermore, prior admissions were associated with future arrest, and vice versa.

The conclusion is that when an offence is committed by someone about whom there is a suggestion of mental abnormality, the fate of the offender may be decided by arbitrary judgements. The criminologist thus argues that associations between mental illness and offending are frequently artefacts of the ways in which both groups are dealt with by the criminal justice and mental health systems.

So far the studies reviewed have identified factors associated with an increased risk of offending, and have shown how the positive association between these factors and criminal behaviour is common to mentally ill and non-mentally ill samples. The complementary perspective is provided by studies that find no positive association between psychiatric variables and criminal behaviour. These include studies that did not demonstrate increased risk of criminal behaviour in those with a psychiatric diagnosis (e.g. Sosowsky, 1978; Steadman et al., 1978), or identified an increased risk, but found that it was restricted to those with diagnoses of personality disorder and/or substance abuse but not of psychosis (e.g. Brill & Malzberg, 1962; Rappeport & Lassen, 1965; Harry & Steadman, 1988). Guze and colleagues undertook a series of cross-sectional and follow-up studies on criminals serving prison sentences and concluded that 'sociopathy, alcoholism and drug addiction were the only psychiatric disorders found more frequently among the index subjects [felons] than in the general population' (Guze, Goodwin & Crane, 1969; Guze, 1976). They reached the same conclusions after studies of the criminal histories of patients in mental hospitals (Guze, Woodruff & Clayton, 1974). Such data may simply mean that the selection system operated by the courts was reasonably effective, but the data have been widely cited in support of the criminological position. There remain substantial objections to such conclusions.

The most comprehensive and elegant summary of the criminological position was given by Monahan and Steadman (1983), who concluded by saying 'There is no consistent evidence that the true prevalence rate of criminal behaviour among former mental patients exceeds the true prevalence rate of criminal behaviour among the general population *matched for demographic factors and prior criminal history* [our italics]'. They also wrote that the 'same factors that relate to the rehospitalisation of civil mental patients also relate to the rehospitalisation of mentally disordered offenders'. The implication is that crime in the mentally ill is but one association of general antisocial behaviour and is determined by social disadvantages common to the mentally ill and the mentally normal (although this ignores the possibility that such disadvantages among the mentally ill post-date the onset of illness). They concluded that mental illness plays little part in the aetiology of criminality in the mentally ill*.

The Psychiatric View

The criminological approach tends to concentrate on demonstrating the presence or absence of a quantitative association between offending and mental illness. Such an approach cannot address the qualitative relationship between crime and mental disorder. The psychiatric literature might be expected to favour such an approach, but

*It must be pointed out that in the light of more recent research Professor Monahan has altered his views (Monahan, 1988).

in practice this is rarely the case, and psychiatric researchers have usually looked for the same numerical associations as criminologists. It is therefore surprising that on many occasions psychiatric researchers have found evidence that apparently contradicts the conclusions of the previous section.

The fragmentation of samples found in the criminological literature is even more pronounced for psychiatric studies. It is necessary to divide the field according to the nature of the sample under study.

Offending Within the Mental Health Care System

Prior to Hospital Admission

A number of studies show that mental illness is associated with a substantial risk of violence before hospital admission. Of 321 admissions (excluding personality disorder and substance abuse), 18% had been accompanied by actual violence (Lagos, Perlmutter & Saexinger, 1977); in a separate series of consecutive hospital admissions 23% had assaulted their partner (Post, Willet, Franks, House, Back & Weissberg, 1980). A retrospective survey of 9000 mixed admissions showed that 10% had been violent before admission (Tardiff & Sweillam, 1980).

Other studies that find similar rates of pre-admission violence also report a specific association with schizophrenia (Craig, 1982; McNeil, Binder & Greenfield, 1988). In a sample restricted to first episodes of schizophrenia (Johnstone, Crow, Johnson & Macmillan, 1986), 94 (37%) had been violent in the previous month and 22% had police contact (MacMillan & Johnson, 1987).

In Hospital

Many studies have shown high rates of violent behaviour in psychiatric hospitals. A series of retrospective studies of samples of the mentally disordered have found that schizophrenics are disproportionately likely to be violent (Albee, 1950; Ekblom, 1970; Shader, Jackson, Harmatz & Appelbaum, 1977; Rofman, Askinazi & Fant, 1980; Tardiff & Sweillam, 1982; Tardiff, 1983; Pearson, Wilmot & Padi, 1986; Karson & Bigelow, 1987; Noble & Rodger, 1989), confirmed by one prospective study (Edwards, Jones, Reid & Chu, 1988). Only Evenson, Altman, Stetten and Brown (1974) and Binder and McNeil (1988) disagree, an over-representation of organic and personality disorder diagnoses being found in the former and of manic patients during acute hospitalisation in the latter. Furthermore, even these discouraging rates are likely to be underestimates, because most derived from a retrospective analysis of violent incident forms or registers, a method associated with significant under-reporting (Lion, Snyder & Merril, 1981; Convit, Isay, Gadioma & Volavka, 1988), especially of the less severe assaults (Infantino & Musingo, 1985). Only Ekblom's (1970) meticulous study of Swedish inpatients found that for serious violence false negatives and false positives were infrequent.

In the Community

Most follow-up studies of discharges from US state mental institutions show an over-representation of mentally ill offenders, which in at least one study was associated with a diagnosis of schizophrenia (Zitrin, Hardesty, Burdock & Drossman, 1976). Although we have already discussed the argument that this is the result of increased numbers of those possessing arrest records in these cohorts (i.e. confounding), anomalies remain. In a sample at high risk of violence, for example, although overall self-report of arrests for violent crimes generally predicted subsequent arrest, this did not hold true for the schizophrenics (Klassen & O'Connor, 1988a,b). Future violence in the schizophrenic group was associated not with previous arrest, but with previous self-reported violent behaviour, implying either that schizophrenics are differentially less able to recall (or perhaps admit to) arrests than violence or that the criminal justice system is behaving differently towards schizophrenics than towards other mentally ill people. The former explanation was not substantiated in a study of remanded prisoners (Taylor, unpublished data). This study also shows that violence is not synonymous with offending.

Swanson, Holzer, Ganju and Jono (1990) analysed the self-reports obtained during a large community survey (the Epidemiologic Catchment Area (ECA) Program) of a limited range of violent behaviours. They found that all psychiatric diagnoses, including schizophrenia, were associated with a substantially increased risk of recall of violent behaviour, even controlling for confounders such as age, gender, drug abuse and social class. In an English study of all schizophrenics identified by a community case register, 49% showed harmful behaviour during a 1-month period (Gibbons, Horn, Powell & Gibbons, 1984).

Mental Health within Samples of Offenders

A study of the mental health of male offenders was carried out in Brixton Prison (a large English remand prison), in which most were pre-trial and all were pre-sentence. The records of 1241 men were examined (Taylor & Gunn, 1984), and a sample of 203 were interviewed (Taylor, 1985). The prevalence of psychosis was 8.7%, of which 70% were schizophrenic. Of those remanded for homicide 11% had schizophrenia, an important finding because all of those accused of homicide in London and its surrounds were remanded to Brixton. This was an over-representation of schizophrenia, because the 1-year prevalence of schizophrenia in Camberwell (an area typical of the catchment area of the prison) is around 0.4% (Wing & Fryer, 1976).

Further evidence supporting an over-representation of schizophrenia has been found in samples restricted to the most serious offenders. Hafner and Boker (1973) assessed the records of all mentally abnormal homicidal offenders in West Germany over a 10-year period. Interpretation of their statistics is complex: the percentage of the sample with schizophrenia varies from 1.2% to 7.7% depending on which baseline statistic is chosen; the true figure is probably somewhere in between. This suggests around a threefold increase in the risk of serious violence, although the authors preferred to draw the more reassuring conclusion that there was no excess of severe violence among the mentally disordered over that expected from national rates. In a study of all homicides in a prosperous California county, 10% of all murderers were schizophrenic (Wilcox, 1985).

Such findings would be supported by evidence of different patterns of offending between those with and those without serious mental illness. Evidence for the differing nature of criminal behaviour among the mentally ill comes from studies of the age at which subjects begin offending. The importance of the issue is illustrated by West (1982), who showed in a random community sample that those who begin offending after 18 years old do not share the same deprived backgrounds as those who begin offending earlier. Turning to mentally ill populations, patients detained in mental hospitals in the UK under the criminal provisions of the Mental Health Act were older and had begun their offending considerably later in life than those not so detained (Walker & McCabe, 1973). The mean age of first conviction of male schizophrenics was 23.0 years (compared with 17.2 years for the personality disordered patients), and 33.4 years for females. (G. Robertson, unpublished data). Women in Holloway Prison who were psychotic had an average age at first conviction of 30 years (Robertson, 1990), considerably higher than non-psychotic prisoners. Similar differences in age have been noted between psychotic and non-psychotic subjects charged with homicide (Gottlieb, Gabrielsen & Kramp, 1987), and between those identified by the police as 'mentally ill' and those not so labelled (Arboleda-Florez & Holley, 1988). Hafner and Boker (1973) found an 8-year difference in the mean age of mentally disordered and non-disordered offenders; Taylor (1987) also found that, among those remanded in custody, psychotic subjects had commenced offending later than those without psychosis. Finally, in offender samples, the prevalence of mental disorder increases with the age of the offender (Inghe, 1941; Taylor & Parrott, 1988).

The Nature of the Relationship between Psychosis and Violent Offending

Evidence of an association between schizophrenia and offending would be strengthened if the links could be extended to clinical features of the illness. These have been reviewed by Taylor (1982), but can be reconsidered in the light of new studies of psychosis and violence. At least some of this relationship can be explained by the actual content and experience of mental illness.

A series of selected case-record studies found that between one-third and two-thirds of homicidal violence committed by schizophrenics can be ascribed to their abnormal mental state (Gibbens, 1958; Lanzkron, 1963; Gillies, 1965; McKnight, Mohr, Quinsey & Erochko, 1966; Hafner & Boker, 1973; Wong & Singer, 1973; Gudjonnson & Petursson, 1982; Wilcox, 1985). An important part of the Brixton Prison studies (Taylor & Gunn, 1984; Taylor, 1985) was the information obtained directly from the prisoners, independent of the legal process and within a few weeks of the offence. Taylor concluded that 'only 9 of the 121 with psychosis were symptom free when they offended' (Taylor, 1985).

Studies in non-offender patients confirm that the strongest association of violence in the acute situation is the presence of the active symptoms of psychosis, rather than the diagnosis of psychosis itself (Planansky & Johnson, 1977; Craig, 1982; Yesavage, 1983; McNeil & Binder, 1987; Krakowski, Jaeger & Volavka, 1988). It may be associated with low serum neuroleptic levels, which can indicate inadequate treatment (Yesavage, 1984). Conversely, violence decreases shortly after admission (McNeil & Binder, 1987) and when psychopathology is treated (Krakowski et al., 1988); this may be a consequence of the reduction in the intensity or prevalence of psychopathology, or a result of the associated improvement in social functioning.

The links between illness and offending can be further clarified, as evidence is now emerging that the risk of violence is at least partly associated with one particular feature of illness – the presence of delusions (Taylor, Mullen & Wessely, 1992). The public health importance of this association becomes clear when it is recalled that delusions are the most common symptoms of acute psychosis (Lucas, Sainsbury & Collins, 1962; Berner, Gabriel & Schanda, 1980). In one sample of chronic schizophrenics only 11% had never suffered from delusions (Taylor, Dalton & Fleminger, 1982).

Several studies have found that the presence of delusions significantly increased the risk of homicidal violence in schizophrenics (Hafner & Boker, 1973; Benezech, Bourgeois & Yesavage, 1980; Addad, Benezech, Bourgeois & Yesavage, 1981). In a follow-up study of patients seen in a Canadian forensic assessment centre, one of the variables associated with subsequent dangerous behaviour was a composite measure of delusions and hallucinations (Menzies, Webster & Sepejak, 1986). This association may be particularly marked for disorders such as paranoia, delusional disorder, morbid jealousy and erotomania, which are all unusual forms of psychosis characterised by a fixed delusional system (Mowat, 1966; Hafner & Boker, 1973; Benezech et al., 1980; Benezech, Yesavage, Addad, Bourgeois & Mills, 1984). All such studies, however, used information obtained in retrospective record searches. Taylor (1985) avoided this bias, and determined that 19%

of 123 psychotic offenders had definite, and a further 24% probable, delusional motivation.

In contrast to the criminological position, evidence from psychiatric and psychological studies suggests that the association between mental illness and offending behaviour is more than can be explained by chance. Nevertheless, any psychiatric researcher will willingly concede that a direct association can explain only part of the findings. Among other possibilities, most of which require further elucidation, is a common predisposition (either social or organic adversity) to mental illness and offending behaviour. The substantial differences in age of onset of criminal behaviours between mentally ill and non-mentally ill samples suggests that social adversity consequent upon mental illness may be a mediator between illness and the observed increased rates of offending.

The Epidemiological Approach – A Possible Solution

How has this confusion arisen? The discipline of epidemiology can provide at least part of the answer. Epidemiology is the study of disease in populations, and the epidemiological approach is always concerned with relating research findings to the appropriate population. In this context it implies attention both to case definition and to the various types of bias and confounding, and emphasises the differences between cross-sectional (case-control) and longitudinal (cohort) designs.

Case Definition

Much of the post-war research in psychiatry has been concerned with the issue of case definition in mental illness. Although problems remain, there is now consensus that schizophrenia can be diagnosed with sufficient reliability for research purposes (although the problem of validity remains). Unfortunately, it is not always carried out, and until recently most studies concerned with crime and mental illness did not give adequate diagnostic information, attempted retrospective diagnoses or relied on often idiosyncratic diagnostic practices of a wide range of psychiatrists (Monahan, 1988). This is illustrated by one study which used a recognised research diagnostic system for retrospective assessment of a series of murderers, but reported an inter-rater reliability of zero (Langevin, Paitich,

Orchard, Hardy & Russen, 1982). More recent attention to case definitions of mental illness has largely been restricted to the psychiatric and psychological literature, whilst the criminological literature has paid scant attention to the issue of specific, let alone standardised, diagnosis, tending instead to view mental disorder as a unitary concept.

Defining psychosis seems almost simple compared with the difficulties of defining offending and criminality, which are fundamentally insoluble, as there is no single definition of crime, nor can there be. Perhaps the most important reason for confusion in this area lies in the problem of case definition for criminologically based studies, which is essentially the same problem as the choice of outcome measure in studies based on psychiatric patients. Crime, offending and violence are three distinct categories and, although they have considerable overlap (Farrington, 1990b), they represent different concepts. Much of the conflict between studies may be traced to this fundamental issue: the criminological emphasis on offending contrasted with the psychiatric emphasis on violence.

Fortunately, it is still possible to use epidemiological techniques in analysing criminal behaviour. The answer is to insist on operational (case) definitions. The researcher must define what is meant by 'crime' or 'violence', and ensure that whatever definition is chosen, it is reliable and consistent. Reliability is a necessary precursor to validity.

Information Bias in the Recording of Crime

No-one will dispute that the true rates of crime vastly exceed the official statistics, the so-called 'dark figure' (Hough & Mayhew, 1983). In the UK less than 15% of all self-reported criminal acts result in police contact with the offender (West & Farrington, 1973). The exact proportion of true to reported crimes is less clear in the USA. One authority (Monahan, 1981) states that 66% of all criminal acts are reported, and 33% result in arrest, but the figure of 20% is quoted by Cohen (1980). The latest official figures conclude that fewer than half of crimes are reported to the police (Bureau of Justice Statistics, 1986).

Thus, even when a crime is officially recorded, few lead to the identification of the perpetrator. Out of 700 000 crimes reported in Greater London in 1982 only 100 000 were cleared up (Commissioner of Police, 1982). This reduction of the true rate of crime to the levels quoted in official statistics is known as the 'shrinkage' in the criminal process, best illustrated graphically (Figure 1) (Stevens & Willis, 1979). A similar process has been demonstrated for the specific offence of rape – the proportion of such sexual assaults that result in a custodial sentence has been estimated at between 6% and 8% in both the USA and the UK (Polk, 1985).

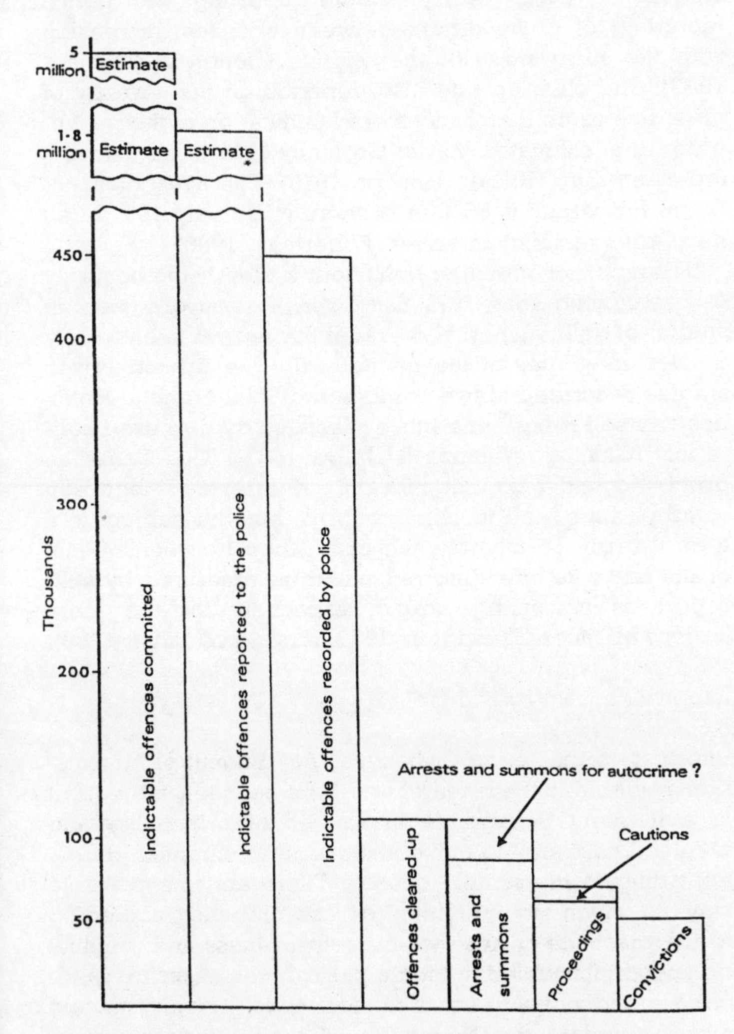

Figure 1 Shrinkage in the criminal process. (Reproduced, with permission, from the Home Office.)

The question of epidemiological interest is how random this shrinkage is. Is the proportion of crime reported or solved a random figure, or are some crimes more likely to be reported/solved than others, which would introduce systematic bias? If the latter, some criminals are more likely to be identified than others. Several lines of evidence suggest that the process of shrinkage is far from random.

As Inghe pointed out, 'the police, as well as the prosecutor, act more efficiently in the case of serious crimes than otherwise' (Inghe, 1941). Victim reporting and police recording of crime differs between offences, increasing with the seriousness of the offence (Hough & Mayhew, 1983). The clear-up rate also depends on the severity of the crime as do the chances of identification of the perpetrator. It is estimated that in Germany 97% of all murders are cleared up (Hafner & Boker, 1973). The latest clear-up figure for assault is 50% in London, while only 10% of all burglaries result in an arrest (Robertson, 1988).

Self-report of offending behaviour is clearly the best way of overcoming bias, and has been extensively used in studies of delinquency. However, it has not yet been widely utilised in studies of the mentally ill. The Brixton Prison studies described above combined official criminal statistics and self-report; one other recent study also used self-report (Chuang, Williams & Dalby, 1987). This Canadian group found no significant differences between schizophrenics and medical controls, but was subject to a type II error. Fortunately, the correlation between official crime and true offending behaviour, as measured by self-report, is reasonably strong, especially for the more serious offences (Farrington, 1973; Huizinga & Elliot, 1986).

Information Bias (by Sample)

Information bias occurs whenever the amount of information available to the researcher differs between subjects. It is a frequent occurrence in studies of criminality and mental illness and, to make matters more complex, differs according to the sample chosen. There are four possible ways in which any individual can be classified according to the presence or absence of mental illness and criminal behaviour, illustrated in Figure 2. Error can occur in classifying an individual in any of the four cells. To make matters more complex, the frequency of such misclassification differs in each. For example, a researcher interested in

	Criminal	**Non-criminal**
Mentally ill	A: rare	B: common
Non-mentally ill	C: common	D: very common

Figure 2 The likelihood of misclassification in studies of criminality and mental illness, arranged by sample.

studying those recorded as criminally insane might recruit a sample of those in group A (those labelled as both criminal and mentally ill). The amount of bias is given by the proportion of those labelled as criminally insane who are incorrectly identified or misclassified. Despite popular prejudice to the effect that criminals regularly manipulate psychiatrists to escape punishment (Appleby, L.S. & Wessely, unpublished data), it is probably a rare event. Surveys of units for the criminally insane in many countries rarely find false positives: most of those in such facilities have committed offences and are mentally ill. The researcher can be confident that the sample consists largely of those who are both mentally ill and have committed a crime (although it is not inevitable that they have committed the crime of which they are accused).

Information bias is more common in the other cells in Figure 2. Category B contains mainly those who are labelled mentally ill and non-criminal, but who have actually committed criminal acts. This is a common occurrence. When a local US attorney rated the records of patients to a state mental hospital, he concluded that 71% of patients had committed illegal acts before admission (Levine, 1970). In the previously mentioned study of Lagos et al. (1977), although 36% had threatened or committed violence, less than 1% had been arrested. Those who have committed unrecorded acts of violence within mental hospitals will also be misclassified (see p. 201).

Category C covers 'normal' criminals, but may actually contain unrecognised cases of mental illness. The relevant literature concerns the psychiatric epidemiology of offender populations (see Gunn, Robertson, Dell & Way, 1978). Again, misclassification occurs. In a unit for violent prisoners, which claimed to have excluded cases of psychosis, researchers found that 13 out of 62 prisoners had 'subtle delusional systems', although no formal diagnoses were made (Bach-y-Rita & Veno, 1974). It is clear that prisons contain individuals with undetected mental illness, often serious (Swank & Winer, 1976; Guy, Platt & Zwerling, 1985; Steadman, Fabisiak, Dvoskin & Holohean, 1987). Coid (1988) has shown that within the criminal justice system chronic psychosis can often be relabelled 'personality disorder', while much real personality disorder goes undiagnosed (Travin & Protter, 1982; Taylor & Gunn, 1984). Whether or not there is an excess of serious mental abnormality in sentenced prisoners is a separate and contentious issue, but not relevant here.

Category D includes all false negatives: those who are not recorded as mentally ill or criminal but who are one or the other. The number of undetected crimes suggests that misclassification of criminality is a common occurrence. For example, Climent and Erwin (1972) assembled a cohort of non-violent persons, chosen from those accompanying patients attending with orthopaedic emergencies, to act as controls for a study of violence – over 25% had to be excluded because on further enquiry they were actually cases, not controls. What can be inferred about those responsible for such undetected crimes? On superficial inspection the false negative rate appears to be twice as high as the true positive rates; in fact the situation may not be quite as serious because many criminologists argue that those who commit the detected one-third are probably not very dissimilar to those who commit the undetected two-thirds (Monahan & Steadman, 1983). In the Cambridge study of delinquent development there was sufficient overlap (in terms of identifying offenders) between self-report of delinquency and official records that 'conclusions about characteristics of offenders based on convictions were generally similar to conclusions based upon self-reports of offending' (Farrington, 1988).

The reverse situation, that those who are labelled as committing crime may not have done so (false positives), probably introduces even less bias into the process. Most criminologists agree that arrest is associated with a high probability of individual criminality (Blumstein & Cohen, 1979). From the epidemiological point of view (although not from the individual) the problem of false positives is not an important one.

Information bias is thus common, especially in categories B and D. This implies that studies that utilise samples of either non-criminal mentally ill or those who are neither mentally ill nor criminal (usually as controls) may contain a proportion of misclassification. The next question is whether or not the error is systematic. All bias is undesirable, but there is a difference in the consequences of random and systematic bias. Random bias will tend to reduce the observed relative risk (non-differential misclassification, which is not welcome), but will not lead the researcher to assume an association where none is present, instead leading to a higher risk of a type 2 error. Systematic bias has an unpredictable effect on the calculation of relative risk and may lead to type 1 or type 2 errors. Thus, in the presence of systematic bias, any finding must be regarded as suspect (Hennekens & Buring, 1987). Is bias random (equally affecting all four groups) or is it systematic? It will already be clear that in practice much bias is systematic.

Systematic Bias

The Effect of Psychosis on the Detection of Criminality

The effect of psychosis on the detection and recording of criminality has several components. First, mental illness renders many individuals more likely initially to be labelled as criminal, i.e. caught (known in the USA as the 'turkey effect', but better described epidemiologically as a positive selection bias). Robertson (1988) showed that schizophrenic offenders were more likely to be arrested at the scene of the crime. Furthermore, 28% of the schizophrenic offenders had given themselves up to the police, compared to 1.2% of 'normal' offenders. In contrast Teplin (1985) looked at police–citizen encounters and concluded that the police did not suspect the mentally ill to be criminal at a disproportionate rate (which is evidence against systematic bias), although the presence of mental illness did increase the probability of arrest. Furthermore, the sample was extremely small and it can also be suspected that the presence of the researcher in the police car influenced police behaviour (Teplin, 1985).

An opposite bias is suggested by evidence that mental illness may decrease the probability of the individual being labelled a criminal. People viewed by the police or the courts as mentally ill may be less likely to be prosecuted. In the USA, Klassen and O'Connor (1988a) found that released patients who were violent were twice as likely to be sent back to hospital as rearrested. Mackay and Wight (1984) noted a similar trend in the UK.

Finally, the risk of offending after release is not fixed at outset, and depends upon subsequent circumstances. The presence of effective after-care, either from the probation service or the mental health system, is intended to influence the risk of reoffending. Differences in after-care will have substantial effects on comparisons between follow-up studies in different places at different times, a point which is almost invariably neglected.

Effect of Criminality on Detection of Mental Illness

Being an established criminal increases the likelihood of arrest, and having a previous record increases the risk of further prosecution (Landau, 1981). Once prosecuted, being labelled as a criminal may lessen the chances of detecting mental illness, because once a person has entered the criminal justice system he or she may remain within it. The exception is extreme violence or homicide, when the rate of psychiatric referral increases (Philips, Wolf & Coons, 1988), and in the UK becomes mandatory for homicide.

Random versus Systematic Bias – Conclusions

Bias is introduced throughout the so-called 'shrinkage' in the criminal process. It is non-random, and is influenced by the presence of both serious mental illness and serious criminality. Given the complexity of these interactions, it is impossible to say whether the different biases cancel out. The relative importance of each will depend on the specific criminal justice system. The result is that nearly all samples contain examples of misclassification, the exact nature of which depends upon the setting and stage of the criminal process reached.

Selection Bias

It is axiomatic for epidemiological studies that cases and controls come from the same population. If differences exist in the way the two groups were selected for study, selection bias is present.

Selection bias accounts for many of the opposing conclusions on the risk of violence among hospital patients. Studies in acute mental hospitals or on admission wards, for example, regularly show an association between schizophrenia and violence, which becomes stronger with the severity and range of observed psychopathology. Retrospective studies of mentally abnormal offenders tend to reveal an association between previous extreme violence and chronic, delusional psychosis, rather than acute psychosis (see Taylor et al., 1991). Studies in secure, long-term forensic psychiatry units find no significant correlation between schizophrenia and current violent incidents; instead an association with a diagnosis of personality disorder has been found (Dietz & Rada, 1982; Barnard, Robbins, Newman & Carrerra, 1984; Dooley, 1986), and in fact Dietz and Rada (1983) conclude that no single diagnostic category is disproportionately associated with interpersonal violence within such facilities. All these differences may be explained by selection bias.

A particularly important example of selection bias has already been introduced, when studies of the rates of psychiatric disorder in convicted prisoners were considered (p. 199). Selection bias is present because at least some psychiatrically ill offenders will have been filtered out of the criminal justice system, either at the time of arrest or at sentencing, and will not appear in samples of convicted prisoners. Once again, it is impossible to quantify the relative contributions made by differing biases, but if the studies of Guze and colleagues on sentenced prisoners are compared with the studies by Gunn and Taylor on those prior to sentencing, it will be apparent that some, but not all (see Roth & Ervin, 1971), populations of sentenced prisoners contain a bias against finding the mentally ill. Thus, conclusions relating to specific samples can rarely be generalised beyond that sample, although attempts are often made to do so.

Turning to discharge follow-up studies, selection bias is apparent in the choice of controls. Valid case-control studies can only be conducted if the controls are typical of the population from which the cases derive (Schlesselman, 1982). In the American discharge studies cited earlier this principle was ignored – like was not being compared with like (Rabkin, 1979; Cohen, 1980). To avoid bias controls must be chosen who would have gone to the same facility as the cases if the controls in turn had become cases. Monahan and Steadman (1983) pointed out that the controls chosen by Sosowsky (1980) came from a different area from the cases, one with a substantially lower crime rate. Overall, only one follow-up study (Harry & Steadman, 1988) uses cases that are not discharged from the US state mental hospitals: the rest have an uncontrolled bias towards single, unemployed, poor, homeless, black men (Cohen, 1980). Violence may itself have played a part in the decision to admit, hence the variable upon which cases and controls are being compared (violence) may have already determined the choice of cases. This is known as *ascertainment bias*, and can be an insuperable flaw in case-control studies (Schlesselman, 1982). The choice of cases has been a further source of bias: in most discharge studies patients are released with the consent of the authorities, and thus selected for predicted good outcome, which greatly reduces their generalisability. In the first of the follow-up studies (Ashley, 1922) a different bias was introduced as 66% of the cases were female, whilst in most since then they have been male.

Inadequate details of the population at risk are also responsible for another frequent problem, that of the *floating denominator*. This is exemplified by the occasional hospital study of violence and schizophrenia that gives no information on the proportion of such patients in the institution. A similar problem has been pointed out by Schipkowensky (1973), who showed that apparent national differences in the proportion of homicide committed by the mentally ill ('abnormal' homicide) is an artefact of genuine differences in the rates of 'normal' homicide.

Confounding

A *confounding factor* is anything that is associated with the exposure of interest and is also a risk factor for the outcome under study. Confounding is thus an alternative explanation for an observed association. Previous arrest, for example, which in the US studies previously reviewed was associated with both mental illness and subsequent criminality, confounds any observed relationship between mental illness and criminality. Perhaps the most common, and most difficult to control, confounder is substance abuse. The problem of confounding is illustrated by one discharge study of a (mainly schizophrenic) cohort in which 66% had an alcohol problem (Giovannoni & Gurel, 1967). Of the 42 schizophrenics arrested for violent crime in the follow-up study of Zitrin et al. (1976), 20 had a history of drug abuse and a further 8 were drug dependent (Rabkin, 1979). The need to record substance abuse adequately is confirmed by Swanson et al. (1990), who found that not only was it an independent risk factor for violent behaviour, but also that there was a significant interaction between serious mental illness and substance abuse.

The issue of confounding is at the heart of the criminological argument (Monahan & Steadman, 1983; see above). Other confounders include class, gender, unemployment and being single. The last needs some elaboration, however, as in certain circumstances living alone decreases the risk of violence: thus, although being married reduces the risk of arrest and conviction in so-called 'normal' criminality, it increases the risk of psychotic violence (Planansky & Johnson, 1977; Hafner & Boker, 1973; Taylor, 1987; McNeil et al., 1988). The reasons are probably multiple: being married is associated with increased age and hence greater maturity; it is also associated with a greater risk of delusionally motivated crime because it is related to an increased chance of a prolonged, intense relationship with the potential victim that carries an additional risk of violence (Taylor, 1987).

The simplest way to deal with confounding is stratification, in which the sample is divided by the presence or absence of the confounding variable. This soon becomes impossible with the number of potential confounders that need to be considered. Multivariate analysis is one solution, but remains imperfect, because the relevant data invariably contain multiply correlated variables. Many measures of social deprivation, such as school failure, poor interpersonal relationships, are correlated, and all are potential confounders, but few consider the problem of multiple co-linearity. Log-linear models can assist, but, as Farrington (1988) has pointed out, the variables of interest are also non-interval, non-linear and non-independent. Finally, many variables influential in the aetiology of violence, such as low social class, parental loss and neurological impairment are not independent variables for a diagnosis of schizophrenia (Taylor, 1982; Edwards et al., 1988).

Relative or Attributable Risk?

As shown earlier (p. 196), part of the evidence in favour of the 'criminological' position is the robust association between current and previous offending in both the mentally normal and abnormal, but *how* important it is is difficult to judge, and depends upon a comparison of relative and attributable risk. The former measures the strength of an association – thus it appears that possessing an arrest record is associated with a 3–13-fold increased chance of reoffending. Attributable risk is a measure of the impact of a variable on the total population, in this instance of how much of the total offending in the mentally ill is associated with prior criminality; Harry and Steadman (1988), for example, found that even when those with antisocial personality disorder were included in the mentally disordered sample, the number of those with previous arrests and of younger age (both of which had highly significant effects on the probability of further offending) still only accounted for 5% of the observed variance in post-discharge offending, although it is true that percentage of explained variance is a crude measure of effect (Rosenthal & Rubin, 1982). Similarly weak predictor variables were noted in an English study of post-discharge offending of those committed to hospital under the criminal provisions of the 1959 Mental Health Act (Walker & McCabe, 1973; Gibbens & Robertson, 1983). Further, previous offending can be no guide to first offending. Thus, the attributable risk of previous offending, which is a more sensitive indicator of the overall impact, may be rather smaller than the relative risk.

The Epidemiologic Catchment Area Program provides a further opportunity to compare relative and attributable risks; Swanson et al. (1990) calculate that the relative risk of a limited range of self-reported violent behaviours in those with only schizophrenia or schizophreniform disorder is four, a substantial figure. However, the population attributable risk percentage of 3% can be obtained from their data, which implies that, although being diagnosed as schizophrenic means that recall of violent behaviour is increased four-fold, such illnesses are associated with only 3% of all the violent behaviours recorded in the ECA Program.

Time at Risk

Few (an early exception being Giovannoni and Gurel, 1967) realise that when comparing rates of offending between the mentally ill and 'normals', the mentally ill may have less chance of offending because of time spent in hospital or prison. Accurate calculations of person-time at risk are therefore important. The most meticulous such assessment was Ekblom's (1970) study of acts of violence committed by inpatients in Swedish mental hospitals. By counting the number of hours people were exposed to patients, and thus their risk of attack, he derived the true rates for seriously violent assault by patients on staff or other patients, which were in fact remarkably low. A related matter – opportunity and exposure to crime – is less quantifiable. One explanation for increased rate of offending in the mentally ill is that it is the product of increased opportunity for both criminality and its detection, which are themselves products of the social drift and deterioration associated with severe psychosis.

The Longitudinal Perspective

Much of the evidence on the relationship between mental illness and abnormal behaviour studies that has been reviewed above follows a particular design. Groups of 'mentally ill' cases are compared with groups of 'normal' controls at a specific time, and the proportions of variables are compared – see the classic case-control study by Schlesselman (1982). Some of the methodological drawbacks of this approach have been discussed. Realisation of these problems has led both criminologists (e.g. Farrington, 1988) and developmental psychiatrists (e.g. Rutter, 1988) to conclude that little further purpose will be served by more studies of 'the mentally ill' and 'normals' looking for evidence of differences in criminal activity, however defined. Using the case-control design to study the rates of mental illness in 'criminals' and 'non-criminals' is also flawed, because the exposure of interest (serious mental illness) is relatively rare in relationship to the frequency of criminality, a major limitation of the case-control approach (Hennekens & Buring, 1987). A recent joint paper from psychology and criminology (Mulvey, Blumstein & Cohen, 1986), when discussing the problems of cross-sectional studies, concluded: 'The major limitation of this approach is that it cannot adequately address the question of how mental illness and criminality may be related on the individual level of analysis'. How can such information be obtained?

The favoured approach is to take a longitudinal perspective. By studying the development of offending over time many of the methodological shortcomings of previous studies can be avoided. Just one of many examples of this in practice can be illustrated by returning to the relationship between offending and age in the whole population, and in particular the age–crime curve.

The age–crime curve is well known in the USA and the UK (Blumstein & Cohen, 1979; Farrington, 1986). It shows a dramatic peak during the teenage years. A natural interpretation is that offenders will commit most crimes during their teenage years.

However, taking the same problem and using longitudinal data, a different picture emerges. A graph of offending by age does not then look like the age–crime curve, and in many individuals does not show any decrease with age until the 30s or 40s, because the number of events in a population (in this case the overall arrest rate in the criminal statistics) is the result of the number of people causing these events and the number of times that they do this: the peak is a measure of prevalence × intensity. Farrington (1986) has shown that the peak in the age–crime curve reflects the intensity of offending during the teenage years less than the prevalence (proportion who are offenders). The rate of individual offending in the teenage years is lower than previously thought. These conclusions would have been obscured by a cursory inspection of the cross-sectional data.

Thus, in 'normal' populations attention has shifted to a longitudinal analysis of offending history, rather than the cross-sectional approach exemplified by the age–crime curve, and in particular a longitudinal strategy called the 'criminal career'. 'The concept of a criminal career structures the longitudinal sequence of criminal events associated with an individual in a unified and systematic way. It is a method for conceptualising the sequence of criminal activities in a person's lifetime as a bounded entity with its own properties' (Mulvey et al., 1986). This has obvious advantages over cross-sectional data, enabling movement from statements of association to models of causation. It may give valuable clues to the continuities (and discontinuities) in the development of abnormal behaviour. Such strategies will also allow the role of social disadvantage as a potential mediator between mental illness and criminality to be assessed.

A further advantage of longitudinal studies is that they permit the direct calculation of incidence rates – in this case the rate of offending over time for individuals/

groups*. The criminal career method allows comparison between subgroups with high and low offending, as well as the identification of social and psychopathological variables associated with high, 'normal' and low offending, rather than have such effects cancel out. That opposing trends may obscure significant differences has rarely been considered yet it is probable that certain features of mental illness (such as apathy, loss of initiative etc.) are associated with decreased offending behaviour, just as other features are associated with increased risk. Longitudinal designs also permit the identification of variables associated with changes in rates. Blumstein and Cohen (1987) have demonstrated that the rate of offending is influenced by drug use: 'during periods of heavy drug use offenders commit crimes at frequencies six times as high as non-using offenders'. A similar figure could be generated for periods of active psychosis, social adversity (such as unemployment), duration of after-care and so on. By using what is in fact a within-subjects comparison, subjects are effectively being used as their own control, which has considerable benefits.

Criminal Careers of the Mentally Ill

To date there is little information on the criminal careers of the mentally ill. What may be expected? The pattern of offending may be identical to that of the normal population; it may differ from normals, but not between diagnostic groups; each diagnostic group may have its own characteristic pattern.

Two studies begin to shed light on the matter. In a short-term study of a group of people originally evaluated by a forensic psychiatric unit in Toronto, Menzies (1987) found a high recidivism rate among a few patients, suggesting a disproportionate influence of a small number. More informative is the study of Lindquist and Allebeck (1990), the first to address directly the topic of criminal careers and psychosis. Using a form of record linkage system, they obtained long-term data on the criminal careers of 644 schizophrenics identified during their first hospitalisation. The expected rates of offending were determined by

*The individual rate of offending, lambda (Blumstein, Cohen, Roth & Visher, 1986), is the conventional term for rates estimated from cohort studies. A high lambda suggests that the overall crime rate may reflect a group of active offenders, whilst a low lambda indicates that the overall proportion of offenders in the population is contributing most to the crime rate. Farrington's studies concerning teenage offending can be summarised as demonstrating a lower lambda in the teenage years than previously thought.

indirect standardisation with national statistics, and were then compared to the observed values. The 95% confidence limits for the relative risk of offending in males was 0.7–2.1 (not significantly elevated) in contrast to the value for females, which was 1.5–3.6. However, when restricted to violent offending the value for both was 3–5.1, meaning that there is an approximately four-fold increase in the risk of violent offending in schizophrenics compared with normals. Although outcome data were restricted to official records, and the sample contained a bias towards the more seriously ill by excluding those schizophrenics never admitted to a psychiatric hospital, this is probably the soundest evidence to date of such a risk, although Taylor (1991), re-analysing data from the Brixton prison study, has shown that violence rather than offending in general almost invariably postdates the onset of illness.

Heterogeneity and Motivation

The concept of heterogeneity within the mentally ill has already been emphasised in the context of diagnosis. Taylor (1985) divided psychotic and non-psychotic offenders by motive (for example, whether delusional or more rational motives such as material gain, panic or immediate retaliation were judged to be responsible). The validity of the distinction was suggested by the finding that none of the non-psychotic men claimed psychotic motives for their behaviour. Furthermore, within the psychotic group those with offences judged to be of delusional motivation had more severe mental illness, indicated by the intensity of current psychopathology, but were less likely to have a criminal history.

Further validation for this difference comes from data concerning the duration of illness. In those judged to have acted for delusional motives, the risk of violence increased with the duration of illness, in contrast with the non-delusional group. The distinction between delusional and non-delusional crime is important because those with delusional motives were more likely to engage in serious violence (Taylor, 1985). Other evidence of a changing symptomatic profile and violence risk over time comes from Hafner and Boker (1973), who found that only 16% of their sample had been ill for less than a year when they committed their very serious offence, and that 55% had been ill for at least 5 years.

Some studies have found the opposite (e.g. Planansky & Johnson, 1977), but these differences can be explained by selection factors. In a study of violence on an acute admission ward, Aitken (1984) gives sufficient information to determine motivation: of 41 recorded assaults only 5 appeared to have had any basis in delusions; the others arose from the circumstances surrounding compulsory detention, such as requests to leave the ward or arguments over medication. In general, these and similar studies record violence that is usually some form of simple assault resulting in relatively minor injury. In contrast, studies of chronic delusional violence often record more considered and dangerous acts. An interaction of several years may be required before a delusional belief is likely to be translated into action: delusional violence is unusual early in the course of a psychotic illness. Longitudinal studies may provide most information about the aetiology of serious psychotic offending.

Conclusions

This review has illustrated the difficulties of accurately assessing the relationship between offending behaviour, violence and mental illness. These are such that no single study will ever overcome all the methodological problems described; it will remain necessary to interpret studies in the light of their methodological limitations and to utilise a variety of research strategies rather than a single 'ideal' study. Researchers must make every effort to define their interest as clearly as possible, and to specify precisely what areas of abnormal behaviour, and what types of mental illness, are being studied. More weight should be given to the results of longitudinal than cross-sectional studies.

Despite these caveats, it is still possible to draw some practical conclusions from the data so far. Certain groups of mentally ill possess an increased risk of criminality and violent behaviour, with a particular risk associated with schizophrenia with a predominantly delusional presentation of long duration. The precipitation of violent behaviour is nevertheless complex, because even within that group further risk is conveyed by, for example, the combination of delusional phenomena and emotional intimacy. One should also beware of concluding that these issues are only of relevance to forensic psychiatrists; the importance of psychotic assaultiveness is illustrated by a meticulous follow-up study of a non-selected sample (McGlashan, 1986) which found that such a history emerged as one of only three consistent predictors of overall poor outcome in schizophrenia.

Most important of all, the relationship between mental illness and abnormal behaviour is dynamic. Strauss, Hafez, Lieberman and Harding (1985) have argued that the longitudinal history of schizophrenia is a continually changing interaction between the person, his or her illness and the environmental response, and that prognosis is never predetermined at the onset of illness (in contrast to the situation in medical epidemiology, when, for example, the long-term risk of cancer after irradiation is determined by the level of initial exposure). This is particularly relevant to the area of serious violence. Mullen (1988) has written: 'The majority of violent offences occur in established schizophrenics who have drifted out of any ongoing care and supervision.' Better understanding of the relationship between psychosis and offending remains essential, but this should not obscure the evidence suggesting that perhaps the single most effective preventive measure would be a better standard of after-care (Hafner & Boker, 1973; Walker & McCabe, 1973; Monahan, 1988).

Acknowledgements

SW was supported by a Wellcome Training Fellowship in Epidemiology. Support during the preparation of this paper was also received from the Peter Scott Memorial Trust. We wish to thank Dr David Farrington, Professor John Monahan, Professor Paul Mullen and Dr Graham Robertson for help and assistance.

References

Addad, M., Benezech, M., Bourgeois, M. & Yesavage, J. (1981). Criminal acts among schizophrenics in French mental hospitals. *Journal of Nervous and Mental Diseases* **169**, 289–293.

Aitken, G. (1984). Assaults on staff in a locked ward: prediction and consequences. *Medicine, Science and the Law* **24**, 199–207.

Albee, G. (1950). Patterns of aggression in psychopathology. *Journal of Consulting and Clinical Psychology* **14**, 465–468.

Arboleda-Florez, J. & Holley, H. (1988). Criminalisation of the mentally ill: part II. initial detention. *Canadian Journal of Psychiatry* **33**, 87–95.

Ashley, M. (1922). Outcome of 1000 cases paroled from the Middletown State Hospital. *State Hospital Quarterly* **8**, 64–70.

Bach-y-Rita, G. & Veno, A. (1974). Habitual violence: a profile of 62 men. *American Journal of Psychiatry* **131**, 1015–1017.

Barnard, G., Robbins, L., Newman, G. & Carrerra, F. (1984). A study of violence within a forensic treatment facility. *Bulletin of the American Academy of Psychiatry and Law* **12**, 339–348.

Benezech, M., Bourgeois, M. & Yesavage, J. (1980). Violence in the mentally ill. A study of 547 patients at a French hospital for the criminally insane. *Journal of Nervous and Mental Diseases* **168**, 698–700.

Benezech, M., Yesavage, J., Addad, M., Bourgeois, M. & Mills, M. (1984). Homicide by psychotics in France: a five year study. *Journal of Clinical Psychiatry* **45**, 85–86.

Berner, P., Gabriel, E. & Schanda, H. (1980). Nonschizophrenic paranoid syndromes. *Schizophrenia Bulletin* **6**, 627–632.

Binder, R. & McNeil, D. (1988). Effects of diagnosis and context on dangerousness. *American Journal of Psychiatry* **145**, 728–732.

Blumstein, A. & Cohen, J. (1979). Estimation of individual crime rates from arrest records. *Journal of Criminal Law and Criminology* **70**, 561–585.

Blumstein, A. & Cohen, J. (1987). Characterising criminal careers. *Science* **237**, 985–991.

Blumstein, A., Cohen, J., Roth, J. & Visher, C. (1986). *Criminal Careers and Career Criminals*. Washington DC: National Academy Press.

Bradford Hill, A. (1965). The environment and disease: association or causation? *Proceedings of the Royal Society of Medicine* **58**, 295–300.

Brill, A. & Malzberg, B. (1962). Statistical report on the arrest record of male ex patients released from the New York State mental hospitals during the period 1946–48. In: *Criminal Acts of Ex-mental Hospital Patients* (Suppl. 153). Washington DC: American Psychiatric Association.

Bureau of Justice Statistics (1986). *Criminal Victimisation 1985*. Washington: US Department of Justice.

Chuang, H., Williams, R. & Dalby, T. (1987). Criminal behaviour among schizophrenics. *Canadian Journal of Psychiatry* **32**, 255–258.

Climent, C. & Erwin, F. (1972). Historic data in the evaluation of violent subjects. *Archives of General Psychiatry* **27**, 621–624.

Cocozza, J. & Steadman, H. (1974). Some refinements in the measurement and prediction of dangerous behaviour. *American Journal of Psychiatry* **131**, 1012–1014.

Cohen, C. (1980). Crime among mental patients – A critical analysis. *Psychiatric Quarterly* **52**, 100–107.

Coid, J. (1988). Mentally abnormal prisoners on remand. 1. Rejected or accepted by the NHS? *British Medical Journal* **296**, 1779–1782.

Commissioner of Police of the Metropolis (1982). *Report of the Commissioner of Police of the Metropolis for the year 1982*. Cmnd 8928. London: HMSO.

Convit, A., Isay, D., Gadioma, R. & Volavka, J. (1988). Underreporting of physical assaults in schizophrenic inpatients. *Journal of Nervous and Mental Diseases* **176**, 507–509.

Craig, T. (1982). An epidemiological study of problems associated with violence among psychiatric patients. *American Journal of Psychiatry* **139**, 1262–1266.

Dietz, P. & Rada, R. (1982). Battery incidents and batterers at a maximum security hospital. *Archives of General Psychiatry* **39**, 31–34.

Dietz, P. & Rada, R. (1983). Interpersonal violence in forensic facilities. In: J. Lion & W.H. Reid, eds. *Assaults Within Psychiatric Facilities*. New Jersey: Grune & Stratton.

Dooley, E. (1986). Aggressive incidents in a secure hospital. *Medicine, Science and the Law* **26**, 125–130.

Durbin, J., Pasewark, R. & Albers, D. (1977). Criminality and mental illness: a study of arrest rates in a rural state. *American Journal of Psychiatry* **143**, 80–83.

Edwards, J., Jones, D., Reid, W. & Chu, C. (1988). Physical assaults in a psychiatric unit of a general hospital. *American Journal of Psychiatry* **145**, 1568–1571.

Ekblom, B. (1970). *Acts of Violence by Patients in Mental Hospitals.* Uppsala: Scandinavian University Books, Almqvist and Wilsolls Boktryckeni AB.

Evenson, R., Altman, H., Stetten, I. & Brown, M. (1974). Disturbing behaviour: a study of incident reports. *Psychiatry Quarterly* **48**, 266–275.

Farrington, D. (1973). Self-reports of deviant behaviour: Predictive and stable? *Journal of Criminal Law and Criminology* **64**, 99–110.

Farrington, D. (1981). The prevalence of convictions. *British Journal of Criminology* **21**, 173–175.

Farrington, D. (1986). Age and Crime. In: M. Tonry & N. Morris, eds, *Crime and Justice*, Vol. 7, pp. 189–250. Chicago: University of Chicago Press.

Farrington, D. (1988). Studying changes within individuals: The causes of offending. In: M. Rutter, ed. *Studies of Psychosocial Risk: The Power of Longitudinal Data*, pp. 158–183. Cambridge: Cambridge University Press.

Farrington, D. (1990a). Implications of criminal career research for the prevention of offending. *Journal of Adolescence* **13**, 95–113.

Farrington, D. (1990b). Childhood aggression and adult violence; early precursors and later life outcomes. In: D. Pepler & K. Rubin, eds, *The Development of Childhood Aggression*, pp. 5–29. Hillsdale, NJ: Erlbaum.

Gibbens, T. (1958). Sane and insane homicide. *Journal of Criminal Law, Criminology and Police Science* **49**, 110–115.

Gibbens, T. & Robertson, G. (1983). A survey of the criminal careers of hospital order patients. *British Journal of Psychiatry* **143**, 362–369.

Gibbons, J., Horn, S., Powell, J. & Gibbons, J. (1984). Schizophrenic patients and their families: a survey in a psychiatric service based on a DGH unit. *British Journal of Psychiatry* **144**, 70–77.

Gillies, H. (1965). Murder in the west of Scotland. *British Journal of Psychiatry* **111**, 1087–1094.

Giovannoni, J. & Gurel, L. (1967). Socially disruptive behaviour of ex-mental patients. *Archives of General Psychiatry* **17**, 146–153.

Gottlieb, P., Gabrielsen, G. & Kramp, P. (1987). Psychotic homicides in Copenhagen from 1959 to 1983. *Acta Psychiatrica Scandinavica* **76**, 285–292.

Gudjonsson, G.H. & Petursson, H. (1982). Some criminological and psychiatric aspects of homicide in Iceland. *Medicine, Science and the Law* **22**, 91–98.

Gunn, J., Robertson, G., Dell, S. & Way, C. (1978). *Psychiatric Aspects of Imprisonment.* New York: Academic Press.

Guy, E., Platt, J., Zwerling, I. et al. (1985). Mental health status of prisoners in an urban jail. *Criminal Justice and Behaviour* **12**, 29–53.

Guze, S.B. (1976). *Criminality and Psychiatric Disorders.* London: Oxford University Press.

Guze, S., Goodwin, D. & Crane, J. (1969). Criminality and psychiatric disorders. *Archives of General Psychiatry* **20**, 583–591.

Guze, S., Woodruff, R. & Clayton, P. (1974). Psychiatric disorders and criminality. *Journal of the American Medical Association* **227**, 641–642.

Hafner, H. & Boker, W. (1973). *Crimes of Violence by Mentally Abnormal Offenders: A Psychiatric and Epidemiological Study.* Cambridge: Cambridge University Press. (Translated by Helen Marshall, 1982).

Harry, B. & Steadman, H. (1988). Arrest rates of patients treated at a community mental health center. *Hospital and Community Psychiatry* **39**, 862–866.

Hennekens, C. & Buring, J. (1987). *Epidemiology in Medicine.* Boston: Little Brown & Co.

Hough, M. & Mayhew, P. (1983). *British Crime Survey: First Report.* Home Office Research Report No 76. London: HMSO.

Huizinga, D. & Elliot, D. (1986). Reassessing the reliability and validity of self report measures. *Journal of Quantitative Criminology* **2**, 293–327.

Infantino, J. & Musingo, S. (1985). Assaults and injuries among staff with and without training in aggression control techniques. *Hospital and Community Psychiatry* **36**, 1312–1314.

Inghe, G. (1941). Mental abnormalities among criminals. *Acta Psychiatrica Neurologica Scandinavica* **16**, 421–458.

Johnstone, E., Crow, T., Johnson, A. & Macmillan, F. (1986). The Northwick Park study of first episodes of schizophrenia. 1: presentation of the illness and problems relating to admission. *British Journal of Psychiatry* **149**, 51–56.

Karson, C. & Bigelow, L. (1987). Violent behaviour in schizophrenic inpatients. *Journal of Nervous and Mental Diseases* **175**, 161–164.

Klassen, D. & O'Connor, W. (1988a). Predicting violence in schizophrenic and non-schizophrenic patients. *Journal of Community Psychology* **16**, 217–227.

Klassen, D. & O'Connor, W. (1988b). Crime, inpatient admissions and violence among male mental patients. *International Journal of Law and Psychiatry*, **11**, 305–312.

Kolvin, I., Miller, F., Fleeting, M. & Kolvin, P. (1988). Social and parenting factors affecting criminal offence rates. *British Journal of Psychiatry* **152**, 80–90.

Krakowski, M., Jaeger, J. & Volavka, J. (1988). Violence and psychopathology: a longitudinal study. *Comprehensive Psychiatry* **29**, 174–181.

Lagos, J., Perlmutter, K. & Saexinger, H. (1977). Fear of the mentally ill: empirical support for the common man's response. *American Journal of Psychiatry* **134**, 1134–1137.

Landau, S. (1981). Juveniles and the police. *British Journal of Criminology* **21**, 27–46.

Langevin, R., Paitich, B., Orchard, B., Handy, L. & Russen, A. (1982). Diagnosis of killers seen for psychiatric assessment. *Acta Psychiatrica Scandinavica* **66**, 216–228.

Lanzkron, J. (1963). Murder and insanity: a survey. *American Journal of Psychiatry* **119**, 754–758.

Levine, D. (1970). Criminal behaviour and mental institutionalisation. *Journal of Clinical Psychology* **26**, 279–284.

Lindquist, P. & Allebeck, P. (1990). Schizophrenia and crime. A longitudinal follow-up of 644 schizophrenics in Stockholm. *British Journal of Psychiatry* **157**, 345–350.

Lion, J., Snyder, W. & Merrill, G. (1981). Underreporting of assaults on staff in a state hospital. *Hospital and Community Psychiatry* **32**, 497–498.

Lucas, C., Sainsbury, P. & Collins, J. (1962). A social and clinical study of delusions in schizophrenia. *Journal of Mental Science* **108**, 747–758.

Mackay, R. & Wight, R. (1984). Schizophrenia and anti-social (criminal) behaviour – some responses from sufferers and relatives. *Medicine, Science and the Law* **24**, 192–198.

MacMillan, J. & Johnson, A. (1987). Contact with the police in early schizophrenia: its nature frequency and relevance to the outcome of treatment. *Medical Science and Law* **27**, 191–200.

McGlashan, T. (1986). The prediction of outcome in chronic schizophrenia: IV. The Chestnut Lodge follow-up study. *Archives of General Psychiatry* **43**, 167–176.

McKnight, C., Mohr, J., Quinsey, R. & Erochko, J. (1966). Mental illness and homicide. *Canadian Psychiatric Association Journal* **11**, 91–98.

McNeil, D. & Binder, R. (1987). Predictive value of judgements of dangerousness in emergency civil commitment. *American Journal of Psychiatry* **144**, 197–200.

McNeil, D. & Binder, R. (1989). Relationship between threats and violent behaviour by acute psychiatric patients. *Hospital and Community Psychiatry* **40**, 605–608.

McNeil, D., Binder, R. & Greenfield, T. (1988). Predictors of violence in civilly committed acute psychiatric patients. *American Journal of Psychiatry* **145**, 965–970.

Melick, M., Steadman, H. & Cocozza, J. (1979). The medicalisation of criminal behaviour among mental patients. *Journal of Health and Social Behaviour* **20**, 228–237.

Menzies, R. (1987). Cycles of control: the transcarceral careers of forensic patients. *International Journal of Law and Psychiatry* **10**, 233–249.

Menzies, R., Webster, C., & Sepejak, D. (1986). Hitting the forensic sound barrier: predictions of dangerousness in a pretrial psychiatric clinic. In: C. Webster, M. Ben-Aron & C. Hucker, eds. *Dangerousness: Probability and Prediction*, pp. 236–261. Cambridge: Cambridge University Press.

Monahan, J. (1981). *The Clinical Prediction of Violent Behaviour.* Washington: US Government Printing Office.

Monahan, J. (1988). Risk assessment of violence among the mentally disordered: generating useful knowledge. *International Journal of Law and Psychiatry* **11**, 249–257.

Monahan, J. & Steadman, H. (1983). Crime and mental illness: an epidemiological approach. In: N. Morris & M. Tonry, eds. *Crime and Justice, Volume 4*, pp. 145–189. Chicago: University of Chicago Press.

Mowat, R. (1966). *Morbid Jealousy and Murder.* London: Tavistock.

Mullen, P. (1988) Violence and mental disorder. *British Journal of Hospital Medicine* **44**, 460–463.

Mulvey, E., Blumstein, A. & Cohen, J. (1986). Reframing the research question of mental patient criminality. *International Journal of Law and Psychiatry* **9**, 57–65.

Noble, P. & Rodger, S. (1989). Violence by psychiatric in-patients. *British Journal of Psychiatry* **155**, 384–390.

Payne, C., McCabe, S. & Walker, N. (1974). Predicting offender patients' reconvictions. *British Journal of Psychiatry* **125**, 60–64.

Pearson, M., Wilmot, E. & Padi, M. (1986). A study of violent behaviour among inpatients in a psychiatric hospital. *British Journal of Psychiatry* **149**, 232–235.

Philips, M., Wolf, A. & Coons, D. (1988). Psychiatry and the criminal justice system: testing the myths. *American Journal of Psychiatry* **145**, 605–610.

Planansky, K. & Johnston, R. (1977). Homicidal aggression in schizophrenic men. *Acta Psychiatrica Scandinavica* **55**, 65–73.

Polk, K. (1985). A comparative analysis of attrition of rape cases. *British Journal of Criminology* **25**, 280–284.

Post, R., Willet, A., Franks, R., House, R., Back, S. & Weissberg, M. (1980). A preliminary report on the prevalence of domestic violence among psychiatric inpatients. *American Journal of Psychiatry* **137**, 974–975.

Rabkin, J. (1979) Criminal behaviour of discharged mental patients: a critical appraisal of the research. *Psychological Bulletin* **86**, 1–27.

Rappeport, J. & Lassen, G. (1965). Dangerousness – arrest rate comparisons of discharged patients and the general population. *American Journal of Psychiatry* **121**, 776–782.

Reiss, A. (1986). Why are communities important in understanding crime? In: A. Reiss & M. Tonry, eds. *Communities and Crime*. Chicago: University of Chicago Press, pp. 1–33.

Robertson, G. (1988). Arrest patterns among mentally disordered offenders. *British Journal of Psychiatry* **153**, 313–316.

Robertson, G. (1990). Correlates of crime among women offenders. *Medicine, Science and the Law* **30**, 165–174.

Robins, L. (1978). Sturdy childhood predictors of adult antisocial behaviour: replications from longitudinal studies. *Psychological Medicine* **8**, 611–622.

Rofman, E., Askinazi, C. & Fant, E. (1980). The prediction of dangerous behaviour in emergency civil commitment. *American Journal of Psychiatry* **137**, 1061–1064.

Rosenthal, R. & Rubin, D. (1982). A simple, general purpose display of magnitude of experimental effect. *Journal of Educational Psychology* **74**, 166–169.

Roth, L. & Ervin, F. (1971). Psychiatric care of federal prisoners. *American Journal of Psychiatry* **128**, 424–430.

Rutter, M. (1988). Epidemiological approaches to developmental psychopathology. *Archives of General Psychiatry* **45**, 486–495.

Schlesselman, J. (1982). *Case-control Studies: Design, Conduct, Analysis.* New York: Oxford University Press.

Schipkowensky, N. (1973). Epidemiological aspects of homicide. In: S. Arieti, ed., *World Biennial of Psychiatry and Psychotherapy, Volume 2.* New York: Basic Books, pp. 192–215.

Shader, R., Jackson, A., Harmatz, J. & Appelbaum, P. (1977). Patterns of violent behaviour in schizophrenic inpatients. *Diseases of the Nervous System* **38**, 13–16.

Shore, D., Filson, R., Johnson, W., Rae, D., Muehrer, P., Kelley, D., Davis, T., Waldman, I. & Wyatt, R. (1989). Murder and assault arrests of White House cases: clinical and demographic correlates of violence subsequent to civil commitment. *American Journal of Psychiatry* **146**, 645–651.

Sosowsky, L. (1978). Crime and violence among mental patients reconsidered in view of the new legal relationship between the State and the mentally ill. *American Journal of Psychology* **135**, 33–42.

Sosowsky, L. (1980). Explaining the increased arrest rate among mental patients: a cautionary note. *American Journal of Psychiatry* **137**, 1602–1605.

Steadman, H. & Keveles, G. (1972). The community adjustment and criminal activity of the Baxstrom patients 1966–1970. *American Journal of Psychiatry* **129**, 304–310.

Steadman, H., Cocozza, J. & Melick, M. (1978). Explaining the increased arrest rate among mental patients: the changing clientele of state hospitals. *American Journal of Psychiatry* **135**, 816–820.

Steadman, H., Fabisiak, S., Dvoskin, J. & Holohean, E. (1987). A survey of mental disability among state prison inmates. *Hospital and Community Psychiatry* **38**, 1086–1090.

Stattin, H., Magnusson, D. & Reichel, H. (1989). Criminal activity at different ages; a study based on a Swedish longitudinal research population. *British Journal of Criminology* **29**, 368–385.

Stevens, P. & Willis, C. (1979). *Race, Crime and Arrests. Home Office Research Unit Report No 58.* London: HMSO.

Strauss, J., Hafez, H., Lieberman, P. & Harding, C. (1985). The course of psychiatric disorder. III. Longitudinal principles. *American Journal of Psychiatry* **142**, 289–296.

Swank, G. & Winer, D. (1976). Occurrence of psychiatric disorder in a county jail population. *American Journal of Psychiatry* **133**, 1331–1333.

Swanson, J., Holzer, C., Ganju, V. & Jono, R. (1990). Violence and psychiatric disorder in the community: evidence from the Epidemiologic Catchment Area Surveys. *Hospital and Community Psychiatry* **41**, 761–770.

Tardiff, K. (1983). A survey of assault by chronic patients in a state hospital system. In: J. Lion & W. Reid, eds. *Assaults Within Psychiatric Facilities.* New York: Grune & Stratton.

Tardiff, K. & Sweillam, A. (1980). Assault, suicide and mental illness. *Archives of General Psychiatry* **37**, 164–169.

Tardiff, K. & Sweillam, A. (1982). Assaultive behaviour among chronic inpatients. *American Journal of Psychiatry* **139**, 212–215.

Taylor, P. (1982). Schizophrenia and violence. In: J. Gunn & D. Farrington, eds. *Abnormal Offenders, Delinquency, and the Criminal Justice System.* Chichester: Wiley, pp. 269–284.

Taylor, P. (1985). Motives for offending amongst violent and psychotic men. *British Journal of Psychiatry* **147**, 491–498.
Taylor, P. J. (1987). Social implications of psychosis. *British Medical Bulletin* **43**, 718–740.
Taylor, P. J. (1991). Schizophrenia and crime: distinctive patterns in association. In: S. Hodgins, ed., *Crime and Mental Disorder*. Netherlands: Kluwer Academic, in press.
Taylor, P. J. & Gunn, J. (1984). Violence and psychosis 1 – risk of violence among psychotic men. *British Medical Journal* **288**, 1945–1949.
Taylor, P. J. & Parrott, J. (1988). Elderly offenders: a study of age-related factors among custodially remanded prisoners. *British Journal of Psychiatry* **152**, 340–346.
Taylor, P. J., Dalton, R. & Fleminger, J. (1982). Handedness and schizophrenic symptoms. *British Journal of Medical Psychology* **55**, 287–291.
Taylor, P. J., Mullen, P. & Wessely, S. (1991). Psychosis, violence and crime. In: J. Gunn & P. J. Taylor, eds, *Forensic Psychiatry: Clinical, Ethical and Legal Issues*. Oxford: Heinemann, in press.
Teplin, L. (1985). The criminality of the mentally ill: a dangerous misconception. *American Journal of Psychiatry* **142**, 593–599.
Travin, S. & Protter, B. (1982). Mad or bad? Some clinical considerations in the misdiagnosis of schizophrenia as antisocial personality disorder. *American Journal of Psychiatry* **139**, 1335–1338.
Walker, N. & McCabe, S. (1973). *Crime and Insanity in England: 2: New Solutions and New Problems*. Edinburgh: Edinburgh University Press.
West, D. (1982). *Delinquency: Its Roots, Careers, and Prospects*. London: Heinemann.
West, D. & Farrington, D. (1973). *Who Becomes Delinquent?* London: Heinemann.
Wilcox, D. (1985). The relationship of mental illness to homicide. *American Journal of Forensic Psychiatry* **6**, 3–15.
Wing, J. & Fryer, T. (1976). *Statistics from the Camberwell and Salford registers 1964–1974*. London: Institute of Psychiatry.
Wong, M. & Singer, K. (1973). Abnormal homicide in Hong Kong. *British Journal of Psychiatry* **123**, 295–298.
Yesavage, J. (1983). In patient violence and the schizophrenic patient. *Acta Psychiatrica Scandinavica* **67**, 353–357.
Yesavage, J. (1984). Correlates of dangerous behaviour in schizophrenics in hospital. *Journal of Psychiatric Research* **18**, 225–231.
Zitrin, A., Hardesty, A., Burdock, E. & Drossman, A. (1976). Crime and violence among mental patients. *American Journal of Psychiatry* **133**, 142–149.

Address correspondence to Dr S. Wessely, Senior Lecturer, Department of Psychological Medicine, King's College Hospital, Denmark Hill, London SE5 9RS, UK.

Part III
Aspects of Process

[14]

International Journal of Law and Psychiatry, Vol. 15, pp. 139–156, 1992
Printed in the U.S.A.
0160-2527/92 $5.00 + .00

Police as Streetcorner Psychiatrist:

Managing the Mentally Ill

Linda A. Teplin* and Nancy S. Pruett*

Managing mentally disordered people in the community historically has been a part of police work (Bittner, 1967). Police play a major role in referring persons for psychiatric treatment, particularly within the lower socioeconomic strata (Cobb, 1972; Gilboy & Schmidt, 1971; Hollingshead & Redlich, 1958; Liberman, 1969; Sheridan & Teplin, 1981; Sims & Symonds, 1975; Teplin, Filstead, Hefter, & Sheridan, 1980; Warren, 1977; Wilkinson, 1975). Over the years, police handling of the mentally ill has been complicated by public policy modifications, for example, deinstitutionalization, more stringent commitment criteria, and cutbacks in treatment programs. As a result, the numbers of mentally ill persons involved with police have increased while, at the same time, the police officer's dispositional options have decreased (Teplin, 1983, 1984a, 1984b).

This paper examines police handling of the mentally ill within the current public policy structure. Based on data from an observational study of 1,396 police–citizen encounters, this paper will describe the decision-making normative framework police use to manage the mentally ill within the community.

Background

Involvement of police with the mentally ill is based on two legal principles: (1) the police power function, that is, to protect the safety and welfare of the public; and (2) *parens patrie*, which involves protection for the disabled citizen (Fox & Erickson, 1972; Shah, 1975). Most mental health codes specify the parameters of police involvement with the mentally ill and instruct police to initiate an emergency psychiatric apprehension whenever the person is either "dangerous to self or others" or, "because of his illness is unable to provide for his basic physical needs so as to guard himself from serious harm" (cf. California Welfare and Institutional Code, 1980; Illinois Revised Statutes, 1981). Thus, police involvement with the mentally ill is mandated by the law.

---

*Department of Psychiatry and Behavioral Sciences, Psycho-legal Studies Program, Northwestern University Medical School, Northwestern Memorial Hospital, 215 E. Chicago Avenue, Room 708, Chicago, IL 60611.

Research support for this paper was provided by National Institute of Mental Health grants RO1MH32294 and RO1MH37988.

However, the actual disposition of a mentally disordered person is inherently a complex social process. While the law provides the legal structure and decrees the police officer's power to intervene, it cannot dictate the police officer's response to that situation (Bittner, 1967, 1970). Unlike other professionals, the police do not have a body of technical knowledge with respect to psychiatry which they use as formulae in the performance of their role (Rumbaut & Bittner, 1979). As with all law enforcement decisions, the police must exercise discretion in choosing the most "appropriate" disposition in a given situation (Goldstein, 1979; Gottfredson & Gottfredson, 1980; Manning, 1977, 1984; Smith, 1986; Smith & Visher, 1981; Wilson, 1968).

In mental health cases, the situation is further complicated by the nebulous definition of "mental disorder." There is a large gray area of behavior which, depending upon cultural values, community context, and administrative practice, might be labelled criminal, psychiatric (Stone, 1975), or merely "odd" (Monahan & Monahan, 1986). In short, dispositional decisions vis-à-vis the mentally ill are an inherently problematic social judgement. As a consequence, police have developed a shared understanding of how things "should" be done (i.e., an informal operative code) in order to "manage" the mentally disordered citizen.

Bittner's (1967) study is considered to be the seminal work in this area. He found that police made psychiatric referrals reluctantly; police initiated hospitalizations only when the situation had the potential to escalate into a "serious problem" (e.g., danger to life, physical health, property, and/or order). Bittner found that there needed to be indications of external risk accompanied by signs of serious psychological disorder (e.g., suicide, distortions in appearance, violent acts, bizarre behavior, public nuisances) for the police to justify a psychiatric referral. He concluded that, except for cases of suicide attempts, the decision to take someone to the hospital was based on overwhelming conclusive evidence of illness.

Several other investigators have confirmed police reluctance to initiate an emergency psychiatric apprehension (cf. Matthews, 1970; Rock, Jacobson, & Janepaul, 1968; Schag, 1977; Urmer, 1973). Schag (1977) reported that most police-initiated commitments to mental hospitals were precipitated by an overt act or threat of self-harm. Like Bittner, he found that an act of self-injury was a *prima facie* justification for commitment. In those cases in which an overt act or threat was not present, the presence of a psychiatric history, creation of a public disturbance and/or bizarre conduct were considered in initiating a commitment.

The probability of the police initiating a hospitalization was also affected by the structural constraints governing hospitalization versus other dispositional alternatives. Rock and associates (1968) found that the more procedural steps there were between the street and hospital, the less likely that police would make an emergency apprehension. Similarly, Matthews (1970) noted that the police officer must calculate how much time alternative courses of action would consume as compared to hospitalization. In sum, the literature documents the pivotal role the police have played historically with regard to the mentally ill.

Police involvement with the mentally ill has become further complicated by several major public policy modifications vis-à-vis mental health delivery. First, the deinstitutionalization of mental patients over the last 30 years has increased the sheer number of mentally ill persons (both deinstitutionalized and "never institutionalized") who may potentially become involved with police.

Second, recent cutbacks in mental health services across the United States have meant that outpatient care often means "no care." Fiscal reductions in mental health programs have resulted in an increasing number of mentally ill persons who are denied treatment because of a lack of available programs and/or a paucity of financial resources (Kiesler, 1982; National Institute of Mental Health (NIMH), 1985). Reductions in mental health funding have also reduced the available number of inpatient beds in public hospitals (NIMH, 1985) as well as the breadth of treatment alternatives (Kiesler & Sibulkin, 1987). These reductions in service are all the more critical when we take into account the changing demographic characteristics. Because of the "coming of age" of post-World War II babies, the absolute number of young persons at risk for developing psychotic disorders is overrepresented in the population (Bachrach, 1982).

Third, the recent, more rigorous legal standards for involuntary mental hospitalization have meant that the simple presence of mental illness and need for service are insufficient to warrant commitment. Rather, the individual must be seriously mentally ill and dangerous to self or others. Many mentally ill persons who would have been committed in years past may now choose to live in the community without treatment.

In sum, the juxtaposition of demographic changes and deinstitutionalization have increased the burden of the mentally ill on police. At the same time, more stringent mental health codes and the diminished treatment options have reduced the police officer's available referral alternatives. Clearly, police now operate in a very different community context than in years past.

This paper will examine the police officer's role as streetcorner psychiatrist within the current sociopolitical milieu. Specifically, we will explore the basic decision rules governing the three major dispositional alternatives available to the police: (1) hospitalization; (2) arrest; and (3) informal disposition. In so doing, it will be demonstrated that the disposition of a mentally disordered citizen is based less on the degree of apparent psychiatric symptomatology than on a complex array of contextual and situational variables.

Method

A large-scale observational study of police activity was conducted to observe firsthand how police officers manage mentally ill persons. Police officers in a Midwestern city in the United States (Standard Metropolitan Area over 1,000,000) were observed in their routine interactions with citizens for 2,200 hours over a 14-month period during 1980–1981; 283 randomly selected officers were included. Observers included the first author as well as five clinical psychology PhD students (three male, two female).

Observations were conducted during all hours of the day; evenings and weekends were oversampled to obtain a maximum of data in a minimum of time. Data were collected in two busy urban police districts; these districts were chosen because of their socioeconomic and racial/ethnic diversity, as well as because they were fairly typical of this particular city. All types of police-citizen interactions were observed, irrespective of any involvement with mentally disordered persons. This procedure was necessary to obtain data on situations unrelated to mental disorder to use for baseline comparisons.

While a standardized mode of assessment to test for the presence of mental disorder would have been preferable, the naturalistic setting of the research obviously precluded making in-depth psychological assessments. In view of the limitations posed by the naturalistic setting, the presence of severe mental disorder was ascertained by the field-worker via a symptom checklist, which listed the major characteristics of severe mental illness, for example, confusion/disorientation, withdrawal/unresponsiveness, paranoia, inappropriate or bizarre speech and/or behavior, self-destructive behaviors.

The observed citizen was defined to be mentally ill if he or she possessed at least one of the symptoms on the checklist *and* was given a global rating of "mentally disordered" by the field-worker. Both indications were necessary to avoid categorizing persons as mentally ill when they were merely exhibiting bizarre or unusual behavior. Thus, the environmental context as well as a number of psychiatric clues were taken into account. For example, a "streetperson" who is found by police shouting and running down the street in the nude on a cold night in January would have been coded as mentally disturbed (assuming someone had not just stolen his clothes). However, similar behaviors exhibited on a warm June evening by a group of drunken college students were recognized as being bizarre, albeit not indicative of mental disorder. It should be noted that the definition of mental disorder was made conservatively to err in the direction of making false-negative (Type II) rather than false-positive (Type I) errors.

To insure that this assessment method accurately discriminated between persons who did and did not exhibit signs of serious mental disorder, a separate validity study was undertaken. Using a sample of 61 randomly selected jail detainees, the results of the method used in the present investigation were compared with those generated via a standardized psychiatric assessment instrument, the NIMH Diagnostic Interview Schedule (Robins, Helzer, Croughan, Williams, & Spitzer, 1981). The two were found to be highly correlated; Fisher's Exact Test, $p < .001$; Kendalls Tau-b = .739; Yule's Q = .997. There was a 93.4% agreement between the two measures as to the presence/absence of severe mental disorder.

To maintain the natural ambience of the data collection procedure, neither tape recording devices nor extensive note taking were permitted during the observations. The apparent lack of an obvious formal data-collection procedure appeared to enhance cooperation between police officers and field-workers. To ease recollection of the data for subsequent transcription, field-workers were allowed to make a list of all police–citizen encounters that occurred during the observational period. The data were later recorded in two ways.

Quantitative Data

The objective characteristics of the encounter were coded according to an instrument developed expressly for this purpose, the "Incident Coding Form"

(ICF). This instrument was designed to record the concrete behaviors and descriptive categories central to the police officers' handling of all police-citizen interactions. An ICF was completed for every encounter between a police officer and a citizen, which involved at least three verbal exchanges. The ICF was extensively pilot tested prior to data collection. To maximize interobserver reliability, all field-workers were given 3 months of special training using both videotapes and field situations. In addition, reliability was subsequently monitored via periodic spot checks. Tests of interrater reliability exceeded 97%.

Qualitative Data

Each field-worker was given a dictaphone for home use so that a narrative of the shift could be reconstructed within 24 hours of the observation period. These qualitative data were recorded according to a specified format, which included general shift information, impressionistic data concerning the officer, and most importantly, a complete narrative of each police–citizen encounter. This last data component included the reasoning underlying police officers' discretionary judgements in relation to their management of the mentally ill. Approximately 3,500 pages of qualitative information were recorded.

Overall, 1,396 police–citizen encounters involving 2,555 citizens were observed and coded. This is a rate of approximately one citizen for every observational hour. Excluding traffic-related incidents, the database included 1,072 police–citizen encounters involving 2,122 citizens.

Findings

Tables 1 and 2 show that of the 2,122 citizens observed, 85 persons (30 suspects and 55 nonsuspects) were judged by the field-worker to be mentally disordered. The marginals indicate that police tend to resolve situations informally, irrespective of the person's state of mental health. However, Table 1 illustrates that, for suspects, the presence or absence of mental disorder significantly determined the type of disposition; chi-square = 13.66, $p < .001$. Mentally ill suspects had an arrest rate nearly double that of non-ill

TABLE 1
Presence/Absence of Severe Mental Disorder by Disposition: Suspects Only

	Disposition, % and (*N*)			
Suspects	Hospitalized	Arrested	Informal Disposition	Total
Ill	13.3 (4)	46.7 (14)	40.0 (12)	5.9 (30)
Non-ill	0.0 (0)	27.9 (133)	72.1 (343)	94.1 (476)
Total	0.8 (4)	29.1 (147)	70.2 (355)	100.0 (506)

*Fisher's Exact Test, $p < .0001$, $df = 1$. Since the expected values were too small to perform a chi-square statistic, we used an analogy to Fisher's Exact Test for a three by two table (Mehta & Patel, 1983).

TABLE 2
Presence/Absence of Severe Mental Disorder by Disposition: Nonsuspects Only[a]

	Disposition, % and (*N*)[b]		
Nonsuspects*	Hospitalized	Informal Disposition	Total
Ill	10.9 (6)	89.1 (49)	3.4 (55)
Non-ill	0.0 (0)	100.0 (1561)	96.6 (1561)
Total	0.4 (6)	99.6 (1610)	100.0 (1616)

[a]Includes victims, witnesses, complainants, objects of concern, and subjects of assistance.

[b]The category, "Arrested," does not appear in this table because, by definition, nonsuspects cannot be arrested. The police officer's definition of citizen role was used.

*Fisher's Exact Test, $p < .0001$, $df = 1$.

suspects (46.7% vs. 27.9%). Perhaps what is most striking about both Tables 1 and 2 is the relative rarity of hospitalization; hospitalization was initiated for only 13.3% of the mentally ill suspects (Table 1) and 10.9% of the nonsuspects (Table 2). Not surprisingly, police never sought to hospitalize any citizen who was defined by the field-worker as "nonmentally disordered."

Given the disruptive nature of many symptoms of severe mental disorder, it is interesting that police rarely resort to hospitalization. The data presented in Tables 1 and 2 suggest a number of questions. Under what circumstances are hospitalizations initiated? Is the type of disposition (hospitalization, arrest, or informal) determined largely by the degree of apparent disorder? What extrapsychiatric factors affect the police officer's choice of disposition? To explore these questions the following section presents qualitative data relevant to each of the three major dispositions shown in Table 1. Two types of data are presented: (1) information ascertained via direct observation of the 85 mentally disordered citizens, and (2) anecdotes communicated to the field-worker by the officers about their prior experience in handling mentally disordered persons.

Hospitalization

Our finding concerning the rarity of emergency hospitalization is strikingly similar to Bittner's (1967) finding of more than 2 decades ago. However, the infrequent utilization of the hospital in the present investigation was a result of a number of structural characteristics peculiar to the current postdeinstitutionalization milieu.

Police were acutely aware of the reduced number of psychiatric placements available to them. While state hospitals were once the primary treatment facility, they have been replaced by community-based mental health centers. Unfortunately, these mental health centers (many housed within private hospitals) often have very strict admission criteria. We found that virtually every police officer was aware of the stringent requirements for admission into the local psychiatric hospital: the person must be either actively delusional or suicidal. Police knew that persons who were alcoholics, narcotic addicts, or defined by hospital staff to be "dangerous" were *persona non grata* at the hospitals, even if they also exhibited signs of serious mental disorder. Persons with criminal charges pending, no matter how minor, were deemed unacceptable. It was common knowledge among officers that if a citizen met the above-mentioned exclusionary criteria, hospitalization was not an available disposition.

The following vignette illustrates one of the few situations that met the criteria for hospitalization. Hospitalization was initiated because the citizen was seriously delusional and too public in her deviance to be ignored by the police:

> At 22:00 a radio call came on saying there was a white female, age 28, who was taking off her clothes in front of the ______ building. She was dressed in dirty clothes and was very disheveled. She was repeatedly pulling up her T-shirt and exposing herself and making obscene gestures at the crowd that had gathered. Several officers helped her into the wagon. She kept saying, "Fuck [the mayor]." She said she had walked from [the suburbs] to make some statements to the mayor . . . she continued yelling things [profanities] out of the back [of the wagon]. . . . There was no evidence of alcohol or drugs, so it looked like a straight psychiatric case . . . the woman said she had been in a psychiatric hospital and that she was manic-depressive. . . . (Shift #171, Encounter 2)

Even those mentally disordered individuals who meet admission criteria and seek voluntary admission are rarely hospitalized without bureaucratic impediments. The following vignette illustrates the structural constraints, which often impede police when initiating even a voluntary hospitalization. This case is notable because it illustrates the frequent situation in which the services offered do not match those that are required:

> Between 22:00 and 23:00, call for suicide risk. Dispatcher said this was the third call . . . Citizen, male, age 73 . . . approached the officers and said other officers had been there several times that night. He said he had talked with the Human Service people, but was still feeling suicidal. . . . Human Service people had gotten him an appointment for Monday morning to see if they could get him in a nursing home. Citizen had agreed, but now said he could not handle the situation so he had gone out and started drinking. On one of the earlier calls that evening, the police had confiscated several knives and other items Citizen had planned to use to commit suicide. . . . He had tried to commit suicide twice before. He had old scars on his wrists . . . after one suicide attempt he was hospitalized. . . . It was clear that Citizen was not getting the help he felt he needed . . . he said he'd been drinking this night in order to get up the courage to

> kill himself . . . asked to go to [hospital] . . . so officers drove to [local hospital] . . . the psychiatric unit at the hospital was full so they could not take him and said we should try another hospital . . . police called the wagon . . . Officer I said Citizen needed to go to [state mental hospital]. The wagon officers looked at each other disgustedly and one asked why the man needed to go. . . . The wagon officers then reluctantly had Citizen climb in the back [of the wagon] . . . Officers I and II felt they really didn't have any means of handling the situation and that there were no resources in the community to help them out . . . mental health system . . . is only geared for people who have already made a suicide attempt and can be taken to the hospital, or who represent a definite danger to others. . . . (Shift #326, Encounter 11)

While suicidal risk may be insufficient for hospitalization, persons who have already attempted suicide are readily admitted by the hospital, as indicated in the following vignettes:

> Radio call for an injured person at a nursing home. Citizen 1 . . . a double amputee in a wheelchair . . . was sitting holding his head between his knees . . . he had broken a bottle and cut part of what was left of his leg with the bottle . . . Officer I took Citizen 2 [a nurse] aside and asked her what [amputee's] problem was and whether he had done this before. He asked her if she thought [man] was suicidal . . . [and if he] had been referred for psychiatric help. He said obviously the man needs some kind of help and the nurse said, "Well, if he needs it he'll be referred for it." Officer I said no, "I'm asking you if he has been referred for psychiatric help?" . . . Officer I said that he obviously had some deep problems . . . he needs help. [Nurse] had recontacted the doctor and was making arrangements for [amputee] to go to ______ hospital for a psychiatric evaluation. She was going to call the ambulance and have him transported tonight. . . . In sum . . . Officer I took the time to talk things over and find out about the situation. He was instrumental in getting the patient transferred to the [psychiatric] hospital. (Shift #397, Encounter 2)
>
> Three months ago, Officer I was working the midnight shift [with a partner]. It was about 2:30 a.m. [They] . . . happened to notice a man standing on a corner wearing a sweatshirt, parka and slacks. He was about thirty-years-old, white. As they drove by, they noticed him wave. They said it was the kind of reaction where he probably didn't really need the police until he saw them, and decided to stop them. They . . . came back, and pulled up, with the passenger-side officer rolling down his window and asking what he wanted. The man responded that he wanted to go to the ______ hospital. They asked him why. Before anyone could do anything, he pulled out a knife and plunged it into his chest. The man was admitted to the hospital. (Shift #38)

Despite the importance of the police in aiding the mentally ill, "managing mentals" was not regarded by the officers as a "good pinch." Since the officer's activity index and criminal arrest quota excluded psychiatric dispositions, involvement with the mentally ill was unrecognized and unrewarded by the police department. Coupled with the scarcity of placements and the hospitals' strict admission criteria, the lack of rewards tended to inhibit the police from making psychiatric referrals.

An added complication was that the current philosophy of community-based treatment apparently discouraged police from using the hospital as a resource. Police did not understand the policy of community care. They perceived rapid release of "their mentals" to be a personal slight on their judgement, a waste of their time, and an unwillingness by the mental health profession to "do something." Police frequently lamented that "no place will take them" or "how nuts does someone have to be?" In short, the current normative structure discourages police from initiating hospitalizations. Without the aid of the mental health system, police of necessity incorporate streetcorner psychiatry to maintain the mentally ill in the community.

Arrest

Although there is a stereotype that police spend the bulk of their time making arrests, our data show that arrest occurs relatively rarely. However, the arrest rate for the mentally ill is significantly greater than for non-ill persons (see also Teplin, 1984b) because arrest is often the only disposition available that will bring the situation under control. For example, arrests would take place when persons were not sufficiently mentally disordered to be admitted by the hospital, but were too public in their deviance to be ignored. In such situations, the probability of arrest was increased whenever it was thought that the mentally ill person would continue to annoy "decent people," and therefore result in a subsequent call for police service.

Our data indicate that it was common practice for the police to obtain a signed complaint from a third party (thus facilitating arrest) even in situations where psychiatric hospitalization was thought to be the more appropriate disposition. The police officer's rationale for this procedure was to ensure the ready availability of an alternative disposition (arrest) in the event that the hospital found the individual unacceptable for admission. The police officer's ingenuity was apparently born out of necessity since, as noted above, the hospitals had very specific criteria for admission. The following vignette illustrates a situation in which the person was apparently mentally ill, but was thought to be insufficiently ill to be admitted to the hospital and was subsequently arrested:

> The officer indicated that this man had been on the street calling women names, calling them whores, and shouting at black people, calling them "niggers" and chasing them. The officer said he thought the guy was crazy, "you know paranoid". . . . A woman had signed a complaint and asked that he be arrested because he was bothering her. . . . The man sounded like a paranoid schizophrenic . . . both

> from my observation of him and his response to questions the officer put to him in the station. He was very vague about himself and who he was, and felt that people were out to get him. He couldn't understand why he was in the police station. When he was taken to his cell he began shouting to be let out, and kept shouting the rest of the time he was there. The officer said the man denied having any psychiatric treatment or being under psychiatric care. In this situation he was charged with disorderly conduct. The officer said that there wasn't enough to take him into the mental health center, because his behavior wasn't that severe for the hospital to accept him. (Shift #119)

Arrest is also the only disposition available to the officer in cases where the person is defined as "too dangerous" by the hospital or has any type of pending criminal charge, as indicated by the following two vignettes:

> A young man was banging on his mother's door with a meat cleaver. . . . He was threatening to kill someone else and was trying to get into this mother's home for a gun. She wouldn't let him in, and had called the police to get rid of him and/or calm him down. When the police got there, Officer II decided that the man needed to be hospitalized as he was dangerous to himself and others. So they called for a wagon to take the man to [state mental hospital] . . . but they also wanted a complaint signed by the mother for disorderly [conduct] in case [the hospital] wouldn't take him. It turned out that [the hospital] would indeed not take the man so he ended up being locked up for disorderly conduct. (Shift #180)

> Citizen I was the victim of the knifing assault by Citizen 2 and had suffered some minor cuts on her face, arms, and hands. . . . They were drinking beer and [victim] decided that she would go to the store to buy more beer. Upon her return she found [the other woman] beating her [own] children. . . . A quick look at the kids showed they had been severely beaten. [The victim] stated that, upon finding [other woman] beating the children, she attempted to restrain [her] and the latter woman grabbed a knife blade from a kitchen drawer and attacked [the victim who] called the police . . . demanding the officers arrest [the other woman]. She stated that [the assailant] had beaten her children before, was on some sort of probation for this and has a history of psychiatric treatment. . . . There was evidence in her behavior of a psychiatric problem. Officer I had to restrain [the assailant] a number of times as she tried to bolt from the apartment and return to . . . reclaim her children . . . [She] was verbally abusive, resistant. . . . At the station, [she] was charged with assault . . . Officer I stated that [this] was clearly a psychiatric case, should probably go to [psychiatric hospital]. However, because she had [criminal] charges against her, [hospital] won't accept her. It's hospital policy not to accept police referrals with charges pending against them. (Shift #148, Encounter 2)

These vignettes illustrate the inconsistency between the legal structure and streetcorner implementation of the law. Although "dangerousness to self or others" is one of the major criteria for commitment in most mental health codes, this characteristic renders citizens undesirable by many hospitals. Once rejected for hospitalization, the only available disposition is often arrest.

Mentally ill persons who have additional problems (e.g., substance abuse) are also likely candidates for arrest. For example, mental health programs find that people who have been drinking are disruptive to the patient milieu and often will not accept them for treatment. Conversely, detoxification programs feel that they are not equipped to deal with persons suffering from a psychiatric impairment. The following narrative is illustrative of a rather typical situation in which the jail was the last stop of several in an attempt to find a placement for a person who was both mentally ill and intoxicated.

> At 8:00 p.m. we . . . saw that an ambulance was stopping in back of a parked bus. . . . They [ambulance personnel] ran inside the bus and brought out a large burly black man. The officers exclaimed, "Charlie, what are you doing?" Charlie greeted them with equal friendliness. Evidently, Charlie was the neighborhood character. . . . The bus driver, not realizing Charlie was drunk, was afraid he was ill and had called for an ambulance. The paramedics, seeing that Charlie was only drunk, left him in our charge. The officers asked Charlie if he wanted to go to detox and he said "sure". . . . The people [at detox] took one look at Charlie and would not accept him. Evidently, he was potentially violent and disruptive. . . . The officers asked if they would sign a complaint. They said yes. Evidently he had been [to the jail] so often that they already had a sheet on him so it was easy to get him into a cell. The officer explained to me that Charlie was a problem because he wasn't crazy enough to go to the mental hospital. The people at [the mental hospital] wouldn't accept him because he was potentially violent and often drunk. The detox people didn't want him, even though he was an alcoholic, because he was potentially violent and bothered other patients with his crazy ways. So that left the jail. They would put him in lock-up overnight; he would go to court in the morning and then would be released. In the meantime, they would get him off the street. Charlie was booked for disorderly conduct. The detox facility was the complainant, although he had done nothing disorderly. (Shift #81, Encounter 3)

The qualitative data indicate that multiply impaired persons (such as those described above) are more likely to be arrested because of the overall organization of the mental health care delivery system. Although our public health system is composed of a complex array of services, each subsystem designs its programs to fit a specific need. Thus, the majority of programs are designed as if clients are "pure types," for example, they are *either* alcoholic or mentally ill. Because of the narrowly defined parameters of each of the various subsystems, a number of multiply impaired persons are deemed unacceptable for treatment in each of the service delivery facilities. In this way, many potential users "fall through the cracks" of the various care-giving subsystems into the criminal justice net. As illustrated in the above vignette, police would often make the rounds of the various service agencies before resorting to arrest.

"Serious" incidents were also more likely to culminate in an arrest. However, unlike Bittner's (1967) study, the definition of "seriousness" in the present investigation was not always correlated with the severity of the offense. A number of sociopsychological contingencies determined whether or not the serious criterion would be invoked. For example, situations in which the citizen was disrespectful of the police officer were nearly always thought to be serious as illustrated by the following two vignettes:

> Radio call for a disturbance at a bar. . . . The bartender . . . stated to the officer that a lady sitting at the bar . . . had been trying to get people to buy her drinks and had been bothering the other customers and creating a disruption. . . . The officers asked her if she would leave. The lady said no. The officer then radioed for a wagon. . . . The officer then asked her if she wanted to leave or would she rather go to jail. She said she didn't care. . . . When the wagon arrived, he told her, "Let's go" . . . her behavior had been rather strange but, as Officer I stated later, there was no reason to take her to the hospital because she was just causing a disturbance and was not endangering herself or anyone else. . . . The sergeant commented that . . . even though he suspected that she had some sort of mental problem, the fact that she wouldn't leave the area made a legal disposition necessary. (Shift #125, Encounter 2)
>
> We received a call to investigate a disturbance at the el [elevated train] station. . . . When we arrived at the scene we were met by a female newspaper dealer who said earlier . . . a woman was in the el station, screaming and trying to take some of the newspapers. . . . As we were walking out, the woman who caused the original problem came back into the station . . . she ran amuck. She jumped on the police officer and started hitting him with closed fists and she was really landing blows. He was taken by surprise, but after a brief struggle . . . he led her out of the el station to the car. . . . During this time she began screaming at him that he was an agent of the devil and that she was a messenger from God; that she would see to it that he was punished by God for having her arrested. Nevertheless . . . he arrested her on a disorderly conduct charge. (Shift #291, Encounter 2)

Similarly, situations that were public, which offended "decent people," and those with a willing complainant were nearly always defined by police to be serious:

> Batman is seriously syphillitic, a streetperson well known to the officers. He used to be entirely painted green, but has stopped doing that. He is bug-infested. There is a hole in the side of his face where

the spirochyte has caused his face to become disfigured. He goes into [expensive department stores] and scares the customers because he's so unsightly, but sometimes will steal petty things. . . . Officer I said that [hospital] had gotten tired of taking Batman, they felt he was a hopeless case and had given up on him. So now, the only thing to do with him was send him to lock-up. He said, "Police don't give up on patients the way doctors, psychiatrists or psychologists do. They keep locking people up and the court system doesn't give up on people. The recidivism rate is extremely high." (Shift #170, Encounter 4)

We . . . were met by an elderly woman who said there was a man sleeping in a car behind the apartment building. She said that the night before, this man had been acting real crazy and had thrown rocks at the building. . . . We saw the suspect sleeping in the back seat of a rather old Dodge. The suspect presented a very bizarre sight. . . . Most of his hair was off, but there were ridges of hair all over his head . . . actual gouges in his scalp. There were also numerous slash marks up and down his wrists, extending up to the elbows. [He] looked disoriented, was very filthy, but looked physically fit, perhaps a body builder at one time. He was quite acquiescent. . . . They [officers] put cuffs on him and told him they were going to take him in for damage to property and, probably, disorderly conduct. At this point, the woman who called the police made the general comment that this man didn't belong in jail, but in a hospital as he was sick . . . [However,] the man was taken away . . . to the station and booked. (Shift #284, Encounter 1)

In sum, arrest was used as a disposition in three types of situations: (1) when the police officer's first choice would have been hospitalization, but the officer felt that there was a strong probability that the potential patient would be judged unacceptable by the hospital; most often, they were rejected because they fell into the cracks between the narrowly defined parameters of the various service subsystems; (2) in encounters which were characterized by their publicness and visibility which, at the same time exceeded the tolerance for deviant behavior within the community and offended "decent people;" and (3) in situations in which the police felt there was a high likelihood that the person would continue to "cause a problem" (and thus result in a "callback"). In such encounters, police resorted to arrest as a way of managing the person by removing him or her from the scene.

Overall, formal dispositions were made (either hospitalization or arrest) when police felt that the situation was likely to escalate and require subsequent police assistance. Clearly, the large gray area between behavior that is mentally disordered and that which is merely disorderly allows a great deal of discretion in choosing the final disposition. It is frequently unclear whether the individual is "bad" and should be arrested, "mad" and should be hospitalized, or simply "odd" and would be tolerated within the community. Nevertheless, the data indicate that the degree of psychiatric symptomatology is only one of many predictive variables determining the police disposition of the case.

Informal Dispositions

Our finding that informal dispositions were the predominant resolution is consistent with prior studies (Bittner, 1967; Schag, 1977). Police handled over seventy percent of all mentally ill persons via informal means. Requiring neither paperwork nor unwanted "downtime" (time off the street), informal dispositions are the police officer's resolution of choice.

There are three major categories of mentally disordered persons who are likely to be handled by informal means: (1) neighborhood characters, (2) "troublemakers," and (3) quiet "crazies."

Neighborhood Characters. Police are familiar with "neighborhood characters," that is, persons who reside within the community and whose idiosyncratic behavior(s) and/or appearance set them apart from "decent people." Virtually any officer can tell you about "Crazy Mary," "Mailbox Mollie," "Dirty Dean," and "Ziggy." These are neighborhood characters who are defined by the police as "mentals" but who are not hospitalized because the familiarity, predictability, and consistency of their eccentricities enable the police and local community to tolerate their deviant behavior. Interestingly, familiarity with the citizen's particular psychiatric symptomatology enables the officers to act as a streetcorner psychiatrist. In this way, police play a major role in maintaining the mentally ill within the community. The following vignettes depict common encounters of this type in which the neighborhood character is greatly comforted by the police officer's apparent concern:

> A man called the police to inform them that he was being monitored by another man. He said the man had planted a microdot in his apartment and kept track of his every action. The complainant had a lot of electronic equipment in his apartment. . . . He claimed the man who was monitoring him was able to jam his CB radio and call the man obscenities over the radio. He asked the officers to listen. . . . The man said he's also called the FBI and wanted to file a report with the police. Officer I said he went along with the man, letting him think the officers would take such a report, but he didn't do anything. . . . The man seemed appreciative of their efforts and they told him to let them know if he got any more information on the threatening man. The man was clearly disturbed, but as he was not dangerous to himself or others, he was not taken to [hospital]. The police just humored him. Officer II agreed that there's a necessity for deception in some cases. (Shift #213)
>
> A lady in the area claims she has neighbors who are beaming rays up into her apartment. Usually . . . the officer handles the situation by telling the person, "we'll go downstairs and tell the people downstairs to stop beaming the rays," and she's happy. Officer II seemed quite happy about this method of handling the problem. (Shift #220)

Troublemakers. Troublemakers, like neighborhood characters, are known to the police and are most likely to be managed by informal means; in other words, they are unlikely to be arrested or hospitalized. However, unlike the neighborhood character, the police officer's use of informal dispositions with troublemakers is not dictated by their predictability. Rather, informal dispositions are the resolution of choice because troublemakers are thought to be too difficult to handle via either arrest or hospitalization. The symptoms of their mental disorder are such that they cause disorder and disrupt the routine of the police. Police related the following vignettes:

> Whenever she came into the [police] station she caused an absolute disruption. She would take off her clothes, run around the station nude, and urinate on the sergeant's desk. They felt it was such a hassle to have her in the station, and in lock-up, that they simply stopped arresting her. (Shift #036)
>
> I think Harry is paranoid. Whenever the police go near him for any reason, even if it had nothing to do with him, he would get very upset and begin calling downtown, causing all kinds of flak in the department. So they leave him completely alone, even though they feel he is a certified cashew nut. (Shift #036)

These vignettes indicate that being labelled a troublemaker allows the individual to act in ways that would otherwise tend to result in either arrest or hospitalization. Police feel that although formal intervention may be periodically warranted in such cases, such persons are usually not worth the hassle and disruption.

Quiet "Crazies." Persons whose symptoms of mental disorder are relatively unobtrusive are also likely to be handled informally. Such persons offend neither the populace nor the police with vocal or visual manifestations of their illness. Their symptoms are not seen as being serious enough to warrant hospitalization. Moreover, quiet crazies are seen as more disordered than disorderly and are unlikely to provoke arrest, as the following vignettes illustrate:

> She [complainant] said the man down the block . . . had been trying . . . the door next to her restaurant. . . . Both officers recognized the man as a street person. . . . This was clearly a mental health case not going to [the hospital] based on discretion used by the officers . . . the man was wearing several stocking caps underneath the helmet, a pair of hexagonal shaped glasses, over safety goggles, several scarfs around his neck . . . 4–5 layers of shirts, sweaters, jackets topped by an overcoat . . . carrying a brown shopping bag . . . and a cardboard box. . . . Officer I searched him . . . as Officer I was talking information . . . the man kept saying "thank you" after he found out he was not going to be arrested . . . The man said he'd seen a psychiatrist in Kentucky and Indiana. The man said he'd never been to [local hospitals]. . . . Officer II said, "[hospital] probably wouldn't have wanted that man anyway." He said they would have let him go when they saw he was coherent and

> they don't care about the street or shopping bag person. . . . It was clear that Officer II saw [hospital] making clear discriminations about who were likely prospects for being kept there. (Shift #213, Encounter 1)
>
> As [a citizen] waved to us, Officer I identified her as a "crazy lady," stating he had seen her in the neighborhood, gesturing at passers by. . . . by appearance, [she] was fairly identifiable as a mental health case . . . dressed bizarrely, wearing many layers of clothing. She spoke in a hyperactive, excited way. . . . She told a story about having friends who were afraid to come back to [city] . . . They went out of town and had left their car on the streets . . . the car had picked up a lot of parking tickets . . . her friends were afraid to come back because they thought something terrible would happen to them because they had all these tickets. It became clear very quickly that [her] story didn't make any sense. . . . In response to [her] distress, [officer] became quite placating, sympathetic and reassuring. Rather than arguing that there was no reason for her friends' fear, he told her what to tell her friend to do about these tickets . . . Officer I gave up after she wasn't placated, ending by saying, "okay it will be alright dear. We have to go now." She remained as revved up as in the beginning. . . . Afterwards, Officer I expressed feelings of resignation about such situations. He said . . . either they are victims of crime or just in need of something which the police are not able to provide. (Shift #278, Encounter 5)

In both vignettes, the citizens were judged neither sufficiently disordered to warrant a mental health referral nor sufficiently disruptive to warrant an arrest.

Conclusion

Managing mentally disordered persons in the community has always been a necessary part of police work. In recent years, the police officer's role as streetcorner psychiatrist has expanded as a result of deinstitutionalization and other public policy modifications. However, the legal structure does not dictate the resolution of encounters with the mentally ill. Whether the disordered individual is defined by police to be "bad" (and should be arrested), "mad" (and therefore hospitalized), or merely "eccentric" is decided by discretion rather than by rules of law. Of necessity, police have developed an informal operative code to implement the legal structure.

This paper has demonstrated the importance of extrapsychiatric variables in determining the informal operative code. The police officers' decision to hospitalize, arrest, or manage a mentally ill citizen informally is based less on the degree of psychiatric symptomatology than on the sociopsychological and structural factors pertinent to each situation. By and large, the police do not rely on conventional mental health resources; arrest, too, is a relatively infrequent disposition. Rather, informal dispositions are the resolution of choice.

Further investigations of police decision-making are needed to determine the extent to which the present findings can be generalized. Studies of rural areas are of particular importance to determine if and how the exigencies of rural life alter the police officer's choice of management strategies. Multijurisdictional studies are also needed to investigate the impact of the legal structure on police management of the mentally ill. For example, how do commitment criteria, whether restrictive or liberalized, affect the police officer's choice of disposition? The extent of mental health services and the availability of outpatient commitment as a treatment alternative are also likely to affect police decision-making (Mulvey, Blumstein, & Cohen, 1987), and warrant further study.

Police departments must be made aware of their pivotal role as a mental health resource. Programs to educate and train police about extralegal dispositions for mentally ill citizens have been advocated by a number of mental health professionals (cf. Finn & Sullivan, 1987; Monahan & Monahan, 1986; Teplin, 1984a, 1984b, 1991) and in the Criminal Justice Mental Health Standards adopted by the American Bar Association. Accordingly, police departments in the United States have begun to include mental health training in their programs (Finn & Sullivan, 1987). In this way, law enforcement agencies are acknowledging and preparing police for their legitimate role as "streetcorner psychiatrist."

References

Bachrach, L. L. (1982). Young adult chronic patients: An analytical review of the literature. *Hospital and Community Psychiatry, 33*, 189–197.

Bittner, E. (1967). Police discretion in emergency apprehension of mentally ill persons. *Social Problems, 14*, 278–292.

Bittner, E. (1970). *The function of police in modern society*. Washington, DC: National Institute of Mental Health.

California Welfare and Institutional Code 5150 (West 1980).

Cobb, C. W. (1972). Community mental health services and the lower socioeconomic classes. *American Journal of Orthopsychiatry, 43*, 404–414.

Finn, P., & Sullivan, M. (1987). *Police response to special populations*. Washington, DC: U.S. Department of Justice, National Institute of Justice, Office of Communication and Research Utilization.

Fox, R. G., & Erickson, P. G. (1972). *Apparently suffering from mental disorder*. Toronto, Canada: University of Toronto Centre of Criminology.

Gilboy, J. A., & Schmidt, J. R. (1971). "Voluntary" hospitalization of the mentally ill. *Northwestern University Law Review, 66*, 429–453.

Goldstein, P. J. (1979). *Prostitution and drugs*. Lexington, MA: Lexington Books.

Gottfredson, M., & Gottfredson, D. (1980). *Decision making in criminal justice: Toward the rational exercise of discretion*. Cambridge, MA: Ballinger Publishing Co.

Hollingshead, A. B., & Redlich, F. C. (1958). *Social class and mental illness*. New York: John Wiley & Sons.

Illinois Revised Statutes. chap. 91 1/2 3-606 (1981).

Kiesler, C. A. (1982). Public and professional myths about mental hospitalization: An empirical reassessment of policy-related beliefs. *American Psychologist, 37*, 1323–1339.

Kiesler, C. A., & Sibulkin, A. E. (1987). *Mental hospitalization: Myths and facts about a national crisis*. Beverly Hills: Sage Publications.

Liberman, R. (1969). Police as a community mental health resource. *Community Mental Health Journal, 5*, 111–120.

Manning, P. (1977). *Police work: The social organization of policing*. Cambridge, MA: MIT Press.

Manning, P. (1984). Police classification and the mentally ill. In L. Teplin (Ed.), *Mental health and criminal justice* (pp. 177–198). Beverly Hills: Sage Publications.

Matthews, A. (1970). Observations on police policy and procedures for emergency detention of the mentally ill. *Journal of Criminal Law, Criminology, and Police Science, 61*, 283–295.

Mehta, C. R., & Patel, N. R. (1983). A network algorithm for performing Fischer's Exact Test in R × C contingency tables. *Journal of the American Statistical Association*, June, 427–434.

Monahan, J., & Monahan, B. (1986). Police and the mentally disordered. In J. Yuille (Ed.), *Police Selection and Training* (pp. 175–186). The Hague, The Netherlands: Martinus Nijhoff.

Mulvey, E. P., Blumstein, A., & Cohen, J. (1987). Reframing the research question of mental patient criminality. *International Journal of Law and Psychiatry, 9*, 57–65.

National Institute of Mental Health. (1985). *Mental health, United States, 1985* (DHHS Publication No. ADM 85-1378). Washington, DC: U.S. Government Printing Office.

Robins, L., Helzer, J., Croughan, J., Williams, J., & Spitzer, R. (1981). *NIMH Diagnostic Interview Schedule: Version III*. Rockville, MD: NIMH, Division of Biometry and Epidemiology.

Rock, R., Jacobson, M., & Janepaul, R. (1968). *Hospitalization and discharge of the mentally ill*. Chicago: University of Chicago Press.

Rumbaut, R. G., & Bittner, E. (1979). Changing conceptions of the police role. In N. Morris & M. Tonry (Eds.), *Crime and justice: An annual review of research* (Vol. 1) (pp. 239–288). Chicago, IL: University of Chicago Press.

Schag, D. (1977). *Predicting dangerousness: An analysis of procedures in a mental center*. Unpublished doctoral dissertation, University of California, Santa Cruz.

Shah, S. (1975). Dangerousness and civil commitment of the mentally ill: Some public policy considerations. *American Journal of Psychiatry, 132*, 501–505.

Sheridan, E. P., & Teplin, L. A. (1981). Police-referred psychiatric emergencies: Advantages of community treatment. *Journal of Community Psychology, 9*, 140–147.

Sims, A., & Symonds, R. (1975). Psychiatric referrals from the police. *British Journal of Psychiatry, 127*, 171–178.

Smith, D. A. (1986). The neighborhood context of police behavior. In M. Tonry & N. Morris (Eds.), *Crime and justice: An annual review of research* (Vol. 8). Chicago, IL: University of Chicago Press.

Smith, D. A., & Visher, C. A. (1981). Street-level justice: Situational determinants of police arrest decisions. *Social Problems, 29*, 167–177.

Stone, A. (1975). *Mental health and law: A system in transition*. Washington, DC: U.S. Government Printing Office.

Teplin, L. A. (1983). The criminalization of the mentally ill: Speculation in search of data. *Psychological Bulletin, 94*, 54–67.

Teplin, L. A. (1984a). Managing disorder: Police handling of the mentally ill. In L. A. Teplin (Ed.), *Mental health and criminal justice* (pp. 157–176). Beverly Hills, CA: Sage Publications.

Teplin, L. A. (1984b). Criminalizing mental disorder: The comparative arrest rate of the mentally ill. *American Psychologist, 39*, 794–803.

Teplin, L. A. (1991). The criminalization hypothesis: Myth, misnomer or management strategy. In S. Shah & B. Sales (Eds.), *Law and mental health: Major developments and research needs* (DHHS Publication No. ADM 91-1875). Washington, DC: U.S. Government Printing Office.

Teplin, L. A., Filstead, W., Hefter, G., & Sheridan, E. (1980). Police involvement with the psychiatric emergency patient. *Psychiatric Annals, 10*, 202–207.

Urmer, A. (1973). *The burden of the mentally disordered on law enforcement*. Sacramento, CA: ENKI Research Institute.

Warren, C. A. (1977). *The social construction of dangerousness*. Los Angeles, CA: University of Southern California.

Wilkinson, G. S. (1975). Patient–audience social status and the social construction of psychiatric disorders: Toward a differential frame of reference hypothesis. *Journal of Health and Social Behavior, 16*, 28–38.

Wilson, J. Q. (1968). The police and the delinquent in two cities. In S. Wheeler (Ed.), *Controlling delinquents* (pp. 9–30). New York: John Wiley & Sons.

[15]

The Howard Journal Vol 34 No 4. Nov 95
ISSN 0265–5527, pp 291–313

Mentally Disordered Offenders: Finding a Focus for Diversion

ELIZABETH BURNEY and GEOFFREY PEARSON
Elizabeth Burney is Research Fellow and Geoffrey Pearson is Wates Professor of Social Work, Goldsmiths' College, University of London

Abstract: The paper is based on an ongoing evaluation of a court-based diversion scheme for mentally disordered offenders in a busy inner-London magistrates' court. It begins with a review of the field, in particular the different decision-making points at which diversion schemes of this kind might be situated. This is followed by an account of the early experience of the Islington Mentally Disordered Offenders Project which began in the early 1990s. Attention is focussed on four areas of special need: homelessness; drug misuse; personal violence, and race and ethnicity.

The aim of this paper is to discuss the most suitable means for diverting mentally disordered offenders from the criminal justice system, where this is deemed appropriate, and providing adequate mental health services and supports to this sometimes difficult group. In part, the paper is derived from the ongoing evaluation of a court-based advice scheme in an area of inner-London.[1] Some features of this initiative, and what it can tell us both about mentally disordered offenders and the needs of magistrates' courts, are described at a later point. The paper begins, however, with a discussion of some general issues.

Difficult Decisions: The Growth and Diversity of Diversion Schemes

The mentally disordered offender has received more attention in the early 1990s than at any time since the publication of the Butler Report in 1975. Funding has been made available, through a variety of means, for prototype schemes to address the needs of mentally disordered offenders. Stimulated by the Home Office Circular 66/90 (*Provision for Mentally Disordered Offenders*) and the investigations of the Reed Committee (Department of Health and Home Office 1992a) practical initiatives are proliferating, particularly with the aim of diversion from custody and/or from prosecution.

Two major difficulties can be immediately identified in schemes of this sort. The first is the variety of possible definitions and types of mental disorder, in part as a result of the definitions employed by the 1983 Mental Health Act, together with the differing perceptions of the problem in the different agencies involved. The second is the very large number of potential diversion points within the criminal justice system through which a relatively tiny number of people pass at any one time.

The first issue was illustrated clearly in the catalytic study of 2,042 sentenced prisoners by Gunn and his colleagues. This showed that psychiatric disorder was endemic in the prison population, with 37% of males and 56% of females serving over six months suffering from some form of identifiable difficulty (Gunn *et al.* 1991a, b). However, the breakdown by diagnosis revealed a very varied group of people, who would evoke quite different responses under mental health law and psychiatric practice. For almost two-thirds of the 37% of men receiving a diagnosis, for example, this involved a substance-related disorder – and would therefore be excluded from the scope of the Mental Health Act, as would the 5% described as sexual deviants. Also, a further 20% of these mentally disordered prisoners were identified as suffering from a 'personality disorder', whom many psychiatrists would define as 'untreatable' thereby also falling outside the scope of the Act.

Only 4% of mentally disordered prisoners (amounting to 2% of the sentenced prison population) were diagnosed as 'psychotic', most commonly involving the diagnosis of schizophrenia. As Gunn *et al.* (1991b) indicate, however: 'the low prevalence of psychosis among sentenced prisoners should not obscure its importance' (p. 13). When extrapolated to the total prison population, this would amount to several hundreds of people scattered through the system who should be in hospital rather than prison. Nevertheless, given the relatively small numbers this also indicates that a major problem of diversion schemes is a logistical one of the needle in the haystack. Moreover, despite a small number of high profile cases which capture the headlines, most mentally disordered offenders are neither very seriously ill nor dangerous, thus prompting the question of how much intervention is justified.

The difficulty presents itself at every level of decision-making within the criminal justice system. Where the police are concerned at the point of arrest, it would appear that they are quite good at recognising mental disorder when they encounter it, which as Walker (1992) suggests they do so not infrequently. As indicated by a recent study for the Royal Commission on Criminal Justice, however, there is considerable variation: 'Suspects suffering from schizophrenia were most readily identified by the police, while those suffering from clinical depression were least often identified' (Gudjonsson *et al.* 1994, p. 32). It is what happens after the recognition of mental disorder, of course, which determines whether or not the mentally disordered person enters the criminal justice system, with Walker's survey suggesting that less than one-half of those to whom the police are called are likely to be detained. Following detention, successive filters operate of different kinds: whether section 136 of the Mental Health Act is invoked, taking the person to a 'place of safety' for assessment; whether they are enabled to enter hospital voluntarily; or whether they are either cautioned, prosecuted, or simply released without charge. Local practices vary a great deal (Fahy 1989; Walker 1992).

The most common type of formal diversion scheme established to date would appear to be those involving court-based psychiatric assessment teams. A survey conducted for the Department of Health by Blumenthal and Wessely (1992) identified 48 schemes of this type serving magistrates' courts with 34 more being planned. The authors noted an uneven spread of activity across the regions, however, which seemed largely dependent on the availability and interest of forensic psychiatrists, rather than the assessment of local need. Perhaps this helps in part to explain why in 1993 15 out of 18 inner-London courts had either their own psychiatric assessment scheme or access to one nearby, whereas in outer-London this was true of only eight out of 18 courts (Williams 1993).

Court-based psychiatric assessment schemes will sometimes rely on the co-operation of the Crown Prosecution Service where it may be decided that it is not in the public interest to pursue a less serious offence where the defendant is mentally ill. The decision to discontinue or withdraw a case can facilitate the work of psychiatrists conducting court assessments, followed by the use of a 'civil' section of the Mental Health Act to take the ex-defendant to hospital. Because hospitals sometimes resist admissions under the forensic sections of the Act, for fear of violence, this method is the one most commonly used at Clerkenwell Court and other inner-London assessment schemes (James and Hamilton 1991; Joseph 1992).

Court-based diversion schemes of this kind can be extremely expensive. Nevertheless, they have demonstrable value for some of the most worrying cases such as the small minority of obviously psychotic defendants who in the past would have spent weeks in custody awaiting psychiatric reports. For this group, the availability of on-the-spot assessment in court can make dramatic reductions in the length of remand sentences by compressing the time needed for psychiatric reports from weeks to a few days (James and Hamilton 1991, 1992; Joseph 1992; Joseph and Potter 1993). Such schemes are therefore not difficult to justify in humanitarian terms, for as indicated in a recent study of psychotic men in Brixton prison, many aspects of current practice with psychiatric remands are 'quite inexcusable' (Robertson *et al.* 1994, p. 60). If the humanitarian and psychiatric justifications are clear, the financial burden of court-based psychiatric assessment schemes remains a difficulty. It can be argued that they are cost-effective in terms of prison remands avoided or reduced (Joseph and Potter 1993). The obvious problem, common to multi-agency work, is that the potential savings are made in one part of the system, whereas the cost of assessment and hospitalisation are picked up elsewhere.

Because court-based schemes are often led by psychiatrists, it is commonly assumed that diversion from custody means the provision of a hospital bed – one reason why there might sometimes be coolness on the part of health authorities towards developing diversion for mentally disordered offenders. However, this has been found not to be so for a large proportion of those assessed in such schemes (James and Hamilton 1991,

1992; Joseph 1992; Burney 1992). Nor is a psychiatrist's opinion always needed for the mentally disturbed who appear in court, who may already be receiving treatment, or are neither so ill nor so dangerous as to require that level of professional and institutional intervention.

The question then arises whether some (or indeed many) of these mentally distressed people should have arrived at court in the first place, and whether or not 'diversion' could be arranged at an earlier stage. By the time that a defendant comes to the notice of a court-based assessment team, a whole variety of informal filtering mechanisms will already have been at work, suggesting different possible points in the chain of decision-making at which diversion schemes might be situated.

One approach which has attracted interest in some areas involves the creation of volunteer panels of 'appropriate adults' to support mentally ill or mentally handicapped people under the Police and Criminal Evidence Act. Hampshire Constabulary, for example, has a model scheme in operation. However, diversion at these stages of police decision-making will not be possible for more serious offences or where consideration of the victim requires the matter to be publicly aired. Such cases will still have to go through the court process at least part of the way.

In these circumstances a more appropriate model of diversion might be the inter-agency panel, similar to those operating successfully in the juvenile justice field. A probation survey in 1992 revealed that eight out of 55 probation areas had some form of panel scheme, of which three have been subject to in-depth evaluation (Hedderman 1993; Gordon and Hedderman 1993). Panel schemes provide a multi-disciplinary assessment team which considers the options and makes a recommendation to the court. They can also provide information for bail risk assessment. One distinct advantage is that multi-agency panels involve from the start representatives of those agencies and interest groups who will implement the plan to be recommended for the individual concerned. It is, however, not clear to what extent service-user perspectives have been incorporated in panel decision-making, which is an increasing trend in other systems of community care planning and provision for the mentally ill (WHO 1989; Campbell 1990).

Most current panel schemes are co-ordinated by a probation officer, which may have a bearing on the type of case which gets referred. Panel schemes appear to handle a wider range of mentally disordered defendants than court-based assessment schemes. In the Home Office evaluation 13% of panel cases involved 'mental impairment' (Hedderman 1993, p. 17) whereas those people with 'learning difficulties' are seldom referred to psychiatric-led assessment schemes. The point was further illustrated by Joseph and Potter (1993) who found that ony 2% of people referred to two such schemes in London were suffering from mental handicap/learning difficulties as opposed to mental illness. This is not dissimilar to the way in which those offenders with a diagnosis of 'personality disorder', while being shunned by mainstream psychiatric services often become the clientele of the probation service (Bartlett *et al.* 1992).

The earliest point at which there is a potential for diversion, of course, is that of arrest and charge by the police. One problem with diversion schemes employed at police station level is that, although the police will see more potential 'divertees' than at any later stage of decision-making within the criminal justice system, it is still a very thin scatter. Precise estimates vary. One Home Office study observed all detainees over a six-month period (n = 2,947) at seven London police stations and mental disorder was assessed or suspected in 3% of cases (Robertson *et al.* 1993). A somewhat higher estimate was arrived at in a study for the Royal Commission on Criminal Justice which assessed the psychological vulnerability of 156 suspects held at two London police stations. Here mental illness was found in 7% of cases, with a further 3% suffering from a mental handicap (Gudjonsson *et al.* 1994). A study of custody records by the Revolving Doors Agency (1994) in the Paddington area of London, on the other hand, identified only 2% of detainees over a six-month period as 'people with mental health problems', and only 13 of the 70 identified cases actually went to court. The thin trickle of cases identified by these different methods is thus broadly consistent with the experience of the community psychiatric nurse assessment scheme at Bournville police station in Birmingham where only 25 mentally disordered detainees were noted in the first six months of operation (Spurgeon 1993). Helpful as such a service might have been for those 25 individuals, it is hardly conceivable in resource terms that it could be replicated across the country.

As these varied estimates might suggest, it is extremely difficult to know how much diversion actually takes place while decision-making is still in the hands of the police. There are no reliable estimates of formal arrangements between local psychiatrists and police stations, for example, although according to Blumental and Wessely (1992) this was more likely to be part of the strategy adopted in health authority plans, rather than the provision of psychiatric services at courts or in prisons. Even the use of the formal powers embodies in s. 136 of the Mental Health Act is often inadequately recorded (Burney 1993; Revolving Doors 1993). Provided that the abuses commonly alleged against the use of s. 136 are avoided (cf. Rogers and Faulkner 1987), and that adequate safeguards and guidelines are in place to prevent its disciminatory use, it is a procedure which deserves closer scrutiny. A police power which enables a mentally disordered person to be taken directly to hospital or another 'place of safety' for assessment without being charged would seem to offer the most sensible and readily accessible diversion route in many situations.

From the above discussion, a number of key themes emerge. First there is the question of numbers. Set against common stereotypes we need to ask how many people are we talking about under the label 'mentally disordered offenders'? How many of these are either truly dangerous (to themselves or to others) or in need of full-blown psychiatric intervention? What sort of offences bring them to court and what sort of sentences or orders result? How often, instead of a prosecution or caution, are they diverted by the police to a 'place of safety' or simply released with 'no further action'? It is surprising how often services are set up on sheer guesswork, although perhaps this is inevitable given the current state of knowledge.

Secondly, it is necessary to clarify the question of needs. The shortcomings of funding and organisation with regard to 'care in the community' have been well rehearsed and will not be repeated here (Barham 1992; Hawker and Ritchie 1990; NACRO 1993). When resources are scarce, efficient use of what exists becomes imperative. But how can 'efficiency' be achieved without knowing the prevalence of different types of need and the priorities which apply in individual cases? This is particularly true in those cases which bridge across different categories of need, such as when mental health problems overlap with drug or alcohol misuse.

Finally, there is the vexed issue of responsibility. To whom do these people 'belong' when they enter the criminal justice system? Rhetoric about 'inter-agency co-operation' often fails to match the complexities and realities on the ground (Blagg *et al.* 1988; Pearson *et al.* 1992). Where the mentally disordered offender is concerned, there is a pressing need for a lead responsibility within any system of multi-agency work. The health service has an explicit responsibility for mental illness, although there is every reason to believe that it is only the most acute cases – whether offenders or not – who receive attention. Such a view was powerfully reinforced by the recent observations of the Mental Health Act Commission (1993, pp. 17–19) on the overloading of the psychiatric hospital service which has reached crisis point in many inner-city areas, with scenes in some hospital wards resembling those of Bedlam. Pressures such as these can only reinforce the already existing reluctance of health authorities to regard potentially troublesome patients with a history of offending as priorities for scarce resources (cf. Fennell 1991). At the same time, the common assumption within the criminal justice system that psychiatrists must always be involved in the assessment and care of mentally disordered offenders will sometimes be found to be erroneous. More basic forms of social support including a reliable degree of security in terms of accommodation and personal finances might in many cases be a better guarantee of diversion from custody, reflecting the more general experience of what 'community care' (or just simply 'living in the community') means for the mentally ill (Barham and Hayward 1995). Non-specialist agencies such as social services and housing departments, together with a variety of supports provided through agencies in the voluntary sector, occupy a crucial (but often underdeveloped) role in these respects.

It is clear that there is considerable scope for the development and extension of diversion schemes and a wide variety of 'filter mechanisms' competing for the attention of the mentally disordered offender, although each with its own attendant difficulties. What is less clear however is that there is an invisible army of the mad tramping daily through our courts, as is so often assumed.

The Islington Experience: The Project and its Clientele

Some of the problems identified above, and some of the possible ways round them, can be illustrated by one of the few court-based diversion schemes to be subject to research and evaluation. The Islington Mentally Disordered Offenders Project (IMDOP) was established in April 1992 at Highbury Corner magistrates' court initially for a three-year trial period. Funded by a charitable trust, and involving collaboration between the Inner London Probation Service and the Mental After Care Association, the scheme employs a psychiatric nurse as a 'Mental Health Court Worker' on a full-time basis. She is located in the court probation office, with a desk also in the court foyer, with a remit to assess offenders with possible mental disorders, to assist the court in dealing with them appropriately, and to offer support and training to probation staff. The court is also able to refer relevant cases to the psychiatrist-led assessment team which operates once a week at the neighbouring Clerkenwell court.

The research attached to IMDOP has involved a number of objectives, including an ongoing evaluation of the initiative. In its initial phase the aim of research was to provide a 'baseline' estimate of the numbers of identified mentally disordered offenders appearing at Highbury Corner court, together with a profile of their known social characteristics. This was largely based on the various records and reports maintained by the court probation team, and interviews were conducted with a number of probation officers and a few of their mentally disordered clients. Also, access was given to the Inner London Probation Service (ILPS) database of key variables extracted from social enquiry reports (SIRs) concerning 546 cases in the Islington area over a period of nine months in 1991. Overall, some kind of mental health problem was identified for 12% of those registered on the SIR database.

When the court advisory post was first conceived, it was thought that a large part of the work would consist of preventing those defendants with an acute psychosis from receiving long custodial remands or inappropriate prison sentences. In the event, neither the number of acute psychotics nor the attitude of the court towards them has made this more than a minor – though still crucial – part of the role. Broadly speaking, our initial impression was that mentally disordered offenders seen at Highbury Corner magistrates' court fell into three categories.

(i) A very small number of people diagnosed as psychotic and with pressing treatment needs, amounting to no more than maybe 20 per year, who now go to hospital via the Clerkenwell court assessment scheme.

(ii) A larger, indefinite, number of offenders with a history of psychotic illness who may exhibit mildly psychotic behaviour but who do not require hospitalisation. These tend to commit petty offences for which they receive a small fine, 'one day in lieu', or are discharged.

(iii) A much larger and more amorphous group of depressed, anxious or 'personality disordered' individuals whose mental health difficulties are often bound up with social conditions and who are likely to end up in the arms of the probation service.

In the event, this preliminary analysis was largely borne out by the Mental Health Court Worker's experience in her first twelve months of work. Altogether she processed 101 referrals of whom 85 cases (84%) were assessed by her as mentally disordered. Of the total cases referred, 86 were men and 15 were women.[2] In terms of age, where this was known (n = 77) two-thirds were in the 21 to 35 years age group with almost one-half over 30 years of age. Reflecting national trends, mentally disordered offenders within this sample tended to be older than the average group seen by the courts and the probation service (cf. Hudson *et al.* 1993, p. 28). Similarly, in the ILPS SIR database the median age of offenders with mental health problems was five years older than that of other offenders.

Among the initial year's referrals, 16 cases fell into the first category described above and were deemed sufficiently ill to justify referral to the Clerkenwell psychiatric assessment team, although not all ended up in hospital. This team – consisting of two psychiatrists, an approved social worker, and a psychiatric nurse – meets once a week and is well-geared to obtaining on-the-spot hospitalisation for those who need it. The team takes referrals from mentally ill offenders who have been remanded in custody, and judging from the Highbury Corner experience these cases are almost always obvious from the moment that they appear in the police cells. Consequently, there is rarely any difference of opinion about the appropriateness of a referral to the Clerkenwell scheme.

The second category mentioned above is the one which probably takes up most of the Mental Health Court Worker's time, and includes a handful of repeated petty offenders with whom she is closely involved. Most of this group are already well known to the mental health services, but not so ill as to require immediate hospitalisation. Because their mental condition has already been assessed, and they may already be receiving community-based treatment, there is no need to refer them to the Clerkenwell team, especially as this usually involves a few days in custodial remand awaiting the next weekly session.

On their first court appearance, some time on the telephone by the Mental Health Court Worker will establish their status and involvement with the health service, and her follow-up often proves to be the vital link with support services on the ground, where these exist. In this respect her work resembles that of other CPN based schemes. However, while lack of such support occasionally results in petty offences which can be linked to the onset of a more serious psychotic episode, the Mental Health Court Worker can sometimes obtain the required health service intervention where the court would have no power to order it. For example, in response to a summary offence which is not imprisonable, there is no access to the Clerkenwell assessment team via a custodial remand, even though the defendant might by that stage be becoming a danger to himself or others.

The third category is much more amorphous, reflecting the spectrum of mental illness and distress other than the more obviously recognised psychoses. Depression is the most familiar, and courts are rightly concerned to identify people who may be a risk of self-harm or suicide. In other cases there is a grey area where intervention on mental health grounds may or may not be thought appropriate. Many of these sad and difficult people find their way onto probation caseloads, where the Mental Health Court Worker may be called upon in her support role. Generally speaking, this can enable probation officers to feel more confident in dealing with mentally disordered offenders – or those bordering on this category. As one survey has shown, probation officers are poorly equipped by their education and training to respond to the needs of mentally disordered offenders, and express a high level of demand for appropriate forms of training and professional support (Hudson *et al.* 1993).

One final expection at the outset of IMDOP was that there would be a large number of perpetually re-appearing individuals – petty offenders for whom the court had no solution and who were clogging up the system. Earlier research (Fairhead 1981) had shown this 'petty persistent' group to be associated with a range of social difficulties such as poverty, accommodation problems and alcohol misuse, together with a history of mental illness. More recently, this perception has been fuelled and reinforced by awareness of the effects of the mental hospital closure programme, and fears that the courts were bearing the brunt of the consequences; although no doubt many other professionals such as housing managers and general practitioners feel likewise.

In practice, Highbury Corner sees very few mentally ill people appearing on repeat charges. In the first year of the project only twelve clients reappeared. Of these, fewer than one-half could be said to represent a hard core whose frequent offending and chaotic lifestyle can arouse a sense of frustration in the courtroom. For lack of available services, the Mental Health Court Worker has been forced to establish close, long-term contacts with some of these, and others on prison after-care. Unknown numbers, of course, may reappear in different courts – and increasingly she has found it necessary to act as a reference point for their encounters in other parts of London and elsewhere. Even so, the very few local 'regulars' who are clearly mentally disordered contribute quite insignificantly to the caseload at Highbury Corner, although the baggage of problems that such people carry with them is far from insignificant. Many of these relate, predictably, to inadequate support from mental health and social services – representing a tight bundle of multiple social need, although merely a pin-prick within the overall shortcomings of 'community care' for the mentally ill. One priority for the project evaluation will be to identify more clearly the key issues surrounding the care management of this tiny, but time-consuming group.

Special Areas of Need: Housing, Race, Drugs and Alcohol, and Violence

What can be learnt from the Islington project about the most persistent areas of need and difficulty associated with mentally disordered offenders and the institutional responses involved? We have set out above some of the general characteristics, in terms of mental state and patterns of offending. In the following pages we will address four main areas which emerge from the Islington experience, and which can be seen both to reflect and illuminate issues which have give rise to much concern and debate. These are: the precarious accommodation situation of many mentally disordered offenders; the relationship between mental disorder and substance misuse; the vexed question of the over-representation of black people among those diagnosed as psychotic; and the role which violence plays in the offending pattern of mentally disordered offenders.

In addressing these issues, our sources of information include court and probation records, the SIR database for the Islington area, and the information systems used by the Mental Health Court Worker. We will also make some use of the outcomes of the Black Offenders Project which had been conducted in the Islington area of ILPS just prior to the establishment of the mentally disordered offenders initiative (cf. Lawrence *et al.* 1992).

Overall, 12% of those offenders registered in the ILPS SIR database (n = 546) were identified as having mental health problems although it must be remembered that this does not provide a complete record of offenders appearing before the court. Probation reports are not required for most petty offences, for example, and nor are they usually supplied for people pleading not guilty. Even so, the SIR database points to a number of areas of special need, albeit with varying degrees of clarity.

(i) Housing and Homelessness

One of the most striking differences revealed by the SIR database between mentally disordered offenders as against the general offender population was their accommodation situation (see *Table 1*). The majority of

TABLE 1
Accommodation Situation
(n = 546)*

	Mental Health Group %	Remainder %
Permanent accommodation	45	74
Temporary accommodation	28	16
Hostel	8	3
No fixed address	20	7

(*Note*: *The figures are taken from the ILPS SIR database where a certain amount of double counting can be discerned by a close scrutiny of individual entries. These figures must therefore be used advisedly. Overall, 12% of the total (that is, 65 cases) were identified as having mental health problems.)

offenders with mental health problems did not have permanent accommodation, and compared with the remainder of the offenders they were twice as likely to be living in temporary accommodation or a hostel, and three times as likely to have no fixed abode.

In the first year of the Mental Health Court Worker scheme, information on accommodation was not routinely recorded. However, of the 57 cases where information was held, approximately one-half were living in permanent accommodation, with one-quarter of no fixed abode, and the remainder in some form of temporary accommodation. Even so, individual casework revealed that some of the accommodation described as 'permanent' could be most precarious. Some of the referrals requiring most support are psychotic individuals living without electricity or hot water because of unpaid bills, and with virtually no furniture. One man in such a position had received no help from social services for over a year in spite of requests from the Mental Health Court Worker. It was only her intervention that enabled him to receive a disability allowance, and cases such as this point to the potential fragility of 'community care' arrangements. In one admittedly exceptional case, a man with intermittent paranoid tendencies was placed by the local authority in 14 different bed-and-breakfast hotels in a period of only six months, each placement quickly breaking down because of his aggressive behaviour, assaults on other residents, threats or vandalism. Even when the police had been called none of these incidents had led to arrest, however, although his 'petty' misconduct must have been a considerable nuisance and difficulty for the victims of his outbursts.

Other cases reveal offence-related instability in accommodation. Loss of accommodation resulting from personal violence, threats or damage in the home, whether against family, neighbours or fellow hostel dwellers, seems not to be uncommon. Such individuals are also seen as a bad bail risk, increasing the likelihood of custodial remand. This combination of circumstances underlines not only the importance of stable accommodation for mentally disordered people, but also that support of the right kind should be available where possible to minimise the behaviour which can undermine that stability where it might already exist. Work undertaken in the inner London area of Hammersmith by the Revolving Doors Agency (1993) bears out this scenario where the difficulties that the mentally ill have in coping with housing allocation procedures, and the corresponding problems experienced by officials trying to fit 'hard to place' tenants into the over-stretched social housing sector are well described. Lack of long-term support once a tenancy had been achieved was seen as contributing to frequent breakdowns resulting from rent arrears and neighbour disputes.

The stress associated with homelessness or the threat of eviction can itself be a contributing factor to the onset of an episode of acute mental illness, thus reinforcing the vicious cycle. As research has confirmed, there is a significant link between 'life events' and both psychotic and depressive episodes leading to hospital admission, a finding which was established 20 years ago (Bebbington *et al.* 1993; Brown and Birley 1968; Brown *et al.*

1973). In such circumstances, as people lurch from one form of crisis to another, incidents which carry the potential of criminal charges are always an added hazard – thus underscoring the vital contribution of an effective social housing policy and associated support mechanisms to the lives of mentally disordered offenders.

(ii) Drug and Alcohol Related Problems

One further outcome of the analysis of the SIR database which invites attention is that one-half of all those cases with mental health problems were also identified as having problems with drugs and/or alcohol. Moreover, in half of these cases the defendant's offence was stated to be drug or alcohol related. This echoes the findings of other studies, and was highlighted in one of the discussion papers prepared for the Reed committee (Department of Health and Home Office 1992b, Discussion Paper 3, para. 3.5).

It is not possible to know from the ILPS database how many of those offenders who were identified as having problems with both mental health and substance misuse would fall into the category of drug dependency. Nor has the issue of substance misuse been particularly prominent in the first year's work of the Mental Health Court Worker, although this is now being closely monitored. As a consequence, it is not always clear how our evidence should be interpreted on this matter. One key issue would seem to be whether or not the one-half of mentally disordered offenders for whom drug or alcohol misuse was also recorded were suffering from both mental illness *and* a substance related disorder. In this respect Joseph and Potter (1993) suggest that 'the most common multiple diagnoses were combinations of schizophrenia, personality disorder, and alcohol dependence' (p. 327). However, it is possible that some cases in the SIR database have a multiple classification because probation staff took the view that a defendant had a mental health problem because he or she was misusing drugs or alcohol. This difficulty is not dissimilar to that found in the prison study by Gunn *et al.* (1991b) where in almost two-thirds of cases the prisoner's primary diagnosis was one of drug or alcohol problems. It is also reflected in the report of NACRO's Mental Health Advisory Committee (NACRO. 1993, p. 4) which, commenting on the sometimes confused terminology, opts for a global definition of 'mentally disturbed offender' to include some whose difficulties originate in drug or alcohol misuse.

In the case of probation officers, of course, theirs were judgments made by people who would often have received little if any formal training in psychiatric assessment. Even so, systems of classification and differential diagnosis traditionally employed by British psychiatrists have a tendency to obscure the presence of over-lapping difficulties such as an identifiable mental illness together with substance misuse. These questions of 'dual diagnosis' or the co-morbidity of symptoms have received much more attention in North America (for example Mueser *et al.* 1990; Ridgley *et al.* 1990) and might warrant closer scrutiny in Britain. As the experience in the USA has shown, quite apart from any other considerations those with a dual diagnosis of mental illness and drug misuse can easily fall between different systems of health care and management.

(iii) Race and Ethnicity

A third area of special need which emerges from the Islington experience is the striking over-representation of black defendants referred to the IMDOP scheme. This, as will become apparent, is a thorny topic which is hedged about by all kinds of difficulties of evidence and interpretation. A useful context for the discussion is provided by the Black Offenders Project (BOP) which had been conducted in the same area of inner London, involving among its other activities a scrutiny of the same ILPS SIR database (Lawrence *et al.* 1992).

The ILPS SIR database employs a race and ethinic coding system of White/Black/Other. As indicated by the Black Offenders Project this system has some serious drawbacks (Lawrence *et al.* 1992; Pearson and Lawrence 1995). Setting these to one side, however, on this basis it was estimated that black people accounted for approximately one-fifth (19%) of all offenders (n = 455). Those classified as white constituted the large majority (75%), with the 'other' category comprising 6%.

Where mental health issues are concerned, the SIR database identified fewer black offenders as having mental health problems than whites: 9% as against 12%. It should be added that BOP found few differences between black and white offenders in terms of other personal and social factors. Both groups were predominantly unemployed (76% of black as against 64% of white offenders) and one-half of both groups had finance difficulties. One-quarter of each group (25% of whites and 24% of blacks) had drug-related problems, whereas fewer black offenders (20% as against 28%) had alcohol-related problems. Approximately the same percentage (40% of whites and 37% of blacks) experienced family problems, with similar proportions living with no fixed abode (8% of whites and 7% of blacks).

On this basis, approximately one-in-eight of all mentally disordered offenders on whom probation reports had been compiled were black. Quite a different profile is found, however, in the cases referred to the Mental Health Court Worker. Of 101 cases in the first year, one-third (n = 33) of these were black, which even allowing for the imperfections in the race and ethnic coding system adopted by the probation service clearly represents a considerable over-representation of black people. Moreover, among those cases where the diagnosis was psychosis or schizophrenia (n = 33) one-half were black: 17 cases, compared with 13 white and 3 'other'. This is reflected in the Clerkenwell psychiatric assessment scheme where 39% of referrals from all sources were of African-Caribbean descent (James, personal communication, cited in Burney 1992).

The discrepancies described above arise partly because the SIR database, which does not indicate an over-representation of black mentally disordered offenders, would be likely to exclude people remanded from Highbury Corner to the Clerkenwell scheme and would also exclude people pleading not guilty which black people are more likely to do on the available evidence (Walker 1988, 1989; Hood 1992). It is also possible that some kind of 'negative filtering' system operates by which black mentally disordered offenders assume a higher visibility within the criminal justice system, and thus figure more prominently than might otherwise be expected both in cases brought to court by the police and in subsequent referrals to the Islington mental health project.

We do not feel that it would be appropriate, especially in view of the limited basis of our evidence, to enter into the complex debate on the well-documented controversy concerning the over-representation of people of African-Caribbean descent within the diagnostic category of schizophrenia, and in compulsory admissions under the Mental Health Act (Cope 1986; Fernando 1991; Littlewood and Lipsedge 1982). Where mentally disordered offenders are concerned, however, one possibility which should not be overlooked is evidence from the British Crime Survey which has shown that white people are more likely to report minor acts of violence which lead to no harm to the victim if these result from black assailants than if the assailant had been white (Shah and Pease 1992). The relationships between offence, race and the likelihood of reporting to the police as revealed by this research are complex, but there is an indisputable 'race factor'. We know more generally that racial prejudice and the negative stereotyping of black people within the police service mean that interactions between the police and public are significantly different at the point of arrest (Smith and Gray 1983; Skogan 1990; Reiner 1993). For these kinds of reasons, it is reasonable to suppose that the conduct of black mentally disordered offenders assumes a much higher 'visibility' resulting in an over-representation within the criminal justice system.

Whatever the mechanisms which produce this, it is equally important to recognise the special needs of black mentally disordered offenders within the system. One outcome of the Islington Black Offenders Project was to establish the need for black support groups, and work within the Inner-London Probation Service has subsequently begun on a black empowerment initiative of this kind (Lawrence *et al.* 1992; ILPS 1993). Where mentally disordered offenders are concerned, support mechanisms both within and outside the criminal justice system have a particular relevance, especially where an individual might be subject to persecutory delusions which could easily be exacerbated by not only the actions of the police and penal institutions, but also by perceptions of racism. This is not solely a matter for the criminal justice system, however, and also relates to the lack of responsiveness of health care systems and helping agencies to black people's needs. As indicated by one research study: 'due to a lack of assistance or referral at an early stage, black clients were more likely to have to reach a crisis requiring hospitalisation before action was taken' and that 'help at an earlier stage might have avoided this' (Browne *et al.* 1993, p. 111). Where the criminal justice system itself is concerned, the inclusion of a mental health dimension as part of the ethnic monitoring now required under s. 95 of the Criminal Justice Act 1991 would also be helpful.

(iv) Violence and Mental Disorder

A culturally dominant stereotype of mentally ill people is that they are prone to violence, and popular images linking violence and madness – whether in the form of news items or fictional dramatisations in television and the cinema – are not only widespread in our society but also continually reproduced and reinforced by a variety of means (cf. Scheff 1966). One of these is through high profile cases of mentally disordered offenders, such as that recently of Christopher Clunis, which arouse considerable and justifiable anxiety that the lack of effective care and control can pose a threat to the very lives of those around them.[3] These are rare but shocking cases involving mentally ill people, and as Barham (1992) remarks: 'While the overall picture does not exhibit a distinct pattern of violence, it is none the less clear that in a minority of cases tragedies could all too easily occur if vigilance is not exercised' (p. 26). The Clunis inquiry has supported the idea of special supervision arrangements for the small minority of patients in the community identified as potentially dangerous. It also emphasised, however, that 'the vast majority of those people who suffer from schizophrenia live safely in the community' (DOH 1994, p. 115).

In these respects the Islington experience reflected other recent evidence, suggesting a higher proportion of violent offences among mentally disordered offenders than the average (cf. Taylor and Gunn 1984; Mendelson 1992; Hudson *et al.* 1993) Among those offenders for whom pre-sentence reports had been written, the SIR database indicated that those identified as having mental health problems were almost three times more likely to have committed crimes involving personal violence, with slightly more than one-third (37%) of all charges against people with mental health problems involving personal violence, threats or the possession of an offensive weapon. The large proportion of these offences, however, were of a relatively minor nature. Of the total (n = 20), there were ten cases of common assault or threatening behaviour, two cases of assault on a police officer, seven cases of actual bodily harm or carrying an offensive weapon, and only one case of grievious bodily harm.

The cases referred to the Mental Health Court Worker in the first years show an even higher proportion of personal violence, although again predominantly in the minor categories. A few very serious cases weigh heavily at the other end of the scale, however, such as one murder and two attempted murder charges appearing before magistrates on their way to a higher court. In such cases the Mental Health Court Worker can sometimes play a key role in obtaining a prompt forensic psychiatric assessment.

A simple breakdown of offences (see *Table 2*) shows that personal violence accounted for as much as 48% of the total, but that serious violence (including indecent assault and robbery) accounted for less than 14%. Most other types of offence were correspondingly lower than average, with the exception of criminal damage.

It is likely that the higher proportions of mentally disordered offenders

TABLE 2
*Charges Against Mentally Disordered Offenders**

	No.	%
Violence or threat (minor)		35
Common assault/public order offence	17	
Assault on police	1	
Actual bodily harm/offensive weapon	10	
Violence (serious)		14
Indecent assault	2	
Robbery	4	
Grievious bodily harm/wounding	2	
Murder/attempted murder	3	
TOTAL PERSONAL VIOLENCE	39	48
Damage		19
Criminal damage	11	
Arson	4	
Theft		20
Shoplifing	9	
Theft of motor vehicle	1	
Other theft	6	
Burglary (including attempts)	5	6
TOTAL PROPERTY OFFENCES	34	45
Other		7
Drink/drive	3	
Drugs possession	1	
Non-payment fine/breach order	2	
TOTAL OFFENCES	81	100

(*Note*: *Defendants referred to the Mental Health Court Worker and positively assessed as mentally disordered or probably so. The cases cover a twelve-month period to mid-April 1993. The charges against a further four referred cases in the same period are not recorded.)

appearing before the court on charges of relatively minor violence is once more a consequence of the enhanced 'visibility' of such offences. As already noted, the mentally ill are popularly conceived of as inherently violent. When a mentally disordered person then actually commits a violent act, he or she comes to embody this fearful stereotype. Stereotypes of violence by the mentally ill imply 'unpredictability' (the 'maniac' running 'amok' or going 'berserk') and hence are less likely to be dealt with in a confident way by either the public or professionals. Any study of the mentally disordered offender, or any practical scheme of assistance, will therefore on some occasions run headlong into this set of powerfully charged emotions. Indeed, more carefully balanced concepts of 'dangerousness' seem frail adversaries to such powerful sentiments.

The large bulk of those mentally disordered offenders charged with offences involving minor violence or disorder, however, do not appear to present any great difficulty for the courts. Most of the cases seen are dealt with by penalties such as a conditional discharge, a small fine, or 'one day in lieu' where someone has been held overnight in the police cells. A rare exception was a case where, as a result of an interview conducted by the Mental Health Court Worker, it became apparent that the defendant was harbouring delusions which could have resulted in harm to someone known to him. In this case the original charge had been non-violent, and although it should be emphasised that the outcome was a rarity in the Highbury Corner experience it offers proof that the presence of a skilled worker (whether in court or at some other point of contact) to whom a mentally disordered person could express their feelings may be an important first step in securing appropriate and prompt treatment.

The question of violence by mentally disordered offenders is, thus, both a mixture of the humdrum and dangerous – whether potential or actual. It is clearly necessary to guard against stereotypes, while ensuring adequate care and control. One final point of interest and special need is where the stereotypes of mental illness, violence and race collide.

We have already noted the over-representation of black people in referrals to the IMDOP scheme, although on the available evidence we are unable to offer a coherent explanation of this. What can be said with confidence, however, is that even within the SIR database (where black offenders with mental health problems are *not* over-represented) the black mentally disordered offender represents a small but concentrated area of multiple social difficulty. In all, only nine black offenders with mental health problems were identified in the SIR database. As many as seven of these cases involved personal violence, however, of whom three had served previous prison sentences and four were of no fixed abode. As indicated by BOP these seven cases accounted for one-third of all black offenders within the SIR database who had been charged with personal violence (Lawrence *et al.* 1992, p. 8). So that while the 'violent' black mentally disordered offender is hardly a big problem in numerical terms, this represents a tight concentration of high-profile social problems. Perhaps it is out of such acorns that the mighty oaks of stereotypical judgments grow.

Conclusions

Within the criminal justice system, even in a busy inner-city court, mentally disordered offenders appear to be many fewer in number than has been sometimes assumed, but the complexity and apparent intractability of their needs renders inadequate the aim of 'diversion' alone. As argued by Fennell (1991, p. 333), the likelihood that mentally disordered offenders will continue to find their way to prison means that 'there is an urgent need to consider how a humane and therapeutic psychiatric service might be provided within the prison system'. Moreover diversion, if seen in terms of services located at individual entry points such as police stations or courts, is a logistical nightmare. A relatively tiny number of people passing through a myriad of decision-making points in the criminal justice system cannot be dealt with by posting a gatekeeper, like a cat at a mousehole, at every opening.

Court-based psychiatrists are clearly very valuable for the minority within this minority – the acute psychotics who need immediate access to a hospital bed. For less acute cases, psychiatric assessment alone does little if unaccompanied by effective follow-up to community resources. That is where panel assessment schemes, or court schemes employing psychiatric nurses such as that at Highbury Corner, offer more chance of active liaison.

Given the relative infrequency and wide scatter of mentally disordered offenders, what is needed is a combination of access to specialised advice and assessment services at key centres or on-call to serve a wide area, combined with (as the Reed report made clear) a high level of generalised awareness at all levels of decision-making within the system. Even this will not produce lasting results without a much greater degree of permeability between the relevant service providers, although in view of the experience of inter-agency co-operation in other spheres it is perhaps too much to hope for a shared view of the issues (Pearson *et al.* 1992).

The three major problem areas highlighted in this paper by the Islington experience – accommodation needs; the apparent overlap between mental health problems and substance misuse; and the over-representation of black people with psychotic illness – are all matters which challenge perceptions and practices across a range of agencies of the criminal justice and penal systems, health, housing and social services. The fourth identified issue of violence – which occasionally involves serious risks, but which is also more commonly a matter of relatively minor incidents stirred with a stereotypical spoon – so often clouds and overshadows these other matters for the lack of effective systems of care and control where these are truly needed, and obstructs progress in other spheres.

We have focussed on these particular issues because we believe that they act in various combinations to provide the main social obstacles to the goal set by the Reed committee, that mentally disordered offenders should be cared for 'as far as possible in the community, rather than in institutional settings' (Department of Health and Home Office 1992a, p. 40). As Jill Peay (1994, p. 1119) has recently remarked in a review of the field, such a stance is 'disarmingly straightforward'. Quite apart from the need to provide effective controls as well as to promote community care, it is a position which risks glossing over numerous difficulties in terms of how mentally disordered offenders secure access to services:

> In some cases mentally disturbed offenders may need access to specialist services, such as a specialist bail hostel. However, many will simply need access to those community care services which exist to meet the needs of mentally disturbed people in general. *Involvement in the criminal justice system is often a reason why these services are denied to them.* (NACRO 1993, p. 19, italics added)

Especially, we might add, if you are homeless, black, involved in drugs or alcohol, or perceived as violent. It is possible, even where a person is not an offender, for the perceived risk of future violence to outweigh the legal rights of mental patients appearing before Mental Health Review Tribunals and thus deny the person's release from hospital into the community (Peay 1989, p. 182–4), thereby providing a form of 'custodial detention by other means'.

Besides changes in understanding and attitude, the necessary changes in access to community services will not come about without the nuts and bolts of inter-agency co-operation envisaged by the Reed Report. There has to be more than lip-service recognition that the solutions for the great majority of mentally disordered offenders do not lie in psychiatric wards and special hospitals, but in local support of a low-key nature provided by a combination of health, housing and social services at ground level. Establishing structures which are properly resourced in terms of both personnel and material benefits is what will prevent more mentally disturbed people from acquiring the role and status of 'disordered offender'. Ironically, as things stand at present, for many a court appearance may be the only way that their needs will become apparent.

Notes

[1] The initiative, based at Highbury Corner Magistrates' Court, is run jointly by the Inner London Probation Service and the Mental After Care Association. Research and evaluation of the initiative has been funded by grants from the Home Office through the Islington Safer Cities Project, the Inner London Probation Service, and the Mental After Care Association.

[2] Differences have often been noted in the ways in which both the courts and psychiatry regard women as against men. These are matters with considerable historical precedent (Showalter 1987) and are reflected in the increased likelihood for the courts to request psychiatric reports for women (Allen 1987). Equally, while the male:female ratio in the prison population is 28:1 in the special hospitals it is only 5:1 (Peay 1994). While the number of referrals of women to the Highbury Corner scheme are too small to allow meaningful comparisons, gender differences such as these do not appear to show through. In the first year's referrals, however, one striking observation is that women were much less likely to be charged with offences involving personal violence: one-fifth of women as opposed to one-half of men (cf. *Table 2*). For a recent study of psychiatric assessments of women remanded to Holloway prison see Dell *et al.* (1993).

[3] Christopher Clunis killed Jonathan Zito in a random stabbing at Finsbury Park Underground Station, North London, on 17 December 1992. He was a paranoid schizophrenic with a history of violence and hospital admissions who had been discharged from Guy's Hospital twelve weeks previously. An inquiry found that

all agencies involved, including hospitals, social services, and the police must share the blame for what happened. There was no effective care plan and responsible professionals who should have known about his violent history did not. Clunis, who had never kept an outpatient appointment, did not see a psychiatrist at any time after his discharge. Social services failed to achieve a home assessment, and the police did not arrest him although only a few days before the killing he had attacked a man in the street with a screwdriver and in another incident chased children and adults brandishing a screwdrivr (cf. DOH 1994; *The Independent*, 19 July 1993 and 25 February 1994).

References

Allen, H. (1987) *Justice Unbalanced: Gender, Psychiatry and Judicial Decisions*, Milton Keynes: Open University Press.

Barham, P. (1992) *Closing the Asylum*, Harmondsworth: Penguin.

Barham, P. and Hayward, R. (1995) *Relocating Madness From the Mental Patient to the Person*, London: Free Association Books.

Bartlett, A., Eastman, N., Backhouse, A. and Evans, C. (1992) *The National Health Service, the Criminal Justice System and the Penal System: Evaluation of the Interface in the South West Thames Health Region* (Interim Report), London: St. George's Hospital Medical School, University of London.

Bebbington, P., Wilkins, S., Jones, P., Foerster, A., Murray, R., Toone, B. and Lewis, S. (1993) 'Life events and psychosis: initial results from the Camberwell Collaborative Psychosis Study', *British Journal of Psychiatry, 162*, 72–9.

Blagg, H., Pearson, G., Sampson, A., Smith, D. and Stubbs, P. (1988) 'Inter-agency cooperation: rhetoric and reality', in: T. Hope and M. Shaw (Eds.), *Communities and Crime Reduction*, London: HMSO.

Blumenthal, S. and Wessely, S. (1992) 'The extent of local arrangements for the diversion of the mentally abnormal offender from custody' (Report to the Department of Health from the Institute of Psychiatry and King's College Hospital Medical School, unpublished).

Brown, G. W. and Birley, J. L. T. (1968) 'Crises and life changes and the onset of schizophrenia', *Journal of Health and Social Behaviour, 9*, 203–14.

Brown, G. W., Harris, T. and Peto, J. (1973) 'Life events and psychiatric disorder', *Psychological Medicine, 3* (2), 159–76.

Browne, D., Francis, E. and Crowe, I. (1993) 'The needs of ethnic minorities', in: W. Watson and A. Grounds (Eds.), *The Mentally Disordered Offender in an Era of Community Care*, Cambridge: Cambridge University Press.

Burney, E. (1992) *Mentally Disordered Offenders: From Court to Community: A Study in an Inner London Magistrates' Court*, London: Goldsmiths' College, University of London.

Burney, E. (1993) *Islington Mentally Disordered Offenders Project: Evaluation Report Number One*, London: Goldsmiths' College, University of London.

Butler, Lord (1975) *Report of the Committee on Mentally Abnormal Offenders*, Cmnd. 6244.

Campbell, P. (1990) 'Mental health self-advocacy', in: L. Winn (Ed.), *Power to the People: The Key to Responsive Services in Health and Social Care*, London: King's Fund Centre.

Cope, R. (1989) 'The compulsory detention of Afro-Caribbeans under the Mental Health Act', *New Community, 15* (3), 343–56.

Dell, S., Robertson, G., James, K. and Grounds, A. (1993) 'Remands and psychiatric assessments at Holloway Prison, I & II', *British Journal of Psychiatry*, *163*, 634–44.

Department of Health (1994) *The Report of the Inquiry into the Care and Treatment of Christopher Clunis*, London: HMSO.

Department of Health and Home Office (1992a) *Review of Health and Social Services for Mentally Disordered Offenders Requiring Similar Services: Final Summary Report*, Cm. 2088.

Department of Health and Home Office (1992b) *Review of Health and Social Services for Mentally Disordered Offenders Requiring Similar Services: Report of the Official Working Group on Services for People with Special Needs*, London: Department of Health/Home Office.

Fahy, T. (1989) 'The police as a referral agency for psychiatric emergencies: a review', *Medicine, Science and Law*, *29* (4), 315–22.

Fairhead, S. (1981) *Persistent Petty Offenders* (Home Office Research Study No. 66), London: HMSO.

Fennell, P. (1991) 'Diversion of mentally disordered offenders from custody', *Criminal Law Review*, *May*, 333–48.

Fernando, S. (1991) *Mental Health, Race and Culture*, London: Macmillan.

Gordon, D. and Hedderman, C. (1993) 'Panel assessment schemes and other responses to mentally disordered offenders: a survey of probation areas', *Home Office Research Bulletin*, *34*, 9–12.

Gudjonsson, G., Clare, I., Rutter, S. and Pearse, J. (1994) 'Persons at risk during interviews in police custody: the identification of vulnerabilities', *Home Office Research Bulletin*, *35*, 31–2.

Gunn, J., Maden, T. and Swinton, M. (1991a) *Mentally Disordered Prisoners*, London: Home Office.

Gunn, J., Maden, T. and Swinton, M. (1991b) 'How many prisoners should be in hospital?', *Home Office Research Bulletin*, *31*, 9–15.

Hawker, C. and Ritchie, P. (1990) *Contracting for Community Care: New Strategies*, London: King's Fund Centre.

Hedderman, C. (1993) *Panel Assessment Schemes for Mentally Disordered Offenders* (Research and Planning Unit Paper 76), London: Home Office.

Hood, R. (1992) *Race and Sentencing*, Oxford: Clarendon Press.

Hudson, B. L., Cullen, R. and Roberts, C. (1993) *Training for Work with Mental Disordered Offenders*, London: CCETSW.

Inner London Probation Service (1993) *Black Groups Initiative*, London: ILPS.

James, D. V. and Hamilton, L. W. (1991) 'The Clerkenwell Scheme: assessing efficacy and cost of a psychiatric liaison service to a magistrates' court', *British Medical Journal*, *303* (6797), 282–5.

James, D. V. and Hamilton, L. W. (1992) 'Setting up psychiatric liaison schemes to magistrates' courts: problems and practicalities', *Medicine, Science and Law*, *32* (2), 167–76.

Joseph, P. L. A. (1992) *Psychiatric Assessment at the Magistrates' Court*, London: Home Office and Department of Health.

Joseph, P. L. A. and Potter, M. (1993) 'Diversion from custody, I & II', *British Journal of Psychiatry*, *162*, 325–34.

Lawrence, D., Pearson, G. and Aina, C. (1992) *Black Offenders Project: Report to the Inner London Probation Service and the Islington Safer Cities Project*, London: Goldsmiths' College, University of London.

Littlewood, R. and Lipsedge, M. (1982) *Aliens and Alienists: Ethnic Minorities and Psychiatry*, Harmondsworth: Penguin.

Mendelson, E. F. (1992) 'A survey of practice at a regional forensic service', *British Journal of Psychiatry*, *160*, 769–76.

Mental Health Act Commission (1993) *Fifth Biennial Report 1991–1993*, London: HMSO.

Meuser, K. T. *et al.* (1990) 'Prevalence of substance abuse in schizophrenia', *Schizophrenia Bulletin, 16* (1), 31–55.

NACRO (1993) *Community Care and Mentally Disturbed Offenders* (NACRO Mental Health Advisory Committee, Policy Paper 1), London: NACRO.

NACRO (1994) *Diverting Mentally Disturbed Offenders* (NACRO Mental Health Advisory Committee, Policy Paper 2), London: NACRO.

Pearson, G., Blagg, H., Smith, D., Sampson, A. and Stubbs, P. (1992) 'Crime, conflict and community: the multi-agency approach', in: D. Downes (Ed.), *Unravelling Criminal Justice*, London: Routledge.

Pearson, G. and Lawrence, D. E. (1995) 'Race and ethnic monitoring: how not to do it', *Criminal Justice, 13*(1), 1–2.

Peay, J. (1989) *Tribunals on Trial: A Study of Decision-Making Under the Mental Health Act 1983*, Oxford: Clarendon Press.

Peay, J. (1994) 'Mentally disordered offenders', in: M. Maguire, R. Morgan and R. Reiner (Eds.), *The Oxford Handbook of Criminology*, Oxford: Clarendon Press.

Reiner, R. (1993) 'Race, crime and justice: models of interpretation', in: L. R. Gelsthorpe (Ed.), *Minority Ethnic Groups in the Criminal Justice System*, Cambridge: Institute of Criminology.

Revolving Doors Agency (1993) *An Initial Assessment of the Scale and Nature of Contact Between Mentally Distressed People in Hammersmith and Fulham and the Criminal Justice System*, London: Revolving Doors.

Revolving Doors Agency (1994) *The Management of People with Mental Health Problems by the Paddington Police*, London: Revolving Doors.

Ridgely, M. S., Goldman, H. H. and Willenbring, M. (1990) 'Barriers to the care of persons with dual diagnosis', *Schizophrenia Bulletin, 16* (1), 123–32.

Robertson, G., Pearson, R. and Gibb, R. (1993) 'Entry of mentally disordered people to the criminal justice system' (Interim report to the Home Office Research and Planning Unit, unpublished).

Robertson, G., Dell, S., James, K. and Grounds, A. (1994) 'Psychotic men remanded in custody to Brixton Prison', *British Journal of Psychiatry, 164*, 55–61.

Rogers, A. and Faulkner, A. (1987) *A Place of Safety: MIND'S Research into Police Referrals to Psychiatric Services*, London: MIND.

Scheff, T. J. (1966) *Being Mentally Ill*, New York: Aldine.

Shah, R. and Pease, K. (1992) 'Crime, race and reporting to the police', *Howard Journal, 31*, 192–9.

Showalter, E. (1987) *The Female Malady: Women, Madness and English Culture, 1830–1960*, London: Virago.

Skogan, W. (1990) *The Police and Public in England and Wales: A British Crime Survey Report* (Home Office Research Study No. 117), London: HMSO.

Smith, D. J. and Gray, J. (1983) *Police and People in London*, London: Policy Studies Institute.

Spurgeon, D. (1993) *Diversion at Point of Arrest: CPN Attachment at Bournville Lane Police Station* (Interim Report), London: Mental Health Foundation.

Taylor, P. and Gunn, J. (1984) 'Violence and psychosis I: risk of violence among psychotic men', *British Medical Journal, 288*, 1945–9.

Walker, J. (1992) *Police Contact with the Mentally Disordered*, London: Home Office Police Department.

Walker, M. A. (1988) 'The court disposal of young males, by race, in London in 1983', *British Journal of Criminology, 29*, 441–60.

Walker, M. A. (1989) 'The court disposal and remands of white, Afro-Caribbean, and Asian men', *British Journal of Criminology, 29*, 353–67.

Williams, J. (1993) 'Report to No 17 Area Criminal Justice Liaison Committee: Sub-Committee on Mentally Disordered Offenders' (unpublished).
World Health Organisation (1989) *Consumer Involvement in Mental Health and Rehabilitation Services* (WHO/MNH/MEP 89, 7), Geneva: Division of Mental Health, WHO.

Date submitted: May 94
Date accepted: October 94

[16]

Mentally Disordered Suspects in the Criminal Justice System

PHILIP W. H. FENNELL*

The risk of wrongful conviction is particularly acute for suspects suffering from mental disorder. Because mentally disordered people sometimes behave in a way which attracts attention, they become suspects. Once they are suspects, their demeanour may lead investigating officers to believe that they are being evasive or telling lies. They may be vulnerable in that they may make false admissions, whether because they have the type of personality that is anxious to please investigating officers or because they are compulsive confessors.

Drawing strongly on the work of Gudjonsson, who has pioneered much forensic psychological work on suggestibility, the Runciman Commission refers to the substantial body of research showing four different categories of false confession:

> (i) people may make confessions voluntarily as a result of a morbid desire for publicity or notoriety; or to relieve feelings of guilt about a real or imagined previous transgression; or because they cannot distinguish between reality and fantasy;
> (ii) a suspect may confess from a desire to protect someone else from interrogation and prosecution;
> (iii) people may see a prospect of immediate advantage from confessing (e.g. an end to questioning or release from custody) even though the long term consequences are far worse (termed coerced compliant confessions); and
> (iv) people may be persuaded temporarily by the interrogators that they really have done the act in question (coerced-internalised).[1]

Concern about the vulnerability of mentally disordered suspects as regards making false confessions has grown dramatically since the late 1970s. Colin Lattimore, one of the defendants in the miscarriage of justice which led to the appointment in 1978 of the Royal Commission on Criminal Procedure (the Philips Commission) had a learning disablity. He was convicted on an alleged confession which it later emerged could not have been true. At the time of his arrest, Colin Lattimore was an eighteen-year old with a learning disability who, along with two other boys, was convicted of the killing of Maxwell Confait. Lattimore's conviction was based almost wholly on a

* *Cardiff Law School, University of Wales, P.O. Box 427, Museum Avenue, Cardiff CF1 1XD, Wales*

confession allegedly made to the police, which he claimed he had been frightened into making. His case was referred to the Court of Appeal after he had spent over two years in Rampton, and his conviction was quashed on the basis of evidence (which had been available at the time of the trial) showing that he could not possibly have been at the scene of the crime. The Philips Commission report described how it began its work in 1978 in a climate of concern raised by the Confait murder case which, 'by implication, raised serious questions about the way in which the police had handled the investigation, particularly in relation to the treatment of juveniles and mentally handicapped suspects.'[2]

Scarcely more than a decade after the Philips Report we find that, of the recent wave of miscarriages of justice straddling the appointment of the Royal Commission on Criminal Justice, a considerable number have involved confessions taken from mentally disordered people. These include Stefan Kiszko,[3] convicted before PACE came into force, Engin Raghip,[4] David Mackenzie,[5] Stephen Miller (one of the Cardiff Three),[6] and Judith Ward.[7] There have been a large number of others too where confessions made by mentally disordered people have been found to be unreliable.[8] Given this background, it is perhaps surprising that there is very little discussion in the Runciman report which relates specifically to the needs of mentally disordered offenders.

The Commission did however stress that its concern for the situation of mentally disordered suspects was an important factor in its decision to recommend retention of the right of silence:

> There is the risk that, if the police were allowed to warn suspects who decline to answer their questions that they face the prospect of adverse comment at trial, such a power would sometimes be abused. It is now well-established that certain people, including some who are not mentally ill or handicapped, will confess to offences that did not commit, whether or not there has been impropriety on the part of the police. The threat of adverse comment at trial may increase the risk of confused or vulnerable suspects making false confessions.[9]

The Commission was only too well aware that it is the less experienced and more vulnerable suspects against whom the threat of adverse comment would be likely to be more damaging. It concluded by saying that: 'There are too many cases of improper pressures being brought to bear on suspects in police custody, even where the safeguards of PACE and the Codes of Practice have been supposedly in force, for the majority to regard this with equanimity.'[10]

Since the Commission wrote those words, however, Home Secretary Michael Howard's package of radical, right-wing criminal justice reforms has been presented to Parliament as the Criminal Justice and Public Order Bill. Its most notorious criminal justice provisions are clauses 27–30. Clause 27 allows adverse inferences to be drawn from a suspect's failure to mention a fact when questioned or charged if he or she subsequently relies on the fact in his or her defence, and could reasonably be expected to have mentioned it. Adverse inferences would also be drawn by virtue of clause 29 if an accused fails to account for objects, substances or marks at the time of arrest, or by virtue of clause 30 if the accused fails to account for his or her presence at any place.

Clause 28 deals with the right of silence at trial. It provides that where the accused has not informed the court that he or she will offer evidence in his or her defence at the trial, the court is required to call upon the accused to give evidence and the court or jury may draw such inferences as are proper from the accused's refusal to give evidence. This provision would introduce a novel rite into the trial, with a potentially powerful influence on the minds of jurors. The accused would be called on to give evidence and warned of the consequences of not doing so. The ritual undermining of the accused's case can only be avoided if the accused declares an intention to testify, or where it appears to the court that the physical or mental condition of the accused make it undesirable for him or her to be called upon to give evidence. If passed, this provision will generate much work for forensic psychologists and psychiatrists, and an early question will be just how bad an accused person's mental condition needs to be before it will be undesirable. Presumably this means that it would be undesirable in the interests of the accused and in the interests of justice, for him or her to be called on to give evidence. All four clauses have the potential to increase pressure on already mentally vulnerable suspects to confess, and to generate false confessions. All of which leads to a number of questions and speculations. How effective are existing safeguards? What impact will clauses 27–30 have on the existing safeguards? And what safeguards would we have recommended to the Runciman Commission for mentally disordered suspects had it been known that the right of silence was to be abolished? The rest of this essay discusses the development and application of the safeguards in PACE and its code C for the protection of mentally disordered suspects, and the recommendations of the Commission.

The unreliability of confession evidence is often revealed because some other piece of evidence comes to light which is inconsistent with its truth. This happened in the case of Stephen Kiszko, who died this Christmas less than two years after his release following sixteen years in prison. In terms of both the disgrace to English criminal justice and the tragic consequences for its victim, this was perhaps the most appalling of all the miscarriages of justice. His case occurred before the PACE safeguards were introduced, and his imprisonment stretched from before the appointment of the Philips Commission until after the Runciman Commission was set up. He was released in February 1992, sixteen years after his conviction in 1975 of the murder of an eleven-year-old girl. The victim had been brutally stabbed, and the murderer had masturbated over her body. Stefan was arrested and questioned for two days without a solicitor present, before he finally confessed to the murder, and to exposing himself to three girls shortly before the killing.

It was known at the time by the police surgeon in charge of the forensic tests that Stefan was infertile, and that the sample taken from the victim's clothing could not have come from an infertile man. Although the significance of this information was apparently made known to the police, it was not disclosed to the defence and did not emerge at the trial. Kiszko's alibi was disbelieved because it came from members of his family. He retracted his confession, alleging it had been intimidated out of him. The police, expressing a desire 'to get this wrapped up by Christmas', had presented him with a statement and told him to sign it. His lawyer, David Waddington QC, later Home Secretary and now Lord Waddington, Governor of Bermuda, entered a plea of diminished responsibility, which contradicted his steadfast denials and his alibi evidence. The girls later retracted their allegation of flashing, saying they had made it all up. In 1992, the forensic evidence came before the Court of Appeal, his conviction was quashed, the investigation of the murder was re-opened, and another investigation into the original inquiry was set up.

THE BACKGROUND TO THE PACE SAFEGUARDS FOR MENTALLY DISORDERED SUSPECTS

At the time of the interrogations of both Colin Lattimore and Stefan Kiszko, the administrative directions appended to the *Judge's Rules on the Interrogation and taking of Statements by Police* required the interviewing officer to decide whether the suspect was mentally handicapped; if so, the mentally handicapped person was 'as far as practicable' required to be interviewed in the presence of an adult. There were all sorts of problems in implementing this protection, not least of which was that senior investigating officers in the Confait case professed never to have heard of the Judge's Rules.

Secondly, there was the factor identified by the Philips Commission that the identification of people with disorders requiring the presence of an adult was not an easy task for the police officer under 'the pressures of custody' with 'only his common sense and experience to go on.'[11] They went on to say that 'mental handicap may be a condition that is easy to diagnose in a consulting room, although even then there may be areas of dispute', noting that problems could arise with people suffering from mental illness, but that was 'not a matter for a lay person to try and diagnose.'[12] A doctor should be called in.

Thirdly, the requirement for a mentally handicapped person or a juvenile to be interviewed in the presence of an adult was limited by the words, 'as far as practicable'; finally, it was not clear exactly what the role of the adult was, beyond that of being a non-police witness.

The Philips Commission rejected two proposals for monitoring the conduct of all police interviews by the presence of an independent person. One option was to use defence solicitors, which they saw as too expensive, and involving the solicitors in an irresolvable role conflict between representing their client and independent monitoring of the interview. The other was using magistrates, solicitors or some other class of person to provide an independent account at trial of what went on during an interview. This too would be costly, as some sort of a paid service would have to be created if people were to be available round the clock, and the Commission doubted how long the public's impression of such a body would last.

The Confait affair made it inevitable that the protection of vulnerable juvenile and mentally handicapped suspects would be a central concern for the Philips Commission and, in this respect, they pinned their hopes on beefing up the 'adult' provisions, and making non-compliance a matter on which the jury would be warned.

The only permitted exception to the requirement that an independent adult should be present would be where a senior officer authorized the interview to proceed by certifying that there were reasonable grounds for believing that to wait for the arrival of an adult would involve a risk of serious harm to persons or damage to property.[13] It was envisaged that the adult required to be present with a mentally handicapped person or a juvenile should be a parent, guardian or somebody else known to them, if possible. A parent was felt to be the appropriate adult for a juvenile because, in the Commission's view, parents had a right to be present at the interrogation of their child.

The Philips Commission went on to suggest placing some obligation on local authorities to make provision for social workers always to be available out of ordinary working hours to act as independent adults. Here, at last, was an acceptable form of independent monitoring for the cost-conscious Commission. Parents would come free, and the cost of social workers could be met through local authority social services budgets. The role envisaged for the adults was partly parental, and partly to facilitate the interview. They were to provide support and advice, and to be present during the interview to ensure that the person being interviewed understood the questions being put to him or her. In the Commission's view they were emphatically *not* to attempt to act as the person's legal adviser.

VULNERABLE PEOPLE, CONFESSIONS, AND PACE

Section 77(1) of PACE specifes the circumstances in which the jury should be warned about the potential unreliability of a confession. It applies specifically to mentally handicapped defendants. Mental handicap means a state of arrested or incomplete development of mind which includes significant impairment of intelligence and social functioning,[14] what is now called 'learning disability.' Where the case against a mentally handicapped person depends wholly or substantially on his or her confession, unless the confession was made in the presence of an independent person, the judge must warn the jury of the special need for caution before convicting in reliance on it. The 'independent person' of s. 77 is the 'appropriate adult' of the PACE codes, required for all suspects who appear to be mentally disordered, a much wider group than just mentally handicapped people.

Mental disorder has a much wider meaning than mental handicap. It includes 'mental illness' which takes in all the psychotic illnesses, depressive disorder, dementia, and Alzheimer's Disease among others; 'arrested or incomplete development of mind' which includes all learning disability; 'psychopathic disorder', meaning a persistent disorder or disability of mind which results in abnormally aggressive or seriously irresponsible conduct on the part of the person concerned; and, in case there was something that had not been thought of, 'any other disorder or disability of mind'.[15]

Although appropriate adults are required by the codes to be present at the interviews of all mentally disordered suspects, s. 77 only requires a warning to be given to a jury where no adult was present at the interview of a mentally handicapped person. This is an inconsistency which the Runciman Commission has rightly recommended should be removed, but there are no proposals to extend the scope of s. 77 to all people with mental disorders in the Criminal Justice and Public Order Bill 1994.

Section 77 is narrow in scope and requires only a warning to the jury. If a defendant is mentally disordered, it is much better to have the confession excluded altogether under s. 76(2) of PACE if (a) it was made or obtained by oppression or (b) if something was said or done which was likely, in the circumstances existing at the time, to render unreliable any confession which might be made in consequence thereof. Something said or done for the purposes of s. 76(2)(b) can include failure to bring in an appropriate adult. The question under s. 76(2)(b) centres on whether something said or done was likely to render the confession unreliable, and not the likelihood that the confession is either true or false.[16] The burden of proof is on the prosecution to disprove an allegation of oppression or that something was said or done which was likely to render the confession unreliable. The court also has a discretion under s. 78 to exclude from the jury any evidence if it appears in all the circumstances, including those in which it was obtained, that the admission of the evidence would have such an adverse effect on the proceedings that the court ought not to admit it. Again, failure to bring in an appropriate adult can constitute grounds for the exercise of this discretion to exclude. Section 78 does not require there to have been misconduct on the part of the police before a confession can be excluded.[17] It is hardly surprising, then, that the strategy of defence advocates in such cases is to argue for exclusion, with s. 77 as a fall-back.[18]

Sections 76 and 78 have been applied in a number of cases involving patients with mental disorder of different types. In *R.* v. *Moss*,[19] the defendant, who was borderline mentally handicapped, had been in custody for nine days, had been denied access to a solicitor, and had not made any admissions until the fifth of nine interviews. The Court of Appeal held that the confession evidence should have been excluded under ss. 76 and 78. In *R.* v. *McKenzie*,[20] the appellant had a personality disorder which made him a compulsive confessor. He was also of below average intelligence. He confessed to a large number of serious crimes which he could not have committed. Lord Taylor CJ, delivering the judgment of the Court of Appeal, said that where:

> (1) the prosecution case depended wholly upon confessions;
> (2) the defendant suffered from a significant degree of mental handicap; and
> (3) the confessions were unconvincing to a point where a jury properly directed could not convict upon them,

then the judge, assuming he had not excluded the confessions earlier, should withdraw the case from the jury. A confession may be unconvincing if it lacks the incriminating details to be expected of a guilty and willing confessor, if it is inconsistent with other evidence or is otherwise inherently improbable. Although the court was invited by counsel for the appellant to extend the scope of the ruling to people with mental disorder generally, the judgment refers to defendants with a significant degree of mental handicap. However, it may be that the term was being used in a general rather than a technical sense, since it is doubtful whether McKenzie could have been regarded as suffering from a significant degree of learning disability.

There have also been cases where confessions of defendants with personality disorder have been declared unreliable. In 1988 a judge excluded a confession to murder made by a woman suffering from psychopathic disorder aggravated by alcohol abuse, because she might have been motivated by a childlike desire to protect her lover whom she had overheard confessing to the crime. In 1992 the Court of Appeal found that Judith Ward's admissions, made at a time when she had been suffering from severe personality disorder, could not be relied upon as being true, and her conviction of terrorist bombing offences was overturned as unsafe and unsatisfactory.[21]

As to psychotic illness, in *R.* v. *Miller*,[22] a case decided in 1986, the Court of Appeal held that a trial judge had discretion to refuse or to admit to evidence a confession which he was satisfied was a voluntary one even though it had been made by a person who was possibly in an irrational state of mind where much of what was said was the product of delusions or hallucinations. The appellant had confessed to the murder of his girlfriend following questioning by a police officer who knew him to be suffering from paranoid schizophrenia. He described how the killing took place and then said he had done it at the behest of the screams of 'arbitrised humans and small molecular people'. The judge, in deciding to admit the confessions, was found by the Court of Appeal to have carefully exercised his discretion on the grounds that the confession was not obtained by oppressive conduct, that the case was not so extreme that it would be proper to exclude the confession because of the suspect's mental condition, and that the jury, if properly directed would have no difficulty in separating the factual statements from the delusional material and could therefore rely on those statements. The confessions were not so unconvincing that no jury properly directed could possibly convict on them.

An important question has been the extent to which the court's decision to exclude under ss. 76 or 78 should be based on medical evidence of the defendant's likely mental state at the time of the confession. In 1988, in *R.* v. *Everett*,[23] the defendant, a forty-two-year-old with a mental age of eight, pleaded guilty to indecent assault after the trial judge ruled that evidence of admissions made to the police should not be excluded. He appealed on the grounds that the evidence had been wrongly admitted. His appeal was allowed because the judge had decided the question by reference only to the tapes of the interviews and had not taken into account the expert medical evidence of the mental condition of the accused. Everett was followed in *R.* v. *Raghip*,[24] the appeal of one of the Tottenham Three, a case described by the Runciman Commission as establishing the role of expert medical and psychological testimony in cases involving ss. 76 and 78.

In October 1985 there were serious disturbances at Broadwater Farm estate, London, sparked off by the death of a middle-aged black woman, Mrs Cynthia Jarrett, from a heart attack during a police raid on her house. During the violence, PC Keith Blakelock was set upon by a large group of men and brutally murdered. Over 300 officers were drafted into the area, and a large number of juveniles and young men were arrested, three of whom were later convicted. Their convictions were overturned when the senior officers were found to have falsified interview records in the case of one of the defendants, Winston Silcott, tainting the convictions of all three men.

Engin Raghip was nineteen when he was arrested. He was illiterate and, according to the expert testimony at the trial, was 'in the middle of the mildly mentally handicapped range'.[25] He was questioned for four days without either an appropriate adult or a solicitor present. It was argued at the trial that the evidence of the interviews should be excluded on the grounds that Raghip had been denied access to a solicitor, and that to interview him on ten separate occasions over four days without a solicitor, knowing that he was illiterate, and allowing him no visits until he had confessed, amounted to oppressive conduct, a submission which was rejected by the trial judge.

Considering whether the confession ought to be excluded under s. 76(2)(b), the judge heard expert evidence of Raghip's mental condition. However, he then declared the confession admissible on the basis of his own view, after hearing a tape recording of the interview, that the defendant understood the questions and had made rational answers. The expert psychological evidence of Raghip's mental ability did not go before the jury to assist them in their assessment of the confession.

The Court of Appeal held that the circumstances to be considered by the trial judge on a submission under s. 76(2)(b) include the mental condition of the defendant at the time of interview, and that that decision was to be taken on the basis of the medical evidence rather than the trial judge's own assessment of the defendant's performance at interview. Once the confession had been declared admissible, the judge was required to give a s. 77 warning, and the psychological evidence would have been required to assist the jury in their assessment, since they would not have been able accurately to judge Engin Raghip's mental condition at the time of the interview from his comparatively confident demeanour in court. The Runciman Commission welcomes the prospect that as a result of this judgment, the courts are more likely than in the past to admit expert evidence of a defendant's likely mental state at the time of interview,[26] recognizing that this made it essential that expert witnesses in forensic psychiatry and psychology continue to be provided by the relevant departments in hospitals and universities.[27] Since the implementation of PACE, the safeguards for defendants with mental health problems have increased significantly, with an increasing willingness on the part of the judiciary to acknowledge the factors which make mentally disordered defendants vulnerable to making false confessions. The central figure in those safeguards is the appropriate adult.

APPROPRIATE ADULTS

If a police officer has any suspicion or is told, in good faith, that a suspect of any age may be mentally disordered, mentally handicapped or mentally incapable of understanding the significance of questions put to him or her, or any replies made to them, then the person must be given special treatment under the code and this includes securing the attendance of an appropriate adult.[28] Research evidence has shown that the number of occasions on which appropriate adults are summoned to the police station is very low by comparison with the numbers of suspects known to be vulnerable by reason of mental disorder.[29] The research carried out for the Runciman Commission by Gudjonsson, Clare, Rutter, and Pearse found 6 per cent of suspects in the study had a reading age of below nine years, were illiterate, and needed an appropriate adult.[30] A further 7 per cent were suffering from mental illness, 3 per cent from mental handicap, and one or two had brain damage. The study found that, while police were able to identify juveniles and people with serious mental disabilities, they were understandably less able to identify people with more minor disorders and handicaps. This is what we would expect from the cases which have reached the Court of Appeal, where appropriate adults have not been present at interviews. This is one area in which greater training for custody officers would be of potentially great benefit.

If a suspect appears to be suffering from a mental disorder, the custody officer must immediately call in the forensic medical examiner (newspeak for police surgeon) or, in an urgent case, send the person to hospital or call in the nearest available doctor.[31] Robertson's study of the role of police surgeons, which covered three London and twelve provincial police stations, found that mental illness accounted for about 9 per cent of examinations and mental handicap for about 0.5 per cent.[32] He noted a difference between London and elsewhere in the assessment and treatment of people who might be considered unfit for interview on grounds of mental health. Outside London, it was more frequently the case that suspects were considered unfit for interview but less frequent that an appropriate adult was called in. In London, on the other hand, few of those detained were declared unfit for interview but doctors advised the police to call in an appropriate adult in almost a quarter of cases referred to them for assessment of possible mental disorder. If a suspect's mental disorder is not identified, the safeguards in PACE code C will not be implemented, so it is important that police surgeons are `properly trained in the recognition of different forms of mental disorder.The Reed Committee reported at the end of 1992 on health and social services for mentally disordered offenders and others requiring similar services, recommending that there should be closer links between forensic medical examiners and local psychiatric services, that forensic examiners should be encouraged to develop better understanding of the needs of mentally disordered offenders, and that specialist panels should be established to enable them to gain relevant experience.[33] The Runciman Commission recommend that duty psychiatrist schemes should be piloted in busy police stations in city centres, and every police station should have arrangements for calling upon psychiatric help when this is needed. Police surgeons should be able to obtain advice from a psychiatrist about cases where they have doubts about the mental state of suspects.[34]

Having secured any necessary medical attention for the suspect, the custody officer must as soon as possible identify and call in an appropriate adult.[35] A mentally disordered person must not be interviewed or asked to sign a statement without an appropriate adult attending.[36] The only exception is where an officer of the rank of superintendent at least certifies that delay will involve a serious risk of harm to persons or serious loss or serious damage to property. Even then, questioning may not continue in the absence of the appropriate adult once sufficient information to avert the risk has been received. A record must be made of the grounds for any decision to begin an interview in such circumstances.[37]

A significant problem for the police in cases where mental disorder has been identified is finding someone to act an appropriate adult. Research by Brown, Ellis, and Larcomb, published in 1993, found that specialist and psychiatric social workers were increasingly being called in as appropriate adults in such cases of mental disorder as were identified (about 1 per cent of their sample or 110 cases).[38] Local authority social services are increasingly being asked to provide appropriate adults but they may not have the staff available, especially if the questioning is prolonged over a period of days or even weeks.

The role of the appropriate adult is not to act simply as an observer and this is to be explained to him or her. The code states that the role has three aspects: (i) to advise the person being questioned; (ii) to observe whether or not the interview is being conducted properly and fairly; and (iii) to facilitate communication with the person being interviewed.[39] Appropriate adults who have no training and experience in the role may be unclear about what the role actually involves. One danger is that the role of facilitating communication may be over-emphasized to the extent that the adult becomes an agent of the interrogating officers, to the detriment of the advisory role.[40] The voluntary organization MENCAP now has a policy of not providing appropriate adults because of the difficulties experienced by their staff.

The Runciman Commission's attention was expressly drawn to a serious difficulty with the role, namely, that where the suspects make admissions in the presence of the appropriate adults, the adults are not covered by the same protection of legal professional privilege as would be a solicitor. It was not clear to the Commission whether the same privilege should apply as to communications between a client and his or her solicitor or whether, given that an appropriate adult may not be a solicitor, different rules should apply. As far as social-worker appropriate adults are concerned, the relevant social services and professional guidance put a duty on them to disclose. As the Runciman Commission put it:

> If . . . the appropriate adult must, if required by a court, give evidence of any incriminating material, a proposition which clearly undermines the whole purpose of the role, then this needs to be clearly stated. The suspect should not be given the impression that whatever he or she says to the appropriate adult will be entirely in confidence if that is not the case.[41]

The Commission recommended a comprehensive review of the role, functions, qualifications, training, and availability of appropriate adults, and saw as an urgent task for that review the formulation of an unambiguous rule on the confidentiality of communications to appropriate adults.

The fundamental question is whether we should continue to have appropriate adults, in view of the difficulties in finding suitable people and the internal contradictions between advising the suspect and facilitating the investigation inherent in the role. Their primary function should be to protect the suspect from oppression and unfairness in the conduct of the interview by offering advice and support.

Are these not roles which could be performed by fully qualified solicitors with special training in advising mentally disordered clients? A solicitor who is present at the police station in a professional capacity may not act as the appropriate adult.[42] The Runciman Commission was not clear why solicitors should not be able to act as appropriate adults.[43] The thinking behind the prohibition appears to be that it was felt they would lack the necessary independence. The need for vulnerable people to have access to a solicitor who is properly equipped to deal with the difficulties of advising and representing a mentally disordered person has been made clear by the fact that, in a number of miscarriages where defendants have been pressured into confessing, they have waived their right to a solicitor until after the confession had been elicited from them. If mentally disordered suspects can be induced to confess to serious crimes which they have not committed, how easy must it be to convince them that they do not need a solicitor.

If solicitors who were properly trained in representing mentally disordered clients were automatically made available for mentally disordered suspects, many of the problems with the appropriate adult system for this group could be resolved. They would need to be properly trained, as the Cardiff Three case[44] reminds us. The suspect Miller's solicitor sat passively by while police shouted at Miller what they wanted him to say after he had denied involvement over 300 times. Miller was on the borderline of mental handicap. He had an IQ of seventy-five, a mental age of eleven, and a reading age of eight. His eventual confession, which incriminated his co-defendants, was excluded as oppressive under s. 76. The court of Appeal was critical of both the police, who had adopted techniques of interrogation which were wholly contrary to the spirit and the letter of PACE and the codes, and of the solicitor who seemed to have sat in on the interviews and done little else. The Court of Appeal felt that his presence might actually have rendered a disservice since the officers might have taken the view that unless and until the solicitor intervened, they could not be criticized for going too far. The Court stressed that 'a solicitor fulfilling the exacting duty of assisting a suspect during interviews should not remain passive but should discharge his function responsibly and courageously.'[45] A specialist section of the duty solicitor panel to provide solicitors who would automatically be called in to represent mentally vulnerable suspects deserves serious consideration.

However, it is not simply a matter of improving or replacing the appropriate adult safeguards. If they are enacted, the proposals in the Criminal Justice and Public Order Bill throw a large spanner in the works of the protection provided by PACE and the codes. Appropriate adults have to be present during the interview of a mentally disordered suspect; there has been a significant case law on what is an interview for the purposes of PACE.[46] Code C defines an interview as questioning a person regarding his involvement or suspected involvement in a criminal offence or offences.[47] In *R.* v. *Maguire*[48] Otton J. said that the requirements of the code applied to interviews held not only at police stations, but also on other premises, and premises include any vehicle,[49] but that the code did not prevent a police officer from asking questions at or near the scene of a crime to elicit an explanation which if true or accepted would exculpate the suspect. If, in the course of such questions, a juvenile made admissions, they would be prima facie admissible even though no adult was present. These statements were considered in *R.* v. *Weekes*[50] where the Court of Appeal drew a distinction between an enquiry that a police office has to make on the spot when he asks a suspect to account for his or her movements and presence, and a more formal type of questioning that might take place in the police station. In this case, the appellant responded to the initial questions put to him in the car by denying being involved in the robbery and implicating another youth. The questions continued and he admitted being on the look out. The first part of the conversation was not an interview, but once the appellant started making admissions the police already had an explanation from him and therefore there should have been an appropriate adult present. The Court of Appeal held that the whole conversation was an interview and accordingly there had been a breach of the PACE code and the judge ought to have excluded the confession under s. 78. The essence of the question was whether fairness demanded that, in the circumstances of a particular case, the provisions of the code of practice should be implemented.

In an effort to clarify the definition of interview, the code was amended, but in a way which only served to deepen the confusion. The new definition states that questioning a person only to obtain information or his or her explanation of the facts or in the ordinary course of the officer's duties does not constitute an interview for the purposes of the code. In *R.* v. *Cox*, McCullough J. said that whether a conversation amounted to an interview had to be considered within the framework of the officer's decision to arrest, the suspect's arrest, his or her arrival at the police station, notification of his or her right to free legal advice, and the interview. Fairness should be the guide. This follows the purposive approach advocated by Birch in her commentary on *Maguire* where she advocated abandoning the search for a definition in favour of asking whether questioning is of a kind at which the safeguards on interviewing in the code were likely to be directed. As she said then:

> Once people have been arrested and loaded into police cars it is likely that they were intended to benefit from these provisions in respect of questions put to them about the offence under investigation.[11]

The clauses in the new Bill cast that assumption into doubt. The impact of the provisions on mentally disordered and juvenile suspects have clearly not been though through or, if they have, the Government is prepared to pay the price of a further series of miscarriages of justice involving mentally disordered suspects.

Apart from the proposals on appropriate adults, and the proposals for warnings in a prescribed form to be given to juries of the dangers of convicting on uncorroborated confession evidence where the prosecution is relying wholly or mainly on a confession, which would apply to all suspects, the Runciman Commission has made few proposals specifically directed to the protection of mentally vulnerable suspects. It has expressed broad and tentative support for the proposal of the CPS and other witnesses to combine caution with a requirement that the offender co-operate with social work agencies or the probation service or to agree to consult a doctor or to attend a clinic. Referring to one police area where an informal system has already been developed, it recommends that this topic should be looked at further. The imposition of an obligation to accept interventions of this nature without due process would risk breach of Article 6 of the European Convention, and any such schemes would need to be carefully drawn to avoid this possibility.

One of the most important statements of principle in the Runciman Report is that 'the protection of suspects from unfair or unreasonable pressure is just as important to the criminal justice system as the thoroughness with which the police carry out their investigations.'[52] With its Criminal Justice and Public Order Bill, the Government has launched a full-scale attack not only on this principle but on the PACE regime. Unless urgent action is taken to safeguard the position of mentally disordered suspects, there will undoubtedly be a further sorry procession through the Court of Appeal of miscarriages involving false or unreliable confessions by this vulnerable group.

NOTES AND REFERENCES

1 *Report of the Royal Commission on Criminal Justice* ('RCCJ') (1993; Cm. 2263; Chair, Lord Runciman) 57.
2 *Report of the Royal Commission on Criminal Procedure* (1981; Cmnd. 8092; Chair, Lord Phillips) para. 1.5.
3 Unreported, 18 February 1992.
4 Unreported, 5 December 1991.
5 *Independent* 28 July 1992.
6 *R.* v. *Miller, R.* v. *Paris, R.* v. *Abdullahi, Times,* 24 December 1992.
7 *Independent,* 5 June 1992.
8 Including *R.* v. *Harvey* [1988] *Crim Law Rev.* 241; *R.* v. *Delaney* [1988] Cr. App. R. 338; *R.* v. *Everett* [1988] *Crim. Law Rev.* 826; *R.* v. *Lamont* [1989] *Crim Law Rev.* 813; *R.* v. *Moss* [1990] 91 Cr. App. R. 371; *R.* v. *Brine* [1992] *Crim. Law Rev.* 122.
9 RCCJ, op. cit., n. 1, 52.
10 id., pp. 54–5.
11 id., para. 4.106.
12 id.
13 id., paras. 4.104 and 4.107.
14 Police and Criminal Evidence Act (PACE) s. 77(3).
15 Mental Health Act 1983, s. 1(2).
16 *R.* v. *Cox* [1991] *Crim Law Rev.* 276.
17 *Brine,* op. cit., n. 8.
18 See Diana Birch, note to *Lamont,* op. cit., n. 8, which is one of the few appeal cases dealing with the duty under s. 77. Most have been upheld on the grounds that the confession should have been excluded under s. 76(2)(b) or s. 78.
19 *Moss,* op. cit., n. 8.
20 [1993] 1 W.L.R. 453; *Independent,* 28 July 1992.
21 *Independent,* 5 June 1992.
22 [1986] 1 W.L.R. 1191.
23 *Everett,* op. cit., n. 8.
24 *Times,* 9 December 1991.
25 Two of the other defendants whose confessions were ruled inadmissible at the trial were more severely learning disabled than Raghip.
26 RCCJ, op. cit., n. 1, p. 58.
27 id., p. 152.
28 PACE code C, para. 1.4.
29 B. Irvine and I. MacKenzie, *Police Interrogation* (1989) 70-3; K. Bottomley, *The Impact of PACE on Policing in a Northern Force* (1991).
30 G. Gudjonsson, I. Clare, S. Rutter, and J. Pearse, *Persons at Risk During Interviews in Police Custody: The Identification of Vulnerabilities,* RCCJ research study no. 12 (1993).
31 PACE code C, para. 9.2.

32 RCCJ, op. cit., n. 1, p. 44; G. Robertson, *The Role of Police Surgeons*, RCCJ research study no. 6 (1992).
33 Department of Health and Home Office, *Review of Health and Social Services for Mentally Disordered Offenders* (1992; Cm. 2088).
34 RCCJ, op. cit., n. 1, p 45.
35 PACE code C, para. 3.9.
36 id., para 11.14.
37 id., also annex C.
38 D. Brown, T. Ellis, and K. Larcombe, *Changing the Code: Police detention under the Revised PACE Codes of Practice* (1993).
39 PACE code C, para. 11.16.
40 For example, *R.* v. *Jefferson* (*Times* 22 June 1993) where the suspect's father had been a critical observer of his son's performance during his interview, and had intervened to tell him to tell the truth. The Court of Appeal held that encouragement by an appropriate adult of a juvenile who was being fairly interviewed to tell the truth should not normally be stigmatized as a failure of the adult to fulfil the duty to advise the suspect, nor would it have the consequence of changing him or her from an appropriate to an inappropriate adult for the purposes of the code.
41 RCCJ, op. cit., n. 1, p. 44.
42 PACE code C, notes for guidance 1F.
43 RCCJ, op. cit., n. 1, p. 44.
44 *Times*, 24 December 1992.
45 id.
46 For a discussion of this, see S. Field, 'Defining Interviews under PACE' (1993) *J. of Legal Studies* 254-63.
47 PACE code C, notes for guidance, para. 11A.
48 [1990] 90 Cr. App. R. 115.
49 PACE 1984, s 23.
50 [1993] 97 Cr. App. R. 222.
51 [1989] *Crim Law Rev.* 815.
52 RCCJ, op. cit., n. 1, p. 25.

[17]

Insanity and fitness to stand trial in Canada and England: a comparative study of recent developments

RONNIE MACKAY

ABSTRACT The legal provisions relating to those persons who are found unfit to be tried or who successfully plead the defence of insanity have recently undergone radical change in both Canada and England. This article seeks to compare and critically evaluate the operation of these analogous but very different reforms which have resulted from major dissatisfaction about the way in which the law of both countries has treated this group of vulnerable offender patients.

Keywords: insanity, fitness to stand trial, Canada, England, medicolegal

In a previous article, 'Insanity and Fitness to Stand Trial in Canada and England: a Comparative Study' (Mackay, 1990), which sought to investigate Anglo-Canadian responses to the complex problems surrounding the disposal and treatment of those who are either mentally unfit to stand trial or who successfully plead the defence of insanity, I concluded:

> In Canada and England reform is long overdue. It is now up to the governments of both countries to ensure that such reform is implemented as a matter of priority. Which of these countries will be the first to achieve a fairer and more balanced way of treating those who are or ought to be found unfit to stand trial or legally insane? Only time will tell.

The Journal of Forensic Psychiatry Vol 6 No 1 May 1995 121–138

ISSN 0958–5184

Since these words were written there have been remarkable developments in both countries which have transformed the law relating to the disposal of these two categories of persons. English law has been altered by virtue of the enactment of the Criminal Procedure (Insanity and Unfitness to Plead) Act 1991 which came into operation on 1 January 1992 while in Canada radical changes to the Criminal Code (mental disorder) came into force on 4 February 1992 (Department of Justice, 1992).

The English reforms were prompted by concern over the way in which the law failed to protect those who were found unfit to plead (Mackay, 1991a) while the Canadian mental disorder amendments were prompted by the Supreme Court of Canada's decision in *R.* v *Swain* which decided that the provision of the Criminal Code requiring the mandatory and indeterminate hospitalization of any accused acquitted on the grounds of insanity violated ss. 7 and 9 of the Canadian Charter of Rights and Freedoms.[1]

The first part of this article will review these statutory changes and compare them with the analogous reforms in England, taking account of relevant Canadian case law developments. The second part will attempt to place these reforms in perspective by briefly considering what the available empirical data reveal about the first year of the operation of these new measures in each country.

R. v *SWAIN*

On 4 February 1992 a major legislative reform package, in the form of Bill C-30, was proclaimed. These reform measures had been under consideration for some time by the Department of Justice but were made a reality by the Supreme Court of Canada's decision in *R.* v *Swain* (1991) where the accused, who was charged with assaulting his family, was found to have been suffering from a psychotic episode at the time. After receiving treatment at a mental health centre the accused's condition improved to such a degree that he was released into the community until the time of his trial some 18 months later in June 1985. At the trial the judge ruled that the Crown could lead evidence of insanity despite the accused's objections, with the result that an insanity verdict was returned which in turn meant that Swain received automatic and indeterminate detention at the pleasure of the Lieutenant Governor. It was this inflexible form of disposal, modelled on the English Criminal Lunatics Act of 1800, which led to the appeal in *Swain*.

The Supreme Court made it clear that this form of 'strict custody' was unconstitutional owing to its failure to provide procedural safeguards for those found legally insane. Thus, even if the trial judge had contemporaneous evidence relating to the accused's present state of mind which showed clearly that detention was not required, 'strict custody' would still result. In short, the mandatory nature of such a disposal gave the court no opportunity to enquire whether the accused actually needed confinement. Chief Justice Lamer speaking for the majority of the Supreme Court made the position very clear when he said:

> The detention order is automatic, without any rational standard for determining which individual insanity acquittees should be detained and which should be released. . . . I cannot imagine a detention being ordered on a more arbitrary basis [as] not all of these individuals will be dangerous.

The court also held that the rule which permitted the Crown to raise insanity despite the accused's objections could no longer stand as it violated s. 7 of the Charter. The majority of the court concluded that the prosecution should in future be permitted to raise insanity in only two situations. The first would be where the accused himself had put his mental capacity for criminal intent in issue as part of his defence strategy. In essence, therefore, this brings Canadian law into line with the position in England (Mackay, 1990). However, Lamer, C. J. went further by introducing a second novel situation which he described as follows:

> the Crown may raise evidence of insanity after the trier of fact has concluded that the accused is otherwise guilty of the offence charged. In these circumstances the Crown's ability to raise evidence of insanity cannot interfere with the conduct of the accused's defence because the Crown's ability to do so will not be triggered until after the accused has concluded his or her defence.

In effect this rule restricts the prosecution from independently raising the issue of insanity until after the jury have concluded that the accused was otherwise guilty of the offence in question but prior to a conviction being entered. There is no analogous procedure in England with the result that in such a situation a conviction would be entered while in Canada if the court 'subsequently found that the accused was insane at the time of the offence' an insanity verdict would be returned. While it is difficult to predict what effect this new rule may have in increasing the number of insanity defences in Canada, what it does do is ensure that the insanity issue cannot be circumvented by a guilty verdict as is the position in England. The essence of the Canadian approach is encapsulated by Lamer, C. J. when he remarked:

> it is a principle of fundamental justice that the criminal justice system not convict a person who was insane at the time of the offence. That it is so dispels any suggestion that an accused somehow has a right to be wrongly convicted.

THE NEW CANADIAN PROVISIONS

In view of the serious repercussions which could flow from its decision in *Swain*, namely that by declaring the indeterminate detention provision to be of no force 'judges will be compelled to release into the community all insanity acquittees, including those who may well be a danger to the public', the court gave Parliament a 6-month period in which to implement new legislation during which any detention ordered would be for a maximum of 60 days.

The result of this ruling meant that the Canadian government was required urgently to bring forward reform proposals which the Department of Justice had been working on for a number of years (Mackay, 1990). These important measures sweep away the mandatory disposal which was originally mandated after a finding of unfitness or an insanity verdict, replacing this with flexibility of disposal which is given to the court or to a review board. Further unlike their English counterpart, the new provisions, together with recent case law, make important changes to the substantive law governing fitness to stand trial and the insanity defence (O'Mara, 1993; Davis, 1993).

(a) The fitness issue (Davis, in press)

The new code's provisions define the phrase 'unfit to stand trial' in a new s. 2 of the Criminal Code which reads:

> 'Unfit to stand trial' means unable on account of mental disorder to conduct a defence at any stage of the proceedings before a verdict is rendered in respect of an offence charged against the accused or, the inability to instruct counsel to do so and, in particular, the inability of the accused to
> (a) understand the nature or object of the proceedings,
> (b) understand the possible consequences of the proceedings, or
> (c) communicate with counsel.

Further, s. 2 states that '"mental disorder" means a disease of the mind'. This together with the abolition of the natural imbecility provision[2] might seem to indicate that the fitness provisions no longer apply to those who are mentally handicapped (Hitchen, 1993). If this is so then there would seem to be a major gap in the new Canadian law.

One of the first cases to examine the new statutory test of fitness to stand trial is *R.* v *Taylor* (1993) where the accused, a paranoid schizophrenic, was able to understand the nature and object of the proceedings and their possible consequences and thus met the first two criteria specified above. However, there was disagreement over his ability to communicate with counsel in the sense that it was argued for the Crown that the accused 'suffered from delusions so pervasive and irrational that he was "unable to perceive his own best interests and how those interests should be addressed in the course of a trial"'. In essence this means that the court was being invited to adopt an 'analytic capacity' test rather than a 'limited cognitive capacity' test. In rejecting the former, Lacouriere, J. A. considered that it 'established too high a threshold . . . by requiring that the accused be capable of making rational decisions beneficial to him'. In the judge's opinion to require this high threshold would interfere with the liberty of the accused to conduct his own defence 'even if this meant that the accused may act to his own detriment in doing so'. It seems clear therefore that Canadian law has retained a test for fitness to stand trial which remains similar to that adopted by the common law of England in *R.* v *Pritchard* (1836) and *R.* v *Robertson* [1968].

A further important issue which was raised in *R.* v *Taylor* concerned the fact that at the initial fitness hearing the judge did not require the Crown to show that it had a prima-facie case against the accused but instead proceeded with the fitness hearing before any proof was offered by the Crown. In this connection s. 672.25(2)(b) of the code contains a provision similar to that of English law in s. 2 of the Criminal Procedure (Insanity and Unfitness to Plead) Act 1991, namely that the judge has discretion to postpone the fitness issue until the Crown has completed its case. Having regard to the fact that the accused had denied the allegation against him it was argued that the trial judge had been wrong not to postpone the fitness hearing. On this matter Lacourciere, J. A. took a strong view, deciding that in the exercise of his discretion under s. 672.25(2)(b):

> a trial judge must consider whether there is any dispute as to the Crown's ability to demonstrate that the accused committed the act or acts alleged in the indictment. If there is a dispute, the trial judge should not decide the question of fitness without being satisfied that the Crown is in a position to establish that the accused committed the act or acts alleged.

In many ways this important judgment brings Canadian law into line with the newly enacted provision in the English Criminal Procedure (Insanity and Unfitness to Plead) Act 1991 which not only contains a similar postponement provision but also requires the court to conduct a 'trial of the facts' in all cases where there has been a finding that the accused was unfit to plead, thus requiring that a jury be satisfied that the accused did the act or made the omission charged before he can be subject to the court's disposal powers. If the jury is not so satisfied then a verdict of acquittal must be returned. This new procedure is designed to ensure that unfit defendants are not subject to the court's disposal powers unless the prosecution can prove the act or omission alleged against them. However, there is no need for the Crown to prove any element of *mens rea* and in that sense the enquiry is of a limited nature.

Clearly there is a difference in emphasis here between the English and Canadian provisions, for while the 'trial of the facts' arises only after an unfitness finding and is limited to proof of the act, the Canadian decision in *Taylor* mandates in cases where there is any dispute over the allegation, that the Crown be required to establish its case against the accused before proceeding with a fitness hearing. Further, there is no reason to suppose that this should not include proof of *mens rea*. In which case Canadian law seems more generous to the accused in not proceeding with any fitness hearing until after the Crown can make out the essence of the charges.

(b) The new insanity defence (Verdun-Jones, 1994)

The insanity defence under s. 16 of the Criminal Code has been repealed[3] and replaced with a new 'not criminally responsible' plea. The new s. 16(2) reads as follows:

> No person is criminally responsible for an act or omission made while suffering from a mental disorder that rendered that person incapable of appreciating the nature and quality of the act or omission or of knowing that the act or omission was wrong.

Clearly, the major change here is a modernization of the old test by a removal of the terms 'insanity' and 'natural imbecility'. As far as 'disease of the mind' is concerned, this term, as with the new unfitness provision, is retained in the definition of mental disorder. This means that the new defence will continue to be based on the requirement of 'disease of the mind', which in turn has evolved through a complex series of Supreme Court decisions the most recent of which is *R.* v *Parks* (1992) where it was decided that sleepwalking should not be classed as a disease of the mind where the cause of the accused's state of mind was sleep, a condition which must be regarded as normal, with the result that an unqualified acquittal was the correct verdict. By way of contrast, however, the court referred to the English Court of Appeal's decision in *R.* v *Burgess* [1991] where the expert testimony was different in that it supported the fact that the accused's somnambulism was caused by an abnormal mental condition, namely a sleep disorder, with the result that the condition was classed as disease of the mind and an insanity verdict returned. This distinction between normal and abnormal sleepwalking seems less than satisfactory but once again shows the continuing difficulty which the courts experience when considering the phrase 'disease of the mind'.

The new s. 16(2) retains the word 'appreciate' as opposed the use of the word 'know' in the English McNaughton Rules. This in turn means that the broader interpretation which the Supreme Court of Canada has given to the former term will be maintained (Mackay, 1990). Similarly, the word 'wrong' remains unaltered in the new provision and in this connection a major shift has taken place in Canada as a result of the Supreme Court's decision in *R.* v *Chaulk* (1990) where the court boldly overruled its earlier decision in *R.* v *Schwartz* (1989) which had decided to follow the English approach in *R.* v *Windle* [1952] towards the interpretation of the word 'wrong'; namely to restrict the word's meaning to encompass only 'legal' and not 'moral' wrongfulness. In arriving at his conclusion Lamer, C. J. said:

> it is plain to me that the term 'wrong' as viewed in s. 16(2) must mean more than simply legally wrong. In considering the capacity of a person to know

> whether an act is one that he ought not to do, the enquiry cannot terminate with the discovery that the accused knew that the act was contrary to the formal law. A person may well be aware that an act is contrary to law but, by reason of . . . disease of the mind, is at the same time incapable of knowing that the act is morally wrong in circumstances according to the moral standards of society.

Having laid down this new rule the Chief Justice was anxious to allay fears that it might open the floodgates to amoral offenders. Thus, he emphasized:

> First, the incapacity to make moral judgments must be causally linked to a disease of the mind; if the presence of a serious mental disorder is not established, criminal responsibility cannot be avoided. Secondly . . . [T]he accused will not benefit from substituting his own moral code for that of society. Instead, he will be protected by s. 16(2) if he is incapable of understanding that the act is wrong according to the ordinary moral standards of reasonable members of society.

This aspect of the decision in *Chaulk* clearly favours a more extensive interpretation of the word 'wrong' than that of English law. Indeed, the English approach in *Windle* may be so narrow that there is every possibility that it is being ignored in practice (Mackay, 1990). However, if this is the case then it would be infinitely preferable if the English Court of Appeal could follow the lead of the Supreme Court of Canada by disposing of *Windle* in the same manner as Chief Justice Lamer dealt with *Schwartz*.

A second important issue considered by the court in *Chaulk* turned on the question of whether s. 16(4), which places the burden of proving insanity on the accused, infringed the presumption of innocence guaranteed by s. 11(d) of the Charter. In deciding that this was the case the Chief Justice pointed out that s. 16(4) allows a factor which is an essential element of guilt to be presumed. However, he also concluded that this exception to the burden of proof being on the Crown was justified, *inter alia*, so as to avoid placing on the Crown the impossibly onerous burden of disproving insanity.

The result of this aspect of the decision in *Chaulk* is now reflected in the new Canadian legislation which provides in s. 16(2) that 'Every person is presumed not to suffer from a mental disorder so as to be exempt from criminal responsibility . . . until the contrary be proved on the balance of probabilities'. While this mirrors the position under the English McNaughton Rules, s. 16(3) contains a difference in approach by stating that 'The burden of proof that an accused was suffering from a mental disorder so as to be exempt from criminal responsibility is on the party that raises the issue'. This indicates that if the Crown is able to raise insanity then it need only satisfy the civil rather than the criminal burden. By way of contrast the position in England would appear to be that if the Crown seeks to establish insanity then it must do so beyond reasonable doubt (see *R.* v *Grant*). This would seem to give an English defendant more protection from an unwanted finding of insanity than his Canadian counterpart for, despite the decision of the Supreme Court in *Swain*, it would seem that once the Canadian accused has put his mental capacity in issue or the allegation is proved against him, then the Crown may succeed in having a mental disorder verdict returned if it can prove this on the balance of probabilities.

Another important change to the insanity defence in Canada concerns the nature of the verdict. This change is the direct result of Department of Justice's conclusion that:

> Consultation and press reports over the last few years both have demonstrated that the general public finds it difficult to understand why an accused is found not guilty when he or she clearly committed the act. (Department of Justice, 1986)

The result of this has been to alter the verdict from one of 'not guilty by reason of insanity' to a 'verdict that the accused committed the act or omission but is not criminally responsible on account of mental disorder' (NCRMD). Although it is further stated in s. 672.35 that the effect of such a verdict is that 'the accused shall be deemed not to have been acquitted or found guilty or convicted of the offence' this change of verdict is clearly a compromise which could be viewed as prejudicial to the mentally disordered (Mackay, 1990). However, a point which should not be overlooked here is that by focusing on the need for proof that the accused committed the act in question this in turn may influence the Crown in its selection of a charge. Further, if and when the capping provisions are introduced, the length of time a NCRMD offender may be detained will again depend upon the act the proof of which gave rise to the verdict of not criminally responsible.

(c) The disposal provisions

The new Canadian provisions contain a comprehensive and complex framework dealing with the disposal of those found unfit to stand trial or NCRMD. First, independent review boards (RB) have been created in each province to replace the old boards which merely acted in an advisory capacity to the Lieutenant Governor.

Prior to any disposition the court is permitted under s. 672.11 to order an assessment of the accused if there are reasonable grounds to believe that he is unfit to stand trial or not criminally responsible. While the court may make such an order on its own motion, the prosecution may only apply for such an order where the accused raises the issue of fitness (s. 672.12(2)) or mental capacity (s. 672.12(3)) or where the prosecution can satisfy the court that there are reasonable grounds in support of either issue. Further, the period of assessment has been reduced to 5 days in fitness cases and to 30 days for other purposes with a possible maximum increase to 60 days (s. 673.13(2) and (3)). As will be noted later these limitations particularly in fitness cases are having a marked practical effect on the numbers of assessments.

When it comes to disposal the court or the RB can now make such an order. If the court is to make such an order it must be satisfied that it can readily do so and without delay (s. 672.45(2)). However, the court may defer the matter to a RB under s. 672.47 which provides that the RB must hold the hearing as soon as is practicable but not later than 45 days after the verdict. It would appear that in practice courts more often than not prefer to adopt this latter practice so that the majority of dispositions are made by the RB.

Before making a disposition the court or review board is required under s. 762.54 to 'take into consideration the need to protect the public from dangerous persons, the mental condition of the accused, the reintegration of the accused into society and the other needs of the accused and shall make . . . [the disposition] that is the least onerous and least restrictive to the accused'.

The disposal options include an absolute discharge but only for those found NCRMD, a conditional discharge or an order that the accused be detained in custody in a hospital (Burt, 1993). While on the face of it this much-needed flexibility of disposal bears a marked resemblance to the flexibility contained in the Criminal Procedure (Insanity and Unfitness to Plead) Act 1991, the refusal of the Canadian provisions to permit an absolute discharge in unfitness cases is a distinction which merits later discussion. Further, an absolute discharge is available only after a finding of NCRMD where in the opinion of the court or RB 'the accused is not a significant threat to the safety of the public' (s. 672.54(a)). This particular requirement was the subject of litigation in *Orlowski* v *Attorney-General of British Columbia* (1992) where three accused appealed against being discharged subject to conditions rather than absolutely. In allowing the appeals and remitting the cases back to the RBs for further consideration, the court concluded that before any disposition can be made an opinion must be expressed on the issue of 'significant threat' as it is impossible to make a disposal other than an absolute discharge, which of necessity is the least restrictive alternative, without first forming an opinion on the former issue. However, the court made it clear that 'the board need not order an absolute discharge when it has doubts as to whether the accused is a significant threat or not' which means that if an opinion was formed that he could become such a threat if he did not take his medication then 'the board cannot be said to have an opinion that the accused is not a significant threat. The word "threat" . . . has a future connotation.' Clearly, this judgment fulfils one of the major purposes of the Canadian statutory provisions which is to protect the public and does so in a much more express and forthright manner than its English counterpart.

In dealing with those who are unfit the court has no power to make an absolute discharge but has been given the authority to make a limited treatment order under s. 672.58. Before this can be done the court must hear medical testimony under s. 672.59 which indicates, *inter alia*, that the course of treatment is likely to render the accused fit within 60 days and that without it the accused is likely to remain unfit. If the court makes such a disposition then the treatment in question can be given without the accused's consent up to the 60-day maximum after which the accused will be remitted to court to stand trial provided he or she is fit. If he or she remains unfit the court may proceed to make an alternative disposition under s. 672.45.

It is quite clear that the primary policy of the new Canadian provisions dealing with the unfit is to send the accused back for trial as soon as is practicable. In this connection s. 672.48 ensures that the RB as part of its function must decide whether the accused is fit to stand trial and if so he must be sent back to court so that the fitness issue may be retried, although he may be detained in hospital up to the time of trial if the RB 'has reasonable ground to believe that the accused would become unfit to stand trial if released' (s. 672.49(1)). This policy of enquiring into fitness with a view to the speedy return of the accused to court stands in marked contrast to the position under English law where the power to remit for trial resides with the Home Secretary and applies only in cases where the unfit accused has been given a hospital order with restrictions. Further, s. 672.33 requires a Canadian court to 'hold an enquiry, not later than two years after the verdict [of unfitness] is rendered and every two years thereafter . . . to decide whether sufficient evidence can be adduced at that time to put the accused on trial'. If the prosecution cannot satisfy the court on this matter then according to s. 672.33(6) the court must acquit the accused. This is an important provision as it ensures that the prosecution has a good case against the unfit accused irrespective of time-lapse. There is no similar provision in England which means that unfit defendants who are not remitted for trial cannot clear their names. However, it is noticeable here that the philosophy behind the English provisions surrounds the best method of disposing of the unfit defendant rather than attempting to ensure, as in Canada, that he or she is rendered fit and sent back for trial.

At the time of writing two important aspects relating to disposal have not yet been implemented by the Canadian government, the first because of its controversial nature and the second due to fiscal implications. However, both deserve brief comment.

The first concerns the creation of a 'cap' for both unfitness and insanity findings beyond which detention under the Criminal Code must cease. The basis of the 'cap' was described by the Department of Justice as follows:

> In the case of a charge of murder in the first degree, this outer limit would be life. In the case of offences against the person or that endanger public safety, the outer limit would be ten years or the maximum penalty, whichever is the shorter. In the case of all other offences, the outer limit would be two years or the maximum penalty, whichever is the shorter. (Department of Justice, 1986)

After the expiry of this outer limit it was originally recommended that if further detention was thought to be required this would then have to be effected through the civil commitment process.

These 'capping' provisions are clearly intended to bring some degree of proportionality into the period of detention of mentally disordered offenders. However, the retention of life for murder and a 10-year cap for a whole host of serious offences means that such offenders continue to be subject to the risk of being detained for very long periods. The only analogy under the 1991 Act concerns murder where such a charge continues to result in hospitalization for an indeterminate period. By way of contrast, however, while a person found NCRMD in Canada may be hospitalized indefinitely, a judge has discretion to dispose of the case in some other manner. Thus, in *R.* v *Trueman* (1992) a conditional discharge was immediately ordered after the accused was found NCRMD on a charge of first degree murder. As already indicated, such an approach has been made impossible by the 1991 Act.

There is no doubt that at the root of the Canadian Government's choice of capping periods lies the aim of protecting the public from the premature release of 'dangerous mentally disordered persons who come into conflict with the law' (Department of Justice, 1991). As a result the legislation introduces the possibility of increasing the cap to life in cases of insanity acquittals where the offence in question is a 'serious personal injury offence' and in consequence an application has been made to the court that the accused be declared 'a dangerous mentally disordered accused'.[4]

This is certainly a sting in the tail as far as the whole capping system is concerned and is sure to be the subject of marked constitutional challenge.

Secondly, for the first time the new provisions will give Canadian criminal courts the power to make a hospital order (s. 736.11). However, this power is very different from its English counterpart in that it can be made only where immediate treatment is urgently required at the time of sentencing for a period not exceeding 60 days[5] after which the accused is to be sent to prison to serve the unexpired portion of the sentence (s. 736.15). It is clear, therefore, that Canadian hospital orders are of very limited duration and are reserved for those suffering from acute mental disorder at the time of sentence. In many respects they are more akin to interim hospital orders than ordinary hospital orders in the sense that under s. 38 of the Mental Health Act 1983 the maximum detention period is likewise 6 months but with the important difference that while detention in hospital counts towards the term of imprisonment in Canada (s. 736.16) the same is not true in England. Thus, if after making an interim hospital order an English court decides to imprison the accused the time spent in hospital does not necessarily reduce the term of imprisonment.

The first year of the reforms in Canada and England

Prior to the enactment of the Canadian reforms the Department of Justice funded a major research project designed to collect data about every Lieutenant Governor's Warrant (LGW) over the 3-year period 1988–90. The data were collected through the board offices in each province (Hodgins, 1993), for the purpose of studying what effect the reforms might have. The results can be summarized as follows.

1. The number of warrant patients was 1,007 in 1988, 1,120 in 1989 and 1,156 in 1990. This slow but steady increase was felt by the authors to be likely to continue and might even increase in the light of the new reforms.
2. Of the 1,007 patients *detained* in 1988, 91% were found not guilty by reason of insanity (NGRI). However, of the 309 warrants *issued* during 1989, only 45% were NGRI. Of the 251 warrants *vacated* during 1988, 41% were NGRI patients. This balance of more unfit warrants being vacated remained constant in the other years reflecting the swifter turnover for unfit patients many of whom are sent back for trial.
3. The most prevalent diagnoses were schizophrenia (64%), personality disorders (10%) and affective disorders (8%). Thereafter diagnoses varied widely. The most prevalent index offences were homicide (just over 30%), attempted murder (17%), other assaults (24%).
4. Unfit patients were detained in hospital, on average, for 9.3 months compared to around 53.0 months for NGRI patients.
5. There were no marked changes in the characteristics of the warrant population over the 3-year period.

The authors conclude that the new reforms could result in an expansion of the warrant population if prosecutors make extensive use of the 'dangerous mentally disordered accused' provisions thus making it very difficult for such persons to be released. Further, the number of unfitness and insanity findings could well rise partly because of the new procedural safeguards and flexibility of disposal which might make such findings more attractive to defendants but also because the new law applies equally to those accused of summary offences.[6]

By way of contrast analogous empirical research in England (Mackay, 1991b) prior to the 1991 Act shows how very small the combined number of unfitness and insanity findings is when compared with Canada. Thus in 1988 there was a total of 17 such findings compared to 309 warrants issued in Canada during a similar period. The reasons for this marked difference in numbers were explored in an earlier paper (Mackay, 1990) and can be traced, *inter alia*, to the marked use of hospital orders in England.

The impact of the reform measures

It is still too soon to make confident predictions as to the exact nature of the impact which these reform measures in England and Canada may have. Further, while comprehensive research is being undertaken in England to monitor the first 5 years of the operation of the 1991 Act (Mackay and Kearns, 1994), it is a matter of regret that no similar research is currently being undertaken in Canada which is especially unfortunate as given that the Department of Justice was prepared to fund a study into LGWs during 1988–90 it would surely have been desirable to extend this study in order to assess the effect of the changes. Given that there is no such comprehensive study one must turn to particular provinces in order to discover more about the impact of the Canadian reforms.

In British Columbia research is underway which does help to shed some light on this issue. During the first 3 months of the reform measures there appears to have been a drop in the number of patients being referred by the courts for inpatient psychiatric evaluation with no increase in findings of unfitness (Smith and Grant, 1993). However, possibly as the courts in British Columbia become more familiar with the new Criminal Code provisions, the numbers began to rise, with the result that figures comparing the first full year of the reform measures with the last year of the old law reveal not only an increase in psychiatric remands from 298 to 340[7] but also an increase in the number of admissions to the Forensic Psychiatric Institute (FPI) by virtue of unfitness findings from 20 to 31 and NCRMD verdicts from 9 to 15.[8] With regard to NCRMD the increase from 9 to 15 (40%) should be treated with caution as earlier research has shown that in 1989 there were 14 findings of not guilty by reason of insanity in British Columbia (Ogloff, 1991). However, while it might be thought possible that this 40% increase has little to do with the impact of the new code provisions, what these figures fail to take account of is the number of cases which did not result in admission to the FPI. In this connection it is very interesting to note that during the first year of the new law 'five persons found NCRMD were given immediate conditional discharges' (Davis, draft PhD thesis) while only one unfitness case was disposed of in this manner during the same period. In effect, therefore, this increases the total of NCRMD cases to 20 and unfitness cases to 31 which leads to the conclusion that there does seem to be an overall upward trend in numbers and that if this is reflected in other provinces throughout Canada then the impact of the reform measures could be significant.

A further significant impact of the Canadian reform measures concerns the fact that the number 'of insanity acquittees given absolute discharges rose dramatically in the first year of the new law, to 31, from a total of two the previous calendar year' (Davis, draft PhD thesis). The explanation for this is given as a clearing up of older cases by the review board of those who were being detained unnecessarily, which shows the impact which the Supreme Court's decision in *Swain* is continuing to have in practice.

As far as England is concerned, a comparison between the final year of the old law and the first year of the operation of the 1991 Act reveals a somewhat different picture, with a reduction in the number of findings of unfitness but with a strange increase in the number of insanity verdicts.

Thus in 1991 there were a mere 7 findings of unfitness with the same number of insanity verdicts leading to a total of 14 cases. Strangely, although this is the smallest number of cases yet found in any one year, it also accounts for the highest number of insanity findings. There is no ready explanation for this especially as the very small number of unfitness cases can be explained away by the fact that a number of the 1991 cases had been adjourned with a view to taking advantage of the flexibility of disposal under the new legislation. Surprisingly, no similar attempt at delay seems to have been made in any of the 1991 insanity cases. In any event, the number of unfitness cases in 1992 was 13, with a total of five insanity verdicts leading to a combined figure of 18 cases. However, two of the unfit cases were disposed of under the old law owing to the fact that the trial judges in these cases refused to accept the delay tactics referred to above. This meant that only 11 unfitness cases were disposed of under the new law, making a total of 16 cases. This means that there has been a slight reduction in the number of unfitness cases, with the number of insanity cases remaining about the same. This is especially strange as it has become quite clear that the courts have begun to take full advantage of the new disposal powers under the 1991 Act. Thus, in the 16 cases dealt with during the first year of the new law, only three cases resulted in indefinite hospitalization with the other cases being dealt with as follows:

> four supervision and treatment orders; three ordinary hospital orders without restrictions; two acquittals after the trial of the facts: two absolute discharges and one guardianship order. The final case would have been one of indefinite hospitalization but for the fact that the Home Secretary was not informed quickly enough about the case by the court with the result that the accused had to be freed through lapse of time. (Mackay and Kearns, 1994)

To date, therefore, although the 1991 Act has not yet had an effect as far as any increase in the number of cases is concerned, it is clear the courts are happy with the new flexible disposal powers.

CONCLUSION

There is no doubt that major dissatisfaction about the way in which the law in both England and Canada treated this group of mentally vulnerable offenders led to the reform measures which have been the subject of this article. However, while Canada has enacted an ambitious and comprehensive legislative package which transforms the legal position, by way of contrast England has done the complete opposite by implementing a minimal number of procedural changes but in all other respects leaving the substantive law intact. Further, while the Government of Canada was compelled to take action, as a result of the Supreme Court's decision in *Swain*, the English changes came about in the form of a Private Member's Bill which was supported by all concerned, including the Home Office.

There is no doubt that a major period of adjustment will take place in Canada while the new Criminal Code provisions become more familiar. Certainly, these new measures contain the potential for a system to be developed which will ensure that the mentally unfit and NCRMD are dealt with in a just and humane manner. However, the other side of the equation is the concern for public safety which is clearly evident within the Canadian provisions, particularly those which are yet to be proclaimed. These unproclaimed measures demonstrate the tension between replacing indeterminate custody with maximum detention periods and the need to protect the public from dangerous mentally disordered offenders. What remains to be seen is whether these measures will survive constitutional challenge as they do seem to demonstrate a somewhat punitive response towards the mentally disordered. Certainly, a 10-year cap in respect of a long list of designated offences that are prosecuted on indictment, including, for example, 'stopping mail with intent' and 'dangerous operation of a motor vehicle', seems excessive. Further, the labelling of certain individuals as 'dangerous mentally disordered accused' and the implications which follow this seem to pander unduly to public fear of the danger which mentally disordered persons pose. The result is a somewhat uneven reform package with the balance tipping in favour of public safety. However, with the Supreme Court of Canada having shown its preference for restricted detention periods in *Swain*, there is every chance that a greater degree of proportionality may have to be introduced into these capping measures.

Finally, although it is still too early to make confident predictions about the overall impact of each country's reform measures, what the preliminary figures from British Columbia seem to show is that there has been an increase in the use of both unfitness and the new NCRMD verdict. So far as England is concerned, the first year of the new law reveals a decrease in the overall number of cases, which is strange as one would have expected an increase owing to the new disposal flexibility which has been given to the courts. In closing, two important points need to be made. First, it is to be hoped that the type of research which is currently being conducted in British Columbia is being mirrored in other Canadian provinces, for only then will it be possible to measure the broader impact of the reforms. In this connection, it is most regrettable that apparently there is no national research, similar to that commissioned by the Department of Justice from 1988 to 1990, being conducted in Canada at present. Second, with regard to the operation of the 1991 Act in England, it is vital that all those who are professionally concerned with this small group of mentally vulnerable offenders should realize that the courts are already making full use of their new flexible disposal powers. Once this message is communicated it is to be hoped that full advantage will be taken of these new measures. This should lead to a marked increase in the number of cases of unfitness to plead and insanity which in turn would ensure that the 1991 Act achieves its full purpose.

ACKNOWLEDGEMENTS

The Canadian aspects of this article resulted from a visit to Canada made possible by the generosity of the Canadian High Commission in the form of a Canadian Studies Research Award.

Many people assisted me during my stay in Canada and I should like to record my thanks to the following:

Professor Simon Verdun-Jones, School of Criminology, Simon Fraser University, British Columbia
Professor Chris Webster, Professor Jim Ogloff and Professor Ron Roesch of the Department of Psychology, Simon Fraser University, British Columbia
Simon Davis and Denise Hitchen, respectively doctoral and masters candidates, School of Criminology, Simon Fraser University, British Columbia
Dr Derek Eaves, executive director, Forensic Psychiatric Services, Burnaby, British Columbia
Ms Faye Grant, policy and programme analyst, Forensic Psychiatric Services, Burnaby, British Columbia
Norman Prelypchan, chairperson, British Columbia Review Board
Lyle Hillaby, crown counsel, Review Board, British Columbia
Dr Steven Hucker, Professor of Forensic and Correctional Psychiatry, Queen's University, Kingston, Ontario, lately head, Forensic Division, the Clarke Institute of Psychiatry, Toronto

In relation to the English aspects of this paper I owe a continued debt of gratitude to the following:

C3 Division of the Home Office, the Crown Prosecution Service and the Lord Chancellor's Department
Gerry Kearns, research assistant, De Montfort University
the Economic and Social Research Council for funding ongoing research into the 1991 Act in the form of Grant No. R000 23 3773.

Professor Ronnie Mackay, BA, MPhil, Professor of Criminal Policy and Mental Health, Department of Law, De Montfort University, The Gateway, Leicester LE1 9BH

NOTES

1 Section 7 gives 'the right to life, liberty and security of the person and the right not to be deprived thereof except in accordance with the principle of fundamental justice', while s. 9 ensures 'the right not to be arbitrarily detained or imprisoned'.

2 The original s. 16 defined insanity to include those 'in a state of natural imbecility'; see R. D. Mackay (1990).

3 Section 16(2) of the Canadian Criminal Code originally provided: 'For the purposes of this section a person is insane when he is in a state of natural imbecility or has disease of the mind to an extent that renders him incapable of appreciating the nature and quality of an act or omission or of knowing that an act or omission is wrong.

4 Further, transitional provisions will permit those detained under a LGW for more than 10 years in respect of a designated offence to be declared dangerous mentally disordered accused in which case detention will be increased to a life maximum. Inevitably, such transitional applications will be hotly contested.

5 Section 736.14 makes it clear that a hospital order cannot be made where the accused has been sentenced to a non-custodial sentence or a term of imprisonment of less than 60 days.

6 There is no such similar provision in England which means that unfitness and insanity only apply to indictable offences tried in the crown court.

7 This increase may not reflect the true number of remands in that there appear to have been difficulties in calculating the number of short 5-day remand orders owing to the fact in many such cases the patient was returned to court quickly with a court-ordered extension taking place thus changing the legal status of the order (Faye Grant, personal communication).

8 I am grateful to Faye Grant, policy and programme analyst at the Forensic Psychiatric Institute, Burnaby, British Columbia for supplying me with comparative statistics for 1990–1 and 1992–3 admissions to forensic services in that province.

REFERENCES

Burt, L. (1993) 'The Mental Order Provisions: Community Residence and Dispositions under Section 672. 54(c).' *Criminal Law Quarterly*: 40–8.

Davis, S. (1993a) 'Changes to the Criminal Code Provisions for Mentally Disordered Offenders and their Implications for Canadian Psychiatry'. *Canadian Journal of Psychiatry* 38: 122–6.

Davis, S. (1994) 'Fitness to Stand Trial in Canada in the Light of Recent Criminal Code Amendments'. *International Journal of Forensic Psychiatry*: 17: 319–29.

Department of Justice (1986) 'Mental Disorder Amendments to the Criminal Code', information paper, Minister of Justice and Attorney General of Canada, Ottawa.

Department of Justice (1991) press release, Ottawa, 10 July.

Department of Justice (1992) communiqué, Ottawa, 30 January 1992.

Hitchen, D. (1993) 'Fitness to Stand Trial and Mentally Challenged Defendants: A View from Canada'. *International Bulletin of Law and Mental Health* 4: 5–7.

Hodgins, S. (1993) 'Mental Health Treatment Services in Quebec for Persons

Accused or Convicted of Criminal Offences'. *International Journal of Law and Psychiatry* 16: 179–94.

Mackay, R. D. (1990) 'Insanity and Fitness to Stand Trial in Canada and England: a Comparative Study'. *Journal of Forensic Psychiatry* 1: 277–303.

Mackay, R. D. (1991a) 'The Decline of Disability in Relation to the Trial'. *Criminal Law Review*: 87–97.

Mackay, R. D. (1991b) 'The Operation of the Criminal Procedure (Insanity) Act 1964 – an Empirical Study of Unfitness to Plead and the Insanity Defence'. De Montfort University Law School monograph.

Mackay, R. D. and Kearns, G. (1994) 'The Continued Underuse of Unfitness to Plead and the Insanity Defence'. *Criminal Law Review*: 576–9.

Ogloff, J. R. P. (1991) 'The Use of the Insanity Defence in British Columbia: a Qualitative and Quantitative Analysis', technical report prepared for the Department of Justice.

O'Mara, A. J. C. (1993) 'Hadfield to Swain: The Criminal Code Amendments Dealing with the Mentally Disordered Accused'. *Criminal Law Quarterly*: 49–107.

Smith, J. and Grant, F. (1993) 'Amendments to the Criminal Code of Canada: Impact on Inpatient Psychiatric Remands'. *Journal of Forensic Psychiatry* 4: 355–60.

Verdun-Jones, S. N. (1994) 'The Insanity Defence in Canada – Setting a New Course'. *International Journal of Forensic Psychiatry* 17: 175–89.

ENGLISH LAW REPORTS

R. v *Burgess* [1991] 2 All ER 769.
R. v *Grant* [1960] Crim LR 424.
R. v *McNaughton* (1843) 10 Cl & F 210.
R. v *Pritchard* (1836) 7 C & P 303.
R. v *Robertson* [1968] 3 All ER 557.
R. v *Windle* [1952] 2 QB 826.

CANADIAN LAW REPORTS

Orlowski v *Attorney-General of British Columbia* (1992) 94 DLR (4th) 541.
R. v *Chaulk* (1990) 2 CR (4th) 1.
R. v *Parks* (1992) 75 CCC (3d) 287.
R. v *Schwartz* (1989) 55 DLR (4th) 1.
R. v *Swain* (1991) 63 CCC (3d) 481.
R. v *Taylor* (1993) 11 OR (3d) 323.
R. v *Trueman* (1992) 80 Man R (2d) 72.

[18]

Crim.L.R.

A Rationale for Infanticide Laws

By Daniel Maier-Katkin, J.D., and
Robbin Ogle, M.A.

*Administration of Justice, Pennsylvania State University**

Summary: *This article argues in favour of infanticide legislation. Perseverance in the established practice of lenient treatment for women who murder their own infant children is justified on the basis of psychiatric evidence, ethical considerations and public policy.*

I. Introduction

The murder of infants is among the most disquieting of crimes, at least to the sensibilities of the modern world, in which standards of civilization are generally associated with the protection of the defenceless and innocent.[1] Awareness that the practice of infanticide has been extensive in ancient civilisations and primitive cultures may create the misleading impression that the subject is primarily of historical and anthropological interest. The sad reality, however, is that the killing of infants remains pervasive across cultures, and that it forms a disproportionate element of the homicide statistics in much of the industrialised First World, including England and Wales.[2]

Data compiled by the Home Office reveal that the homicide rate among children under the age of one year is greater than that of any other age group—virtually four times higher than the homicide rate among the general population—and that this has been the case at least.since 1925.[3] In the years between 1984 and 1988, for example, the homicide rate among the general population was just

---

* This work was undertaken while the principal author was a Fulbright Fellow and Visiting Professor at the Institute of Psychiatry, University of London School of Medicine. The financial support of the British Fulbright Commission and The Pennsylvania State University is gratefully acknowledged, as is the intellectual assistance of Dr. Channi Kumar, Dr. Maureen Marks, and Sir Leon Radzinowicz.

[1] In this regard, it might be argued that infanticide and abortion are related phenomena, and that they ought to be considered together. In this article, however, abortion is not discussed, partially because the legal and moral issues associated with infanticide are sufficiently complex and that the heated controversy surrounding the abortion issue would cloud rather than clarify the issue, and partially because the murder of children is a conceptually separable problem of sufficiently great importance in its own right.

[2] An analysis of World Health Organisation data for the year 1975 indicated that babies in the first year of life were of greater risk of becoming victims of homicide than any other segment of the population in many first-world nations, including: Austria, Denmark, Germany, Japan, The Netherlands, Norway and Switzerland as well as England, Wales and Scotland. See D. Lester, "The Distribution of Sex and Age Among Victims of Homicide: A Cross-National Study," (1986) 32 Int. J. Soc. Psychiatry 47. There is also evidence that family planning policies in China have resulted in the widespread practice of killing female infants; analysis of Chinese census data suggests that as many as 600,000 infant girls may have been killed in a single year. "Where Have All The Little Girls Gone? In Rural China No One Knows," *International Herald Tribune*, Rome, Tuesday, June 18, 1991 (p.1, Column 2). See also, "Stark Data on Women: 100 Million Are Missing," *New York Times*, Tuesday, November 5, 1991 (section C, p.1).

[3] *Criminal Statistics for England Wales* 1926–1987, London: HMSO.

over 10 per million population; among infants under the age of one year, the rate was just over 40 per million.[4]

Public attitudes and policy about the killing of infants, particularly by their mothers, have been far from constant in British history. A great period of relative permissiveness was brought to an end by the draconian Stuart Bastardy Act of 1623, which presumed that the deaths of illegitimate children were caused by their mothers and permitted executions even without actual proof that homicide had been committed.[5] The severity of this Act and the oddness of its evidentiary standards brought it into disfavour and it was repealed in 1803; but the killing of infants by their mothers continued to be classified as capital murder.[6] The Infanticide Act of 1938[7] established an independent offence of infanticide, and a presumption that mothers who kill their own children within 12 months of giving birth to them suffer an imbalance of the mind. While the Act authorises penalties comparable to those prescribed for manslaughter, actual sentencing practice has been lenient, with the majority of cases resulting in sentences of probation.[8]

During the past 20 years the Infanticide Act has been a subject of considerable controversy. Professor Nigel Walker and others have argued against the Act on the basis that the psychiatric principles from which it is derived are unsubstantiated.[9] Critics, including the Butler Committee[10] and Professor Walker,[11] have argued that the Act ought to be repealed on the basis that it has been rendered redundant and unnecessary by subsequent legislation abolishing the death penalty and establishing the offence of diminished responsibility manslaughter. While the pattern of lenient sentencing that has arisen under the Act has been frequently supported, some writers have worried about whether the Act and the prevalence of lenient sentences reflect a demeaning attitude about the responsibility of women in general for their behaviour.[12]

Despite all this criticism, the Criminal Law Revision Committee expressed support for the Act and suggested that it be amended to include a broader range of environmental and social stresses.[13] This approach has recently been incorporated into the draft Criminal Code Bill, which provides:

> "A woman who, but for this section, would be guilty of murder or manslaughter of her child is not guilty of murder or manslaughter, but is guilty

---

[4] *Homicide Fact Sheet*, Home Office, Division of Planning and Research, unpublished.

[5] 21 James I, c.27.

[6] 43 George III, c.58.

[7] 1 & 2 George VII, c.36.

[8] Nigel Walker, *Crime and Insanity in England*, vol. 1 (Edinburgh: Edinburgh University Press, 1968), p.133.

[9] *Ibid*. (1968), pp.87–104. See also, K. O'Donovan, "The Medicalisation of Infanticide," [1984] Crim.L.R 259.

[10] Report of the Committee on Mentally Abnormal Offenders, Cmnd. 6244, para. 19.27 (1975).

[11] Nigel Walker, "Butler v. the CLRC and Others," [1981] Crim.L.R. 596.

[12] Osborne, J. "The Crime of Infanticide: Throwing Out the Baby With the Bathwater," (1987) 6 *Canadian Journal of Family Law* 47 (Summer). Also see Ania Wilczynski, "Infanticide—Women Who Kill Their Infants: Debunking the Myth of the Mad and the Bad Offender." Unpublished Masters Thesis, Institute of Criminology, University of Cambridge, 1989.

[13] Criminal Law Revision Committee, Fourteenth Report, Offences Against the Person, Cmnd. 7844 (1980), para. 103.

> of infanticide, if her act is done when the child is under the age of twelve months and when the balance of her mind is disturbed by reason of the effect of giving birth *or of circumstances consequent upon the birth* (emphasis added).[14]

This article argues for the position taken by the CLRC; that is, for a policy of compassionate rather than retributive justice. Evidence is presented to demonstrate that the psychiatric principles from which the legal classification of infanticide is derived are well supported by a sizeable body of evidence. Next, the highly theoretical argument that subsequent legislation has rendered the Infanticide Act redundant is demonstrated to be mistaken as a matter of actual criminal justice practice. The final section consists of a critical review of objections to the Infanticide Act derived from a cluster of intertwined attitudes about punishment in general and the social and legal circumstances of women in particular, and then concludes with a justification for persistence in the established policy of merciful disposal of cases.

II. The psychiatric evidence is compelling

Perhaps the most fundamental criticism of the Infanticide Act is that the psychiatric premise on which it is based is unsubstantiated. Judith Osborne claims that the Act did not recognise the existence of a link between childbirth and infanticide, but created it.[15] Nigel Walker characterises this process as "myth-making by legislation."[16] Evidence for this position can be drawn from the language of the statute itself which requires only: 1) that a mother kill her infant child; and 2) that the balance of her mind be disturbed at the time. The standard employed is clearly much lower than the traditional standard for exculpation through mental disorder in England—that is, the *M'Naghten* rule[17]; and there is no requirement of causality. The defendant is not required to prove that her condition precipitated the homicidal act, but only that she experienced psychiatric distress, which once alleged will be hard to disprove.

Walker argues that the authors of the statute simply presumed, in a manner "quite foreign to English law," that if the balance of a new mother's mind was disturbed at the time she committed an infanticidal act, then there must have been a causal connection sufficient to reduce her responsibility for the offence.[18] Osborne goes further, suggesting that the only justification for the "established tradition" protecting women who kill their babies from the normal legal conse-

---

[14] A Criminal Code for England and Wales, Law Com. No. 177 (1989) Vol. 1 Report and Draft Criminal Code Bill, clause 64(1). See also R. D. Mackay, "The Consequences of Killing Very Young Children," [1993] Crim.L.R. 21.

[15] Osborne, *op. cit.*, p.55.

[16] Nigel Walker (1968), *op. cit.*, p.136.

[17] Nigel Walker (1968), *Ibid*, p.131 reports that the new term was specially chosen in 1922 because it was without established meaning and would have to be interpreted *de nóvo* by the courts. In any event, it is a marked contrast to the pre-existing standard of insanity which requires that a defendant be unable to distinguish between right and wrong, which Walker discusses at pp.87–104.

[18] *Ibid.* (1968), p.135.

quences . . . [is] "a sexist attitude ingrained in the criminal law: women are not to be accorded full responsibility for their actions."[19]

Without denying that there are elements of sexism in law and in society, it remains important to ask whether the psychiatric assumptions of the Infanticide Act are unreasonable. As only women are able to experience pregnancy and childbirth, illnesses associated with these phenomena must inevitably be unique to women. This does not imply inferiority, nor does it deny the possibility that men may be exclusively subject to other disturbances.

Part of the confusion about this issue derives from the fact that the existence of several different postpartum psychiatric conditions has been alleged, and that the quality of the evidence varies substantially. The most common condition is postpartum depression which is described as ranging in severity from mild (characterised by transitory experiences of exhaustion, restlessness and unhappiness), to moderate (characterised by less transient unhappiness, irritability, diminished initiative and clarity of thought, and sometimes by subtle changes of personality).[20] It is estimated that the less severe "baby blues" affect as many as half of all new mothers in the first few days postpartum, while more severe depressions develop more slowly and "insidiously" over the first few weeks postpartum, with an incidence of about 10 per cent.[21] Clinical descriptions of these depressions are abundant in the literature, and the incidence of depression during the postpartum period can be regarded as established fact. The problem, however, is that most people experience transient depressions, and on any given day the incidence within any group (students, secretaries, lawyers) is likely to be considerable. In this light, it is hardly surprising that researchers find that a percentage of new mothers experience depression; it would be more surprising if this were not the case. The interesting questions are whether incidence rates are greater among new mothers than in the general population, and whether the quality of depression during the post-partum period is more intense. Carefully controlled studies indicate that the answers to both of these questions are negative[22]—"baby blues" appear to be more common and no more intense than going-to-work blues. These findings, however, do not address the more fundamental issue: the existence of a relationship between childbirth and cases of severe psychiatric distress.

The most severe postpartum psychiatric illnesses described in the literature are puerperal (or postpartum) psychosis and psychotic depression. While these disorders are much less common than the more usual depressions, they are of much greater psychiatric and legal significance; and the evidence for their existence, while not incontrovertible, is quite strong. Puerperal psychosis is characterised by agitation, confusion, marked disturbance of sleep, hallucinations,

[19] Osborne, *op cit.*, p.57.

[20] J. A. Hamilton, "Postpartum Psychiatric Disorders," (1989) 12 *Psychiatric Clinics of North America* 89 at pp.91–2.

[21] *Ibid.* pp.91–92.

[22] See, for example, M. W. O'Hara, O. J. Neunaber, and E. M. Zekoski, "Prospective Study of Postpartum Depression: Prevalence, Course and Predictive Factors," (1984) 93 J. Abnormal Psychology 158; P. J. Cooper, E. A. Campbell, A. Day, H. Kennerley, and A. Bond, "Non-Psychotic Psychiatric Disorder After Childbirth," (1988) 152 Brit. J. Psychiatry 799.

vivid and sometimes bizarre delusions, violent behaviour and frequent "mercurial" mood shifts.[23] Postpartum psychotic depression combines the qualities of puerperal psychosis with those of severe depression.

> " . . . Over time, the psychotic features become less apparent and the depressive features stabilize at a point that permits the patient to assume some responsibilities and some freedom of action. Psychotic episodes occur occasionally but are concealed and suppressed. The black perspective of depression turns to a shade of grey. The patient believes that she may recover, and her intimates encourage her.
>
> One impediment remains. The episodes of hallucinations and delusions continue to recur. They recur at unpredictable times and on unpredictable occasions."[24]

Estimates of the incidence of these disorders are in the range of 1 or 2 per 1000 postpartum women[25]: Stern and Kruckman[26] review seven studies undertaken on two continents between 1846 and 1975 which describe these phenomena and agree on the rate of incidence.

A 1987 epidemiological study of puerperal psychosis offers additional strong evidence for the existence of a link between childbirth and mental illness.[27] A computer link was established between an obstetric register and a psychiatric case register for the city of Edinburgh (population 470,000). "In this way all Edinburgh women with both a psychiatric contact and an episode of childbirth between January 1, 1970, and December 31, 1981, were identified."[28] By comparing these data with data about psychiatric contacts of these same women during a two-year period before they became pregnant and during the two-year period after childbirth it was determined that the postpartum period does involve special risks. In the first 30 days after childbirth there were nearly seven times as many psychiatric hospital admissions as the average monthly admission rate before pregnancy.[29] More dramatic, and more important, the rate of psychiatric admissions with a diagnosis of psychosis was almost 22 times higher during the 30 days after giving birth than the average monthly rate before pregnancy, and for first-time mothers 35 times higher.[30] On the basis of these data, it seems reasonable to conclude that Professors Walker and Osborne are wrong to assert that the relationship between childbirth and mental disorder is merely a myth created by the authors of the Infanticide Act.

Psychiatrists, however, are unable to agree among themselves about the nature and etiology of these psychoses during the postpartum period. One school maintains that biological changes associated with pregnancy have a role

---

[23] Hamilton, *op. cit.* (note 88), pp.93–4.
[24] *Ibid.* p.96.
[25] Lentz, *op. cit.*, p.532.
[26] Gwen Stern and Laurence Kruckman, "Multi-Disciplinary Perspectives on Post-Partum Depression: An Anthropological Critique," (1983) 17 *Social Science and Medicine* 1027.
[27] R. E. Kendell, J. C. Chalmers and C. Platz, "Epidemiology of Puerperal Psychoses," (1987) 150 Brit. J. of Psychiatry 662.
[28] *Ibid.* p.663.
[29] *Ibid.* p.663.
[30] *Ibid.* p.665.

in precipitating the illness, the other asserts that puerperal psychosis is not a single illness but a collection of types of illnesses that manifest themselves during a period of vulnerability.[31] This distinction may seem insignificant to the layman, but it has had an important impact on the diagnosis of these illnesses (and perhaps indirectly on public policy as well).

In the early part of the twentieth century, psychiatry became engaged in an internal controversy over nomenclature. The group that favoured a system of terminology and diagnosis based on symptoms rather than causes prevailed. Postpartum illnesses, because of their many and changeable symptoms, seemed to defy this type of classification. In the pursuit of internal consistency the term postpartum was expunged from the Diagnostic and Statistical Manual of Mental Disorders published by the American Psychiatric Association.[32] The World Health Organisation followed the example of the American Diagnostic and Statistical Manual in its International Classification of Diseases in 1972.[33] Consequently, there is at present no official diagnosis of "postpartum psychosis" anywhere in the world.

The state of the diagnostic manuals has public policy implications because it can be used to support an assertion that the link between childbirth and mental illness is mythical; but this is misleading. The argument is about the etiology of psychoses during the postpartum period, not about incidence. Furthermore, the awareness of the existence of psychosis during the postpartum period is still reflected in the diagnostic manuals. The Diagnostic and Statistic Manual of the American Psychiatric Association, for example, offers postpartum psychoses as an example of an "Atypical Psychosis,"[34] and describes childbirth as a precipitating factor (possibly of organic etiology) in the onset of "Major Depressive Episodes."[35]

On balance, it seems inappropriate to dismiss the link between childbirth and mental illness as a myth created by the authors of the Infanticide Act. This does not mean, of course, that every person, or even every woman, who kills a child is actually suffering from a disturbance of the balance of the mind. Indeed, an important study by the psychiatrist, P. T. d'Orban, of 89 women charged with the killing or attempted murder of their own children[36] concluded that only 24 suffered from "psychotic illness, . . . acute reactive depression associated with a suicidal attempt and . . . personality disorder with depressive symptoms of sufficient severity to require admission to psychiatric hospital . . . ." The other cases involved fatal abuse (36), neonaticide—the murder of newborns almost immediately after their birth, generally by very young or retarded mothers, frequently after concealed pregnancies sometimes characterised by self-denial[37]—

[31] F. Kane, "Postpartum Disorders," in *The Comprehensive Textbook of Psychiatric Disorders* (4th ed., 1985), pp.1343–48.
[32] Hamilton, *op. cit.* (note 88), p.89.
[33] Hamilton, *Ibid.* p.90.
[34] American Psychiatric Association, *Diagnostic and Statistical Manual of Mental Disorders* (ed. 3-R). Washington, DC: APA Press (1980), p.211.
[35] *Ibid.* pp.218–21.
[36] P. T. d'Orbán, "Women Who Kill Their Children," (1979) 134 Brit. J. Psychiatry 560.
[37] See, Phillip J. Resnick, "Murder of the Newborn: A Psychiatric Review of Neonaticide," *Ibid.*

(11), retaliating mothers (nine), mothers of unwanted children (eight), and mercy killing (nine). But it must be remembered that the Infanticide Act does not presume that all women who kill their children are mentally ill; it merely allows psychiatric evidence to be considered in mitigation. Perhaps most important, the Act does not require psychotic or even severe mental illness to be proven, but only a disturbance of the balance of the mind. It is quite likely that many of the non-psychotic women in d'Orbán's study satisfied this requirement. Among his battering mothers, for example, there were histories of family disruption, abuse, marital discord, housing problems and financial difficulties, all identified by d'Orbán as "sources of stress."[38] Among the retaliating mothers there were extensive histories of psychiatric illness,[39] and the neonaticidal mothers, while not tending to suffer severe mental illness, were generally young, unmarried,[40] and, as Glanville Williams has put it, "suffering from the obvious stress of having an illegitimate child."[41] Thus, even if most of the women who kill their own children do not suffer from psychoses or other extreme mental illnesses, many do; and the others probably suffer from the types of emotional distress contemplated by the statute. Whether the policy of mitigation is wise or necessary may be open to challenge, but the fact that it can be justified in psychiatric terms seems clear beyond question.

III. Infanticide is superior to diminished responsibility as a legal classification intended to promote leniency in sentencing

In 1975, the Butler Committee Report suggested the abolition of the Infanticide Act on the grounds that cases could just as well be settled under the diminished responsibility provisions of the Homicide Act of 1957. Abolishing the offence of infanticide, it was said, would "rationalize and simplify the law."[42] It is important to note that this suggestion was embedded in a cluster of recommendations, the most far-reaching of which also included the abolition of the diminished responsibility section of the Homicide Act and the abolition of the mandatory sentence of life imprisonment for murder.[43] In essence, the Butler Committee recommended a significant extension of the discretionary power of the judiciary in sentencing homicide offenders. By giving the courts unrestricted discretion over sentencing in homicide cases, it was argued, the special extenuating circumstances of each case would be considered and appropriate, individualised penalties could be imposed without need for special legislation.

Thus, in recommending the elimination of the Infanticide Act, the Butler Report still embraced the value of individualised sentences reflecting the special circumstances of each case. It did not renounce the underlying purpose of the Act, nor criticise the pattern of judicial sentencing that has arisen under it. Rather, a broader liberal system was proposed which would serve these pur-

---

[38] *Ibid.* pp.562–64.
[39] *Ibid.* p.562.
[40] *Ibid.* p.561.
[41] Glanville Williams, *op. cit.*, p.124.
[42] Home Office, Department of Health and Social Security, *Report of the Committee on Mentally Abnormal Offenders* (The Butler Committee Report). London: HMSO (1975), p.249.
[43] *Ibid.* p.251.

poses in another way. In any event, none of these recommendations have been implemented. It is not at all clear that the Butler Committee would have favoured the repeal of the Infanticide Act in isolation from all other recommendations.

In 1980, the Criminal Law Revision Committee, noting that a wide range of organisations including the Royal College of Psychiatrists, the National Council of women, the Law Society, the Police Federation, and the Senate of the Inns of Court supported the Infanticide Act, recommended its retention.[44] It may be that the Act is inelegant, or that it is redundant with the terms of the diminished responsibility section of the Homicide Act, and it may be that other approaches to the whole problem of sentencing could render it completely unnecessary. But if it is conceded that the Act serves a desirable purpose in the current legal context, it ought to be preserved. As Oliver Wendell Holmes observed: "the life of the law has not been logic it has been experience."[45]

Nigel Walker, who has been among the critics of the Act,[46] has observed, perhaps somewhat ambivalently, that one of its effects has been "the virtual abandonment of prison sentences as a means of dealing with a crime involving the taking of human life," and has referred to this as "one of the most striking developments in the history of our sentencing policy."[47] Could this dramatic result have been achieved as Walker and other seem to believe through the mechanism of the more generalised diminished responsibility sections of the Homicide Act? There is powerful evidence to the contrary.

Susanne Dell's comprehensive study of the implementation of the diminished responsibility provisions found a steady decrease in the percentage of offenders receiving hospital care (down from 52 per cent. in 1964 to 24 per cent. in 1979) and a concomitant increase in incarceration (up from 39 per cent. in 1964 to 57 per cent. in 1979) with a fairly steady 10 per cent. receiving alternative sentences such as probation.[48] This trend has had the least effect on offenders diagnosed as floridly psychotic, but over the years offenders with other diagnoses including depression and psychotic depression have become increasingly likely to go to prison rather than hospital.[49] This trend towards increased punitiveness is also reflected in the length of sentences for offenders convicted under the diminished responsibility sections, which have grown considerably, with more than 30 per cent. being imprisoned for more than 10 years.[50]

The argument put forward by the Butler Committee, Professor Walker and others that the Infanticide Act has been made redundant and unnecessary by the diminished responsibility sections of the Homicide Act is plausible in theory, but incorrect as an assessment of social reality. Women who kill their own children under the age of one year in England and Wales continue to benefit from an

---

[44] Criminal Law Revision Committee, *op. cit.*

[45] Oliver Wendell Holmes, *The Common Law*. Boston: Little, Brown and Company (1881), p.1.

[46] Nigel Walker (1981), *op. cit.*

[47] Nigel Walker (1968), *op. cit.* (note 65), p.133.

[48] Susanne Dell, *Murder Into Manslaughter*. Maudsley Monograph Series #27 (London: Institute of Psychiatry, 1984), see Appendix, Table 1.1, p.63.

[49] *Ibid.* Table 2.10, p.70.

[50] *Ibid.* Figure 1, p.75.

enlightened, progressive penal policy at a time when the treatment of diminished responsibility offenders is becoming increasingly severe. Unpublished data in the Home Office indicate that 56 women were convicted of having killed their own infant child between 1982 and 1988.[51] Only 36 of these women were convicted of infanticide; 20 were convicted of manslaughter and one of murder. Of these 56 women, 45 were sentenced to probation, four were sent to hospital and seven (12.5 per cent.) were sentenced to prison. One prison sentence was for seven years; the others were all for terms of less than three years. It is especially interesting to note that even women convicted of manslaughter tend to receive lenient treatment, in contrast to the general population of offenders convicted of diminished responsibility manslaughter. Indeed, it is probable that the primary effect demonstrated by Dell's data—increased punitiveness in the disposal of diminished responsibility cases—would be even more powerful if the cases involving these women were disaggregated from the diminished responsibility data base. In such a light the trend towards increased incarceration and decreased hospitalisation of diminished responsibility offenders would be more stark, and it would become apparent that probation is a very rare penal strategy for such offenders.

In short, women who kill their own infant children constitute a distinct class of offender in the English system. They tend to be punished in the community rather than in prison. The retributive and deterrent purposes of the criminal law affect the disposal of their cases less than any other class of homicide offender; and this is so even when they are convicted of manslaughter rather than infanticide. It appears that the long history of infanticide legislation has shaped an attitude or cluster of attitudes within the criminal law and the criminal justice system.

The Infanticide Act emerged from a policy decision to promote leniency for women who murder their own children. Whether it was actually believed that these women were mentally ill, or whether a medical model was adopted to justify moderation in the imposition of punishments, is not clear. But the Act, once legislated, reinforced existing policy with the result, as Nigel Walker put it, that infanticide is now so clearly distinguished from "murder" that in England even criminologists ignore the former when writing about the latter.[52] Is it wise to abolish this distinction by eliminating the Infanticide Act, thus placing these cases back into the larger pool of homicides? The answer lies, in part, in value premises about the purposes of punishment, and in part in attitudes about the appropriateness of special treatment for a class of female offenders.

---

[51] There were actually 57 cases in the Home Office data, but one has since been deleted as a case involving a conviction for murder (with a life sentence imposed) was subsequently reversed on appeal on the basis of inadequacy of evidence. See *The Guardian*, February 29, 1992, p.1.

The author wishes to express gratitude to the Division of Plannng and Research of the Home Office for providing access to these data, and particularly to the Director of the Division, Christopher Nuttall, and to William Burns.

[52] Nigel Walker (1968), *op. cit.* (note 5), p.134.

IV. Conclusion: the case for persistence in the established policy of merciful disposal of cases

The Infanticide Act and the pattern of sentencing that has emerged under it are consistent with the dominant historical trends of the past 200 years in relation to penological principles in general and the punishment of infanticide in particular. Earlier patterns of severe punishment, including widespread use of the death penalty, have been renounced. Increased awareness of the psychological and social causes of criminal behaviour has become a significant element of the criminal law. For more than 150 years before the enactment of the Infanticide Act, judges and juries created legal fictions and ignored obvious facts in order to save mothers who killed their infant children from the rigours of the law. One may say that the sensibilities of the people have favoured mercy. The Infanticide Act provided psychiatric rationale and legislative blessing to a pre-existing pattern of judicial and administrative decision-making.

Interestingly, most criticism of the Act has not challenged the pattern of leniency. The Butler Committee, whose recommendations included the abolition of the mandatory life imprisonment sentence for murder and the development of a system of completely individualised sentences to reflect the circumstances of each criminal case, was actually trying to promote greater leniency throughout the entire criminal justice system. The Committee was not critical of the operation of the Infanticide Act, but felt its purposes might better be served through a completely new approach to criminal sentencing. Professor Walker, perhaps the most distinguished individual critic of the Act, leaves us somewhat uncertain about whether he thinks the system is too lenient. His writings hint at unease with the disposal of cases involving infanticidal mothers, but he is not openly critical of the sentences imposed.

Some feminist writers, on the other hand, have complained that the law is too eager to conclude that a woman who acts out of role must be mentally disordered.[53] These writers object to the view that women are subject to uncontrollable hormonal effects, and assert that infanticide may be viewed as a rational albeit criminal choice in a difficult situation.[54] These concerns, rooted in the observation that women are an oppressed group, may lead to the paradoxical result that more severe punishments are called for so as to make it clear that women are equally responsible for their behaviour.[55]

Some critics of the Infanticide Act have drawn attention to certain internal inconsistencies in the Act to suggest that special treatment for one class of female offenders may be inequitable. Certainly it is true that legislation authorising differential treatment of certain groups in matters of criminal liability deserves special scrutiny.[56] Is it fair, for example, that fathers who might also experience a disturbance of the balance of the mind in response to changes in

[53] A. Wilczynski and A. Morris, "Parents who kill their Children," [1993] Crim.L.R. 31, at p.36.

[54] A. Wilczynski, "Neonaticide," presented at the "Perspectives On Female Violence" National Conference, St. George's Hospital Medical School, London, March, 1991.

[55] Osborne, *op. cit.* See also, the memorandum given in written evidence to the Butler Committee by Feminists Against Eugenics, Select Committee, *op. cit.* vol.3, p.551.

[56] Mary E. Lentz, "A Postmortem of the Postpartum Psychosis defence," (1989) 18 Capital University L. Rev. 525 at p.530.

social circumstances (perhaps intensified by sleep deprivation) cannot claim protection under the Act?[57] Perhaps more to the point, the requirement of the Act that victims must be less than 12 months of age may create invidious distinctions between groups of mothers. A woman whose state of mind satisfies the conditions of the statute cannot claim its protection if the child she killed was one day too old. A mother of several children who killed them all during a period when the balance of her mind was disturbed by the effect "of giving birth . . . or . . . lactation" (the language of the existing Act) or "of giving birth or if circumstance consequent upon the birth" (the language of the Draft Criminal Code Bill) would be protected by the statute in relation to the killing of the newborn only.[58] These arguments are not without merit, but is it not mean-spirited to argue against mercy to one class of offenders on the grounds that there are equally deserving offenders to whom it is not extended? The argument extends equally well in the opposite direction, to suggest that a more progressive, less punitive approach might be appropriate in some broader range of cases. If such a system were legislated and demonstrated to be effective in practice, which was, after all, the goal of the Butler Committee, then the abolition of the Infanticide Act might be appropriate. Failing that, however, perhaps the best that can be hoped for is that the discretionary powers of the judicial and executive branches of government will limit blatant inequality to the extent possible.

It has been demonstrated that the full range of criticism of the Infanticide Act is without merit. The psychiatric principles from which the Act is derived have been shown to be supported by a considerable body of scientific evidence. The assertion that the Act has been rendered unnecessary by subsequent diminished responsibility legislation has been shown to be wrong in fact, however plausible it may be in theory. The various positions that can be made for more severe punishments have been shown to be less than persuasive. But these are all arguments in the negative—defensive positions against the voices that call for change. It is also possible to argue affirmatively in support of the Infanticide Act and/or the revised version proposed in the Draft Criminal Code Bill.

Consider the underlying purposes of criminal punishment. Foremost among these is deterrence. Whether women who kill their infant children are psychiatrically disturbed or responding to social stress, it seems unlikely that the threat of legal sanctions will be a controlling factor in their behaviour. Indeed, the whole history of the law's response to infanticide suggests that deterrence is not likely to be a powerful effect. Nor is there any evidence that these women need to be incapacitated. There is no evidence to suggest that they are a threat to other children or to the community. While no wide-reaching recidivism study has ever been undertaken, probation has been the principal penological strategy for a very long time, and no statistical or even anecdotal evidence has been brought forward to suggest that the protection of the community requires that infanticidal mothers be incarcerated. This leaves us having to choose between retribution on the one hand, and compassion on the other. This is principally a matter of values rather than evidence and logic.

---

[57] K. O'Donovan, *op. cit.*, p.262.
[58] Judith A. Osborne, *op. cit.*, pp.55–6.

Glanville Williams argued that the current approach to the crime of infanticide is insufficiently merciful:

> "it allows the conviction . . . of a woman who may in fact have been afflicted by . . . a real temporary insanity . . . [and] the Act does not save the woman, who may already be in great mental distress, the humiliation, disgrace, and agony of a formal trial before judge and jury."[59]

A justification for compassion, derived from the observation that humanity is weak and the challenges of life severe, was particularly well made by Bertholt Brecht in a story-poem about Marie Farrar who died in the Meissen penitentiary after having been convicted of infanticide. The closing stanza reads:

> "You who bear pleasantly between clean sheets
> And give the name "blessed" to your womb's weight
> Must not damn the weakness of the outcast,
> For her sin is black, but her pain was great.
> Therefore, I beg you, check your wrath and scorn
> For man needs help from every creature born."

[59] G. Williams, *op. cit.*, pp.123–24.

International Journal of Law and Psychiatry, Vol. 12, 1–27, 1989
Printed in the U.S.A.

0160-2527/89 $3.00 + .00

Sentencing the Partly Mad and the Partly Bad: The Case of The Hospital Order in England and Wales

Simon N. Verdun-Jones*

Introduction

> The problem of the mentally disordered offender raises in a particularly acute form the question of the primary function of the courts. (Wootton, 1963, p. 58)

In 1812, after her first meeting with Lord Byron, Lady Caroline Lamb confided to her journal that he was "mad, bad, and dangerous to know." In light of the course of their subsequent relationship, perhaps Lady Caroline Lamb was not entirely lacking in insight; however, her observation does neatly encapsulate the ambiguity that surrounds the whole process of sentencing mentally disordered offenders. Indeed, the mixture of madness, badness and alleged dangerousness creates a remarkably complex brew for sentencers, searching for an appropriate disposition for mentally disordered offenders. As Halleck (1986) comments, in the context of the United States:

> We remain uncertain how to treat them. We are unwilling to leave them alone, yet most agencies seek to avoid responsibility for their care. We confine them to prisons and to prison-like hospitals where they are sometimes treated worse than other offenders. They almost always receive worse treatment than mental patients in public or private mental hospitals. (p. 12)

The combination of madness and alleged dangerousness perhaps poses the greatest challenge to sentencers since it is always possible that harsher measures of restraint will be imposed on the mentally disordered offender, who is alleged to be dangerous, than would be imposed on the serious offender who is consid-

*Professor of Criminology, Simon Fraser University, Burnaby, B.C., V5A 1S6, Canada. Visiting Fellow, Institute of Criminology and Clare Hall, University of Cambridge (1987–88).

The author wishes to acknowledge that his research has been supported by a grant from the Social Sciences and Humanities Research Council of Canada. He also wishes to thank Patricia Ratel (Simon Fraser University) for her expert research assistance. Particular thanks are owing to Dr. Adrian Grounds (University of Cambridge), Dr. Jill Peay (Brunel University), and Dr. John Hamilton (Broadmoor Hospital) for their invaluable help in making it possible for the author to obtain access to various institutions in England. Finally, the author wishes to thank Donna Robertson (of Simon Fraser University) for providing the administrative support necessary for the conduct of his research in England.

ered to be "normal." Furthermore, there is always the danger that such restrictive measures will be imposed upon mentally disordered offenders without the benefit of the due process of law that, in theory at least, is emphasized in the sentencing of "normal" offenders.

Clearly, the question of how best to deal with mentally disordered offenders has vexed policy makers in many different jurisdictions. The present paper examines the approach adopted in England and Wales, where sentencing courts have the option of imposing a hospital order, under which a mentally disordered person who has been convicted of an offence, may be sent directly to hospital rather than to prison.[1] Of course, it is always important to view the use of such sentencing options within the context of all of the various pathways that may be followed by mentally disordered offenders through the criminal justice system (Gostin, 1985; Halleck, 1986) and, for this reason, the paper examines the hospital order against this broader background.

Separating the Mad from the Bad: The Insanity Defence

The inherently controversial task of separating the bad from the mad falls to the insanity defence, which is primarily concerned with the question of the defendant's *criminal responsibility* (Monahan, 1973). The function of the insanity defence is to draw a sharp distinction between the mad and the bad and, in theory, to eliminate all considerations of punishment in dealing with the mad. In countries such as Canada and the United States, the insanity defence is still resorted to as a device for dealing with the grossly mentally disordered offender; however, it must be said that in the United States in particular, the last decade has witnessed an increasing determination on the part of legislators to impose much stricter limitations on the scope of the defence as a means of reducing the numbers of individuals who may benefit from it (Mackay, 1988). In any event, even in these countries, a successful insanity defence is a statistical rarity (Pasewark, 1981) and the vast majority of mentally disordered offenders are found to be criminally responsible for their actions. In this sense, most mentally disordered offenders, in these jurisdictions, are considered to be both "mad and bad" or, more accurately, "partly mad and not all bad." If any concessions are to be made to the mental disorder of the convicted offender, then these will emerge at the sentencing stage as "mitigating factors" (Nadin-Davis, 1982, p. 83; Ruby, 1987, chap. 5).

In England and Wales, the insanity defence has virtually disappeared as an option for dealing with the mentally disordered offender (Dell, 1983; Gordon & Verdun-Jones, 1986; Wells, 1983). The defence of diminished responsibility exists in relation to a charge of murder; however, if successful, the defence does not lead to an acquittal but rather to a conviction of manslaughter and, thereby, a greater degree of flexibility in sentencing (Dell, 1982; Gordon & Verdun-Jones, 1986; Griew, 1988; Walker, 1968). In essence, what has happened in

[1] In an earlier paper (Verdun-Jones, 1987), Canadian proposals to introduce a hospital order system were discussed at length. At present, Canadian courts have no power to sentence a convicted offender directly to a hospital rather than prison. At best, the trial judge may sentence the offender to prison with a recommendation that he/she be transferred to a hospital; *see R. v. Deans* (1977), 39 C.R.N.S. 338 (Ont. C.A.). (See also Wormith & Borzecki, 1985.)

England and Wales is that a defendant's mental disorder is no longer relevant to the issue of criminal responsibility. Instead, the issue has now become relevant exclusively to the process of sentencing (Gordon & Verdun-Jones, 1986, p. 74). In short, all mentally disordered offenders are considered to be partly mad and partly bad.

Sentencing the Partly Mad and the Partly Bad in England and Wales

In England and Wales, sentencing practices have developed which appear to have divided mentally disordered offenders into four major groups: (a) Those who are not considered to be dangerous and who may be sentenced to a hospital order or a psychiatric probation order; (b) those who are considered to be dangerous and who may be sentenced to a hospital order coupled with a restriction on their release; (c) those who are not considered to be dangerous but who, it is felt, deserve punishment rather than treatment; (d) those who are considered to be dangerous, in need of punishment rather than treatment, and who have committed a serious offence.

The Predominantly Mad Who Are Not Considered to Be Dangerous

Those mentally disordered offenders who are considered to be in need of treatment rather than punishment and who are not considered to be dangerous may be the recipients of a variety of sentencing options. Such offenders could be given a psychiatric probation order (Ashworth & Gostin, 1985, p. 225; Hoggett, 1984, pp. 163–165), which requires them to be placed under some kind of medical treatment and may even require residence in a mental health hospital, or they could be made the subject of a guardianship order, although this last option is very rarely used (Ashworth & Gostin, 1985, pp. 219–220; Hoggett, 1984, pp. 182–183). Where an offender requires institutional treatment, the court may impose a hospital order, under section 37 of the *Mental Health Act, 1983* (Ashworth & Gostin, 1984, 1985; Gostin, 1983, p. 32; Hoggett, 1984, p. 166; Stockdale & Devlin, 1987, chap. 11). The criteria for imposing such an order are basically the same as those for civil commitment.[2] The court must be satisfied that the offender is suffering from "mental illness," "psychopathic disorder," "severe mental impairment," or "mental impairment."[3]

---

[2]The Crown Court may impose a hospital order on an offender convicted of any offence punishable by imprisonment (except where the penalty is fixed by law, which means that a hospital order may not be used for murder) (section 37(1)). A magistrate's court may impose a hospital order in relation to an imprisonable offence and it has the power to impose such an order without recording a conviction against the accused (section 37(3); see *R. v. Lincoln (Kesteven) Magistrates' Court, ex parte O'Connor*, [1983] 1 W.L.R. 335.

[3]"Mental disorder" is not defined in the Act. However, section 1(2) specifies that "severe mental impairment" means:

> a state of arrested or incomplete development of mind which includes severe impairment of intelligence and social functioning and is associated with abnormally aggressive or seriously irresponsible conduct on the part of the person concerned

"Mental impairment" means:

> a state of arrested or incomplete development of mind (not amounting to severe mental impair-

Where the offender is found to be suffering from "psychopathic disorder" or "mental impairment," the court must also be satisfied that the proposed treatment is "likely to alleviate or prevent a deterioration of his condition" (the so-called "treatability" requirement).[4]

The offender may be sent to a local psychiatric hospital (Faulk, 1985), a regional secure unit, which provides a greater degree of security than a local hospital (Bluglass, 1985; Faulk, 1979; Snowden, 1986; Treasaden, 1985) or one of the four special hospitals, which provide beds only to those persons who are considered to be a serious risk to the public (Hamilton, 1985; Parker, 1985). An offender may be held for up to 6 months under a hospital order. However, the order is renewable, initially for a further 6 months and, thereafter for periods of 1 year. The offender may be released by the responsible medical officer (RMO), the hospital managers or by a Mental Health Review Tribunal.

The Predominantly Mad Who Are Considered to Be Dangerous

Where a mentally disordered offender is considered to be dangerous, a hospital order may be imposed coupled with a restriction order under section 41 of the Act. A restriction order, in practically all cases, has the effect of rendering the hospital order indefinite in duration and a restricted offender may only be released by the Home Secretary or by a Mental Health Review Tribunal. Furthermore, there is the option to release a restricted offender on conditions which renders the offender subject to recall to the hospital by the Home Secretary.[5] A restriction order may only be imposed where it is considered to be "necessary for the protection of the public from serious harm."[6]

The Predominantly Bad Who Are Not Considered Dangerous

If a mentally disordered offender is not considered to be in need of treatment, and is also not considered to be dangerous, the court may impose a variety of conventional sentencing options, either custodial or noncustodial in nature. If the offender is sentenced to prison, it is very likely that his or her

---

ment) which includes significant impairment of intelligence and social functioning and is associated with abnormally aggressive or seriously irresponsible conduct on the part of the person concerned.

"Psychopathic disorder" means:

a persistent disorder or disability of the mind (whether or not including significant impairment of intelligence) which results in abnormally aggressive or seriously irresponsible conduct on the part of the person concerned.

[4]In theory, the imposition of a hospital order should depend on the present mental state of the accused and not on the degree of criminal responsibility at the time of the commission of the offence. For example, in *R. v. McBride*, [1972] Crim. L.R. 322, the Court of Appeal stated that it is not necessary to establish a causal connection between the offender's mental condition and the offence before a hospital order can be made. However, the courts do not always maintain this distinction; see *Castro* (1985), 81 Cr. App.R. (S.) 212 (C.A.), which involved a conviction of drug smuggling.

[5]Section 42. For the origins of this power of recall in the *Mental Health Act*, 1959, see Department of Health and Social Security, 1978, pp. 45–55; Gunn, 1979, pp. 205–209).

[6]Section 41(1).

mental disorder will act as a mitigating factor, thereby reducing the severity of the punishment (Stockdale & Devlin, 1987; Thomas, 1988).

Mentally Disordered Offenders Who Have Committed a Serious Offence and Who Are Considered to Be Dangerous

There is a group of mentally disordered offenders who may be subjected to a preventive sentence of life imprisonment if they are considered to be dangerous and if they have committed serious offences, particularly manslaughter and violent sexual offences (Stockdale & Devlin, 1987, pp. 165–167). Whereas, in most situations, the mental disorder of the offender serves to *mitigate* the severity of the penalty imposed, the practice of imposing discretionary life sentences on allegedly dangerous offenders could be interpreted, particularly by the offenders themselves, as *increasing* punishment on those who are mentally disordered.[7]

The stated rationale for imposing a life sentence is the contention that such a disposition permits offenders to be dealt with flexibly so that their release may be achieved at the precise moment when the medical and prison authorities no longer consider them to be a danger to the public. The Court of Appeal has indicated that a discretionary sentence of life imprisonment is only justifiable where there is clear evidence of mental instability which would indicate the offender is likely to be a danger to the public.[8] In *Wilkinson*,[9] Lord Lane C. J. set out the basic principles in the following manner:

> It seems to us that the sentence of life imprisonment, other than for an offence where the sentence is obligatory, is really appropriate and must only be passed in the most exceptional circumstances. With a few exceptions, . . . it is reserved, broadly speaking . . . for offenders who for one reason or another cannot be dealt with under the provisions of the Mental Health Act, yet who are in a mental state which makes them dangerous to the life or limb of members of the public. It is sometimes impossible to say when that danger will subside, and therefore an indeterminate sentence is required, so that the prisoner's progress may be monitored by those who have him under their supervision in prison, and so that he will be kept in custody only so long as public safety may be jeopardized by his being let loose at large.[10]

It is by no means clear, however, which mental states will "qualify" an offender as a candidate for a life sentence. Indeed, it would not be unfair to suggest that the selection process resembles something of a lottery in this respect. For

[7]In general, the Court of Appeal has ruled that long determinate sentences should not be given to mentally disordered offenders solely because of their dangerousness to the public. In such circumstances, the Court has recommended consideration of a life sentence, with its provisions for "flexible release." *See Wilkinson* (1983), 5 Cr.App.R.(S.) 105 (C.A.); however, *c.f. Gouws* (1981), 3 Cr.App.R. (S.) 325 (C.A.).

[8]*Blackburn* (1979), 1 Cr. App.R. (S.) 205; *Naylor*, [1988] Crim. L. Rev. 63.

[9](1983), 5 Cr.App.R.(S.) 105.

[10]At 108.

example, in *R. v. Allen*,[11] the "mental state" which justified the imposition of a sentence of life imprisonment was constituted by "strong feelings of passion and jealousy which (the offender) could not control." However, in *Vinagre*, where the offender was alleged to be suffering from the so-called "Othello Syndrome," the Court of Appeal ruled that this was not the kind of "mental imbalance" which would justify keeping him in custody until the Home Secretary and Parole Board thought it was safe to release him.[12] Since the mental states in both the *Allen* and *Vinagre* cases appeared to be based on destructive feelings of jealousy, it is difficult to discern a clear distinction between the two cases.

It appears that personality disorders resulting in sexual deviation are mental states that are likely to attract a life sentence in the appropriate circumstances. In *Pate*,[13] for example, the appellant was convicted of false imprisonment and a number of sexual offences against a 13-year-old boy. The medical evidence was to the effect that he was a homosexual paederast with deviant sadomasochistic interests and that he was not amenable to treatment. He was, therefore, considered to be a danger to small boys. He was sentenced to life imprisonment. In rejecting Pate's appeal, the Lord Chief Justice said that:

> This man is plainly mentally ill and represents a danger to the public. We take the view that this is a case which merits life imprisonment by reason of its gravity. (p. 354)

On the other hand, in *Hercules*,[14] a "personality defect," resulting in aggressiveness, was not considered to be the type of mental imbalance which would attract a sentence of life imprisonment. Lawton L.J. commented[15] that there was a "personality defect; but there is a personality defect in nearly all criminals."

The dangers inherent in the use of life imprisonment as a device for ensuring long term detention of the mentally disordered offender were illustrated very strikingly by a recent case decided by a Divisional Court of the Court of Queen's Bench. Indeed, in *Handscomb and Others*,[16] the contention that the life sentence provides a flexible method of determining the optimal moment for release acquired a very hollow ring indeed. As Watkins L.J. stated, the "real question" raised by such cases was whether there is a "danger, given that there is no right to parole, that a prisoner will serve in custody *more* than he should."[17] The Divisional Court considered the cases of four individuals who had been

---

[11][1987] Crim.L.R. 645 (C.A.). See also *R. v. Dempster*, [1987] Crim.L.R. 647.

[12]In *Vinagre* (1979), 69 Cr. App.R. 104 (C.A.), the trial judge accepted the accused's plea of guilty to manslaughter on the basis of diminished responsibility and sentenced him to life imprisonment, despite the submission of evidence that the condition would be unlikely to recur. The Court of Appeal substituted a definite term of 7 years.

[13](1984), 80 Cr.App.R.349 (C.A.).

[14](1980), 2 Cr.App.R.(S.) 156 (C.A.). However, in other cases, life sentences had been imposed on offenders who had been diagnosed as suffering from a personality disorder: *MacDougall* (1983), 5 Cr. App.R. (S.) 78; *Finney* (1979), 1 Cr. App.R. (S.) 301.

[15]At 158.

[16](1987), 86 Cr.App.R. 59.

[17]At 80.

sentenced to life imprisonment for offences other than murder. In the case of Handscomb himself, the defendant had pleaded guilty to manslaughter (on the basis of diminished responsibility) in relation to the brutal killing of a 52-year-old homosexual man. The major issue considered by the Divisional Court was whether the Home Secretary had followed appropriate procedures in fixing the date for the offender's first parole hearing. Under section 61(1) of the *Criminal Justice Act, 1967*, the "Secretary of State may, if recommended by the Parole Board, release on license a person serving a sentence of imprisonment for life . . . but shall not do so . . . except after consultation with the Lord Chief Justice of England together with the trial judge if available." Under this procedure the Home Secretary consults the Lord Chief Justice and the trial judge to determine what period of incarceration should be served for the purposes of retribution and deterrence. Regardless of the inmate's progress, this period must be served before the Parole Board may consider the question of release in light of whether he or she is still considered to be dangerous. In other words, the life sentence is divided into two separate parts; the time to be served in the first part is based on the appropriate "tariff" for the offence concerned, while the time to be served in the second part is based on the Parole Board's assessment of the offender's readiness for release.

In Handscomb's case, the Home Secretary set the date for his initial parole review in such a way that, even if Handscomb were released on his first parole consideration, the offender would have served some 17 years in custody before being released. If remission were taken into account, then Handscomb would actually have served the equivalent of a determinate sentence of 27 years with full remission. Watkins L.J. pointed out[18] that, since 1978, no determinate sentence in excess of 10 years had been imposed for manslaughter with diminished responsibility. It was apparent that the Home Secretary had not considered the factor of remission in determining how long Handscomb should serve for the tariff purposes and, in addition, evidence was received by the Court which suggested that the Home Office did not consider itself bound by the judicial view of the appropriate tariff sentence. In the view of the Court, if the Home Secretary did not, in fact, consider himself bound by the judicial advice as to the tariff part of the sentence, then there was a "prima facie case" of "irrationality" and "unreasonableness." Indeed, Watkins L.J. stated that if "the Home Secretary is not to be guided by the judges on retribution and deterrence, where else can he look for guidance?"[19] In Handscomb's case, the Court held that the date of his first review should "relate strictly to the judicial view of the tariff" and it was not prepared to assume that the tariff advised by the judge and the Lord Chief Justice in this particular case was 17 years' detention. The Court ruled that Handscomb was entitled to declaratory relief that would ensure the immediate setting of a date for an initial parole review. Subsequently, the procedures adopted by the Home Secretary in such cases, were modified in line with the ruling of the Court in the *Handscomb* case.

[18]At 76.

[19]At 82. The Court also considered that it was "irrational" for the Home Secretary to wait for 3 or 4 years before consulting with the judiciary and stated that the Home Secretary should set in motion the process of selecting the date for the first parole review "at the very outset of custody."

The Problem of Dangerousness

If the rationale for imposing a discretionary life sentence in these cases rests on the alleged dangerousness of the offender, how is dangerousness determined in the courts? It appears that this question is decided primarily on the basis of medical evidence.[20] However, it has been suggested by the Court of Appeal that, while medical evidence is normally required to establish that the offender is likely to be a danger to the public in the future, there may be a limited number of cases where the sentencer can draw this conclusion merely from a history of similar offences or a series of similar offences of which the offender is convicted on the same occasion.[21]

It appears that, in making the decision to impose a discretionary life sentence, there is an unstated assumption that medical or clinical predictions of dangerousness are to be given particular weight, despite the immense body of literature which questions whether medical professionals have any special expertise in prediction at all and suggests that psychiatrists consistently overpredict violence (Steadman & Cocozza, 1974; Thornberry & Jacoby, 1979; Webster, Menzies, & Jackson, 1982). Indeed, Menzies, Webster, and Sepejak (1985) have suggested that, as far as prediction of dangerousness is concerned, there is a "forensic sound barrier" of about ".40" which cannot be breached using existing clinical techniques of prediction. Furthermore, as Bowden (1985, p. 270) points out, most psychiatric predictions are, in any event, based on "non-medical information which others are at least as competent to interpret."

It has been argued that, in order to protect society, there will always be a need for the courts to take some account of potential dangerousness in fixing sentences (Zimring & Hawkins, 1986). However, it has equally been contended that preventive sentences based on alleged dangerousness should only be imposed in a very limited number of cases where there is very strong evidence supporting a prediction of dangerousness. As Zimring and Hawkins (1986, p. 509) state, "only those systems that do not trust themselves can be trusted by others to respect the considerable limitations of a jurisprudence of dangerousness." In recent years, of course, there has been an increasing interest in developing methods of prediction that go beyond the exercise of strictly clinical judgment. Indeed, the development of predictive models combining actuarial data, clinical data, and criminological data appears to offer some degree of hope for the improvement of the success rate of predictions of dangerousness (Binder & McNiel, 1988; Cohen et al., 1988; Klassen & O'Connor, 1988; Monahan, 1984).

Dickens (1985) contends that if dangerousness continues to be the basis for prolonged detention, then, like insanity, it should be considered a legal status that should be determined by the court in accordance with due process of law. Under this approach, the role of medical witnesses would be strictly limited.

---

[20] *Blackburn* (1979), 1 Cr. App.R. (S.) 205 (C.A.); *Naylor*, [1988] Crim. L.Rev. 63 (C.A.).

[21] *Dempster* (1987), 9 Cr. App. R. (S.) 176 (C.A.); *Allen* (1987), 9 Cr. App. R. (S.) 169 (C.A.); *Birch*, [1988] Crim. L.Rev. 182 (C.A.). Note that the Court of Appeal has stated that, if a sentencer is considering imposing a discretionary life sentence, notice should be given to defence counsel so that the latter may make submissions as to the reasonableness of such a sentence: *MacDougall* (1983), 5 Cr.App.R. (S.) 78 (C.A.); *Morgan*, [1987] Crim. L.Rev. 837 (C.A.); *Birch, supra*.

According to Dickens, (1985, p. 200), "they may appear as experts in determining an offender's present characteristics, perhaps aiding a decision on whether they amount in law to dangerousness"; however, they would have no role in making predictions as to the future, since they lack expertise in this area. Clearly, such an approach is far from being adopted in the present system of sentencing mentally disordered offenders to life imprisonment in England and Wales. However, until there is some movement in this direction, discretionary sentences of life imprisonment of the mentally disordered will retain the appearance of being arbitrary and unfair.

Treatment of Offenders in the Prison System

Mentally disordered offenders who are sentenced to prison may be consoled by the thought that they may be transferred by the Home Secretary to a hospital for treatment under section 47 of the *Mental Health Act, 1983*.[22] However, the exercise of this option rests entirely within the Home Secretary's discretion and, even if transferred, an offender can always be sent back to prison.[23] If they are not transferred to a hospital in this way, offenders may always be treated within the prison medical service, although it is a matter of considerable debate as to how adequate this service is for mentally disordered offenders (Gunn, 1985; Home Office, 1987).[24] Similarly, an offender may be accepted into the therapeutic regime at Grendon Prison (Gunn et al., 1978; H. M. Prison Service, 1985). However, whether an offender will obtain treatment within the prison system depends entirely on the discretion of the authorities. Indeed, the Court of Appeal has discouraged courts from passing prison sentences in the expectation that a mentally disordered offender will duly be sent to Grendon Underwood prison. In *Hook*,[25] Ormrod L.J. stated:

> It is most undesirable when passing sentence to make reference to the possibility of treatment at Grendon Underwood. It always raises ex-

[22]The Court of Appeal has held that a trial court should not refrain from making a hospital order in a suitable case merely because it prefers the greater degree of security that is apparently offered by a sentence of imprisonment followed by a transfer to a hospital. In *Cox* (1967), 52 Cr.App.R. 130 (C.A.), the appellant was convicted of manslaughter on the basis of diminished responsibility and sentenced to life imprisonment. The trial judge had indicated that the appellant did not merit punishment but that "in the public interest, I am not prepared to put you anywhere near a place where you could be at liberty." In addition, he referred to the power of the Home Secretary to transfer the appellant to a hospital under s. 72 of the *Mental Health Act, 1959*. The Court of Appeal substituted a hospital order with a restriction order. The Court agreed that there was a "real distinction" between being in Broadmoor (a "special hospital") under a hospital order and being in Broadmoor on a transfer from prison.

[23]*See Castro* (1985), 81 Cr. App.R. (S.) 212 (C.A.).

[24]The extent to which the prisons are occupied by mentally disordered offenders is, of course, a controversial issue. However, there appears to be some agreement that a considerable number of offenders, who require mental health treatment, do not in fact receive it (Anonymous, 1985; Parker & Tennent, 1979; Smith, 1984a, 1984b; Taylor & Gunn, 1984; Taylor, 1986). For a discussion of how standards may be set for the delivery of mental health services within the prison system, see Steadman, McCarty, & Morrissey, 1986. Of course, the widespread infusion of psychiatry into the prison system may not always be viewed as an unqualified good (Burtch & Ericson, 1979; Ericson, 1974; Kittrie, 1971).

[25](1980), 2 Cr.App.R. (S.) 353 (C.A.).

> pectations, and these expectations for good reasons are frequently disappointed.[26]

On the other hand, where a hospital order is imposed, the sentencing court can ensure that an offender is at least sent to hospital, where treatment will be available, and that the offender will not be transferred from hospital to the prison system.

The Hospital Order: Therapy, Punishment, or Both?

There is little doubt that, in general, the hospital order system provides a humane alternative to the sentencing of mentally disordered offenders to prison. In theory, the hospital order is imposed for the explicit purpose of treatment, not for punishment, and it results in the offender being diverted from the criminal justice system to the mental health system. Most important of all, the hospital order is a "one way street" in the sense that there is no possibility that the offender may be transferred from the hospital to prison (Hamilton, 1986).

It is clear that the general view of both the courts and forensic psychiatrists is that the hospital order is properly viewed as a therapeutic, rather than a punitive, measure. Indeed, in a government White Paper (Department of Health and Social Security, 1978, p. 45), it was baldly stated that:

> In making the order the court is placing the patient in the hands of the doctors, foregoing any question of punishment and relinquishing from then onwards its own control over him.

The courts have consistently held that a hospital order is to be considered as a therapeutic disposition, even though some offenders may find that they remain longer in the hospital for treatment than they would have been detained in prison if they had been sent there for punishment.[27]

Of course, it would be somewhat shortsighted to view the hospital order purely in terms of its therapeutic goals. Indeed, Potas (1982) has correctly pointed out that hospital orders may be best conceived in terms of a somewhat uneasy union between punitive and therapeutic elements:

---

[26]At 355.

[27]See *Morris* (1961), 45 Cr.App.R. 185 (C.A.). In *Bennett* (1968), 52 Cr.App.R. 514 (C.A.), the offender had been convicted of 2 charges of indecent assault on a boy and sentenced to 3 years' imprisonment. The appellate court substituted a hospital order and the question arose as to whether this disposition was "a sentence of greater severity than that which was imposed in the court below" and thus, not permitted by the *Criminal Appeal Act, 1966*. Widgery L.J. stated (at 518) that

> In our judgment, a hospital order, which is a remedial order designed to treat and cure the appellant, cannot be regarded as more severe than a sentence of imprisonment, *even though in certain events the hospital order may involve the detention of the appellant for a longer period of time.* [italics added]

In *Sodhi* (1978), 66 Cr.App.R. 260 (C.A.), a trial judge varied a sentence from 6 months' imprisonment to a hospital order with a restriction order. The appellant challenged the variation in his sentence, pointing out that he would have been released after only 4 months under the terms of the original sentence. The appellant was considered to be dangerous. In these circumstances, the Court of Appeal ruled that the variation in sentence was appropriate.

> To assume that a hospital order is not punitive is to misconceive the object of this sanction. It shares with imprisonment the consequences of depriving an individual of his or her liberty. Like imprisonment it offers protection to the community by separating inmates from normal societal intercourse. Unlike imprisonment, however, the aim of this disposition is to provide remedial action in the form of medical or psychiatric treatment in an attempt to rehabilitate or to retard the deterioration of a mentally disordered person. It is here that the object of rehabilitation assumes most meaning. Unfortunately, it is also here that the rights and liberties of individuals are at greatest risk. (pp. 13–14)

Although the courts may intend to spare mentally disordered offenders from punishment by making hospital orders, the deprivation of liberty coupled with the possibility of treatment without their consent may well be interpreted by at least some offenders as a form of punishment. In the case of a "simple" hospital order, the punitive elements are not particularly obvious. However, these elements are much more marked in the case of hospital orders that are coupled with restriction orders. The danger of the restriction order is that it may well result in offenders spending a considerably longer period in hospital than they would have spent in prison if they been sentenced to a determinate term of imprisonment. In particular, there is always the risk that mentally disordered offenders may be detained for a substantial period even though the offences of which they have been convicted are relatively trivial. The restriction order may, in theory, be imposed for a definite period but, in practically all cases, it is of indefinite duration. As Parker L.C.J. stated in *Gardiner*:[28]

> Since in most cases the prognosis cannot be certain the safer course is to make any restriction order unlimited in time. The only exception is where the doctors are able to assert confidently that recovery will take place within a fixed period when the restriction order can properly be limited to that period.[29]

The potential threat posed by the restriction order is well illustrated by Elizabeth Parker's (1980) analysis of restriction orders made by the courts in 1977. Parker (1980, p. 466) discovered that the average period of detention under a restriction order was four-and-a-half years and proceeded to compare the proportion of mentally disordered offenders receiving restriction orders with the proportion of "normal" offenders receiving prison sentences of 5 years or more for similar offences. Parker's conclusions were that:

> For each offence, where there are sufficient numbers to warrant a comparison, a greater proportion of mentally abnormal offenders receive restriction orders than do "normal" offenders receive prison sentences of five years or more. This suggests the courts consider that

[28](1967), 51 Cr.App.R. 187 (C.A.), at 193. *See also Toland* (1973), 58 Cr.App.R. (C.A.)

[29]In *Haynes* (1981), 3 Cr.App.R.(S.) 330, the Court of Appeal stated that it was wrong to seek to equate the length of a restriction order with the length of the tariff sentence that might have been imposed had the trial court chosen a sentence of imprisonment. The appellant's counsel had contended that unlimited restriction orders were wrong in principle. However, Taylor J. reasserted the validity of the approach taken in *Gardiner*.

the public needs more protection from mentally abnormal than from normal offenders, even where their offences are similar.

The *Mental Health Act, 1983* significantly tightened up the criteria for imposition of a restriction order, requiring that it be "necessary for the protection of the public from serious harm"[30] and the Court of Appeal has ruled that there must be evidence of dangerousness before a restriction order may be imposed by a trial judge,[31] although, as in the case of the discretionary life sentence, considerable reliance appears to be placed on psychiatric evidence. However, in 1985, restriction orders were imposed in about 19% of all hospital order cases (Department of Health and Social Security, 1986). Treating psychiatrists do not have the power to release a restriction order patient; therefore, the device tends to be unpopular with them, particularly since each case must be considered by the Home Office. Indeed, there is a real question as to whether the primary decision to release such a patient should be in the hands of the executive branch of government. On the other hand, proponents of such a role for the Home Office would contend that it is necessary to protect the hospital order system from potential abuse, thereby preserving it from political controversy.

One of the major changes wrought by the *Mental Health Act, 1983* was the granting to the Mental Health Review tribunals the power to release restricted patients (cf. Gostin, 1982). The tribunals must discharge such patients if they are not suffering from mental illness, or their disorder is not of a nature or degree that warrants detention in hospital for treatment or it is not necessary for their health or safety or for the protection of the public that they should receive such treatment.[32] Given the criteria for imposing a restriction order, it is surprising that there is no continuing requirement that offenders should continue to pose a threat of "serious harm" or that their conditions should be continue to be considered "treatable" (Ashworth & Gostin, 1985, pp. 224–225).

Initial data suggests that the tribunals have been somewhat conservative in making decisions to release restricted patients in the face of opposition from the Home Office and or the responsible medical officers (Peay, 1988, p. 72). In this respect, it is significant that the Act provides for the presiding member of a tribunal to be specifically approved by the Lord Chancellor when it is considering the cases of restricted patients.[33] In practice, circuit court judges and recorders have been appointed to preside in such cases (Hoggett, 1984, p. 259). Despite the lack of evidence supporting the belief that tribunals may be unduly willing to release dangerous patients, this approach clearly reflects the Govern-

---

[30]Section 41(1).

[31]In *R. v. Courtney*, [1988] Crim.L.Rev. 130, the Court of Appeal held that a restriction order could not be imposed in the absence of evidence that the offender was dangerous to others. In this case, the Court of Appeal apparently had taken the view that danger to oneself is not sufficient for the imposition of a restriction order. *See also, Royse* (1981), 3 Cr.App.R. (S.) 58.

[32]Section 72(1)(b). The tribunal also has a *discretionary* power to discharge a patient. In deciding whether or not to make such a discharge, section 72(2) indicates that the tribunal shall have regard to "the likelihood of medical treatment alleviating or preventing a deterioration of the patient's condition" and, if the patient is suffering from mental illness or severe mental impairment, "the likelihood of the patient, if discharged, being able to care for himself, to obtain the care he needs or to guard himself against serious exploitation."

[33]Section 78(4)(a) and Rule 8(3).

ment's concern to quell public anxiety about the premature release of such patients.[34]

In recent years, the powers of tribunals have increasingly been subjected to examination by the courts. There is now a gradually evolving body of case law that is slowly beginning to clarify the role of the tribunals in relation to the discharge of forensic patients.[35] As yet, the jury still remains out on the question of how effective the tribunals are in protecting restricted patients from excessive detention in the name of therapy (Peay, 1981, 1982; Shapland & Williams, 1984).

Who Makes the Decision to Make a Hospital Order?

It is usually assumed that the decision to make a hospital order rests primarily in the hands of the sentencing court. However, this view is misleading because a hospital order may not be made unless there are favourable recommendations from psychiatrists and a bed is made available in an appropriate hospital by the relevant Health Authority.[36] Where the appropriate recommendations are made and a bed is available, the court will make a hospital order in the great majority of cases. However, it is also clear that the courts have been willing to make hospital orders in a number of cases where beds have not been made available and they have expressed a remarkable degree of frustration at their inability, in these circumstances, to avoid sending a mentally disordered offender to prison.

Even if the necessary psychiatric recommendations have been made and a bed is available, the court may decide that punishment is a more important consideration than treatment. Mentally disordered offenders have been sent to prison, in such circumstances, when offences such as rape[37] and drug smuggling[38] have been involved. However, these cases are comparatively rare and, for

[34]In one of the special hospitals, visited by the author, it was suggested that some of the psychiatrists deliberately used the tribunal hearings to obtain the release of patients whom the Home Office wished to see detained further. However, it was stated that this situation did not exist at the other special hospital visited.

[35]Tribunals' orders have been quashed where they have given inadequate reasons: *R. v. Mental Health Review Tribunal, ex parte Clatworthy*, [1985] 3 All E.R. 699 (Q.B.D.); *Bone v. Mental Health Review Tribunal*, [1985] 3 All E.R. 330 (Q.B.D.); *R. v. Mental Health Review Tribunal, ex parte Pickering*, [1985] 1 All E.R. 99 (Q.B.D.). It has been held that a tribunal has no power to order a conditional release with a condition that the patient live in a hospital and that a decision to order a conditional discharge was a final decision, not a provisional one that could be reassessed in light of the arrangements made for support of the patient after his or her release: *Secretary of State for the Home Department v. Mersey Mental Health Review Tribunal for the Mersey Regional Health Authority; Secretary of State v. Mental Health Review Tribunal for Wales*, [1986] 3 All E.R. 233 (Q.B.D.); *R. v. Oxford Mental Health Review Tribunal and another, ex parte Secretary of State for the Home Department and another appeal*, [1986] 3 All E.R. 239 (C.A.).

[36]The *Mental Health Act, 1983* (Section 37(4)) provides that an order cannot be made unless the court is satisfied that arrangements have been made for the offender's admission to hospital within 28 days of the making of an order.

[37]In *Gunnell* (1966), 50 Cr.App.R. 242 (C.A.), the Court of Appeal upheld the refusal of the trial court to make a hospital order despite the medical evidence that the appellant was a psychopath and that there was a place available for him in a special hospital. The appellant had committed a number of rapes and attempted rapes. The trial judge had stated that "punishment must be an element in this case, and that punishment can only be achieved by imprisonment"; he was sentenced to life imprisonment.

[38]*See e.g., Castro* (1985), 81 Cr.App. R. (S.) 212 (C.A.). In this case, the Lord Chief Justice pointed out that the sentencing decision had to take account of the public interest and, in his view, "people who import drugs into this country deserve punishment."

the most part, the courts will make a hospital order, where the psychiatric recommendations have been made and a bed is available. Indeed, psychiatrists interviewed by the author unanimously agreed that in the great majority of cases in which hospital orders are imposed, the courts willingly accept the psychiatric recommendations and that the Crown is very unlikely to offer any opposition to the proposal to impose such a disposition.

However, sentencing courts, who have before them the necessary psychiatric recommendations, frequently find that although they believe a hospital order is the appropriate disposition for a particular mentally disordered offender, they are unable to make such an order because of a lack of treatment facilities (Brahams, 1985). Indeed, they have frequently expressed extreme frustration at the shortage of beds which forces them to imprison mentally disordered offenders, whom they believe should really be sent to hospital.[39] For example, in *McFarlane*,[40] Scarman L.J. referred to the problems that arise in dealing with offenders who are suffering from an "intermediate degree of mental ill-health"; these individuals are suitable for neither the special hospitals nor the local hospitals. In this particular case, the trial judge had been compelled to impose a sentence of 2 years' imprisonment because there were no suitable facilities available so as to permit the imposition of a hospital order. Scarman L.J. said that the trial judge:

> was driven to impose a sentence of two years' imprisonment in a case which he believed should have been dealt with under the Mental Health Act 1959. The disturbing factor in this case is how it came

[39]*See, e.g., Porter* (1985), discussed in 290 *British Medical Journal* 447 (1985). The offender in this case was "severely mentally disordered" and was convicted of arson and causing criminal damage to a printing works (causing $100,000 worth of damage). The DHSS had refused a bed in a special hospital and no appropriate facilities were available in the county or region. The Crown Court reluctantly imposed life imprisonment. On appeal, a medical reassessment was made and the Court of Appeal eventually imposed a hospital order with a restriction order under section 41 of the *Mental Health Act*. Lane L.C.J. pointed out that there were people for whom neither a special hospital nor a prison could be considered appropriate. Despite the fact that the Butler Committee had made its recommendations more than 10 years before, "still nothing had been done."

See also R. v. Horan, [1974] Crim.L.R. 438 (C.A.). Here, the Court of Appeal substituted a hospital order (with restrictions) for a sentence of life imprisonment. The offender had been convicted of arson and sentenced to prison because there was no place available in a special hospital. Such a place became available before the appeal was heard. The Court of Appeal pointed to the need for semi-secure wings in the ordinary psychiatric hospitals.

See also Officer, [1976] Crim.L.R. 698. The Court of Appeal noted that, "judges took a judicial oath to do justice to all men and when they had to send men to prison because no secure hospital beds were available their judicial consciences were strained almost to breaking point."

It is interesting that the courts have also strongly resisted the pressure from social services to imprison petty offenders, who are mentally disordered but are not being given care in the mental health system. As Bridge L.J. said in *Tolley* (1978), 68 Cr.App.R. 323 (C.A.), at 326:

> . . . the punishment should fit the crime and the fact that an offender's mental condition makes it likely that he may, if at liberty, be a danger to himself or others does not justify the use of the penal system as a kind of long stop to make good the shortcomings of the social services and mental health system.

See also Clarke (1975) 61 Cr.App.R. 320 (C.A.).

[40](1975), 60 Cr. App. R. 320 (C.A.).

about that a judge could be driven to impose a sentence of imprisonment when he believed the facts did not warrant it.

The judicial frustration is mirrored in statistics showing a decline in the use of hospital orders during the past 15 years. Ashworth and Shapland (1980, p. 633) demonstrated that the number of hospital orders fell by some 29% between 1973 and 1978 (from 1162 to 817). The most recent figures indicate that, in 1984, the number of hospital orders reached 1030 and in 1985, it had fallen again to some 916 (Department of Health and Social Security, 1984, 1985).[41] The major reason for the decline in the use of the hospital order are the decreasing willingness of psychiatrists to make recommendations for a hospital order as well as the shortage of beds for mentally disordered offenders rather than a reluctance on the part of the courts to use this sentencing option.

This trend is starkly illustrated by the pattern of dispositions imposed on mentally disordered offenders convicted of manslaughter by reason of diminished responsibility. Dell (1984, p. 3) has recorded that, in 1964, 50% of such offenders were given hospital orders and this proportion rose to 70% by the end of the 1960s. However, that proportion has subsequently fallen dramatically to around only a quarter of such cases. Dell points out that there has been a significant decline in the extent to which psychiatrists are willing to make positive recommendations for hospital orders in relation to such offenders. Whereas, in the mid-1960s, two-thirds of diminished responsibility offenders were being recommended for hospital orders by prosecution psychiatrists, this proportion had dropped, by the mid-1970s, to only 45% (Dell, 1984, p. 15). Dell (1984, p. 17) also suggests that, over this period, the special hospitals became more restrictive in their criteria for accepting hospital order patients (limiting their intake to those offenders who constituted a serious risk to the public). As Dell (1984, p. 17) indicates, psychiatrists probably reduced the number of recommendations for the imposition of a hospital order because they were aware of this policy in the special hospitals and were unwilling to make recommendations in cases where there was no realistic chance of obtaining a bed in such a facility.

As noted elsewhere (Verdun-Jones, 1987), local psychiatric hospitals, with their emphasis on a more open therapeutic regime, became increasingly less willing to accept hospital order patients and there were, until relatively recently, few institutions which provided an intermediate degree of security (somewhere between the high degree of security guaranteed by a special hospital and the open regime of a local psychiatric hospital) (Bluglass, 1985; Faulk, 1985; Prins, 1980).

In light of these trends, it is questionable whether the court is really making the decision as to who should be punished and who should be treated. In many cases, it appears to be the hospital authorities who are effectively making this decision by either providing or refusing a bed in the situation where the court genuinely wants to impose a hospital order. In addition, psychiatrists are also playing a major role in making this sentencing decision since a positive psy-

[41]In 1985, there were also some 43 interim hospital orders. These are discussed, *infra*.

chiatric recommendation is a *sine qua non* for the imposition of a hospital order.

Solutions to Lack of Availability of Beds?

In an interim report, published in 1974, the Butler Committee (1974) recommended the creation of 2000 beds in regional secure units in order to meet the needs of psychiatric patients who require a secure regime; the Butler Committee envisaged that these institutions would provide a lesser degree of security than the special hospitals but would be considerably more secure than ordinary psychiatric hospitals (Parker, 1985; Treasaden, 1985). Although the Government immediately accepted the recommendation that such units be built and specific funds were allocated for construction, the first regional secure unit did not open until November 1980 and a further two and half years passed before the second went into service (Snowden, 1986, p. 792).[42] All 14 regional authorities in England and Wales have now announced plans for establishing regional secure units (Bluglass, 1985) and it is expected that there should be some 800 places available by the end of the 1980s (Snowden, 1986, p. 793).

It is not clear whether the increasing availability of beds in regional secure units will lead to a significant increase in the number of hospital orders made in England and Wales. The regional secure units are not designed to hold patients for long periods, a factor which may render them unsuitable for certain types of offenders. In addition, there is the very real possibility, according to Snowden (1986, p. 796) that, with the closure of an increasing number of long-term mental hospitals in favour of community-based facilities, there will be an increasing demand for chronically disturbed patients, particularly those with behavioural problems, to be housed in regional secure units; this would severely restrict the availability of beds from the point of view of the prospective hospital order offender. Nevertheless, the increasing availability of beds in regional secure units should contribute something towards the alleviation of the bed shortage which is presently inhibiting the courts in their use of the hospital order as a sentencing option.

Another device which may encourage psychiatrists and hospital authorities to be more willing to accept hospital order patients is the interim hospital order which was introduced, in 1983, by amendments to the *Mental Health Act*.[43] An interim hospital order permits a hospital to accept offenders on a trial basis to ascertain whether they are suitable cases for treatment. The order is initially made for 12 weeks and it can be renewed for periods of 28 days up to a maximum duration of 6 months. As noted earlier, a full-blown hospital order is a "one way street." If it should turn out that an offender is not suitable for a hospital regime, the error cannot be rectified. The irrevocable nature of hospital orders probably has inhibited hospital authorities from accepting marginal patients and the option of an interim hospital order should render the authori-

[42]By 1979, three or four hospitals had established *interim* secure units. See Prins, 1980, pp. 342–344; Faulk, 1979; Treasaden, 1985.

[43]Section 38.

ties more willing to consider accepting offenders, who would previously have been rejected outright from consideration as hospital order patients.

A final factor which could contribute, in some way, to an increase in the use of the hospital order is a provision introduced by the *Mental Health Act 1983*. This provision states that, where a court is considering making a hospital order, it may require the Regional Health Authority to furnish the court with information concerning the availability of beds within its jurisdiction.[44] Some psychiatrists have suggested that this can put some pressure on the Health Authority and, in turn, on the individual hospitals to provide more beds for hospital order patients.

The Problem of Consent to Treatment

Since the imposition of a hospital order has the same effect as a civil commitment, mentally disordered offenders sentenced to hospital become subject to the possibility of treatment without their consent; nor are they required to consent to the imposition of the hospital order at the time it is made (Gordon & Verdun-Jones, 1983, 1986; Hoggett, 1985). The *Mental Health Act, 1983* places some significant controls on the administration of mental health treatment without the consent of the patient (Gostin, 1983, pp. 47–55; Hoggett, 1984, pp. 207–213). Psychosurgery and the surgical implantation of sex hormones to reduce sexual drive cannot be administered without the independently verified consent of the patient, while the administration of electro-convulsive therapy or medication, for a *period greater than three months* requires *either* the independently verified consent of the patient *or* the approval of an independent medical practitioner, appointed by the Mental Health Act Commission.[45] In most cases, the patient effectively has a right to a second opinion rather than a right to refuse treatment, and American research suggests that in most cases, the second opinion routinely overrules a refusing patient (Godard et al., 1986; Hargreaves et al., 1987; Veliz & James, 1987); it remains to be seen whether similar findings will emerge in England and Wales.

There are strong arguments to be mounted in favour of the view that a hospital order should not be imposed without the consent of the offender. Indeed, the Law Reform Commission of Canada (1976, p. 31) advocated the principle that, in the absence of a genuine emergency, there should be "no treatment of accused or offenders at any stage of the criminal process without consent." This approach is particularly appropriate in the context of hospital order that lasts for a lengthy period, during which the offender may be perfectly competent to make treatment decisions. Therefore, in recommending the introduction of a hospital order option in Canada, the Commission (1976, p. 46–47) unequivocally stated that the imposition of such an order should be clearly predicated on the consent of the offender concerned. (See also Law Reform Commission of Canada, 1979, 1980, & 1986.)[46] At present, however, there

[44]Section 39.

[45]Sections 56 to 62.

[46]The proposed amendments to the Canadian *Criminal Code*, presented in June 1986, would have provided

does not appear to be any momentum to adopt such a policy in England and Wales.

The Problem of the Psychopathic Offender

As we have seen, a hospital order may be imposed where the Court is satisfied that the offender is suffering from "mental disorder," "severe mental impairment," "mental impairment," or "psychopathic disorder." The latter is defined as "a persistent disorder or disability of the mind (whether or not including significant impairment of intelligence) which results in abnormally aggressive or seriously irresponsible conduct on the part of the person concerned."[47] It is hard to disagree with Wootton (1981, p. 91) who notes that, "it is in fact difficult to think of any form of persistently objectionable behaviour which that formula could not be stretched to cover." It would be an understatement to indicate that there is a marked degree of disagreement among psychiatrists as to the diagnosis and treatability of psychopaths (Grounds, 1987a; Hamilton, 1986) and it is significant that "psychopathic disorder" is not a term which has been included in the mental health legislation of either Scotland or Northern Ireland.

The decreasing willingness of psychiatrists to treat "psychopaths" is clearly reflected in a dramatic decline in the number of hospital orders made in relation to this category of offender. For example, Ashworth and Shapland (1980) showed that, whereas the overall number of hospital orders fell by 29% from 1973 to 1978, the number of such orders relating specifically to psychopaths fell by some 55%. In 1973, almost 14% of hospital orders were made in relation to offenders with psychopathy in their diagnosis. However, by 1985, the percentage of hospital orders made in relation to psychopathic disorder was a meagre 2.5% while fully 95% of such orders concerned offenders diagnosed as being mentally ill (D.H.S.S., 1985).

While the number of psychopathically disordered offenders entering the hospital system under a hospital order has recently declined to an almost negligible level, there are still many such offenders in hospital in the course of lengthy periods of detention. The question arises as to what treatment is being administered to such offenders? Although it seems that innovative treatment regimes exist for a select group of young male psychopaths at two special hospitals, Broadmoor and Park Lane (Grounds, 1987b, p. 22), it appears that very little treatment is actually given to the majority of psychopathic offenders detained in special hospitals. Indeed, a study by Dell and Robertson (1986) of psychopathic offenders in Broadmoor suggested that, while the great majority of "mentally ill" patients were receiving psychotropic medication, very few of the psychopathic patients were doing so. Furthermore, at the time of their study, only one-third of the psychopathic patients were participating in psychological

for the introduction of a hospital order based on the offender's consent (Verdun-Jones, 1987). The treatment order option, that is now available to Youth Courts under section 20 of the *Young Offenders Act*, 1980–81–82–83, c.110, requires the consent of offenders and their parents or guardians (Hatch, 1987, 1988; Leschied & Hyatt, 1986).

[47] Section 1(2).

treatments (such as psychotherapy or skills training). While the sample of psychopathic patients had spent, on average, 8 years in Broadmoor, the average period in which they had been participating in specific treatments was only two years; thus, for 6 out of the 8 years spent in the institution by this group of offenders, "just being in Broadmoor" was the only treatment they received. This situation is somewhat problematic given the criterion of "treatability" which must be satisfied before a court may impose a hospital order on an offender diagnosed as suffering from psychopathic disorder.[48] In these circumstances, it is difficult to resist the conclusion that the hospital order option for the dangerous psychopathically disordered offender is little more than a thinly disguised sentence of preventive detention in a maximum security setting.

This particular interpretation is supported by a study conducted by Dell, Robertson, & Parker (1987) which indicates that, while for the mentally ill group of patients at Broadmoor the length of stay was not significantly related to the seriousness of their offences, the opposite was true for the psychopathic group of patients. As the authors point out:

> That the length of detention in a hospital should mirror the gravity of the patient's offence does raise fundamental questions about the whole process of committing offenders who are not mentally ill into indefinite psychiatric detention. (p. 827)

Some psychiatrists (Grounds, 1987a; Mawson, 1983) have argued that many of the problems associated with the disposition of psychopathic offenders would be eliminated if they were sentenced to prison and, then transferred to a hospital, under section 47 of the 1983 Act, with restrictions placed upon their discharge.[49] The potential advantage for offenders of this device is that the restrictions upon release automatically cease upon the expiry of the original prison sentence,[50] which means that they are much less likely to be subjected to long periods of indeterminate detention.[51] From the point of view of psychiatrists and the hospital authorities, considerable problems are posed by psychopathic offenders who are not amenable to any form of treatment or who refuse to participate in any forms of therapy. Such individuals merely serve long periods of detention in a hospital which can ill afford to lose the beds occupied

[48]Psychiatrists, interviewed by the author in Broadmoor, sharply criticized the narrow definition of treatment adopted by Dell and Robertson. For them, participating in the regulated regime of Broadmoor should be considered as a useful form of treatment for psychopaths.

[49]Section 49. In 1986, a joint consultation document ("Offenders Suffering from Psychopathic Disorder"), prepared by the Department of Health and Social Security and the Home Office considered a variety of options for changing the *Mental Health Act* so as to provide new procedures for dealing with psychopathically disordered offenders. One option was to permit the courts to sentence such offenders to prison with a direction that they be admitted immediately to hospital with the status of an offender transferred under sections 47 and 49 of the Act. However, no action was taken by the Government as a result of this document (Peay, 1988).

[50]Section 50(2).

[51]Some of the psychiatrists interviewed by the author in Broadmoor Hospital objected strongly to such a proposal on the basis that offenders who are mentally disordered should not be punished. They, therefore, viewed the proposal as being inhumane in its effect.

by them. Unlike the hospital order, however, the transfer of an offender to hospital is a decision that may be reversed if it proves to be unsuccessful. Another reform that has been suggested (e.g., by Dell & Robertson, 1986) is that treatment should only be offered to psychopaths on a voluntary basis. This reform is particularly necessary in light of the fact that most, if not all, psychopathic offenders are competent to make treatment decisions.

Conclusions

In England and Wales, the issue of mental disorder has been effectively removed from the arena of criminal responsibility and transferred to the process of sentencing; the insanity defence is virtually dead and buried and the defence of diminished responsibility provides a partial defence only for charges of murder (Gordon & Verdun-Jones, 1986, p. 69).[52] The hospital order clearly plays a major role in the system of sentencing mentally disordered offenders and it does provide a more humane method of dealing with mentally ill offenders than the alternative of sending them to prison. However, the question arises as to whether the availability of the hospital order justifies the abandonment of the attempt to separate the "bad" from the "mad" in terms of their criminal responsibility? Is it enough to separate offenders solely for the purpose of sentencing or should they also be separated for the purpose of determining the extent of their criminal responsibility? One of England's most distinguished legal academics, Glanville Williams (1983), strongly supports the present approach to dealing with the mentally disordered offender in England and Wales:

> With our national genius for compromise, we have solved the problem of distinguishing legal irresponsibility from responsibility by making almost everyone responsible but entrusting the judge with a wide discretion which is exercised on pragmatic grounds. If there are the requisite medical recommendations the judge will normally make a hospital order. (p. 689)

Unfortunately, this rather complacent view conceals a number of flaws in the hospital order system. Most dramatically, it overlooks the fact that, even when a court is willing to make a hospital order, there may be no bed available to receive the mentally disordered offender. The only alternative in many cases is to send such an offender to prison, despite the court's view that the offender should be treated rather than punished. As Dell (1983, p. 434) has aptly stated, in such circumstances, "hospitals refuse to take" such offenders, "knowing that prisons cannot so refuse."

However, there are other strong arguments in favour of resurrecting some form of insanity defence. For example, Dell (1983, 1984) has pointed out that hospital orders may not be imposed in the situation where an offender, who was mentally disordered at the time of the offence, has recovered prior to trial. Dell (1984, p. 22) indicates that this situation arises quite frequently among offend-

[52] Wootton (1981, p. 88) expresses the view that diminished responsibility convictions have "virtually become hardly more than an escape from the mandatory sentence for murder."

ers suffering from depression who may recover fairly rapidly after treatment is administered. Dell (1983) caustically notes that:

> The irony of cases like these is that if the defendant had recovered a little later, or if his trial had taken place a little sooner, then a hospital order would have been made, and the patient would have been discharged from hospital when he recovered. Recovery in hospital is rewarded by imprisonment. (pp. 435–436)

If a viable defence of insanity existed, such offenders could be acquitted by reason of insanity and sent to hospital, from which they could be released if they are considered to have recovered from their mental illness.

It has also been suggested (Dell, 1983; Walker, 1981; Wells, 1983) that the absence of a viable insanity defence creates an unfair situation in which mentally disordered offenders are forced to bear the potentially crippling consequence of conviction in a variety of critical areas such as employment and immigration.

Why did the insanity defence virtually disappear in England and Wales? One prime reason is the traditionally narrow interpretation of the M'Naghten rules by the judiciary in that jurisdiction (Dell, 1983; Gordon & Verdun-Jones, 1986).[53] Another critical reason is that, prior to 1983, the consequence of an insanity acquittal was indefinite detention "at Her Majesty's Pleasure," without any access to independent review. Historically, such detention was often tantamount to a "life sentence," since the Home Secretary would usually be most unwilling to release an individual who had perpetrated an offence of extreme violence (Williams, 1983, p. 647). The 1983 Act changed this situation by placing the insanity acquittee in the same position as a hospital order patient with restrictions, thereby giving the individual concerned access to the mental health review tribunals.[54] Curiously enough, however, this development has not sparked a revival of interest in the insanity defence among defence lawyers. Another contributor to the decline of the insanity defence was the advent of diminished responsibility, in 1957; this defence presented an apparently attractive alternative to pleading insanity in relation to a charge of murder. According to Walker (1968, p. 158), the introduction of this defence "has done no more than take over the sort of case which previously would have been accepted by courts as within the McNaghten rules." In the years immediately following 1957, the alternative was, perhaps, particularly attractive because as we have seen, until the 1970s, the majority of cases of diminished responsibility resulted in the imposition of a hospital order rather than imprisonment.

Can the insanity defence be revived? The Butler Committee (1975) contended that the first step towards revitalizing the insanity defence should be a complete reworking of the criteria for acquittal on the basis of "mental disorder." The

[53]It appears that even those defendants who would meet the criteria for the M'Naghten rules do not plead insanity. For example, Dell and Smith (1983) found that, of a sample of some 250 men convicted of diminished responsibility manslaughter, one or more of the examining doctors believed that the defendant fell within the scope of the M'Naghten Rules in 6% of the cases.

[54]Section 46(3).

Committee recommended (1975) that a jury should be instructed to return a verdict of "not guilty on evidence of mental disorder" if:

> (1) they acquit the defendant solely because he is not proved to have had the state of mind necessary for the offence and they are satisfied on the balance of probability that at the time of the act or omission he was mentally disordered, or (2) they are satisfied on the balance of probability that at the time he was suffering from severe mental illness or severe subnormality. (para. 18.26)

The Butler Committee also recommended that the court be given a variety of options in disposing of a defendant acquitted by reason of mental disorder, ranging from imposing a hospital order to an absolute discharge. One innovative disposition, that was proposed by the Committee, was a psychiatric supervision order that would permit the discharge of the defendant into the community subject to a potential recall to hospital should the circumstances warrant it.[55] To date, no action has been taken over the Butler Committee recommendations concerning the insanity defence. Clearly, the Committee's proposals would provide a much broader set of criteria than the existing M'Naghten rules and would also furnish the courts with the power to impose a broad range of dispositions. The Butler Committee's recommendations could provide the basis for the resurrection of the insanity defence, provided there is the political will to do so. Does such a will exist?

In the United States, the evidence suggests that there is a surprising lack of support for the defence of insanity. Hans and Slater (1983) and Hans (1984), for example, conducted a public opinion survey after the *Hinckley* case and concluded that a high proportion of people felt that the insane should be punished like other criminals and that only a small proportion of them believed that it is wrong to punish insane persons who break the law. At a legislative level, there have been a number of moves to restrict the scope of the insanity defence in the United States (Mackay, 1988) with, perhaps, the most significant development being the introduction of the defence of "guilty but mentally ill" in some 12 states. The "guilty but mentally ill" verdict results in the accused being convicted and sent to prison. The verdict, which is an alternative verdict to acquittal by reason of insanity, assuages the conscience of the jury by requiring that the accused receive treatment in the prison system. In essence, it offers a compromise verdict insofar as the mentally disordered offender is concerned and, for that reason, it may be very attractive to jury members, who have fears in relation to the acquittal of defendants whom they perceive to be dangerous. An interesting study by Roberts, Golding, and Fincham (1987) suggests that:

> Most lay persons would prefer to utilize a GMBI option as a compromise verdict even in the most obvious cases of "real" insanity. Our data suggests that this tendency is probably a reflection of the desire to punish severely disordered persons for their antisocial acts . . .

[55] Considerable experience with this type of supervision has been acquired by the Oregon Psychiatric Security Review Board; see Rogers & Bloom, 1985.

combined with the fear that insane persons may be released prematurely, and present a threat to society. (p. 226)

These developments suggest that, although traditional criminal law theory asserts that grossly mentally disordered individuals should be excused from criminal responsibility (Hart, 1968; Packer, 1968), American society at large feels uncomfortable with this approach and expresses a barely concealed desire for retribution in such cases. To what extent, the recent American experience reflects a temporary response to such high profile cases as that of John Hinckley or a more permanent set of attitudes towards the insanity defence is unknown. It would be interesting to see whether similar attitudes exist in England and Wales. What is clear is the development of a trend in the United States towards acceptance of the English system of removing the question of the accused's mental disorder from the realm of criminal responsibility and transferring it to the sentencing process. Perhaps, the public on both sides of the Atlantic is satisfied by a compromise approach that convicts mentally disordered offenders and then holds out the promise of treatment. This is precisely what the hospital order system does in England and Wales, although, unlike the GBMI verdict in the United States, this system does, at least, ensure that treatment will be available within a hospital environment.[56] It may well be the case that the failure to implement the Butler Committee proposals reflects the belief, apparently held by many members of the public, that mentally disordered offenders really are "mad, bad, and dangerous to know."

References

Anonymous. (1985). Mentally ill offenders in prison. *British Medical Journal, 290*, 447.

Ashworth, A. J., & Gostin, L. (1984). Mentally disordered offenders and the sentencing process. *Criminal Law Review, 1984*, 195–212.

Ashworth, A. J., & Gostin, L. (1985). Mentally disordered offenders and the sentencing process. In L. Gostin (Ed.), *Secure provision: A review of special services for the mentally ill and mentally handicapped in England and Wales* (pp. 211–235). London: Tavistock Publications.

Ashworth, A. J., & Shapland, J. (1980). Psychopaths in the criminal process. *Criminal Law Review, 1980*, 628–640.

Binder, R., & McNeil, D. E. (1988). Effects of diagnosis and context on dangerousness. *American Journal of Psychiatry, 145*, 728–732.

Bluglass, R. (1985). The development of regional secure units. In L. Gostin (Ed.), *Secure provision: A review of special services for the mentally ill and mentally handicapped in England and Wales* (pp. 153–175). London: Tavistock Publications.

Bowden, P. (1985). Psychiatry and dangerousness: A counter renaissance. In L. Gostin (Ed.), *Secure Provision: A review of special services for the mentally ill and mentally handicapped in England and Wales* (pp. 265–287). London: Tavistock Publications.

Brahams, D. (1985, February 2). Too few hospital places for mentally abnormal offenders: Pleas for action by the Lord Chief Justice. *The Lancet*, 269.

Burtch, B. E., & Ericson, R. V. (1979). The control of treatment: Issues in the use of prison clinical services. *University of Toronto Law Journal, 29*, 51–73.

Butler, Lord R. A. (Chairman). (1974). *Interim report of the Committee on Mentally Abnormal Offenders*. Cmnd. 5698. London: H. M. S. O.

---

[56]As Roberts et al. (1987, p. 226) point out, preliminary evidence suggests that the treatment of GBMI defendants is not very different from that given to those who are convicted in the "normal" fashion (citing Harris, 1983; Kelitz & Fulton, 1983; McGraw *et al.*, 1985; Smith & Hall, 1982).

Butler, Lord R. A. (Chairman). (1975). *Report of the Committee on Mentally Abnormal Offenders*. Cmnd. 6244. London: H. M. S. O.

Cohen, M. I., et al. (1988). Predicting outcome of insanity acquittees released to the community. *Behavioral Sciences and the Law, 6*, 515–530.

Dell, S. (1982). Diminished responsibility reconsidered. *Criminal Law Review, 1982*, 809–818.

Dell, S. (1983). Wanted. An insanity defence that can be used. *Criminal Law Review, 1983*, 431–437.

Dell, S. (1984). *Murder into manslaughter: The diminished responsibility defence in practice*. Oxford: Oxford University Press.

Dell, S., & Robertson, G. (1986). *Some aspects of treatment and discharge in Broadmoor Special Hospital*. Unpublished report to the DHSS.

Dell, S., Robertson, G., & Parker, E. (1987). Detention in Broadmoor: Factors in length of stay. *British Journal of Psychiatry, 150*, 824–827.

Dell, S., & Smith, A. (1983). Changes in the sentencing of diminished responsibility homicides. *British Journal of Psychiatry, 142*, 20–23.

Department of Health and Social Security. (1978). *Review of the Mental Health Act 1959*. Cmnd. 7320. London: H. M. S. O.

Department of Health and Social Security. (1985). *Mental Health Act Enquiry, 1984*. London: D. H. S. S.

Department of Health and Social Security. (1986). *Mental Health Act Enquiry, 1985*. London: D. H. S. S.

Dickens, B. M. (1985). Prediction, professionalism and public policy. In C. D. Webster, M. H. Ben-Aron, & S. J. Hucker (Eds.), *Dangerousness: Probability & prediction, psychiatry and public policy* (pp. 177–208). Cambridge: Cambridge University Press.

Ericson, R. V. (1974). Psychiatrists in prison: On admitting professional tinkers into a tinkers' paradise. *Chitty's Law Journal, 22*, 29–33.

Faulk, M. (1979). Mentally disordered offenders in an interim regional secure unit. *Criminal Law Review, 1979*, 686–695.

Faulk, M. (1985). Secure facilities in local psychiatric hospitals. In L. Gostin (Ed.), *Secure provision: A review of special services for the mentally ill and mentally handicapped in England and Wales* (pp. 69–83). London: Tavistock Publications.

Godard, S. L., et al. (1986). The right to refuse treatment in Oregon: A two-year statewide experience. *Behavioral Sciences and the Law, 4*, 293.

Gordon, R., & Verdun-Jones, S. N. (1983). The right to refuse treatment: Commonwealth developments and issues. *International Journal of Law and Psychiatry, 6*, 57–73.

Gordon, R. M., & Verdun-Jones, S. N. (1986). Mental health law and law reform in the Commonwealth: The rise of the "new legalism"? In D. N. Weisstub (Ed.), *Law and Mental Health: International Perspectives* (Vol. 2., pp. 1–82). New York: Pergamon Press.

Gostin, L. (1982). Human rights, judicial review and the mentally disordered offender. *Criminal Law Review, 1982*, 779–793.

Gostin, L. (1983). *A practical guide to mental health legislation: The Mental Health Act 1983 and related legislation*. London: MIND (National Association for Mental Health).

Gostin, L. (Ed.). (1985). *Secure provision: A review of special services for the mentally ill and mentally handicapped in England and Wales*. London: Tavistock Publications.

Griew, E. (1988). The future of diminished responsibility. *Criminal Law Review, 1988*, 75–87.

Grounds, A. T. (1987a). Detention of 'psychopathic disorder' patients in special hospitals: Critical issues. *British Journal of Psychiatry, 151*, 474–478.

Grounds, A. T. (1987b). A unit for 'psychopathic disorder' patients in Broadmoor Hospital. *Medicine, Science and Law, 27*, 21–31.

Gunn, J. (1979). The law and the mentally abnormal offender in England and Wales. *International Journal of Law and Psychiatry, 2*, 209–214.

Gunn, J. (1985). Psychiatry and the prison medical service. In L. Gostin (Ed.), *Secure provision: A review of special services for the mentally ill and mentally handicapped in England and Wales* (pp. 126–152). London: Tavistock Publications.

Gunn, J., et al. (1978). *Psychiatric aspects of imprisonment*. London: Academic Press.

Halleck, S. L. (1986). *The mentally disordered offender*. Washington, DC: U. S. Department of Health and Human Services.

Hamilton, J. (1985). The special hospitals. In L. Gostin (Ed.), *Secure provision: A review of special services for the mentally ill and mentally handicapped in England and Wales* (pp. 84–125). London: Tavistock Publications.

Hamilton, J. (1986). Sentencing the mentally disordered. In R. Mackay & K. Russell (Eds.), *Psychiatry and the criminal process* (pp. 38–48). Leicester: Leicester Polytechnic Law School.

Hans, V. P. (1984). *The insanity defense: Public opinion and public policy*. Paper presented at 92nd Annual Convention of the America Psychological Association, Toronto, Ontario, Canada.

Hans, V. P., & Slater, D. (1983). John Hinckley, Jr. and the insanity defence: The public's verdict. *Public Opinion Quarterly, 47*, 202–212.

Hargreaves, W. A., et al. (1987). Effects of the *Jamison-Farabee* consent decree: Due process protection for involuntary psychiatric patients treated with psychoactive medication. *American Journal of Psychiatry, 144*, 188.

Harris, J. D. (1983). Note: Guilty but mentally ill: A critical analysis. *Rutgers Law Journal, 14*, 453–477.

Hart, H. L. A. (1968). *Punishment and responsibility: Essays on the philosophy of law*. London: Oxford University Press.

Hatch, A. J. (1987, November). *Treatment orders and mentally disordered young offenders: Conflicting philosophies and the implementation of the Young Offenders Act*. Paper presented at the Annual Meetings of the American Society of Criminology, Montreal.

Hatch, A. J. (1988). *Treatment orders and the Young Offenders Act: Theory and praxis in youth justice*. Unpublished Master's thesis, School of Criminology, Simon Fraser University, Burnaby, B. C.

H. M. Prison Service. (1985). *First report of the Advisory Committee on the Therapeutic Regime at Grendon*. London: Home Office.

Hoggett, B. (1984). *Mental health law* (2nd ed.). London: Sweet & Maxwell.

Hoggett, B. (1985). Legal Aspects of secure provision. In L. Gostin (Ed.), *Secure provision: A review of special services for the mentally ill and mentally handicapped in England and Wales* (pp. 236–262). London: Tavistock Publications.

Home Office. (1987). *Report of the Interdepartmental Working Group of Home Office and D. H. S. S. Officials on Mentally Disturbed Offenders in the Prison System in England and Wales*. London: Home Office.

Keilitz, I., & Fulton, J. (1983). *The insanity defence and its alternatives: A guide for policymakers*. Williamsburg, PA: Institute on Mental Disability and the Law, National Center for State Courts.

Kittrie, N. N. (1971). *The right to be different: Deviance and enforced therapy*. Baltimore: Johns Hopkins University Press.

Klassen, D., & O'Connor, W. A. (1988). A Prospective Study of Predictors of Violence in Adult Male Mental Health Admission. *Law and Human Behavior, 12*, 143–158.

Law Reform Commission of Canada. (1976). *A report to Parliament on mental disorder in the criminal process*. Ottawa: Information Canada.

Law Reform Commission of Canada. (1979). *Consent to medical care*. Ottawa: Minister of Supply and Services Canada.

Law Reform Commission of Canada. (1980). *Medical treatment and criminal law*. Ottawa: Minister of Supply and Services Canada.

Law Reform Commission of Canada. (1986). *Report: Some aspects of medical treatment and criminal law*. Ottawa: L. R. C. C.

Leschied, A. W., & Hyatt, C. W. (1986). Perspective: Section 22(1), consent to treatment order under the Young Offenders Act. *Canadian Journal of Criminology, 28*, 69–78.

McGraw, B., et al. (1985). The "guilty but mentally ill" plea and verdict: Current state of the knowledge. *Villanova Law Review, 30*, 117–191.

Mackay, R. D. (1988). Post-Hinckley insanity in the U. S. A. *Criminal Law Review, 1988*, 88–96.

Mawson, D. (1983). "Psychopaths" in special hospitals. *Bulletin of the Royal College of Psychiatrists, 7*, 178–181.

Menzies, R. J., Webster, C. D., & Sepejak, D. S. (1985). Hitting the forensic sound barrier: Predictions of dangerousness in a pretrial psychiatric clinic. In C. D. Webster, M. H. Ben-Aron, & S. J. Hucker (Eds.), *Dangerousness: Probability & prediction, psychiatry and public policy* (pp. 115–144). Cambridge: Cambridge University Press.

Monahan, J. (1973). Abolish the insanity defense?—Not yet. *Rutgers Law Review, 26*, 719–740.

Monahan, J. (1984). The prediction of violent criminal behavior: Toward a second generation of theory and policy. *American Journal of Psychiatry, 141*, 10–15.

Nadin-Davis, R. P. (1982). *Sentencing in Canada*. Toronto: Carswell Co.

Packer, H. L. (1968). *The limits of the criminal sanction*. Palo Alto: Stanford University Press.

Parker, E. (1980). Mentally disordered offenders and their protection from punitive sanctions: The English experience. *International Journal of Law and Psychiatry, 3*, 461–470.

Parker, E. (1985). The development of secure provision. In L. Gostin (Ed.), *Secure provision: A review of special services for the mentally ill and mentally handicapped in England and Wales* (pp. 15–65). London: Tavistock Publications.

Parker, E., & Tennent, G. (1979). Mentally disordered offenders. *British Medical Journal, 6155*, 1–2.

Pasewark, R. A. (1981). Insanity plea: A review of the research literature. *Journal of Psychiatry and Law, 9*, 357–401.

Peay, J. (1981). Mental Health Review Tribunals: Just or efficacious safeguards? *Law and Human Behavior, 5*, 161–186.

Peay, J. (1982). Mental Health Review Tribunals and the Mental Health (Amendment) Act. *Criminal Law Review, 1982*, 794–808.

Peay, J. (1988). Offenders suffering from psychopathic disorder: The rise and demise of a consultation document. *British Journal of Criminology, 28*, 67–81.

Potas, I. (1982). *Just deserts for the mad*. Canberra: Australian Institute of Criminology.

Prins, H. (1980). *Offenders, deviants or patients? An introduction to the study of socio-forensic problems*. London: Tavistock Publications.

Roberts, C. F., Golding, S. L., & Fincham, F. D. (1987). Implicit theories of criminal responsibility: Decision-making and the insanity defense. *Law and Human Behavior, 11*, 207–232.

Rogers, J. L., & Bloom, J. D. (1985). The insanity defence: Oregon's Psychiatric Security Review Board. *Behavioral Science and the Law, 3*, 69–84.

Ruby, C. (1987). *Sentencing* (3rd ed.). Toronto: Butterworths.

Shapland, J., & Williams, T. (1984). Legalism revived: New mental health legislation in England. *International Journal of Law and Psychiatry, 6*, 351–369.

Smith, G. A., & Hall, J. A. (1982). Evaluating Michigan's guilty but mentally ill verdict: An empirical study. *Journal of Law Reform, 16*, 77–113.

Smith, R. (1984a). How many mentally abnormal prisoners? *British Medical Journal, 288*, 308–310.

Smith, R. (1984b). The fate of the mentally abnormal in prison. *British Medical Journal, 288*, 386–388.

Snowden, P. (1986). Forensic psychiatry services and regional secure units in England and Wales: An overview. *Criminal Law Review, 1986*, 791–799.

Steadman, H. J., & Cocozza, J. J. (1974). *Careers of the criminally insane*. Lexington, MA: Heath.

Steadman, H. J., McCarty, D. W., & Morrissey, J. P. (1986). *Developing jail mental health services: Practices and principles*. Washington, DC: U.S. Department of Health and Human Services.

Stockdale, E., & Devlin, K. (1987). *Sentencing*. London: Waterlow Publishers.

Taylor, P. (1986). Psychiatric disorder in London's life-sentenced offenders. *British Journal of Criminology, 26*, 63–78.

Taylor, P., & Gunn, J. (1984). Effect of psychiatric diagnosis on conviction and sentencing of offenders. *British Medical Journal, 289*, 9–12.

Thomas, D. A. (1988). *Current sentencing practice*. London: Sweet & Maxwell.

Thornberry, T. P., & Jacoby, J. E. (1979). *The criminally insane: A follow-up of mentally ill offenders*. Chicago: University of Chicago Press.

Treasaden, I. H. (1985). Current practice in regional interim secure units. In L. Gostin (Ed.), *Secure provision: A review of special services for the mentally ill and mentally handicapped in England and Wales* (pp. 176–207). London: Tavistock Publications.

Veliz, J., & James, W. S. (1987). Medicine court: *Rogers* in practice. *American Journal of Psychiatry, 144*, 62.

Verdun-Jones, S. N. (1987, November). *The hospital order: A panacea for the mentally disordered offender? Canadian proposals in light of the experience in England and Wales*. Paper presented at the Annual Meeting of the American Society of Criminology, Montreal.

Walker, N. (1968). *Crime and insanity in England: The historical perspective*. Edinburgh: University of Edinburgh Press.

Walker, N. (1981). Butler v. the CLRC and others. *Criminal Law Review, 1981*, 596–601.

Webster, C. D., Menzies, R. J., & Jackson, M. A. (1982). *Clinical assessment before trial*. Toronto: Butterworths.

Wells, C. (1983). Whither insanity? *Criminal Law Review, 1983*, 787–797.

Williams, G. (1983). *Textbook of criminal law* (2nd ed.). London: Stevens & Sons.

Wootton, B. (1963). *Crime and the criminal law: Reflections of a magistrate and social scientist*. London: Stevens & Sons.

Wootton, B. (1981). *Crime and the criminal law: Reflections of a magistrate and social scientist* (2nd ed.). London: Stevens & Sons.

Wormith, J. A., & Borzecki, M. (1985). *Mental disorder in the criminal justice system*. Ottawa: Ministry of the Solicitor General.

Zimring, F. E., & Hawkins, G. (1986). Dangerousness and criminal justice. *Michigan Law Review, 85*, 481–509.

[20]

BRIT. J. CRIMINOL. VOL. 31 No. 1 WINTER 1991

THE TRANSFER OF SENTENCED PRISONERS TO HOSPITAL 1960–1983

A Study in One Special Hospital

ADRIAN GROUNDS*

A study was made of the use of the Mental Health Act 1959 to transfer sentenced prisoners to Broadmoor Hospital between 1 November 1960 and 30 September 1983. The sample consisted of 380 cases, of whom 72 per cent had received determinate prison sentences and 28 per cent life sentences. Over the 23-year time period, annual admissions declined but the proportion of cases admitted at a late stage of sentence increased. Figures for length of stay and time of departure revealed that sex offenders stayed significantly longer than other categories of offender; and most of the prisoners who were transferred during determinate sentences and subsequently released from Broadmoor into the community were detained in hospital beyond the expiry of their original sentences. Patients admitted during the 1970s were more likely to be detained beyond the expiry of sentence than patients admitted during the 1960s. The implications of this change, and possible reasons for it, are discussed.

Introduction

This paper describes the main findings of a research study of the use of legal powers to transfer sentenced mentally disordered prisoners to hospital. The study design enabled examination of an almost complete sample of cases admitted to one special hospital during the full period of operation of a specific statutory provision. The study objectives were: (1) to examine the use made of Mental Health Act powers to transfer sentenced prisoners to a maximum security hospital; (2) to describe the characteristics of patients admitted under these powers to Broadmoor Hospital during the period of operation of the Mental Health Act 1959; (3) to examine when the patients were admitted, how long they stayed, and when they left in relation to the sentence originally imposed; and (4) to examine what changes occurred over time in the use of the transfer provisions.

Concern about the inhumanity of housing mentally disordered offenders in prisons has a long history. Accounts of historical developments in the law and hospital provision for mentally disordered offenders are given by Walker and McCabe (1973) and Parker (1985). Broadmoor opened as a state asylum for criminal lunatics in 1863. During the early decades of the twentieth century, sentenced mentally ill prisoners

* University Lecturer in Forensic Psychiatry, Institute of Criminology and Department of Psychiatry, University of Cambridge, 7 West Road, Cambridge, CB3 9DT.

This study was carried out during the tenure of a lectureship in forensic psychiatry, financially supported by the Department of Health and Social Security, at the Institute of Psychiatry, London. I am grateful to many colleagues for their support, particularly Professor John Gunn, Dr John Hamilton (who initially suggested this project), Dr Paul Bowden, Christine Curle, Susanne Dell, Dr Patrick McGrath, Elizabeth Parker, Roger Webster and colleagues in the medical records office at Broadmoor; and to Maureen Bartholomew, Gerry Gane, and Helen Ruddy for their secretarial help. I am particularly indebted to Dr Graham Roberston for his kind and patient advice.

The material forms part of a study submitted as a DM thesis to the University of Nottingham (1986).

The opinions expressed in this paper are those of the author and do not necessarily represent those of Broadmoor Hospital or the Department of Health.

were transferred to Broadmoor under s. 2 of the Criminal Lunatics Act 1884. At the expiry of sentence, these patients could expect to be released from Broadmoor (Partridge 1953); and if further asylum care was considered necessary, the local Justice of the Peace could make an order for the patient's detention in a county or borough asylum (Lushington 1895). Under the nineteenth-century legislation, continued detention beyond the expiry of sentence required a new certification procedure. This requirement ceased under the 1959 (and 1983) Mental Health Acts.

Section 72 of the Mental Health Act 1959 enabled a sentenced prisoner to be transferred to hospital for treatment if two doctors certified that he suffered from mental illness, psychopathic disorder, subnormality, or severe subnormality, of a nature or degree which warranted detention of the patient in hospital for medical treatment. A restriction direction could be added under s. 74 of the Act. If at any time before the expiry of sentence such a patient was considered no longer to require treatment for his mental disorder, he could be remitted to prison or his conditional discharge could be authorized by the Secretary of State. If the patient was still in hospital at the expiry of his sentence—that is on his latest date of release (LDR)—the restrictions on discharge ceased, but he remained detained as if under an ordinary hospital order from that date. However, it did become possible for the Responsible Medical Officer (RMO) or a Mental Health Review Tribunal to discharge the patient, without reference to the Home Office.

Several studies have shown that the use of these powers was less than fully effective. The number of people transferred annually from prison to hospital under s. 72 fell sharply until the mid-1970s (see Figure 1). Parker and Tennent (1979) noted that between 1962–4 and 1972–4 the average daily prison population rose by 22 per cent but the number of transferred prisoners fell by 30 per cent. The decline in transfer orders was mainly due to a fall in admissions to local hospitals rather than special hospitals, as local hospitals became more likely to reject applications (Robertson and Gibbens 1980). Cheadle and Ditchfield (1982) found that psychiatrists in local hospitals were often unwilling to admit offenders with chronic illnesses who had little prospect of rapid recovery, and the need for long-term care and control was a barrier to rather than a indication for psychiatric admission. Although during the late 1970s and early 1980s there was an upward trend in the number of sentenced prisoners transferred to hospital, a recent review by a Home Office and DHSS interdepartmental working group (Home Office/DHSS 1987) noted that this trend has levelled off, with numbers remaining at the same level (about 100 a year) since 1984. The report described a census carried out by prison medical officers on 1 October 1986, which found that 1,497 prisoners serving sentences of over six months (representing 4.8 per cent of the sentenced male population) were judged to suffer from mental disorder within the terms of the Mental Health Act, and the House of Commons Social Services Committee expressed concern forcefully in its report on the Prison Medical Service (House of Commons 1986), recommending that 'immediate steps' be taken to find hospital places for mentally ill and severely mentally impaired sentenced prisoners (para. 64).

Less attention has been paid specifically to transfers to special hospitals. The Butler Committee (Home Office/DHSS 1975) described substantial delays in achieving admission during the early 1970s due to 'the congestion in the special hospitals and the difficulties in obtaining acceptance of prisoner-patients by local National Health

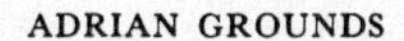

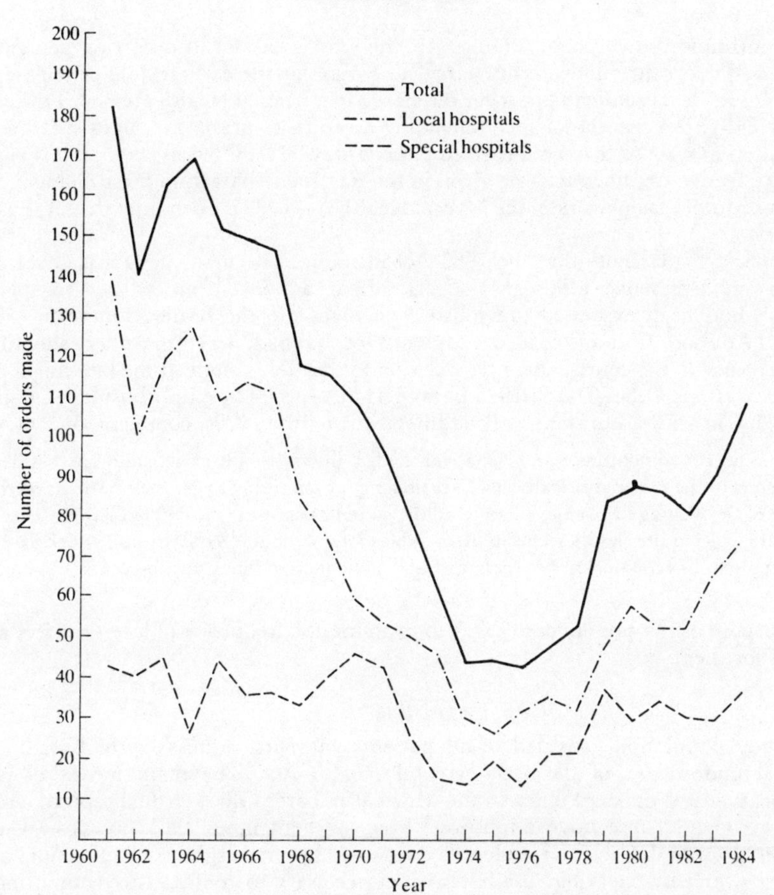

FIG. 1 Number of orders made under s. 72 of the 1959 Mental Health Act (and s. 47 of the 1983 Mental Health Act), 1961–1984. *Source:* Figures from Robertson (1984)

Service hospitals' (para. 3.49). The Committe also considered the proposal that transfers from prison to hospital ought not to be allowed at a late stage of sentence, but dismissed the concern about prolonged detention beyond sentence as 'almost entirely theoretical' (para. 3.42). In contrast, Gostin (1977) argued that a transferred prisoner should not be liable to detention under s. 72 of the Act beyond his earliest date of release, and if continued detention in hospital was required beyond that time it should be done by means of a civil treatment order (s. 26 of the 1959 Mental Health Act). In its *Review of the Mental Health Act 1959* (DHSS *et al.* 1976) the government accepted the recommendation that restrictions on discharge should cease to apply at the earliest date of release (EDR) which allows for remission, rather than at the latest date of release; but it did not accept the view that a new application for a civil order should be made if continued detention in hospital was required at the end of sentence.

The government's proposals were incorporated into the 1983 Mental Health Act, which introduced two main changes to the provisions for transferring sentenced prisoners. First, restrictions on discharge now cease at the earliest date of release, at which point the patient can apply for discharge to a Mental Health Review Tribunal; and secondly, the criteria for recommending a return to prison are slightly extended under the 1983 Act so that a transferred patient may be remitted to prison if it is found that no effective treatment can be given in the hospital. Apart from these changes, the current statutory framework of the Mental Health Act 1983 is essentially the same as its predecessor.

It is of particular note that the 1983 Act introduced no new safeguards governing transfer arrangements, although concern about admission procedures to special hospitals had been expressed previously in evidence to the Butler Committee. The Medical Advisory Committee at Broadmoor Hospital had 'urged that there should be some recourse to the courts where the decision to transfer is made at the late stages of a sentence' (Home Office/DHSS 1975 para. 3.41). A special hospital consultant, noting the decline in s. 72 admissions to Broadmoor during the 1970s, commented:

> There has, at Broadmoor at least, been a waiting list, intermittently closed, and one has heard that doctors in the prison medical service are no longer even trying to get their patients on to it. Because of the waiting list we have had to admit patients very near the end of their sentences, a procedure which quite rightly seems to them to be a form of double jeopardy and which leads to a quite poisonous relationship between staff and patient which may last for years. (Tidmarsh 1978)

One purpose of the present study was to examine the frequency of late transfers and reasons for them.

Methods

The study population consisted of all patients with first admissions to Broadmoor Hospital under s. 72 of the 1959 Mental Health Act. The main means of case identification was the card index in the Medical Records Office at the hospital, which has data on all consecutive admissions from 21 September 1965 onwards. Cases admitted prior to that date were identified from old hospital registers of admissions and discharges, and by checking case notes when necessary to confirm the section under which the patient was admitted. Re-admissions to Broadmoor under s. 72 of the Act were not included in the total figures.

A total of 397 cases was identified from the records. Seventeen were excluded from the analysis. In ten of these (all admitted between 1960 and 1965) there were insufficient data, and six more cases were excluded because the patients, although initially admitted under s. 72, were subsequently detained under hospital orders with restrictions (ss. 60 and 65). One further case was excluded because the original admission had been to another special hospital, with subsequent transfer to Broadmoor. The study population on which data were analysed therefore consisted of 380 patients. The data collected on all the cases consisted of: age on admission; sex; mode of discharge; index offence (in cases of multiple offences the most grave was noted); sentence length; legal category of mental disorder; and the dates of sentencing, admission, departure from Broadmoor, and sentence expiry (LDR).

Preliminary analysis indicated that during the 1970s and 1980s a higher proportion of patients were being admitted at a late stage of sentence. In order to examine this in more detail two groups of forty patients each were selected for comparison, one admitted in the early years and one in the late years of the Act's operation. Data were extracted from their case notes which contained detailed summaries of their psychiatric histories, trial medical reports, and minutes relating to the admission decision.

The data were coded and analysed using SPSSx software (Nie 1983). As the purpose of the study was to examine the application of a particular piece of legislation, the entire population of cases dealt with under the statute in one hospital was selected as the study sample. Results were therefore analysed for male and female cases together.

Results

The study population

The s. 72 cases constituted 15.1 per cent of Broadmoor's 2,623 admissions during the period the 1959 Act was in force (1 November 1960–30 September 1983). Broadmoor took 55 per cent of the total number of s. 72 transfers to all special hospitals between 1961 and 1983.

The characteristics of the population on which results were analysed are summarized in Table 1. The ratio of men to women was 14:1; the corresponding ratio in the sentenced adult prison population in 1983 was 31:1 (Home Office 1984*a*). The mean age of the population was 32 years (range 15–69). Over a quarter of the population had been given sentences of life imprisonment. When compared with those given determinate sentences, there were significantly more cases of mental illness and fewer of psychopathic disorder among the lifers: 82 per cent of the lifers were categorized as mentally ill compared with 67 per cent of the determinate sentence cases ($chi^2=8.69$, $df=1, p<0.01$). The mean length of sentence among those given determinate sentences was four and a half years (range 1 month–22 years).

By 30 September 1983, 317 of the patients (83 per cent of the total admitted) had left

TABLE 1 *Patients Admitted to Broadmoor Hospital under s. 72 of the Mental Health Act 1959 (1 November 1960–30 September 1983); N=380*

	No.	%
Sex		
Male	354	93
Female	26	7
Legal category		
Mental illness	271	71
Psychopathic disorder	109	29
Type of sentence		
Determinate	273	72
Life	107	28
Offence		
Homicide	102	27
Other violence	112	29
Sexual	34	9
Arson	14	4
Acquisitive	84	22
Other	34	9

Broadmoor. Overall, 160 (50 per cent) of the patients who left were released into the community (i.e. were transferred to a local NHS hospital or were given a conditional or absolute discharge). Sixty-eight (22 per cent) returned to prison before the expiry of their sentences, 48 (15 per cent) were transferred to other special hospitals, 29 (9 per cent) were repatriated, and 12 (4 per cent) died.

Admission

The process leading to admission went through three main stages. First, the sentenced prisoner was recognized by the prison medical officer as mentally disordered, and two medical recommendations for transfer were made. Secondly, there was a decision-making stage when the reports were first scrutinized in the Home Office (this period was usually brief) and then sent to the DHSS, where a decision was made about whether to offer a special hospital bed. Finally, if admission was agreed, there was a third stage of waiting until a bed in Broadmoor became available. Transfer to hospital of those serving determinate sentences had to be effected before the EDR. (This did not apply to life sentence prisoners serving indeterminate sentences, and their admissions are separately discussed below.)

An initial analysis of the data indicated that patients admitted during the decade 1961–70 were transferred on average twenty-three months before EDR (SD 24), but patients admitted during the decade 1971–80 were admitted on average ten months before EDR (SD 11) ($t=5.34$, $p<0.001$). This change was not due to any significant reduction in the mean length of their sentences, which remained similar. It therefore appeared that during the 1970s patients were being transferred at a later stage of the sentence.

In order to examine this in more detail, the first forty patients transferred to Broadmoor during the course of determinate sentences were compared with the last forty determinate sentence admissions. The forty 'early cases' were admitted to Broadmoor between 1 February 1961 and 13 May 1963, and the 'late cases' were admitted between 16 January 1974 and 13 September 1983. The different ranges of admission dates in the two groups was not ideal but is explained by the decline in annual admissions during the course of the Act. Thus admission practice during the last ten years of the Act (1974–83) was examined and compared with practice in the early 1960s.

The two groups had similar profiles with respect to age, sex, category of mental disorder, previous psychiatric history, reported diagnosis, and offence group (see Table 2). As mentioned above, length of sentence was not significantly different in the two samples. However, when the time intervals in each stage of the admission process were examined, significant differences emerged. In the later group, patients were being recommended for transfer to hospital at a later stage of sentence, the decision-making process took longer, and, once accepted, the waiting time in prison before transfer was effected lengthened considerably. The differences are summarized in Table 3. Together these delays resulted in patients during the later years being admitted much closer in time to their EDRs.

Delays at each stage contributed to this change. First, cases in the later years were being initially recommended for hospital transfer at a later stage of sentence. This was not explicable in terms of clinical differences between the two groups. Both sets of

ADRIAN GROUNDS

TABLE 2 *Determinate Sentence Cases: Comparison of First Forty Admissions (1961–1963) with last Forty Admissions (1974–1983)*

	Early cases $N=40$	Late cases $N=40$
Mean age	30.4 (SD 6.3)	30.6 (SD 7.5)
Sex		
Male	38 (95.0%)	35 (87.5%)
Female	2 (5.0%)	5 (2.5%)
Category of disorder		
Mental illness	25 (62.5%)	29 (72.5%)
Psychopathic disorder	15 (37.5%)	11 (27.5%)
Previous psychiatric admission	18 (45.0%)	20 (50.0%)
Offence		
Homicide	6 (15.0%)	3 (7.5%)
Violence	15 (37.5%)	17 (42.5%)
Sexual	2 (5.0%)	4 (10.0%)
Arson	11 (27.5%)	8 (20.0%)
Acquisitive	1 (2.5%)	1 (2.5%)
Other	5 (12.5%)	7 (17.5%)
Mean length of sentence (months)	65.1 (SD 49.4)	57.8 (SD 33.9)

TABLE 3 *The Admission Process: Comparison of Time Intervals for Early and Late Cases*

	Early cases $N=40$	Late cases $N=40$	t	p
Mean time (months) from start of sentence to:				
Medical recommendation	12.0 (SD 12.1)	17.9 (SD 14.5)	1.98	<0.05
DHSS acceptance	13.0 (SD 12.2)	21.1 (SD 14.7)	2.69	<0.01
Transfer to Broadmoor	13.3 (SD 12.2)	25.5 (SD 16.4)	3.79	<0.005
EDR	44.9 (SD 32.8)	36.5 (SD 22.8)	1.33	ns
Mean time (months) from				
Medical recommendation to DHSS acceptance	1.0 (SD 0.7)	2.8 (SD 3.4)	3.25	<0.05
DHSS acceptance to admission	0.26 (SD 0.1)	4.4 (SD 4.8)	5.42	<0.05
Medical recommendation to admission	1.3 (SD 0.7)	7.6 (SD 5.8)	6.87	<0.05
Mean time (months) of admission prior to EDR	31.6 (SD 31.9)	11.0 (SD 15.7)	3.67	<0.05

patients had similar psychiatric histories and did not differ significantly with respect to psychiatric diagnosis and symptoms recorded on the medical recommendations. Almost all the mentally ill patients had a diagnosis of schizophrenia or paranoid psychosis, and in both groups, half the mentally ill had shown symptoms within the first three months of sentence, and of these, most (twelve cases in each group) had done so at the start of sentence. The significant delay arose for those patients who developed symptoms of illness after the start of sentence. For these patients the mean time between onset of symptoms and medical recommendation was 3.2 months (SD 3.6) for those admitted in the early years and 12.2 months (SD 14.5) for those admitted in the later years ($t=2.23$, $p<0.05$). The available data do not indicate why in later years those who became ill during sentence had to wait so much longer before being recommended for transfer.

The mean interval at the second stage, between medical recommmendation and the decision by the DHSS to offer a special hospital bed, increased almost threefold in the later years. One change of practice associated with this was a custom in the later years of requesting an assessment by a Broadmoor consultant. A second possible factor may have been increasing difficulty in finding alternative placements in local hospitals for suitable patients. A history prior to transfer of time-consuming and eventually unsuccessful attempts to obtain treatment in a local hospital appeared more common in the later years.

The greatest change over the years occurred at the third stage, between acceptance and admission. The mean time waited by the 'early cases' was eight days (range 1–21 days) and transfer was achieved within three weeks of the Ministry's decision in all cases. In contrast, the mean waiting time for the 'late cases' was four and a half months (range 0–18 months). More than a quarter of them (twelve cases) waited over six months, and four patients (10 per cent) waited over a year between acceptance and transfer.

The reason for these delays was the operation of a waiting list at Broadmoor for s. 72 admissions between the early 1970s and 1983. This was said to be due to serious overcrowding at the hospital. However, it is probable that it was not the overcrowding *per se* but the fact that it had become a matter of political concern which led to the change. The resident population in Broadmoor was substantially higher in the early 1960s than during the 1970s; but in the interval the Estimates Committee of the House of Commons (1968) had reported on 'appalling' overcrowding in Broadmoor and this revelation led to the recognition of a problem which had existed for many years. In this climate, the waiting list was seen as a necessary measure to restrict admissions according to a strict order of priority. In contrast to other categories of patient (such as recalled conditionally discharged patients who had to return immediately because they posed a grave risk in the community), s. 72 cases were given a low priority as it was considered that they were at least being adequately contained under observation while in prison and did not present a risk to the public (Dr P. McGrath: personal communication). However, this state of affairs led to concern among prison medical officers who had to send reminders as EDRs approached.

When all the above time intervals are combined it emerges that the 'early cases' admitted in the 1960s were transferred to Broadmoor on average 1.3 months after the prison medical officer's recommendation for admission, and in no case did the process take more than four months. In contrast, the cases admitted during the decade 1974–83 waited on average 7.6 months between medical recommendation and transfer and a quarter of them (ten cases) waited over a year. Only two of the forty 'early cases' were transferred in the final month before EDR. In contrast, fourteen out of the forty patients admitted during the later decade (35 per cent) were transferred in the last month before EDR, of whom five were transferred within the last week.

Length of stay

The 317 patients who had left Broadmoor by 30 September 1983 had a mean length of stay of just under four years (forty-seven months). One quarter of the sixty-three residents on that date had been in-patients for twelve years or more.

These length-of-stay figures include all modes of departure. The group of patients released from Broadmoor into the community (those conditionally discharged, absolutely discharged, or transferred to local hospitals), was examined separately in order to consider as a specific sub-sample those patients on whom the judgement had been made that they were fit for release from conditions of maximum security. As noted above, there were 160 such cases, fractionally over half the total group of departed patients. For this group, the duration of detention was strongly related to gravity of offence, as shown in Table 4. Sex offenders tended to have particularly long lengths of stay. The mean time spent in Broadmoor by sex offenders before release to the community was 7.4 years, compared with a mean of 4.1 years for the other categories of offender ($t=2.96$, $p<0.005$).

Most of the patients transferred to Broadmoor during the course of determinate prison sentences continued to be detained in the hospital beyond their LDRs—in some cases for many years. In the cohort of determinate sentence cases admitted before 1975 ($N=240$), all but one of the sentences had expired within a period of eight years from admission, but 33 (14 per cent) of these patients were still resident beyond this time.

TABLE 4 *S. 72 Patients who Left Broadmoor for the Community ($N=160$): Length of Stay and Time from Sentence to Departure*

Offence	Mean length of stay in Broadmoor (months)	Mean time from start of sentence to departure from Broadmoor (months)
Homicide ($N=25$)	82.7 (SD 55.2)	144.0 (SD 68.0)
Other violence ($N=43$)	45.2 (SD 33.2)	62.6 (SD 37.8)
Sexual ($N=9$)	89.2 (SD 32.7)	111.7 (SD 44.2)
Arson ($N=6$)	60.1 (SD 64.5)	80.2 (SD 58.3)
Acquisitive ($N=61$)	34.1 (SD 26.0)	50.8 (SD 31.1)
Other ($N=16$)	57.5 (SD 32.5)	68.0 (SD 28.2)
All cases ($N=160$)	51.1 (SD 40.7)	74.8 (SD 53.1)

Departure

Determinate sentence prisoners Departure time in relation to LDR was separately examined in the sub-group of patients given determinate sentences who left Broadmoor for the community ($N=135$). Although the majority of these cases left Broadmoor after their LDRs, there was a strong relationship between the date of departure and the expiry date of the sentence, as shown in Figure 2. Twenty-eight per cent of the 135 patients who left for the community did so within plus or minus six months of the date of LDR, and 43 per cent left within plus or minus one year of LDR. Nevertheless, overall more patients left after the LDR (62 per cent) than before (38 per cent). Conditionally discharged patients left the hospital on average one year before LDR, but those who went into the community by means of an absolute discharge or transfer to local hospital generally left two or three years after LDR. Those discharged by tribunals had a mean length of stay post-LDR significantly longer than those leaving for the community by other means (35.6 and 15.3 months respectively; $t=2.22$, $p<0.005$). Thus the clustering of departure at around the time of LDR for the entire

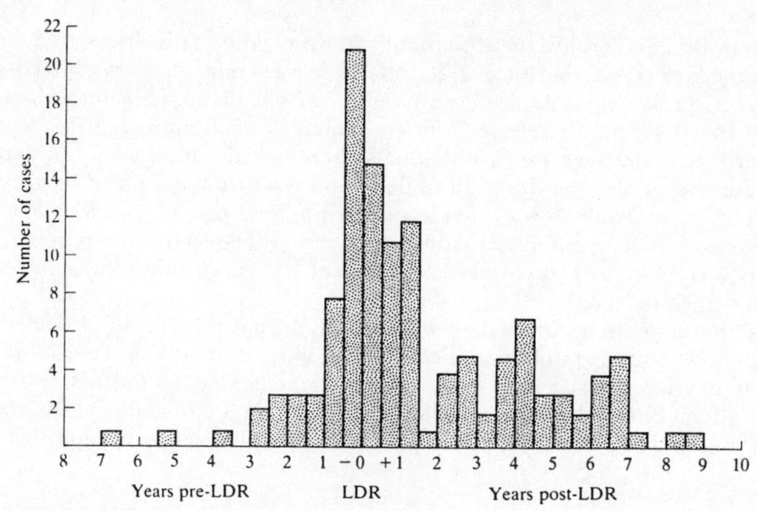

FIG. 2 Determinate sentence cases who left Broadmoor for the community ($N=135$): time of departure in relation to LDR

group results from the combined figures for these modes of departure, three of which were generally well post-LDR, and the other one pre-LDR. Sex offenders left Broadmoor for the community significantly later in relation to LDR than other categories of offender. The eight determinate sentence sex offenders who went into the community left Broadmoor on average almost four years (forty-six months) after LDR, compared with an average of just over a year (sixteen months) for other categories of offender ($t=2.40$, $p<0.02$).

Life sentence prisoners Life sentence prisoners had no fixed release dates against which timing of admission and departure from hospital could be measured. The mean time between sentence and admission to Broadmoor for the 107 lifers admitted was almost four and a half years (range 18 days–30 years). There was a trend towards later transfer for those admitted during later years, with patients admitted during the early 1980s having served over six years on average prior to transfer (see Table 5).

By 30 September 1983, seventy-seven of the 107 lifers had left the hospital and thirty were resident on that date. Twenty-five of the seventy-seven (32 per cent) left Broadmoor for the community, twenty for local hospitals and five by means of conditional discharge. The mean time from the start of sentence to release from Broadmoor for this group was 11.7 years (range 3–28 years). This figure was similar to the average time spent under sentence in prison by life sentence prisoners before release on licence, which was 10.4 years for those released during the five years 1980–4 (Home Office Statistical Department: personal communication).

Changes in the use of the section

During the twenty-three years from 1960 to 1983, Broadmoor's s. 72 admissions, particularly those with determinate sentences, declined. In the decade from 1961 to 70,

TABLE 5 *Life Sentence Prisoners Transferred to Broadmoor under s. 72 of 1959 MHA ($N=107$): Time of Admission after Start of Sentence*

Year of admission	Mean time from sentence to admission (months)	SD
1960–5 ($N=22$)	33.0	(32.6)
1966–70 ($N=26$)	35.0	(46.1)
1971–5 ($N=26$)	61.6	(71.5)
1976–80 ($N=16$)	68.5	(91.6)
1981–3 ($N=17$)	73.3	(55.9)
All cases ($N=107$)	52.1	(61.0)

$F=2.01$; $0.1>P>0.05$.

forty-seven of the 237 admissions (20 per cent) were lifers, compared with 42 of the 108 admissions (39 per cent) in the decade 1971–80 ($chi^2=13.1$, $df=1$, $p<0.001$).

Although the average sentence length of the determinate sentence cases remained fairly constant over the years, the timing of their transfer to Broadmoor became progressively later. Factors associated with this have been described above. In Table 6 sentence length is measured as the total time between start of sentence and LDR. Admission could occur no later than the EDR when normally two-thirds of the sentence had been served. The proportion of cases being transferred to Broadmoor during the last half of sentence increased steadily from under a quarter in the early 1960s to over three quarters during the late 1970s and early 1980s.

TABLE 6 *Changes in the Use of s. 72: Time of Admission in Relation to Sentence for Determinate Sentence Cases ($N=273$)*

Proportion of sentence served at time of admission (% of time from start of sentence to LDR)	Year of admission			
	1961–5	1966–70	1971–5	1976–83
0–25%	34 (35%)	32 (34%)	8 (17%)	1 (3%)
26–50%	42 (43%)	31 (33%)	14 (30%)	8 (22%)
over 50%	21 (22%)	30 (32%)	24 (52%)	28 (76%)

$chi^2=41.84$; $df=6$; $p<0.001$.

This finding raised the question of whether arrival at a late stage of sentence led to later departure in relation to sentence expiry. This was examined by comparing cases admitted in the decades 1961–70 and 1971–80, correcting for follow-up period (i.e. until 30 September 1973 for cases admitted in 1961–70, and until 30 September 1983 for cases admitted in 1971–80). Table 7 shows that the determinate sentence cases admitted in the second decade were transferred at a later stage of sentence, and a higher proportion of them stayed in Broadmoor beyond LDR. There was no reduction in the likelihood of departure to the community: 44 per cent of the 1961–70 admissions returned to the community compared with 50 per cent of the 1971–80 admissions

TABLE 7 *Comparison of Patients Transferred to Broadmoor during Determinate Sentences, 1961–1970 and 1971–1980: Mode and Timing of Departure*

	Year of admission		
	1961–70	1971–80	
Total admissions	190	66	
Proportion of sentence served at time of admission			
0–25%	66 (35%)	8 (12%)	chi² = 24.2
26–50%	73 (38%)	19 (29%)	df = 2
over 50%	51 (27%)	39 (59%)	$p<0.001$
Mean time from sentence to admission (months)	15.6 (SD 16.9)	23.2 (SD 20.2)	$t=2.74$ $p<0.01$
Mean length of sentence (months)	54.3 (SD 43.1)	49.4 (SD 33.0)	$t=0.97$ ns
Residential status	(on 30.9.73)	(on 30.9. 83)	
Departed	155 (82%)	53 (80%)	chi² = 0.05
Resident	35 (18%)	13 (20%)	df = 1 ns
Mode of departure	(N = 155)	(N = 53)	
Conditional discharge	23 (15%)	1 (2%)	
Absolute discharge (RMO)	32 (21%)	11 (21%)	
Absolute discharge (MHRT)	3 (2%)	11 (21%)	
Local hospital	26 (17%)	10 (19%)	
Remit to prison	28 (18%)	8 (15%)	
Other	43 (27%)	12 (22%)	
Mean time of departure, post-LDR for patients going into the community	(N = 84) +12.0 months post-LDR	(N = 33) +21.9 months post-LDR	$t=1.62$ $p<0.05$ (one-tailed)

(chi² = 0.7, *df* = 1, ns). However, for the latter cases there was a reduced likelihood of conditional discharge, and they were likely to have been detained in hospital for longer after LDR before release. Almost half (48 per cent) of the 1961–70 cases who returned to the community did so before LDR, compared with only 18 per cent of the 1971–80 cases released into the community (chi² = 8.61, *df* = 1, $p<0.005$).

Discussion

The findings of the present study are restricted to one special hospital in a particular historical period, and therefore may not be representative either of other hospitals or of current practice. It is possible that aspects of the situation described above have improved: in recent years 70 per cent of transfer warrants have been issued within a month of transfer applications being received, although delays in finding hospital places and Departmental concern about cases referred close to the EDR are still acknowledged (Home Office/DHSS 1987 paras. 6.19–6.20). Further research is needed to determine the current frequency of transfer at a late stage of sentence under the Mental Health Act 1983. Nevertheless, the study highlights a number of general issues.

The major empirical finding was a substantial shift in the use of the transfer powers during the 23-year time period examined. Illustrative cases are given in the Appendix.

The decline in s. 72 transfers to Broadmoor during the early 1970s began later than the much steeper fall in admissions to local hospitals, and probably occurred for different reasons. In local hospitals the reduction was associated with reluctance to accept chronically ill offender patients (Cheadle and Ditchfield 1982), but the decline in Broadmoor's admissions was associated with concern about overcrowding in the hospital and the consequent use of a waiting list which delayed admissions. It is probable that the difficulties experienced by prison medical officers in securing successful transfers led to pessimism and consequent reluctance to initiate the process, futher contributing to the decline in Broadmoor's admissions (Tidmarsh 1978).

The decline in transfers was mainly accounted for by a fall in determinate sentence cases. The change in the relative proportions of determinate sentence and life sentence cases needs to be considered against the background of what was happening in the sentenced prison population. Between 1960 and 1983 the average daily population of lifers within the prison system increased over eightfold from under 300 to over 1,800. (Sapsford and Banks 1979; Parliamentary All Party Penal Affairs Group 1985). In contrast, the population of prisoners serving other custodial sentences increased by a third over the same time period, and stood at approximately 35,000 in 1983 (Home Office 1984*b*). There was also a change in sentencing practice during the two decades, with more mentally abnormal men convicted of diminshed responsibility homicide receiving sentences of imprisonment (Dell 1984). However, overall, the number of Broadmoor transfers declined despite a rise in the sentenced population from which they were drawn.

The timing and process of admission showed striking changes over the two decades. During the early 1960s the transfer process tended to occur relatively quickly and at an early stage of sentence. During the later decade, however, medical recommendations tended to be made at a later stage of sentence, the decision-making process took longer, and the waiting list led to considerable delays in some cases between acceptance for admission and the achievement of transfer. The situation appears to have worsened during the time of operation of the 1959 Act. The relatively efficient admission of cases to Broadmoor during the early 1960s parallels the finding of Walker and McCabe (1973), who showed that most prison transfers under s. 72 in the year 1966–7 were achieved shortly after the beginning of the sentence. However, during 1975 Robertson and Gibbens (1980) noted longer delays in the transfer process to local hospitals, with 20 per cent of cases waiting more than a month between medical recommendation and transfer. They noted that

> the delay between request and completion of transfer is likely to have caused considerable and unnecessary suffering. Such delay may also have caused some ill-feeling and distrust to arise between prison and local hospital medical authorities as a number of the men concerned would no longer have been . . . in the acutely ill condition described by the prison medical officers in their reports. (Robertson and Gibbens 1980: 1266)

For cases transferred to Broadmoor during the last decade of the Act the situation was even worse. As Robertson and Gibbens (1980) pointed out, transfer has to be effected within fourteen days of the Home Secretary's transfer direction, but the real delay occurs before that direction is issued, while a hospital bed is awaited. The situation during the last decade of this study was clinically unacceptable because patients certified as requiring psychiatric treatment in hospital for mental disorder (usually associated with active psychotic symptoms) were not being expeditiously provided with it.

Admission at a late stage of sentence was associated with later departure in relation to the end of sentence. The patterns of admission and discharge therefore suggest that there was a 'shift to the right' in the entire process during the two decades of the Act. The change in departure time was also associated with a marked decline in the use of conditional discharge as a departure route during the later decade. During the 1960s this was seen as a useful means of providing controlled supervision in the community prior to the end of sentence, but it was used rarely in later years; and under the 1983 Act it is no longer a readily available option, because restrictions on discharge are lifted at the EDR rather than the LDR. Some of the prolonged stays in Broadmoor could also be explicable on the basis of clinical factors, and may reflect increasing difficulty in obtaining local hospital places for patients ready to leave special hospitals.

The delays that occurred in the 1970s and early 1980s also raise questions about legal safeguards in the powers for transferring sentenced prisoners to hospital, and this is an issue that also applies to the Mental Health Act 1983 (Grounds 1990). The results of this study show that it was (and remains) administratively possible to transfer a mentally disordered sentenced prisoner to a maximum security hospital on the basis of out-of-date medical reports, at a late stage of sentence, and there is no requirement for renewed authorization of detention at the expiry of the prison sentence. The availability of a Mental Health Review Tribunal hearing at the time of EDR may not be a sufficient safeguard against a *prima facie* injustice because a tribunal requires convincing evidence of *absence* of mental disorder in order to justify discharge, and concern about public safety tends to be the over-riding determinant in tribunal decision-making (Peay 1989).

The findings of the study also emphasize the importance of detecting mental disorder and effecting transfer from prison to hospital at the earliest possible stage of sentence. Not only is this clinically desirable, but it would ensure closer adherence to the spirit of the legislation, the purpose of which is not preventative detention beyond sentence, but the enabling of hospital treatment during sentence.

References

CHEADLE, J. and DITCHFIELD, J. (1982), *Sentenced Mentally Ill Offenders*. London: Home Office Research and Planning Unit.

DELL, S. (1984), *Murder into Manslaughter* (Maudsley Monograph No. 27). Oxford: Oxford University Press.

DEPARTMENT OF HEALTH AND SOCIAL SECURITY, HOME OFFICE, WELSH OFFICE, and LORD CHANCELLOR'S DEPARTMENT (1976), *Review of the Mental Health Act 1959*. London: HMSO.

ESTIMATES COMMITTEE OF THE HOUSE OF COMMONS (1968), *Second Report: The Special Hospitals and the State Hospital*. London: HMSO.

GOSTIN, L. O. (1977), *A Human Condition*, vol. 2. London: MIND.

GROUNDS, A. T. (1990), 'Transfers of Sentenced Prisoners to Hospital', *Criminal Law Review*, 544–51.

HOME OFFICE (1984*a*), *Report on the Work of the Prison Department* 1983. London: HMSO.

—— (1984*b*) *Prison Statistics England and Wales 1983*. London: HMSO.

HOME OFFICE/DEPARTMENT OF HEALTH AND SOCIAL SECURITY (1975), *Report of the Committee on Mentally Abnormal Offenders*. London: HMSO.

—— (1987), *Report of the Interdepartmental Working Group of Home Office and DHSS Officials on Mentally Disturbed Offenders in the Prison System in England and Wales*. London: Home Office/Department of Health and Social Security.

HOUSE OF COMMONS (1986), *Third Report from the Social Services Committee, Session 1985–86: Prison Medical Service*, vol. I. House of Commons Paper 72–1. London: HMSO.

LUSHINGTON, S. G. (1895), *Archbold's Lunacy*, 4th edn. London: Shaw & Sons.

NIE, N. H. (1983), *SPSSx: Statistical Package for the Social Sciences*. New York: McGraw-Hill.

PARKER, E. (1985), 'The Development of Secure Provision', in L. Gostin, ed., *Secure Provision*, 15–65. London: Tavistock.

—— and TENNENT, G. (1979), 'The 1959 Mental Health Act and Mentally Abnormal Offenders: A Comparative Study', *Medicine, Science and the Law*, 19: 29–38.

PARLIAMENTARY ALL PARTY PENAL AFFAIRS GROUP (1985), *Life Sentenced Prisoners*. Chichester: Barry Rose.

PARTRIDGE, R. (1953), *Broadmoor: A History of Criminal Lunacy and its Problems*. London: Chatto & Windus.

PEAY, J. (1989), *Tribunals on Trial: A Study of Decision-Making under the Mental Health Act 1983*. Oxford: Clarendon Press.

ROBERTSON, G. (1984), 'Changes in the Use of the Criminal Provisions of the 1959 Mental Health Act', in T. Williams, E. Alves, and J. Shapland, eds., *Options for the Mentally Abnormal Offender: Issues in Criminological and Legal Psychology*, No. 6. Leicester: British Psychological Society.

—— and GIBBENS, T. C. N. (1980), 'Transfers from Prison to Local Psychiatric Hospitals under Section 72 of the 1959 Mental Health Act', *British Medical Journal* 1: 1263–6.

SAPSFORD, R. and BANKS, C. (1979), 'A Synopsis of some Home Office Research', in D. Smith, ed., *Life Sentenced Prisoners*. Home Office Research Study no. 51. London: HMSO.

TIDMARSH, D. (1978), 'Broadmoor Ins and Outs 1960–1977'. Unpublished paper read to the Forensic Section of Royal College of Psychiatrists, Broadmoor Hospital, 23 May 1978.

WALKER, N. and MCCABE, S. (1973), *Crime and Insanity in England*, vol. 2. Edinburgh: Edinburgh University Press.

APPENDIX

Case 1

Mr A was transferred to Broadmoor under s. 72 of the Mental Health Act (1959) in 1962. He had a previous admission as a transferred sentenced prisoner in 1939 under the Criminal Lunatics Act 1884. This first admission is described below in order to illustrate the use of the legal provisions that preceded the 1959 Mental Health Act.

Mr A pleaded guilty to attempted murder after being charged with attacking a female relative with a hammer. At the time of trial it was recognized that the assault had been associated with persecutory delusions, and this was a mitigating factor in sentencing. A sentence of seven years penal servitude was passed in 1937. Eighteen months later Mr A was reported by a prison medical officer as 'subject to alternating attacks of maniacal excitement and acute mental depression'. He had assaulted staff and made suicidal threats. The Home Office warrant directing removal of the patient from prison to Broadmoor was signed one month later, and required the Superintendent 'to receive and thereto detain the said Prisoner as a Criminal Lunatic until further order or until the expiration of sentence to which he is subject'. The patient was transferred one week later and remained in Broadmoor for five years. His persecutory delusions, explosive outbursts of temper, and assaults on attendants continued throughout his stay without substantial improvement. Three months before the expiry of sentence the Medical Superintendent wrote to the Clerk to the Social Welfare Committee in Mr A's home city informing the Clerk that at the end of the sentence the patient would become due for removal to his local mental hospital as a rate aided certified patient: 'He will become chargeable to your committee as a rate aided person on expiration of sentence, and I would be glad if you would be good enough to confirm this and let me know whether [A] should be removed to the —— mental hospital.'

The Town Clerk replied confirming that the patient should be so transferred. Three weeks before the end of sentence the Broadmoor Superintendent gave written notice to the local Justice of the Peace for Berkshire that the patient was about to cease to be a Criminal Lunatic, and that in the Superintendent's opinion the said patient was 'insane and unfit to be at large', and was 'in such a state of insanity that he can properly be treated in an ordinary mental hospital'. On receipt of these reports the Justice made an order directing that the patient be removed from Broadmoor and detained in his local hospital as a rate aided patient, the order taking effect on the expiry date of the sentence. One week before this date the Broadmoor Superintendent wrote to the local hospital Superintendent informing him of the Town Clerk's acceptance of the patient and the patient's expected time of arrival by train.

Comment

Two points are of interest. First, the requirement that the patient would be transferred to his local hospital on expiry of sentence was accepted by all concerned. His clinical condition and continuing outbursts of violence were not a primary consideration and did not prevent transfer. Secondly, under the 1884 Act the local county or county borough had a legal duty to support the patient financially. If the local authority's hospital facilities were deficient, the authority was required to satisfy the Justice of the Peace that this was so, and would be charged for the cost of the patient's care in another area.

Case 2

Mr B was convicted of shop-breaking and breach of probation, and was sentenced to fifteen months imprisonment in 1960. Within five months of sentence he developed hallucinations, persecutory delusions, and thought broadcasting. He assaulted others and voiced homicidal thoughts. A diagnosis of schizophrenia was made and medical recommendations for transfer to a special hospital were completed after nine months of the sentence had been served. In considering the recommendations the Home Office agreed that special hospital treatment was indicated, but its general reluctance to send to Broadmoor patients with only a few months of sentence to serve was also noted, with the comment that 'Broadmoor would not have much time to do much for him. The restrictions on discharge expire in [six months] and I understand that it is not at present the practice for a patient to remain in Broadmoor after the restrictions have ceased to apply.' It was also noted that in view of the short time remaining until the end of sentence the Home Office would probably not wish to be consulted in the event of a proposal to transfer the patient to a local hospital before the expiry of the restrictions on discharge. One week later the Ministry of Health accepted the patient, who was subsequently admitted. He remained in Broadmoor for four months with some improvement in his psychotic symptoms. One month before the end of the sentence the Broadmoor Superintendent recommended to the Ministry of Health that the patient should be transferred to a local hospital, and one week after the sentence expiry the patient was moved there.

Comment

The case illustrates a transition in thinking and practice during the early years of operation of the 1959 Act. Before 1960 patients generally left Broadmoor at the expiry of their sentences, and this practice continued during the early years under the new Act. The above patient was transferred to his local hospital shortly after the end of his sentence and this was effected without direct consultation between Broadmoor and the receiving hospital. However, clinical considerations were now taken into account, and in considering the request for release from Broadmoor the Ministry of Health asked for evidence that the patient's clinical condition was improved such that his risk of absconding and violence was reduced.

From 1963 onwards the expectation that a patient would normally be released at the end of sentence diminished. If a patient was considered unfit for discharge at the time of LDR it became the practice for the Medical Superintendent to write to the Ministry of Health stating that the patient was still mentally disordered and unfit for discharge into the community, and that it was therefore proposed that he remain in Broadmoor at the expiry of sentence. The Ministry of Health would reply agreeing that the patient should continue to be so detained. In later years, even this formal exchange of correspondence appeared to cease.

Case 3

Mr C was convicted in 1979 of causing actual bodily harm and was sentenced to four and a half years imprisonment. He had a previous history of one conviction for violence and a brief admission to a psychiatric hospital with a diagnosis of schizophrenia. During the first year of sentence his psychotic symptoms recurred and medical recommendations for hospital transfer were completed. In view of his previous history of violence and absconding, admission to a special hospital was recommended. The DHSS accepted Mr C for admission and he was placed on the Broadmoor waiting list.

Ten months later, the prison medical officer requested an assessment by a Broadmoor consultant in order to expedite transfer, but at the time of this assessment Mr C was on regular medication, his symptoms were in remission, and the Broadmoor consultant did not consider transfer to be indicated. The Department of Health withdrew its earlier acceptance of admission. Subsequent approaches by the prison medical officer to the patient's local hospital requesting continuing psychiatric supervision were unsuccessful, and there was concern that Mr C's illness would relapse without regular medication. In the absence of psychiatric care being available locally, the DHSS reconsidered the case and offered a special hospital bed. Mr C was transferred to Broadmoor in 1982, two weeks before his EDR.

In Broadmoor, despite regular medication, his psychotic symptoms fluctuated, with further episodes of aggressive behaviour, and he was still resident and considered unfit for discharge on 30 September 1983.

THE TRANSFER OF SENTENCED PRISONERS TO HOSPITAL

Comment

In this case there was a prolonged delay of twenty months between the initial recommendation for transfer and eventual admission to Broadmoor. The case illustrates a number of features which operated during the later years of the 1959 Act but not in the early years. Admission was delayed because of the waiting list, and while awaiting transfer the patient's condition changed. The opinion of a Broadmoor consultant was then sought to speed transfer, but the condition of the patient had by then improved and the previous acceptance was withdrawn. Finally, the unavailability of suitable local psychiatric facilities for the patient after release from prison led to reconsideration by the DHSS, and to transfer to Broadmoor just before the EDR.

During the early 1960s, such a patient would probably have been transferred to Broadmoor at an early stage of his sentence shortly after completion of the medical recommendations. Cases such as this suggest the need for a statutory limit on the time that can elapse between medical recommendations and transfer to hospital.

[21]

Point prevalence of mental disorder in unconvicted male prisoners in England and Wales

Deborah Brooke, Caecilia Taylor, John Gunn, Anthony Maden

Abstract

***Objectives*—To determine prevalence of mental disorder among male unconvicted prisoners and to assess the treatment needs of this population.**

***Design*—Semi-structured interview and case note review of randomly selected cross section of male remand population. Non-attenders were replaced by the next name on prison roll.**

***Setting*—Three young offenders' institutions and 13 adult men's prisons.**

***Subjects*—750 prisoners, representing 9.4% cross sectional sample of male unconvicted population.**

***Main outcome measures*—Prevalence of ICD-10 diagnoses of mental disorder, and associated treatment needs.**

***Results*—Psychiatric disorder was diagnosed in 469 (63%) inmates. The main diagnoses were: substance misuse, 285 (38%); neurotic illness, 192 (26%); personality disorder, 84 (11%); psychosis, 36 (5%); other and uncertain, 36 (0.5%). Subjects could have more than one diagnosis. The average refusal rate was 18%. In total 414 inmates (55%) were judged to have an immediate treatment need: transfer to an NHS bed, 64 (9%); treatment by prison health care services, 131 (17%); motivational interviewing for substance misuse, 115 (15%); and therapeutic community placement, 104 (14%).**

***Conclusions*—Mental disorder was common among male unconvicted prisoners. Psychosis was present at four or five times the level found in the general population. Extrapolation of our results suggests that remand population as a whole probably contains about 680 men who need transfer to hospital for psychiatric treatment, including about 380 prisoners with serious mental illness.**

Department of Forensic Psychiatry, Institute of Psychiatry, De Crespigny Park, London SE5 8AF
Deborah Brooke, *lecturer*
Caecilia Taylor, *lecturer*
John Gunn, *professor*
Anthony Maden, *senior lecturer*

Correspondence to: Dr Maden.

BMJ 1996;313:1524–7

Introduction

In 1993 about 48 000 people—9% of those awaiting trial—were remanded into custody by the courts to be held as unconvicted prisoners until the trial. About a fifth of all those remanded in custody were acquitted, and a further fifth of males received a community sentence.[1] It is government policy that prisoners on remand who have a serious mental disorder should be transferred to psychiatric hospital, but this is often not done.[2,3] Even when a prisoner is transferred there are delays,[4] during which the patient remains in prison and is at increased risk of self harm and suicide.[5,6] Studies conducted in one London remand centre showed that two thirds of psychotic men were rejected for hospital admission,[4] and the outcome was even worse for other diagnoses.[2]

In addition to causing unnecessary suffering to mentally ill prisoners, this situation creates a risk to the public. Three recent inquiries into killings by mentally ill people described previous remands in custody, during which mental disorder was recognised but not adequately managed.[7-9] Some of the most difficult psychiatric patients in the country are assessed and treated entirely within prisons, which are not designed for this purpose and cannot match the standards of hospitals. For example, the premises of prison health services are not regarded as "hospitals" under the Mental Health Act (1983), and so patients cannot be treated against their will.

Thus, the population of remanded prisoners represents a pool of unmet need for psychiatric treatment of unknown size. About a third of all male prisoners who are sentenced can be given a psychiatric diagnosis, including 2% who are psychotic.[10] Higher levels of morbidity would be predicted in the remand population, because this group have a variety of risk factors for mental illness (such as substance misuse, personality difficulties, and the stress of reception into custody),[11] and the suspected presence of mental disorder may lead to a remand into custody for the preparation of reports. Undocumented demand is likely to remain unmet.

This paper describes the point prevalence of psychiatric disorder in remanded prisoners in England and Wales, together with an assessment of the immediate treatment needs of those prisoners who were given a diagnosis. A list of the prisons visited and copies of the interview schedule and the coding manual can be obtained from us and are included in the report of our study.[12]

Method

SELECTION OF PRISONS AND SUBJECTS

Prisons are grouped by the Home Office into three geographical directorates (North and Midlands; London, East Anglia, and Kent; Central England, Wales, and the West Country). We tried to see a 10% sample from each directorate. It is likely that prisoners with obvious mental disorder will be accommodated in larger prisons with more health services so, in order to reduce bias, we included a cross section from each type of prison (large inner city; smaller, local prisons; purpose built remand centres; and prisons representative of all levels of security) within each directorate. The study was conducted at 13 men's prisons and three young offenders' institutions (holding male prisoners aged under 21) spread throughout England and Wales.

The sample size was chosen to give reasonable confidence intervals, based on the assumption that less than 10% of prisoners would be suffering from psychosis. Within each prison, names were drawn from a list of all remanded prisoners, organised by location within the prison. Selection of (for example) every third name therefore produced a stratified random sample. Each subject was told that the survey was confidential, that it was being conducted by doctors from outside the prison, that participation was voluntary, and that no subject would be identified. In the event of refusal the next name on the roll was selected.

INTERVIEWS

A semistructured interview was administered to each consenting subject by a forensic psychiatrist (CT or DB). The interview had been designed for the project and piloted on 20 prisoners, and items with interobserver reliability of less than 90% had been discarded. The interview was designed to elicit each subject's demographic data, personal and psychiatric history, and evidence of personality disorder. A brief assessment of intelligence quotient (IQ) was included,[13] and current mental state was assessed. Diagnoses were recorded according to the criteria of ICD-10 (international classification of diseases, 10th revision). If relevant, the subject's experiences and views of treatment were noted. After the interview, the prison disciplinary and medical records were consulted.

A previous survey in this department had used a similar methodology.[10] To assess the validity of this method, we included an operational diagnostic psychiatric interview—the schedule for affective disorders and schizophrenia, lifetime version (SADS-L).[14] This was shortened to exclude personality disorder and substance misuse, which were covered by other parts of the interview.

ASSESSMENTS

For subjects with mental disorder, the interviewers allocated current diagnoses taking all this information into account. Subjects could be given more than one diagnosis. A decision was made about immediate treatment needs, based on a clinical approach in which, for example, treatment of psychosis took precedence over concurrent alcohol dependency. In the interests of reliability, all problematic diagnostic or management issues were considered by both interviewers jointly. Any case which was thought to need more discussion was presented at a monthly multidisciplinary meeting convened to oversee the survey. In addition to considering clinical problems, the meeting also reviewed six cases chosen randomly from each month's interviews. This procedure increased validity by reducing the likelihood of idiosyncratic decisions by individual interviewers.[15]

Treatment allocations

Subjects could be allocated one of four treatment options.

Prison health services—Subjects needed continuing care within prison. This included a range of interventions, such as consultations with primary care services and liaison with visiting psychiatrists. This option included transfer to the prison health centre for subjects whose symptoms were too severe to be managed on normal location. Such transfers were expected to be brief. A prison health centre allows greater supervision and opportunities for assessment, but it cannot match the facilities of a psychiatric hospital.

Table 1 — *Prevalence of psychiatric disorder according to ICD-10 criteria among 750 male remanded prisoners*

Diagnosis	No (% (95% confidence interval)) of subjects*
Psychosis	36 (4.8 (3.4 to 6.6))
Neuroses:	
Neurotic disorder	135 (18.0 (15.3 to 20.7))
Adjustment disorder	57 (7.6 (5.8 to 20.7))
Personality disorder	84 (11.2 (8.9 to 13.5))
Sexual deviations	15 (2.0 (1.1 to 3.3))
Harmful or dependent misuse of alcohol or other drugs	285 (38.0 (34.5 to 41.5))
Organic disorder	7 (0.9 (0.4 to 1.9))
Mild mental retardation†	5 (0.8 (0.3 to 1.8))
Diagnosis uncertain	9 (1.2)
No diagnosis	281 (37.5)

*Subjects could have more than one diagnosis, so total exceeds 100%.
†Sample size reduced to 651 because IQ test was not administered to subjects whose first language was not English.

Motivational interviewing for substance misuse—The term "substance misuse" implied that the subject had dependence (that is, pathological or physiological evidence of dependence, such as the acquisition of tolerance) or harmful use (that is, a history of mental or physical harm secondary to use of drugs or alcohol). These two diagnoses, harmful use and dependence, were used as in ICD-10. This treatment option was allocated to those subjects whose dependency or harmful use was uncomplicated by major mental disorder or personality disturbance, and who would benefit from an exploration of their lifestyle and advice on harm reduction. This might be only a single interview, but further treatment options (such as rehabilitation) could be examined with the subject.

Hospital transfer—This option was reserved for those men whose disorder was sufficiently serious to need transfer to NHS inpatient services because of their risk to others or to themselves. It was further refined by stipulating the level of security necessary—low security (open or locked ward), medium security (a regional secure unit), or maximum security (treatment in one of the three special hospitals).

Assessment for therapeutic community—This option was used for those with personality or sexual disorders, and a minority of substance misusers, who were considered suitable for group psychotherapy in a residential setting. Such treatment is currently available in prison (such as at Her Majesty's Prison Grendon) and outside (such as the Henderson Hospital or drug rehabilitation centres). Further assessment would be necessary to confirm suitability.

Results

We interviewed 544 adult men, representing 9% of the adult male remand population, and 206 young offenders (10%). These groups have been combined to give a sample of 9.4% of all male unconvicted prisoners (based on 7973, the number of men held on remand in England and Wales on 31 December 1992). The average refusal rate was 18% (range 4-31% in different prisons). Subjects had a mean age of 27.5 years (range 16.0-60.8, SD 8.9), and the median time spent remanded in custody was 64 days (range 1-501). The subjects did not differ from all male remandees in terms of basic demographic variables.

Demographic and clinical data were abstracted from the prison records of a representative group of 58 prisoners who refused the interview. Of 25 comparisons between these 58 refusers and the 544 adult men, none reached significance at the P<0.05 level.

Table 2—*Recommended treatment for psychiatric disorders among 750 male remanded prisoners*

Treatment	No (%) of subjects
NHS bed	64 (9)
Prison health services	131 (17)
Motivational interviewing for substance misuse	115 (15)
Assessment for therapeutic community	104 (14)
No treatment*	336 (45)

*This comprises subjects without a diagnosis of psychiatric disorder and those with a diagnosis but refusing treatment or who were not thought to need treatment under the Mental Health Act (1983).

PSYCHIATRIC DISORDERS

Psychiatric disorder was diagnosed in 469 (63%) of the subjects, and table 1 shows the prevalence of the different diagnoses made according to ICD-10 criteria. About a third of the subjects could be given more than one diagnosis, mainly due to misuse of several substances and mood disorder. The number of subjects given a diagnosis of neurotic disorder on clinical criteria did not differ significantly from the number obtained with the operational psychiatric interview (192 *v* 184, $\chi^2 = 0.2$, df = 1, P>0.2). The operational interview identified only a minority of the cases of psychosis diagnosed on clinical grounds (14 *v* 36, $\chi^2 = 10.0$, df = 1, P<0.01) because subjects with a psychotic illness were often too disturbed to tolerate the operational interview.

Drug or alcohol misuse formed the largest diagnostic group. Neurotic illness was the next most prevalent. This group included 57 subjects (7.6%) with mild or moderate depression (ICD-10 codes F32.0 and F32.1 respectively) and 14 (1.9%) with severe depression (codes F32.2 and F32.3). Twenty one subjects (2.8%) had anxiety states, and 13 (1.7%) had post-traumatic stress disorder (code F43.1). Of the 36 subjects with psychosis, 24 were known to have a psychiatric history by prison health staff.

Schedule for affective disorders and schizophrenia, lifetime version (SADS-L)—For purposes of comparison, the main findings with this method were schizophrenia, mania, and unspecified functional psychosis (14 subjects, 2%); minor depression (24, 3%); major depression (109, 15%); panic disorder (14, 2%); generalised anxiety and phobic disorders (25, 3%); untestable (25); and missing data (24). These diagnoses are not strictly comparable with those made according to ICD-10 because the operational interview uses different time criteria and different numbers of symptoms. For the purposes of this study, a major difference was the absence of an "adjustment disorder" diagnosis (that is, states of distress in response to life events, lasting not longer than six months); most of these cases were diagnosed by the SADS-L as depression.

IMMEDIATE TREATMENT NEEDS

A total of 414 (55%) subjects were judged to require immediate treatment, and table 2 lists those allocated to different treatments. Most treatment could be provided by health services within the prison. However, 64 subjects (9%, 95% confidence interval 7% to 11%) needed transfer to an NHS bed. Decisions about transfer were made on clinical grounds, using the criteria of severity of disorder, risk of harm to self or others and need for specialist assessment or treatment. On clinical grounds alone, some of these subjects might have been managed by community psychiatric teams. In practice, however, the courts would be unlikely to allow treatment outside hospital because of concern about the risk of reoffending or absconding. Of our 64 subjects requiring transfer, the largest diagnostic groups were psychosis (29 subjects) and neurotic illness (15). The remainder were a disparate group including sexual deviation, organic mental disorder, and learning disability. While 30 of the subjects could have been safely treated in a local hospital, 32 needed medium security and two needed maximum security.

The proportions of subjects given diagnoses, and the proportions allocated to the different treatment options, did not differ between the two interviewers.

Discussion

The most obvious limitation of our study is the 18% refusal rate. Despite our best efforts to show that refusers and non-refusers were similar, the psychiatric status of the refusers remains unknown. The refusal rate is much higher than that obtained in sentenced prisoners.[10] Our impression was that remand prisoners were less cooperative, many being angry that they were detained before being tried. Prisoners have been paid for their participation in some American studies, which introduces new problems.

Our method of sampling probably results in overrepresentation of long stay remandees. These prisoners may have lower rates of neurotic disorders associated with the impact of arrest and imprisonment, but apparent mental disorder can prolong the period of remand for petty offences.[2] We found no difference in length of remand between psychotic and non-psychotic prisoners, but a degree of confounding cannot be excluded.

The results suggest that, in the detection of psychosis in prisons, clinical methods using psychiatrists to conduct assessments are superior to a standardised instrument. A third of prisoners with a psychosis did not give a history of psychiatric contact and so would not be picked up by screening questions on this topic. For diagnoses other than psychosis, the standardised instrument and clinical methods produced similar results. Both approaches depend on self reporting, and psychiatric disorder carries considerable stigma within prison. Any study based on a single interview will underestimate the true level of morbidity. Nonetheless, our figures are greater than those found in the community (psychosis 0.4%, neurosis 14%, alcohol dependence 8%, drug dependence 3%).[16]

Our results are consistent with findings in two other countries: Teplin found 6% of jail detainees to be psychotic in Chicago,[17] and psychiatric symptoms were reported by 57% of remand prisoners in Geneva, although this study did not record diagnoses.[11]

IMPLICATIONS FOR PRACTICE

Of those prisoners requiring treatment, the largest group needed prison health services. This emphasises the need for better training of prison staff and implies a need for increased specialist psychiatric input. Similar recommendations were made in the "Three Colleges" report,[18] which is now being implemented. There is a need for improved liaison between psychiatric services and prisons. The level of severity of illness at which a prisoner requires transfer to hospital must be clarified, in local agreements.

This survey followed two initiatives designed to reduce the number of mentally ill prisoners on remand: the growth of court diversion schemes and an increased use of the Mental Health Act 1983 to transfer unsentenced prisoners to hospital as an emergency. From 1984 to 1994, the number of prisoners transferred annually under this provision increased from 47 to 535.[19] Despite these improvements, there are still substantial numbers of mentally disordered remanded prisoners. Extrapolating from the numbers of prisoners in our survey who required transfer, the number of NHS beds needed for the male remand population lies between 526 and 861. Half of this provision should be in medium security. It must be

Key messages

- Past neglect of unconvicted mentally ill prisoners has led to further violent offending after release
- We conducted a survey of the point prevalence of psychiatric disorder in men remanded in custody in England and Wales and assessed their treatment needs
- A diagnosis of psychiatric disorder was made in 63% of those surveyed, including 5% with psychosis
- Over half of these prisoners were judged to have an immediate treatment need—most could be treated inside prison, but 9% needed transfer to a psychiatric bed outside prison
- By extrapolation, the remand population probably contains about 680 men who need transfer to hospital for psychiatric treatment, including about 380 with serious mental illness
- Prison treatment facilities for unconvicted prisoners need substantial expansion

emphasised that the figure of 526 is a minimum. Our assessments were brief, and more detailed examination would probably reveal higher levels of morbidity.

In its strategy for health the government has identified mental illness as a priority,[20] and there is particular concern about mentally disordered offenders. Remand prisons contain an important pool of unmet need. On the grounds of humanity and public safety, it is unacceptable that mental disorder in this readily accessible group of offenders should go undetected or untreated.

We thank the prison staff, who made it possible to carry out the survey, and the prisoners themselves, who agreed to be interviewed at a time when their lives were in turmoil.

Funding: This work was commissioned by the Research and Planning Unit on behalf of the Directorate of Prison Health Care at the Home Office.

Conflict of interest: None.

1 Home Office. *Prison Statistics, England and Wales, 1993*. London: HMSO, 1995. (Cmnd 2893.)
2 Bowden P. Men remanded into custody for medical reports: the selection for treatment. *Br J Psychiatry* 1978;132:320-31.
3 Coid J. Mentally abnormal prisoners on remand: I—rejected or accepted by the NHS? *BMJ* 1988;296:1779-82.
4 Robertson G, Dell S, James K, Grounds A. Psychotic men remanded in custody to Brixton Prison. *Br J Psychiatry* 1994;164:55-61.
5 Dooley E. Prison suicide in England and Wales, 1972-87. *Br J Psychiatry* 1990;156:40-5.
6 Liebling A. *Suicides in prison*. London: Routledge, 1992: 42-3.
7 *The report of the independent panel of inquiry examining the case of Michael Buchanan*. London: North West London Mental Health NHS Trust, 1994.
8 Ritchie J, Dick D, Lingham R. *The report of the inquiry into the care and treatment of Christopher Clunis; presented to the chairman of North East Thames and South East Thames Regional Health Authorities*. London: HMSO, 1994.
9 Woodley L, Dixon K, Lindow V, Oyebode O, Sandford T, Simblet S. *The Woodley team report: report of the independent review panel to the East London and the City Health Authority and Newham Council, following a homicide in July 1994 by a person suffering with severe mental illness*. London: East London and the City Health Authority, 1995.
10 Gunn J, Maden A, Swinton M. Treatment needs of prisoners with psychiatric disorders. *BMJ* 1991;303:338-41.
11 Harding T, Zimmerman E. Psychiatric symptoms, cognitive stress and vulnerability factors. A study in a remand prison. *Br J Psychiatry* 1989;155:36-43.
12 Maden A, Taylor C, Brooke D, Gunn J. *Mental disorder in remand prisoners*. London: Home Office, Research and Statistics Directorate Information Section, 1996.
13 Ammons R, Ammons C. The quick test provisional manual. *Psychol Rep* 1962;11:111-61. (Monograph supplement I-VII.)
14 Endicott J, Spitzer R. A diagnostic interview—the schedule for affective disorders and schizophrenia. *Arch Gen Psychiatry* 1978;35:837-44.
15 Maden A, Gunn J. When does a prisoner become a patient? [editorial]. *Criminal Behaviour and Mental Health* 1993;3:iii-viii.
16 Meltzer H, Gill B, Petticrew M. *OPCS surveys of psychiatric morbidity. Bulletin 1: the prevalence of psychiatric morbidity among adults aged 16-64, living in private households, in Great Britain*. London: OPCS, 1994.
17 Teplin L. The prevalence of severe mental disorder among male urban jail detainees: comparison with the epidemiologic catchment area program. *Am J Public Health* 1990;80:663-9.
18 *The report of the working party of three medical royal colleges on the education and training of doctors in the health care service for prisoners*. London: Royal College of Physicians, Royal College of General Practitioners, Royal College of Psychiatrists, 1992.
19 *Statistics of mentally disordered offenders, England and Wales 1994. Home office statistical bulletin issue 20/95*. London: Research and Statistics Department, Home Office, 1995.
20 *The health of the nation: strategy for health in England*. London: HMSO, 1992.

(Accepted 15 November 1996)

[22]

Reprinted from the **BRITISH MEDICAL JOURNAL,** *10th August 1991, Vol. 303, Pages 338-341*

Treatment needs of prisoners with psychiatric disorders

John Gunn, Anthony Maden, Mark Swinton

Abstract

***Objective*—To describe the prevalence of psychiatric disorder and the treatment needs of sentenced prisoners in England and Wales.**

***Design*—Population survey based on a 5% sample of men serving prison sentences.**

***Setting*—Sixteen prisons for adult males and nine institutions for male young offenders representative of all prisons in prison type, security levels, and length of sentences.**

***Subjects*—406 young offenders and 1478 adult men, 404 and 1365 of whom agreed to be interviewed.**

***Main outcome measures*—History of psychiatric disorder, clinical diagnosis of psychiatrist, and required treatment.**

***Results*—652 (37%) men had psychiatric disorders diagnosed, of whom 15 (0·8%) had organic disorders, 34 (2%) psychosis, 105 (6%) neurosis, 177 (10%) personality disorder, and 407 (23%) substance misuse. 52 (3%) were judged to require transfer to hospital for psychiatric treatment, 96 (5%) required treatment in a therapeutic community setting, and a further 176 (10%) required further psychiatric assessment or treatment within prison.**

***Conclusions*—By extrapolation the sentenced prison population includes over 700 men with psychosis, and around 1100 who would warrant transfer to hospital for psychiatric treatment. Provision of secure treatment facilities, particularly long term medium secure units, needs to be improved. Services for people with personality, sexual, and substance misuse disorders should be developed in both prisons and the health service.**

Department of Forensic Psychiatry, Institute of Psychiatry, London SE5 8AF
John Gunn, FRCPSYCH, *professor of forensic psychiatry*
Anthony Maden, MRCPSYCH, *research worker*
Mark Swinton, MRCPSYCH, *research worker*

Correspondence to: Dr Maden.

BMJ 1991;303:338-41

Introduction

Staff in our department surveyed sentenced men in the south east prison region in 1972 and found that 31% had psychiatric disorders, 2% of whom were psychotic.[1] The survey's results have been quoted as indicating that a third of all prisoners should be in psychiatric hospitals,[2] but this is not what was found. The survey did not examine the question of treatment in detail, although some men were receiving treatment in prison and many more were reported to be suitable for such treatment, given adequate facilities.

We present the results of a further study that assessed psychiatric need in a 5% sample of the male sentenced population, which in June 1988 consisted of 28 602 men and 8141 male young offenders (aged 17-21 years).[3] Assessment of cases was expanded to include decisions on appropriate treatment. No standard criteria exist for assessing treatment needs, so needs were decided on clinical grounds for each case; the process was similar to that used to decide on treatment in clinical practice.

Methods

Sentenced prisoners are held in over 120 institutions, comprising local, training, and open prisons. Institutions are further subdivided according to sentence length and level of security. Sampling all prisons was impractical so we selected 16 prisons containing adult men and nine containing male young offenders. Sampling within each prison was random, and varied from one in two to one in eight prisoners. We had information on the sentence length of inmates of all prisons and on the prison regimens. We selected prisons and sampling rates so that the sample was representative of the total prison population in terms of length of sentence and type of prison.

All inmates chosen were invited to be interviewed, being informed that the survey was confidential and conducted by doctors from outside the prison, that participation was voluntary, and that no individuals would be identified. Interviews were conducted during

April 1988 to July 1989. We combined male adults and young offenders for analysis, as both were 5% samples of their respective populations.

INTERVIEW AND DATA COLLECTION

Each inmate's prison file was studied before the interview to obtain demographic and criminological information, reports of behaviour within prison, and social inquiry reports. The prisoner was then interviewed by a psychiatrist (AM or MS), in private within the prison. The semistructured interview was designed for the project and piloted on 50 volunteer prisoners; items with inter-rater reliability less than 90% were discarded. Prisoners were asked about past and present medical and psychiatric problems, substance misuse, and self harm. The clinical interview schedule provided a standardised assessment of mental state.[4] The interview could be completed in 30 minutes for subjects without evidence of psychiatric problems, and was expanded as necessary for others. Further information was obtained from the inmate's prison medical record and from NHS hospitals if previous treatment was reported.

Subjects with significant disease had their condition diagnosed on the basis of their present state, according to the ICD code (ninth revision).[5] Questions about substance misuse referred to the six months preceding the index offence. Each individual could have up to three conditions diagnosed.

Every inmate in whom psychiatric disorder was diagnosed was allocated to one of five categories of recommended treatment options:

None—This applied to prisoners with no mental disorder and to those with a disorder who did not want treatment, unless they required involuntary treatment under the Mental Health Act 1983.

Treatment within prison is treatment that a general practitioner or psychiatrist would provide on a mainly outpatient basis—for example, supportive psychotherapy or drugs, or both.

Therapeutic community refers to the type of contract based regimen under which people with personality disorders are treated at Grendon prison and Henderson Hospital and some drug and alcohol rehabilitation centres. No judgment had to be made about whether treatment should be provided in or out of prison, but the prisoner had to recognise he had a problem, be motivated to do something about it, and be capable of entering into a therapeutic contract.

Further assessment was used when there was uncertainty about the diagnosis, treatment, or motivation. We assumed that at least the initial stages of assessment would take place in prison. The outcome of assessment could range from no treatment to transfer to hospital. This category was used only when there was a high degree of suspicion that mental disorder was present.

Hospital meant that the prisoner required inpatient treatment outside the prison system. It included all prisoners needing involuntary treatment under the Mental Health Act 1983 and all inmates willing to accept treatment voluntarily but with a psychiatric disorder that could not be managed adequately and safely in prison.

Recommended treatments were decided on clinical grounds. In many cases the decision was taken by the interviewers, but in all cases of psychosis, in cases where a recommendation for hospital transfer was likely, and in all cases where the interviewers were in doubt about appropriate management, the case was referred to a meeting of the research panel. This consisted of psychiatrists, psychologists, and a social worker, all of whom worked in clinical forensic psychiatry. The panel met monthly, and cases were presented to it as if to a clinical case conference. The panel was asked to select the most appropriate of the five treatment options, and to estimate the level of security required for all prisoners recommended for hospital treatment, again using clinical criteria. The three categories were low security (district psychiatric service); intermediate security (regional secure unit); and maximum security (special hospital).

A list of the prisons visited and copies of the data collection sheet and coding manual can be obtained from us and will be included in a forthcoming report.[6]

Results

We randomly selected 1478 sentenced men and 406 young offenders for interview: 113 men (7·5%) and two young offenders (0·5%) refused to participate. The characteristics of the sampled population were similar to those of the total prison population (table I). Comparisons are not shown for young offenders but the results were similar to those in adults.

Psychiatric conditions were diagnosed in 652 men (table II). Of the 34 psychotic prisoners, 22 were recognised as mentally disordered by the prison authorities (including 18 of the 21 with schizophrenia) and 27 reported treatment for psychiatric problems during their stay in prison.

Table III shows the recommended treatment for all prisoners according to the primary diagnoses. Fifty two men (2·9%, 95% confidence interval for the population 2·1% to 3·7%) were judged to require transfer to hospital. Of the 30 psychotic prisoners recommended for hospital treatment, 21 had schizophrenia, six affective disorder, and three paranoid psychosis; hospital treatment was recommended for three prisoners with organic disorders; two with mild mental handicap and one with a frontal lobe syndrome. Seventeen inmates with schizophrenia and judged by

TABLE I—*Comparison of characteristics in sample and total population of sentenced adult male prisoners*

Variable	% Of total prison population	% (No) of sample
Length of sentence:		
Short (<18 months)	27	27 (367)
Medium (18-47 months)	37	37 (503)
Long (≥4 years)	36	36 (495)
Type of prison:		
Local	34	33 (455)
Training	55	55 (750)
Open	11	12 (160)
Current offence:		
Violence	24	22 (305)
Sexual	9	9 (123)
Burglary	18	21 (281)
Robbery	10	14 (190)
Theft	15	18 (251)
Drugs	10	10 (129)
Other data:		
On rule 43	8	7 (95)
Non-white	15	16 (225)

TABLE II—*Prevalence of psychiatric disorder in 1769 sentenced prisoners**

Diagnosis	No (%) of prisoners	
Psychoses:		34 (1·9)
Schizophrenia	21 (1·2)	
Affective	7 (0·4)	
Paranoid	6 (0·3)	
Neuroses:		105 (59)
Neurotic disorders	71 (4)	
Adjustment reaction	34 (1·9)	
Personality disorders		177 (10)
Sexual deviations	38 (2·1)	
Substance misuse		407 (23)
Alcohol	203 (11·5)	
Drugs	204 (11·5)	
Organic disorders:		15 (0·8)
Epilepsy	8 (0·5)	
Mental retardation	7 (0·4)	
Diagnosis uncertain		18 (1·0)
No diagnosis		1117 (63)

*Prisoners could have up to three conditions diagnosed.

TABLE III—*Recommended management of sentenced prisoners by primary diagnosis*

Diagnosis	Recommended management					Total No (%) prisoners
	None	Prison care	Further assessment	Therapeutic community	Hospital	
Psychoses		4			30	34 (2)
Neurotic disorder	9	72	1	3	4	89 (5)
Personality disorder	38	31	31	39	6	145 (8)
Sexual disorder	4	6	6	9	9	34 (2)
Substance misuse	183	59	31	43		316 (18)
Organic disorders	4	2	3	2	3	14 (1)
Diagnosis uncertain		2	18			20 (1)
No diagnosis	1117					1117 (63)
Total No (%) of prisoners	1355 (77)	176 (10)	90 (5)	96 (5)	52 (3)	1769 (100)

the research panel to require transfer had been identified by the prison doctor as psychotic, including eight who had been referred for transfer and were awaiting assessment or a bed.

Twelve of the 37 inmates recommended for hospital treatment for mental illness or organic disorder had developed their illness after imprisonment; the 25 others had been ill at the time of their offence, 24 of whom were known to their local psychiatric service. Psychiatric evidence had not been considered in the trials of seven of these inmates, and the remaining 18 were judged unsuitable for the treatment facilities available in hospitals, usually because of difficult or violent behaviour. Among prisoners with personality disorder and sexual deviation, the main reasons for failure to reach hospital were disagreements among doctors over treatability and lack of suitable facilities.

Seventeen prisoners were thought to require treatment in special hospitals, 21 in regional secure units, and 14 in district psychiatric service facilities.

Discussion

Our finding that 37% of sentenced prisoners had a psychiatric disorder, including 2% with psychosis, resembles closely the results of the 1972 survey.[1] The overall pattern, with a high level of disorder but a low level of psychosis, agrees with other studies of sentenced prisoners.[7-9]

We found personality disorder in 10% of prisoners, which is comparable with the 13%[7] and 8%[8] found in other prison surveys using clinical criteria, although it is considerably lower than the 22% found in 1972.[1] The most likely explanation for the differences is the low reliability of clinical criteria. All these figures are lower than those from American studies using standardised tools for assessment—for example, Guze labelled 78% of his sample "sociopathic."[10] We used clinical criteria to ensure relevance to psychiatric practice. The cases we identified represent the more severe end of the spectrum of personality disorder, and 74% of men in this category were judged in need of psychiatric treatment (table III). The fact that almost 12% of men had alcoholism diagnosed was not surprising but drug addiction is now equally common.[11]

The prevalence of psychosis in prisons is comparable with that in the community, but this should not obscure its importance. The treatment options available to psychotic prisoners are limited, and the research panel judged that 30 of 34 psychotic prisoners could receive adequate psychiatric care only by being transferred to a NHS hospital. Reasons for recommending hospital transfer included unpredictable violence, life threatening self harm, victimisation by other prisoners, and a refusal to take prescribed drugs (drugs cannot be given compulsorily in prison, even to inmates who meet the criteria in the Mental Health Act 1983). In many cases, the opinion of the research panel was shared by other doctors treating the prisoner.

Two per cent of the sentenced prison population represents a large number of psychotic inmates: roughly 730 men at any one time, about 450 of whom would have schizophrenia. Similarly, by extrapolation about 1100 (95% confidence interval 776 to 1405) prisoners require hospital treatment for psychiatric disorders. The largest proportion of inmates requiring hospital treatment were judged to need medium security facilities. There are currently 600 medium security beds, considerably less than the 2000 recommended by Butler[12] and the 1000 accepted as an initial target by the Department of Health and Social Security.[13]

The problems presented by difficult patients are not new,[14] and hospitals are particularly likely to reject convicted criminals with chronic conditions who have little prospect of recovery.[15 16] Many of the patients we identified fell into this category. More facilities for long term care in conditions of medium security are needed. For prisoners who are accepted by the health service, a study at one special hospital showed that, between 1960 and 1983, the delay between medical recommendation and admission increased sevenfold, mainly because of shortage of beds.[17] Prison doctors often complained of delays in the NHS response to requests for assessment. Proposed changes in the NHS may exacerbate this problem as they contain financial disincentives for health districts to take on chronic, difficult patients. The NHS reforms fail to address the question who will pay for the treatment of such patients in the future.[18] Similar anxieties have been expressed about the funding of care for other "expensive" patient groups[19]; regional funding has been suggested but the issue remains unresolved.

For offenders with sexual deviation or personality disorder, provision of services outside prisons is rudimentary. Despite enormous public concern and the increasing numbers of violent and sex offenders accumulating in prisons[3] psychiatry has failed to provide for these groups. Our figures show considerable unmet need and suggest that expansion of treatment facilities in both prisons and the health service should be a priority.

The treatment needs of many inmates could be met within the prison system. Approximately 6% of men were judged to require treatment in a therapeutic community setting for personality disorders, substance misuse, or sexual disorder. This is available at Grendon prison and the Wormwood Scrubs Annexe[1] but the number of places is limited. Previous work[1] has shown the effectiveness of Grendon prison[1 20] and we believe another prison of this type should be developed. Provision for patients with such disorders has always been limited. Hospitals, especially hospitals with security, also need to develop treatment programmes for patients with personality disorders. Specialised assessment and treatment units for sex offenders would be valuable within both prisons and the NHS.

We studied only sentenced prisoners, excluding those on remand or who had defaulted on fines. The average daily prison population in England and Wales during 1988 was around 50 000 and included 12 000 remand prisoners, a group that is subject to the worst overcrowding and contains many people who have been remanded because of mental abnormality. Surveys of remand prisons show high levels of psychiatric illness[21] and prison suicides are more common in this group.[22] These prisoners add to the demands on psychiatric services in prisons.

This research was commissioned by the directorate of the Prison Medical Service and funded by the Home Office. The views expressed are those of the authors. We thank Dr Graham Robertson for help throughout the study.

1 Gunn J, Robertson G, Dell S, Way C. *Psychiatric aspects of imprisonment.* London: Academic Press, 1978.
2 Weller MP. Mental illness—who cares? *Nature* 1989;**339**:249-52.
3 Home Office. *Prison statistics England and Wales 1988.* London: HMSO, 1989.
4 Goldberg DP, Cooper B, Eastwood MR, Kedward HB, Shepherd M. A standardised psychiatric interview for use in community surveys. *British Journal of Preventive and Social Medicine* 1970;24:18-23.
5 World Health Organisation. *Mental disorders: glossary and guide to their classification in accordance with the ninth revision of the International Classification of Diseases.* Geneva: WHO, 1978.
6 Home Office. *Mentally disordered prisoners.* London: HMSO (in press).
7 Bluglass R. A psychiatric study of Scottish convicted prisoners. [MD thesis]. Edinburgh: University of St Andrews, 1966.
8 Roper WF. A comparative study of the Wakefield prison population in 1948. I. *British Journal of Delinquency* 1950;1:15-28.
9 Roper WF. A comparative study of the Wakefield Prison population in 1948. II. *British Journal of Delinquency* 1950;1:243-70.
10 Guze SB. *Criminality and psychiatric disorders.* New York: Oxford University Press, 1976.
11 Maden A, Swinton M, Gunn J. Drug dependence in prisoners. *BMJ* 1991;302:880.
12 Interim report of the committee on mentally abnormal offenders. HMSO, London: 1974. (Cmnd 5698.)
13 Department of Health and Social Security. *Health service circular (interim series).* London: DHSS, 1974. (HSC(IS)61.)
14 Secure accommodation in psychiatric hospitals. *Lancet* 1986;ii:24-5.
15 Cheadle J, Ditchfield J. Sentenced mentally ill offenders. London: Home Office Research and Planning Unit, 1982.
16 Coid J. Mentally abnormal prisoners on remand. 1. Rejected or accepted by the NHS. *BMJ* 1988;**296**:1779-82.
17 Grounds A. The transfer of sentenced prisoners to hospital 1960-1983. *British Journal of Criminology* 1991;31:54-71.
18 Secretary of State for Health, Wales, Northern Ireland, and Scotland. *Working for patients.* London: HMSO, 1990. (Cmnd 555.)
19 Bentley C, Adler MW. Choice cuts for patients with Aids? *BMJ* 1990;**301**:501-2.
20 Genders E, Player E. *Grendon: a study of a therapeutic community within the prison system.* Oxford: University of Oxford, Centre for Criminological Research, 1989.
21 Taylor PJ, Gunn J. Violence and psychosis. I. Risk of violence among psychotic men. *BMJ* 1984;**288**:1945-9.
22 Dooley E. Prison suicide in England and Wales, 1972-87. *Br J Psychiatry* 1990;156:40-5.

(Accepted 4 June 1991)

 Printed in Great Britain by Meridian Print Centre Ltd., Derby.

Part IV
The Ethics of Forensic Psychiatry: Should Psychiatrists Engage with the Criminal Courts?

[23]

International Journal of Law and Psychiatry, Vol. 13, 281–307, 1990
Printed in the U.S.A. All rights reserved.

0160-2527/90 $3.00 + .00

Mental Health Professionals and the Courts: The Ethics of Expertise

Stephen L. Golding*

The interactions between mental health professionals and the civil and criminal justice systems have a long history, much of which is marked by strident debate and criticism as well as considerable accomplishment (American Psychological Association, 1978, 1980; Appelbaum, 1984b; Bazelon, 1982; Bersoff, 1986; Bonnie & Slobogin, 1980; Ciccone, 1986; Golding & Roesch, 1987; Monahan, 1980; Morse, 1986, 1978a; Resnick, 1986; Stone, 1984; Ziskin, 1981). As the forensic mental health[1] professions become recognized increasingly as specialties, we need to analyze the nature of our role(s) as experts to the court. The central question addressed in this article concerns the nature of the ethical principles which should govern the offering of such expertise by forensic mental health professionals to the courts.

The Diversity of Forensic Expertise

While the forensic mental health profession is a specialty, it is a mistake not to acknowledge the diversity of particular roles and to recognize that expertise within the specialty does not translate to expertise across the domain of roles. Figure 1 represents an initial attempt to characterize the domain of roles in terms of clients, primary roles, issues, and expertise.

The listing is not meant to be exhaustive, but rather illustrative of the di-

---

*Department of Psychology, University of Utah, Salt Lake City, UT 84112.

The *Specialty Guidelines for Forensic Psychologists* have been revised since this article was written; therefore quoted materials may have changed (see also footnote 9). A revised copy may be obtained from the author.

Acknowledgement—The author would like to express his appreciation to the following colleagues for their editorial comments and assistance: J. Dvoskin, T. Grisso, L. Frankel, R. Roesch, C. Slobogin, and W. Winslade.

[1]This section assumes that clinical psychologists, psychiatrists, psychiatric social workers, and possibly other professions have, subject to adequate training and experience, equal and legitimate claims as independent mental health service providers and scholars. It further assumes that forensic assessment, treatment, and research is an interdisciplinary *specialty* within these professions, requiring specialized training, experience, and scholarship. No attention is given to the fundamentally economic argument advanced by some within these professions to restrain individuals from other professions. Such a position reflects guild concerns and is not justifiable on scientific or evidentiary grounds. Accordingly, the phrases "forensic mental health professional," "forensic psychologist," "forensic psychiatrist," and "forensic psychiatric social worker" may be substituted for each other unless specifically noted.

I. Criminal justice system.

  A. Pretrial evaluator on issues of competency, mental state at the time of offense, mental status of other parties (witnesses, alleged victims).

    1. Pretrial therapist (including treatment following indictment, therapist for a defendant who was in treatment and/or evaluation prior to indictment, or therapist for other parties).
    2. Presentence evaluator on issues of disposition, classification, and prediction of future status (dangerousness, treatment response, etc.).
    3. Postconviction evaluator on issues of treatment needs, competency, current mental status, treatment response, etc.
    4. Postconviction therapist.

II. Civil justice system.

  A. Therapist or evaluator on issues of civil commitment (including contact as therapist or evaluator with person subject to commitment prior to the commitment proceeding).
  B. Therapist or evaluator with respect to a party to a civil legal proceeding of any type (child custody, divorce, malpractice, negligence, contracts, wills, etc.).

III. Consultation (criminal and civil).

  A. Expert to the court offering general evidence or testimony based upon one's research or scholarship.
  B. Consultant to a party on issues of legal tactics, voir dire of jurors or other experts, change of venue, etc.
  C. Consultant to a party acting as amicus.

FIGURE 1. Classification of Prototype Roles of Mental Health Professionals.

versity. A full discussion of all ethical issues pertaining to this range of roles is the proper subject of a text, not an article. We therefore concentrate on a set of issues that are central within roles in the criminal justice system, but most generalize within the limits of similar rules of evidence. We begin with a review of those rules of evidence surrounding mental health expertise, rules which provide an integrative structure to our discussion of the ethics of expertise.

An Idealized View of Mental Health Expertise

The sections of the *Federal Rules of Evidence* which pertain to expert testimony provide an idealized view of the role of the mental health expert and a useful context for our analysis of the real world problems and ethical dilemmas of such expertise.

While qualified by many hearsay exceptions, ordinary witnesses may testify only about matters for which they have "personal knowledge."[2] Experts, on the other hand, may testify as to inferences and opinions, and they may rely upon evidence which is not otherwise admissible. The justification for this exception is given in Rule 702 which states:

> If scientific, technical, or other specialized knowledge will assist the trier of fact to understand the evidence or to determine a fact in issue, a witness qualified as an expert by knowledge, skill, experience, training, or education, may testify thereto in the form of an opinion or otherwise.[3]

The nature of the data which the expert may use and testify to is described in Rule 703:

> The facts or data in the particular case upon which an expert bases an opinion or inference may be those perceived by or made known to the expert at or before the hearing. If of a type reasonably relied upon by experts in the particular field in forming opinions or inferences upon the subject, the facts or data need not be admissible in evidence.

Rule 704, modified as part of an attempt to reform expert evidence in insanity cases, provides a limitation on the type of opinions which may be offered:

> No expert witness testifying with respect to the mental state or condition of a defendant in a criminal case may state an opinion or inference as to whether the defendant did or did not have the mental state or condition constituting an element of the crime charged or of a defense thereto. Such ultimate issues are matters for the trier of fact alone. (704[b])

Rule 403 further limits expert testimony by allowing the judge to exclude such testimony, even if relevant when

> . . . its probative value is substantially outweighed by the danger of unfair prejudice, confusion of the issues, or misleading the jury, or by consideration of undue delay, waste of time, or needless presentation of cumulative evidence.

---

[2]Rule 602, *Federal Rules of Evidence*.

[3]See Landis (1988), Giannnelli and Imwinkelried (1988), Giannelli (1980), Moenssens, Inbau and Starrs (1986), Shuman (1986), and *United States v. Downing* (1985) for extended discussions of the application of Rule 702 to various areas of forensic expertise.

Thus, in the ideal, mental health expertise enters the courtroom[4] in the following steps:

1. An area of expertise, which is beyond the ordinary knowledge and understanding of the trier of fact, is accepted as one which will assist the trier of fact in understanding evidence or determining a fact at issue.
2. An expert in that area is qualified by the trial judge after hearing evidence that the individual is an expert, by virtue of "knowledge, skill, experience, training, or education."
3. The evidence upon which the expert will rely must be judged to be "trustworthy" or "reliable" (i.e., of a type "reasonably relied upon") by experts in the area of expertise.[5] Furthermore, the nature of the evidence and the opinion must be judged to be more probative than it is prejudicial, confusing, misleading, or redundant with other evidence.

Summary Critique of Mental Health Expertise.

It comes as no surprise, of course, that the ideal and the real are frequently at variance with one another. Controversy has surrounded the role of mental health expertise in the courtroom for several centuries (Bazelon, 1974; Blau, 1984; Clements & Ciccone, 1984; Diamond & Louisell, 1965; Ennis & Litwack, 1974; Golding & Roesch, 1987; Kaplan & Miller, 1986; Resnick, 1986; Smith, 1981; Walker, 1978). While an exhaustive catalogue of the controversial issues would be quite long, a set of central issues will first be outlined and then discussed under the major section headings which follow.

Moral Advocacy Versus Expertise. While some nihilists argue that mental health expertise simply does not exist or should be banned completely from the courtroom, the more cogent argument has been that such expertise as does exist is quite limited, and that the *real* role of the forensic expert in the courtroom has been that of moral advocate (Morse, 1978b; Morris, 1982). That is, the problem with forensic expertise is identified with a hidden moral agenda in which the moral controversies underlying the ascription of responsibility and blameworthiness are played out through the roles of the experts.

The Qualification of Experts. In principle, a trial judge accepts an individual as a qualified expert only after a thorough hearing as to the person's training, knowledge, and experience with respect to a circumscribed area of expertise. In practice, judges rarely exercise this discretionary authority. The resulting problem is the level of expertise available to courts varies widely with many generically trained mental health professionals giving "expert opinions" on complex

[4]See Anonymous (1988), Landis (1988), and Neumeg (1988) for annotations to these various rules of evidence governing expert testimony.

[5]This is *not* equivalent to ruling that the evidence is admissible in its own right. When an examiner testifies that a defendant told him about symptom X at time Y, this evidence is accepted as a ground for the expert's opinion, not as evidence for the existence of X at Y.

forensic mental health questions. The court is thereby misled into believing that it is hearing opinions based upon the most current scholarship, research, and experience in the area.

Prejudicial Versus Probative Aspects of Expertise. While judges have the discretionary authority to limit expert evidence, even when relevant, on the basis of the balance between its prejudicial versus probative effects, they are rarely asked to evaluate this issue. As a consequence, it has become common practice for both defense and prosecution to (mis)use their experts to introduce evidence that would otherwise be inadmissible, obfuscatory, or prejudicial. A related claim is that the "aura of science" which surrounds expert testimony leads to undue weight being given to the expert's opinions and inferences. Furthermore, since these opinions themselves are frequently seen as "invading the province of the trier of fact," experts are seen as inappropriately influencing the legal system.

Expertise Is Distorted in an Adversarial System. The fundamental structure of evidence production in an adversarial system is seen as incompatible with the basic tenets of expert knowledge systems which are grounded in the scientific methods of evidence appraisal.

Expert Evidence Often Implicates a Number of Constitutional Issues. The fundamental critique is that the nature of the current legal structure allows the process of expert evidence production to touch sensitive constitutional issues, often resulting in an obvious or insidious abridgement of constitutional rights. The most frequently cited problems involve self- incrimination, confrontation, and effective assistance of counsel (effective representation at critical stages, availability, effective cross-examination, and the like).

Expertise Is for Hire. This claim is expressed most stridently as experts are "whores for hire." The more reasoned critiques question whether the combination of economic forces and a strongly structured adversarial system produces the most useful and probative expert testimony. Thus, the combination of "doctor shopping," inadequate qualification of experts, vaguely defined boundaries of expertise, and adversarial as opposed to court-appointed experts may deprive the court of the most probative expertise available.

Moral Advocacy Versus Expertise

By design, our criminal and civil justice systems are built upon fundamental "moral axioms" that derive from our Judeo-Christian heritage. To the extent that critical mental state claims inherently implicate these "moral axioms," forensic expertise may be drawn into a moral arena. For example, as a matter of fundamental "fairness," we assume that judgment of both criminal and civil responsibility for proscribed behaviors is based upon an ethical calculus that assigns individual moral and criminal responsibility as a function of intentionality and mental capacity. The classic legal maxim, *Actus non facit reum, nisi mens sit rea*,[6] can be shown to be rooted in our Judeo-Christian conceptions of moral responsibility (Golding & Roesch, 1987). Technically, forensic mental health professionals are called upon to offer *expert* testimony on the relationship between behavioral, situational, medical, and psychological characteristics, on the one hand, and a defendant's capacities for intending, cognizing, reasoning, appreciating, and controlling on the other. The assumption is that the expert's observations, data, inferences, and opinions are grounded in dispassionate scientific method. While forensic professionals do have many scientifically justifiable skills in observation, assessment and inferential judgments to offer to the ascription process (Bonnie & Slobogin, 1980; Golding & Roesch, 1987; Morse, 1985, 1986), it seems inevitable that they will be drawn into the arena of moral judgment.

In the context of the prediction of dangerousness, Judge David Bazelon (Bazelon, 1974) characterized this as the "hot potato" problem: difficult social/moral judgment problems are "hot potatoes" that judges, juries, and society at large are willing to (covertly) relegate to forensic mental health professionals. On the surface, the trier of fact maintains judgemental authority, and the role of the forensic expert, to quote the United States Supreme Court in *Ake v. Oklahoma* (1985) is to:

> . . . gather facts, both through professional examination, interviews and elsewhere . . . ; (to) analyze the information gathered and from it draw plausible conclusions about the defendant's mental condition, and about the effect of any disorder on behavior; and . . . offer opinions about how the defendant's mental condition might have affected his behavior at the time in question. . . . They know the probative questions to ask the opposing party's psychiatrists and how to interpret their answers. . . . Furthermore, . . . (they) translate a medical diagnosis into language that will assist the trier of fact, and therefore offer evidence in a form that has meaning for the task at hand. (p. 80)

Frequently, however, enormous pressure is placed upon the expert to take on the moral burden, and hence to go beyond their designed role.

The assertion that forensic experts are nothing more than 'whores for hire,"[7] is an historically recurring theme, often found in its most strident form in the public media after a highly visible public trial involving the insanity defense (Hans & Slater, 1983). This argument is frequently comingled with other assertions about the "softness" of psychological knowledge, lack of agreement be-

[6]Golding and Roesch (1987) constructively translate this maxim into modern jurisprudence as: An act is not legally cognizable as evil, and hence punishable, unless it is committed by a person who has the capacity to cognize the act as evil and then freely chooses to do it.

[7]Resnick (1986) has a useful review of many historical examples. A particularly outrageous example, cited by Nigel Walker, was voiced by crown counsel in his cross-examination of a Dr. Leo (who had been previously involved in the famous *Hadfield* trial and who was also a prominent member of the Sephardic Jewish community)—"Have you not been here before as a witness and a Jew physician, to give an account of a prisoner as a madman, to get him off upon the ground of insanity?" *(Rex. v. Lawrence, 1801, cited in Walker, 1968, p.82.)*

tween experts, and the extent to which judges and juries are "duped" by the outrageous and fictionally authoritative claims of experts (Faust & Ziskin, 1988). Empirically, most of these arguments can be shown to be wildly exaggerated (Fukunaga, Pasewark, Hawkins, & Gudeman, 1981; Golding & Roesch, 1987; Melton, Petrila, Poythress, & Slobogin, 1986; Petrila, 1982; Resnick, 1986; Rogers, Wasyliw, & Cavanaugh, 1984; Steadman, Keitner, Braff & Arvanites, 1983) but the perceptions and beliefs continue. One needs to ask why they continue and what steps may be taken to bring public perceptions into line with empirical reality.

I believe that the key to understanding the level of emotionality surrounding this issue can be found in the deeply rooted moral and religious tension which surrounds the attribution of individual responsibility for "good" and "evil." At one end of the responsibility continuum are the "furiously insane" (i.e., those severely and obviously disordered individuals) who would be inappropriately and unjustly punished for losing control over impulses, cognitions, and the distinction between reality and fantasy. By one mechanism or another, our tradition has always been to exempt such individuals from moral blame and criminal responsibility (for an extended discussion see Golding & Roesch, 1987). Indeed, the assumption, codified in the legal maxim, *furiosus furore solum punitur*,[8] has been that the mental anguish and suffering of the insane is sufficient to account for any retributive feelings we might have towards them concerning their misdeeds.

However, one does not have to move far from this end of the continuum before there is a real moral and psychological tension about "irresistible impulses" versus "the impulse not resisted." We all struggle with the distinction between reality and fantasy, and seek to control various impulses, distorted perceptions, and cognitions. Individuals who have the capacity to control their thoughts, perceptions, and impulses and who fail to do so are not only criminally responsible, they are morally condemned as weak, or in the extreme, simply evil. Therefore, when the expert is asked covertly to relieve us of the moral burden of deciding who is on which side of a fuzzy boundary marked by considerable tension and conflict, we displace our anxiety, our punitiveness, and perhaps our resentment about being held to the moral standard and the psychological tension it causes. Poythress (1982) provides an important example, describing the heated reactions of the court and its officers when he declined to accept the implicit role and refused to offer a conclusory opinion. The scholarly treatises on this subject (e.g., Appelbaum, 1984a; Bazelon, 1978; Bonnie, 1984; Dahl, 1985; Golding & Roesch, 1987; Halleck, 1980, 1984; Melton et al., 1986; Morse, 1986) are in agreement that experts ought to confine themselves to presenting the trier of fact with knowledge, data, and perhaps reasoned inferences which *inform* and *advise*, and stay out of the ultimate arena of conclusory moral judgments. Thus, psychological knowledge, however limited, about a defendant plays a critical, but *nonconclusory* role in the moral judgments which distinguish points on this continuum. As forensic mental health professionals, it is proper to call upon us to offer *scientifically acceptable* observations, data, and expert testimony that draws out *reasoned inferences*

[8]"The madness of the insane is punishment enough."

and lends coherence to those data. The court seeks expert evidence on the relationship between psychological characteristics of a defendant, presented in proper scientific context with overt attention to factors which limit the reliability and validity of the evidence, and a defendant's legally relevant capacities for *intending, cognizing, reasoning, appreciating, and controlling*. The boundary between informing and advising the trier of fact about the nature and influence of persecutory delusions and conclusory opinions about a defendant's ability to "appreciate the wrongfulness" of their conduct is admittedly fuzzy, but it is also real. We do a disservice to our professional and to society when we accept the "hot potato" and allow ourselves to become either overt or covert moral agents.

In my view, it is not proper for us, as professionals, to await reform in the legal system with regard to this issue. We also need to reform ourselves by adopting explicit ethical and practice guidelines about the proper role of forensic expertise in the justice system. Existing standards do not adequately consider the issue. The parent professional organizations for psychologists and psychiatrists indirectly give ethical guidance to their members in this area by variously stating that mental health professionals limit their practice to areas of demonstrated competence (American Psychiatric Association, 1981; American Psychological Association, 1981). Forensic subspecialty organizations are more specific. The American Academy of Psychiatry and Law (1987) addresses the issue by stating, "The forensic psychiatrist functions as an expert within the legal process. . . . he adheres to the principles of impartiality and objectivity. (and) . . . his opinion reflects this impartiality and objectivity" (p. 17). In commentary, it is further advised that "the . . . forensic psychiatrist enhances the impartiality and objectivity of his work by basing his forensic opinions, . . . reports, and . . . testimony on all data available . . . (and) . . . by distinguishing, to the extent possible, between verified and unverified information as well as between clinical 'facts,' 'inferences' and 'impressions'"(p.17). The draft standards of the American Academy of Forensic Psychology (1988) similarly stress the scientific bases of expert opinion, and cautions that the forensic psychologist "resists invitations and pressures to practice outside (of) . . . areas of proficiency, or to answer questions which cannot be answered" (p. 3) and "should not render any opinions on legal issues" (p. 11).

These guidelines are an important starting place, but do not go far enough in providing guidance to forensic experts in avoiding either partiality or assuming ultimate "moral agent" roles. Division 41 (Psychology and Law) of the American Psychological Association is currently debating a set of draft guidelines[9] (Golding & Grisso, 1988) which attempt more specific guidance. As part of the definition of *professional competence*, the draft asserts that forensic psychologists have an affirmative responsibility to:

> . . . recognize that their own personal values, moral beliefs, as well as their personal and professional relationships with parties to a legal

[9]The guidelines are currently being debated and do not yet represent the official position of Division 41. At present, these guidelines simply represent a working draft submitted to the Division by its authors. It is available from the author on that basis.

proceeding may interfere with their ability to provide impartial forensic psychological services to parties in a legal proceeding. Under such circumstances, forensic psychologists are obliged to decline participation and to limit their assistance in a manner consistent with professional obligations (Section 3[f]).

Furthermore, with respect to the *methods and procedures* of forensic evaluations:

> Forensic psychologists have an obligation, flowing both from their competence and their special status as a person qualified as an expert to the court, to employ the highest clinical and scientific standards of their profession when selecting data collection methods and procedures for an evaluation, treatment, consultation or scholarly/empirical investigation (Section 6[a]).
>
> Forensic psychologists fully inform prospective clients, relevant parties to a legal proceeding, and other consumers of their professional products and services of the known scientific bases and limitations of the methods and procedures which they employ (Section 6[b]).
>
> In providing forensic psychological services, the forensic psychologist takes special care to avoid undue influence on the outcome of his/her methods, procedures, and conclusions emanating from the party to the legal proceeding by virtue of compensation or otherwise. As an expert conducting an evaluation, treatment, consultation or scholarly/empirical investigation, the forensic psychologist maintains his/her professional integrity by examining the issue at hand from all reasonable perspectives, and actively seeks information which will differentially test plausible rival hypotheses (Section 6[c]).

Finally, with respect to guidelines for *communications* to the court and the public, the suggested guidelines provide that:

> Forensic psychologists are sensitive to the public perceptions of their profession, and are aware that the adversarial nature of the legal system creates inevitable tensions, conflicts, and controversies.
>
> Forensic psychologists conduct their professional services and evaluations in the spirit of impartiality and strict adherence to principles of scientific investigation.
>
> Forensic psychologists have an obligation to all parties to a legal proceeding to present their findings, conclusions, evidence or other professional products in a fair manner. The principle of impartiality with respect to evaluations, investigations or research does not preclude forceful representation of the data and reasoning upon which a conclusion or professional product is based. It does, however, preclude an attempt, whether active or passive, to engage in partisan advocacy. The forensic psychologist does not, by either commission

or omission, allow the nature of their evidence to be misrepresented, nor does s/he participate in partisan attempts to avoid, deny or subvert the presentation of evidence contrary to their own position.[10]

Forensic psychologists, by virtue of their competence and rules of discovery, actively disclose all sources of information obtained in the course of their professional services; they actively disclose which information from which source was used in formulating a particular written product or oral testimony.

Forensic psychologists are aware that their role as expert to the court, under Federal Rule of Evidence 702, is to "assist the trier of fact to understand the evidence or to determine a fact in issue." In offering expert evidence, they make clear the distinction between their own professional observations, inferences and conclusions and legal facts, opinions and conclusions, although they may explain the relationship between their expert testimony and the legal issues and facts of an instant case (Sections 7 [d–f]).

The essence of these ethical guidelines is that they place an affirmative responsibility on the expert to monitor his or her evidence and to remain, as clearly as possible on the "science" side of the boundary between moral judgment and expert evidence.[11,12] Admittedly, as every student of the philosophy of science knows, subjectivity and moral judgments seem an inevitable component of even the most "objective" data, psychological, or otherwise. Such limiting factors do not, however, preclude ethical standards which seek to either minimize such subjective influence or at least mandate alerting the consumer of the expertise to its probable nature and extent.[13]

The Voir Dire of Experts

Authority rests with the court to assure that expert evidence is relevant, properly obtained, likely to assist the trier of fact, and more probative than

[10]The term "impartiality" is used in several ways in the literature. Diamond (1959) uses it to include nonadvocacy on the part of the expert with respect to his or her opinion. Golding and Grisso (1988) use the term as defined in this section.

[11]Attempts to accomplish this by statutorily limiting certain kinds of conclusory statements are unlikely to prove workable. As Melton and his colleagues (1986) point out expert testimony can be scaled from a catalog of simple perceptions to opinions about ultimate legal issues. While most scholarly treatises emphasize the importance of confining expert testimony to drawing the relationship between forensic data and legally relevant decisions and avoiding giving conclusions as to legally ultimate issues, there are strong pressures, and indeed *preferences* on the part of judges, to hearing the expert's "ultimate opinion" (see the extended discussion of these issues in Melton et al., 1986, pp. 13–17; 364–371).

[12]Nationally there is a trend for jurisdictions to restrict conclusory testimony in line with Federal Rule 704(b) and the general consensus in the scholarly literature. However, this is far from uniform and not without significant resistance, as Poythress' (1982) example points out. It would be important to examine empirically the nature of this trend and its impact on judicial decision making.

[13]Competent cross-examination will always attempt to draw out the expert's biases, predilections, and the like. We improve the quality of such examinations and our professional image by stating such contextualizing and limiting factors freely.

prejudicial. After determining that relevant expertise in a given circumscribed area exists and is likely to assist the court, it must determine which experts are qualified. The discretionary authority of the trial judge is quite broad, and examples of reversals based upon an abuse of discretion standard are extremely rare. Nevertheless, it is common knowledge that appropriate discretionary judgment is rarely applied and that many loosely qualified experts are permitted to testify. That is, trial judges rarely scrutinize the qualifications of a proposed expert, and defense and prosecution counsel rarely mount a rigorous examination of the expert during the voir dire. The assumption within the current system is that the rigors of the cross-examination process will be sufficient to discredit inadequate expertise, and that this properly goes to the weight and not the admissibility of the expert's evidence.

For example, at the penalty phase of the trial of Thomas Barefoot for the capital murder of a Texas police officer, Dr. James Grigson was qualified as an expert to testify as to the existence of aggravating factors, such as the "probability that the defendant would commit criminal acts of violence that would constitute a continuing threat to society" as specified in Texas law.[14] Without having either examined Barefoot or having been denied the opportunity to do so, Grigson responded to the state's hypothetical questions and claimed that he could "predict future dangerousness of an individual within reasonable medical certainty," and Barefoot was within the "most severe category of sociopaths," such that Grigson was "one hundred percent and absolutely [certain that] Barefoot would commit future acts of violence that would constitute a continuing threat to society" (*Barefoot v. Estelle*, 1983, p. 919). My point here is not to enter into the argument about whether the data on prediction of future dangerousness is such that it ought to be barred as too unreliable to meet the threshold test for admissibility under Rule 702 (see, for example, Appelbaum, 1983, 1984a; Dix, 1983; Garrett, 1982). For the moment, let us accept the Supreme Court's view that:

> It is, of course, not easy to predict future behavior. The fact that such a determination is difficult, however, does not mean that it cannot be made. Indeed, prediction of future criminal conduct is an essential element in many of the decisions rendered throughout our criminal justice system. . . . What is essential is that the jury have before it all possible relevant information about the individual defendant whose fate it must determine. (*Jurek v. Texas*, 1976, 274–276)

It is patently clear that if such testimony is to be admitted on such a difficult issue, the court has *the obligation to hear the best and most considered evidence, reflecting the highest levels of professional expertise*. This is precisely what did not happen in the *Barefoot* case. Defense counsel did object to the *form* of Grigson's testimony, and was overruled in accordance with *Jurek* and other cases. The United States Supreme Court and the trial judge (like most judges) have consistently ruled that any objections to Grigson-like testimony

[14]Texas Code of Criminal Procedure Annotated 37.071(b)(2).

ought to be handled by cross-examination which would go to its weight. Thus, the facts that Grigson possessed an idiosyncratic and "rogue" understanding of the scientific literature on the predictability of dangerousness, that his assessment methods (none) were scientifically unjustifiable, and that his testimony, based as it was on neither an evaluation nor even an attempted evaluation of the defendant was in clear violation of both the general code of ethics for psychiatrists (American Psychiatric Association, 1981) and the specific code for forensic psychiatrists (American Academy of Psychiatry and Law, 1987), are elements that go to the weight of his evidence in the Supreme Court's view.[15]

The Supreme Court's reliance upon the rigors of cross-examination is more than muddled thinking. It is a dangerous misapplication of the fundamental rules of evidence which govern expert testimony. Having decided that a difficult, but relevant, area of expertise exists, the court must *assert* its authority to guarantee that the expertise offered is the best reasonably available, and the least likely to confuse, distort, prejudice, or mislead. Doctor Grigson may have evaluated "between thirty and forty thousand individuals,"[16] but he clearly could and should have been disqualified on the basis of his lack of expertise (fundamental misunderstanding of the scientific bases of the problem) and his failure to base his testimony on evidence "of a type reasonably relied upon by the experts" (Rule 703).

A further example comes from the area of the insanity defense. While many might dispute the scientific bases upon which professionals could testify in this area, once the principle is admitted, then the court needs to seek out *relevant expertise*. In an unreported case in Champaign, Illinois (discussed in full by Golding & Roesch, 1987), Dr. Thomas Szasz was not qualified as an expert because the defense successfully argued that, whatever else his qualifications, he held a fixed and immutable belief, amounting to dogma not expertise, that mental illness is a myth. In this case, the trial court correctly reasoned that, having decided that the defendant's possible mental illness was a relevant legal issue (under Rule 702), it could not accept as "expert testimony" evidence that denied that core assumption. That is, reasoned and principled disagreement as to the defendant's mental state, based upon accepted methods of assessment and inquiry, would be admissible, and perhaps even desirable. On this issue, however, Szasz could not be qualified as an "expert" within the assumptions of the court.

As professionals we have an obligation to attempt to reform the process of expert qualification. All professional codes have statements which make it unethical to claim expertise outside of one's area of actual knowledge, training, and experience.[17] One cannot argue with so reasonable a claim, except to ob-

---

[15]As the Supreme Court itself notes, "Such testimony could have been presented at Barefoot's trial, but was not" (*Barefoot*, 1983, P. 905, n. 11). This characterization of the problems with Grigson's testimony is mine, not the Court's.

[16]*Barefoot*, 1983, p. 918. This is a surprising claim in its own right.

[17]For example, the *Ethical guidelines for the practice of forensic psychiatry* assert "Expertise in the practice of forensic psychiatry is claimed only in areas of actual knowledge and skills, training, and experience" (p.17).

serve that, as a guideline, it does not appear to have worked well. Many practicing mental health professionals and specialists believe that they are qualified to render inferences and opinions in areas where they have only generic training. Even more problematical is the tendency of some to claim expertise, and for the court to qualify them as such, when they are unwilling to acknowledge or are unaware of the scientific limits of their data and opinions. The result is a cumbersome system that depends too heavily upon the rigors of cross-examination. Additionally, the court is subjected to unnecessary "battles of the experts" which consume time, limited financial and judicial resources, and demean the public image of justice and of the professions. A partial solution is to place an *affirmative duty* on the potential expertise to clarify the bases and limits of their expertise during their voir dire. Instead of passively answering only those questions asked by counsel or the court, the expert should be required to actively produce the bases of their *specific expertise* in the delimited area defined by the court as relevant.[18] It is also incumbent upon the professional to clarify the limits of expertise, per se, in a particular domain through both scholarly outlets and as part of an ethically grounded voir dire.

A prime advantage of this approach is that it does not require the professions to solve or agree upon what constitutes a "subspecialty" or what training and so forth is required to be a "specialist." Rather, the court retains its legitimate role as authority in this matter. However, such activism on the part of the professions forces the court to become more informed, to make its decision upon more uniform and extensive data. The system is thereby encouraged to engage in more issue specific scrutiny. Judge David Bazelon has argued for many years that courts need to assert more authority in this area.[19] With due respect, we cannot wait for such reform. The courts continue to be too liberal in their judgments of the limits of expertise, and have been too willing to accept generic board certification or training as qualifying experts across a variety of issues. By placing an affirmative duty on the potential expert to offer evidence on these issues, we help to ensure that this critical issue will receive the attention it deserves.

---

[18]Golding and Grisso (1988) attempt to incorporate both the "competency" and the "specific expertise" language in their proposed guidelines:

> Forensic psychologists provide services only in areas of psychology for which they are competent by virtue of "knowledge, skill, experience, training, or education."
> While courts have the authority, pursuant to Federal Rules of Evidence 701–706, 403, and others, to determine if an individual will be permitted to offer evidence as an "expert," forensic psychologists have an *affirmative duty* to present to the court the factual bases (knowledge, skill, experience, training, or education) for their qualification as an expert. (Sections 3[a–b])

The draft guidelines of the American Academy of Forensic Psychology (1988) similarly recognize that even specific expertise in one area (e.g., competency) does not imply expertise in another (e.g., dangerousness).

[19]In *Jenkins v. United States* (1962), Judge Bazelon observed that general degrees, training, or experience were not the critical issue. Rather, the issue was whether the individual's specific qualifications were such as to make it probable that his or her observations and opinions would likely aid the judge in the search for the truth on a particular matter.

Prejudicial and Constitutional Aspects of Expertise

These are interrelated problems, and the source of much controversy, in part because the evidentiary and constitutional issues themselves are complex, and the guidance provided by existing guidelines is vague. Attention will be paid to a limited set of issues, but the underlying logic can be applied to other areas without loss of generality. We will concentrate on three central issues: (a) the misuse of experts to introduce evidence that would otherwise be inadmissible, obfuscatory, or prejudicial; (b) undue weight being given to the expert's opinions and inferences (the "aura of science" problem) and "invading the province of the trier of fact;" and (c) aspects of expert evidence which undermine rights to confrontation and effective assistance of counsel.

As experienced attorneys and forensic clinicians know all too well, an expert in court can be either a dangerous foe or a valued ally. One prime reason for this is that experts are permitted in our system to rely upon evidence that is "otherwise inadmissible." Technically, experts may be called upon to testify as to that evidence as the basis upon which they have reached their professional opinion. The trier of fact, under various rules, may not rely upon that "otherwise inadmissible" evidence as facts, but rather as information which goes to the weight of the expert's opinion.[20] Several kinds of evidence are the source of the problem. Hearsay evidence includes information supplied to the expert by other professionals (directly and through reports), hospital records, and information supplied by other third parties including lay persons, relatives, and various agencies with which the examinee may have had contact. While a "careful" trial might involve the direct testimony of the individuals providing this information and their cross-examination (hence converting this information from hearsay to admissible evidence), this usually does not occur. In general, the courts have permitted experts to rely upon this sort of data because it is customary within the profession, and because it has been assumed that the expert is in a position to "screen out" unreliable information, and may be cross-examined on the issues. As O'Toole (1977) and others have pointed out, this is a weak assurance to the court of the reliability and trustworthiness of the data. One solution proposed by O'Toole is for the courts to carefully scrutinize the extent to which it is customary to rely upon such data and further to inquire as to the reliability of the hearsay evidence. We can assist the trier of fact in this regard by making our own standards more rigorous. For example, the guidelines proposed by Golding and Grisso (1988) provide that:

> When forensic psychologists seek data from third parties, prior records or other sources, they do so only with the prior approval of their client, the court, or other relevant legal parties. (Section 6[e]).

[20]It is not clear that this makes any cognitive sense (Carlson, 1987; Rice, 1987; Wardle, 1984; Weinstein, 1986). If the trier of fact gives credibility to the expert's opinion, it follows cognitively if not logically that the evidentiary bases of that opinion will also be given credibility, although the two issues can be technically separated. If a defendant's long history of delusional thinking and hospitalization has been relied upon by the expert in believing the defendant's self-report that he was under the influence of a delusion system at the time of the alleged murder, accepting the expert's opinion that the defendant was delusional during the crime psychologically entails belief in the defendant's history of delusional thinking, although no admissible evidence as to that fact may have been produced.

> Forensic psychologists are aware that the hearsay exceptions embodied in Federal Rule of Evidence 703 places a special burden upon them. While hearsay or otherwise inadmissible evidence may form the partial basis of their opinion, evidence or professional product, they actively seek to minimize their reliance upon such evidence.
>
> (i). With respect to evidence of any type, whether hearsay or otherwise admissible under the rules of evidence, forensic psychologists avoid offering information from their investigations or evaluations that does not bear directly upon the legal purpose of their professional services and which is not critical as support for their product, evidence or testimony, except where such disclosure is required by law.
>
> (ii) Where circumstances reasonably permit, forensic psychologists seek to obtain independent and personal verification of data upon which they rely as part of their professional services to the court or to a party to a legal proceeding. (Section 6[f]).

These guidelines, if adopted by the profession, would increase greatly the reliability of such hearsay bases, and would also provide the opposing counsel with adequate information upon which to base realistic cross-examination. It is not unreasonable to ask the forensic clinician to be sensitive to hearsay information which may be prejudicial, and to seek to limit information contained in a report or in court testimony by asking whether the information is necessary to support their professional opinion. If the information is necessary, then reasonable steps should be taken to ensure its reliability.[21]

The problems associated with the weight of expert evidence are even more complex. With some exceptions[22], the courts have generally adopted an approach which allows wide limits to the admissibility of clinical forensic expertise, allowing the "rigors" of cross-examination to reveal the appropriate weight to be placed upon such evidence.[23] The practicality of this position depends upon the extent to which data which pertain to the reliability of the expert evidence are fully available to the trier of fact. Regrettably, ordinary trial practice falls far short of this standard.[24] Most attorneys are not prepared to mount

[21]Hospital records, intake and interview notes, and telephone conversations are the most likely to be problematic, and may contain reference to "assaults," "threats," prior diagnoses, hospitalizations and the like. Verifying this information, or at least disclosing who wrote the note and in what context goes a long way to improving the quality of the testimony and subsequent cross-examination.

[22]The most noteworthy exceptions have been annotated in a collection by Landis (1988).

[23]In *Barefoot v. Estelle*, the United States Supreme Court summarized this view, by noting that " . . . the rules of evidence generally extant at the federal and state levels anticipate that relevant, unprivileged evidence should be admitted and its weight left to the fact finder, who would have the benefit of cross-examination and contrary evidence by the opposing party . . . " (*Barefoot* at 898). In response to criticisms that much forensic evidence was *too unreliable* to be relied upon, the Court noted that, having found the evidence relevant and *not entirely unreliable*, it was proper to allow the trier of fact to sort out the proper weight since the exclusion argument "is founded on the premise that a jury will not be able to separate the wheat from the chaff. We do not share in this low evàluation of the adversary process." (*Barefoot*, P. 901, Note 7)

[24]In a limited fashion, the Supreme Court acknowledged this by affirming an indigent defendant's constitutional right to be provided with the *expert resources* necessary to effectively introduce mental state evidence in capital trials (*Ake v. Oklahoma*, 1985).

an effective and thorough examination of the expert, many individuals qualified as experts lack sufficient expertise as to the scientific limits of their methods, procedures, and opinions[25], and the adversarial system of evidence production may not be the most effective method, especially when scientific matters are the subject of controversy (Anderten, Staulcup & Grisso, 1980; Appelbaum, 1987; Bersoff, 1986; Loftus & Monahan, 1980; Monahan & Walker, 1986).

In order to assist triers of fact under the current conditions, and not to allow our expertise to be misrepresented by either *over-* or *under-valuing* its scientific bases, we need to adopt stronger ethical standards with regard to evidence production. A large portion of the guidelines proposed by Golding and Grisso (1988) addresses these problems. Some of these have been previously referred to and others are detailed here. The proposed guidelines are based upon the assumption that a qualified expert accepts that his or her special status in the legal system confers upon them a special responsibility to preserve the best evidence of the bases of their testimony and to forthrightly present that evidence contextualized by an accurate statement of its known limitations and qualifications.[26]

Section 3(c)(i)–(iv) addresses the issue of collecting and preserving the "best evidence" as follows:

> Forensic psychologists have an obligation, flowing both from their competence and their special status as a person qualified as an expert to the court, to document and to make available to all parties to a legal proceeding, all data which form the basis for their evidence or services. The standard to be applied to such documentation or recording *anticipates* that the detail and quality of such documentation will be subject to reasonable judicial scrutiny, and so is higher than the normative standard for general clinical and research practice. (Section 3[c]).
>
> All evaluation and treatment procedures, research, and other forms of data which form the basis for the expert's evidence must be available, in reasonable form, for discovery and direct or cross-examination. (Section 3[c][i]).
>
> All data and evidence collected as a consequence of a contractual relationship with an attorney representing a party to a legal proceeding are subject to attorney-client privilege as a "work-product." They may not be released without either the waiver of the party holding the privilege or a lawful order from the court to release or produce the data or evidence (Section 3[c][ii]).
>
> A special problem exists with respect to "personal notes." Notes taken during the course of an examination or interview for the purpose of recording relevant aspects of the individual's demeanor, verbal behav-

[25]See the fuller discussion of this point in the previous section of the *voir dire* of experts.

[26]In essence, the guidelines are based upon "scientific rules of evidence" rather than "adversarial rules of evidence." The expert bears the responsibility to assure that the full scientific bases and limitations are presented (Loftus and Monahan, 1980).

ior and so forth are not considered personal notes, since they are a substitute or augment recordings [see iv(1)]. Personal notes include only notations made for the personal use of the evaluator (e.g., hunches, speculations, areas to pursue) and which do not function as a basis, whether partial or otherwise, for the evaluator's professional product, testimony or other evidence. (Section 3[c][iii]).

When a forensic psychologist conducts an examination or engages in the treatment of a party to a legal proceeding *prior to, or as a consequence of a legal proceeding*, s/he incurs a special responsibility to provide the "best documentation" possible under the circumstances.

Usually, video- or audio-tapes will provide the best documentation of interviews. Because the forensic psychologist has advance knowledge in these circumstances that the evidentiary basis of their opinions, testimony or other evidence will be subject to adversarial examination, they may not intentionally fail to collect and document the "best evidence." Under circumstances where the interviewee refuses consent or where situations, beyond the reasonable control of the examiner, preclude such recordings, the examiner bears a special responsibility to preserve the best record possible, in the form of detailed notes prepared within a reasonable period of time following the interview.

Documentation of the data upon which one's evidence is based is subject to the normal rules of discovery, disclosure, confidentiality and privilege which operate in the jurisdiction in which the data were obtained. The forensic psychologist has an affirmative duty to be aware of those rules and to regulate his/her conduct in accordance with them.

The duties and obligations of forensic psychologists with respect to documentation of data which form the basis for their evidence obtain from the moment they know or have a reasonable basis for knowing that their data and evidence derived from it is likely to enter into legally relevant decisions. (Section 3[c][iv][1–3]).

Our concern here is with assuring that the evidentiary bases of expert testimony are sufficiently preserved so as not to undermine the opposing party's constitutional right to effective counsel and confrontation. Recording interviews or otherwise preserving the best evidence available removes the disadvantage of cross-examining an expert who is not only "in control" of the expertise but also of the *data* to which that expertise is applied. While a medical pathologist would testify ordinarily as to the meaning of a certain pattern of blood stains, the courts would not ordinarily allow such testimony if he were the only one who saw them! Why should not we be held to an appropriately equivalent standard?

This problem is illustrated forcefully in *United States v. Byers* (1984)[27]. At

[27]Parts of this section are adapted from Golding and Roesch (1987) which reports the Byers case in more detail.

Byers' trial for murder, an examining psychiatrist testified that during an interview Byers had told him that his wife had suggested to him that his mental state might have been under the influence of "roots." This statement, if true and not distorted out of context, implied that Byers' "delusions" were suggested to him by his wife. The trial court characterized the testimony as "devastating" and such that it "perhaps will torpedo the (defendant) out of the water" (p. 1144). Unfortunately, the psychiatrist had (a) destroyed his notes of the interview, (b) admitted that he did not record the statement in the destroyed notes because he considered it insignificant, (c) did not tell any of his colleagues of the alleged statement, and (d) did not allude to it or any aspect of malingering in his report to the court.

Byers was unsuccessful in his attempt, on appeal, to have his conviction set aside on the grounds that the testimony violated his Fifth Amendment privilege against self-incrimination and his Sixth Amendment right to effective assistance of counsel. A strongly divided court ruled that Byers statements to the expert were admissible and did not violate his right to avoid self-incrimination. The court distinguished *Estelle v. Smith* (1981) by arguing that, whereas Smith had not raised either competency or sanity, Byers had himself interposed the insanity defense, thus waiving certain aspects of the right against self-incrimination:

> When a defendant asserts the insanity defense and introduces supporting psychiatric testimony, his silence may deprive the State of the only effective means it has of controverting his proof on an issue that he interjected into the case. Accordingly, several Courts of Appeal have held that, under such circumstances, a defendant can be required to submit to a sanity evaluation conducted by a prosecution's psychiatrist (p. 465).

Similarly, the Court rejected Byers' claim that he had been deprived of effective assistance of counsel—"it is enough that Byers had the opportunity to contest the accuracy of both the details and the conclusion of Dr. Kunev's analysis by cross-examining him (pointing out, as he did, that the crucial statement on which Kunev based his conclusion was not reflected in the psychiatrist's summary of the interview)" (*Byers*, p. 1121). Interestingly, the Court concluded, "Recording psychiatric interviews may be a good idea, but not all good ideas have been embodied in the Constitution in general or in the Sixth Amendment in particular" (*Byers*, p. 1121).

Judge Bazelon, in his strongly worded dissent, expressed the underlying logic of our proposed guideline clearly when he concluded that:

> If defense counsel had an accurate, complete record of the clinical interview he could, with the aid of his own experts, attempt to identify the distortions and interactions that may have affected the substance of the interviewer's reports and testimony. But such a com-

> plete, accurate record cannot, by virtue of the very effects I have described, be expected to be forthcoming from the interviewer. The accused, moreover, whatever his mental state, cannot be relied upon to fill in the gaps necessary for a complete and accurate assessment. It is therefore clear that . . . counsel may be unable to detect distortions or to cross-examine meaningfully the government's expert and rebut his conclusions. . . . A complete tape recording or videotape of the interview would provide counsel with exactly the sort of objective and precise record that, as I have previously discussed, is often a prerequisite to detection of distortions and to effective cross-examination or rebuttal at trial. As discussed above, such a taped record would facilitate constitutional aims without impairing the interview process itself. (*Byers*, pp. 1171–1172).

Full access to the evidentiary bases of forensic testimony is becoming an increasing problem as jurisdictions seek to reform the procedures involved in the prosecution of child sexual abuse cases. While a full discussion is beyond the scope of this article (but see Cohen, 1985; Kelly, 1985; MacFarlane, 1985; Miller & Weinstock, 1987; Otto & Melton, 1990; Roe, 1985; Spencer, 1987), many jurisdictions now permit, under increasingly wider circumstances, a child's statements to an examiner to be entered into testimony through the expert and without the child being required to testify. To compound the problem, many jurisdictions also allow expert testimony as to the conclusion that the child has been the victim of sexual abuse (see prior references). In such circumstances, the proper role of the forensic professional and the integrity of the judicial process may be seriously compromised. Whether or not such evidentiary rules are "wise" or based upon scientifically defensible premises,[28], it is clear that in such jurisdictions, the forensic examiner *must*, at a minimum, be required to produce carefully documented data upon which such testimony is based.[29] Otherwise, the role of the forensic professional is seriously compromised.

Obviously, the data upon which forensic testimony is based, no matter how carefully documented, is no better than the reliability and validity of the methods and procedures used to collect such data. Therefore, explicit guidelines are needed by the profession so that the ground is laid to challenge an expert with

[28]Currently, absent certain strong physical signs (e.g., presence of venereal disease or blatant vaginal or anal trauma), there are no scientifically acceptable scientific data on "sexual abuse profiles" based upon psychological data. The expert's role, consistent with Federal Rule 702 and the position advocated here, is properly limited to an analysis of the cognitive, developmental, personality, and situational data which need to be considered in a *judicial* determination of the child's credibility.

[29]Other benefits to careful recording, including videotaping, are discussed at length in Golding and Roesch (1987). For example, approximately 40% of all insanity-pleaders are found unfit for trial (Criss & Racine, 1980; Golding, Eaves & Rogow, 1989; Petrila, 1982) and another 30% may receive treatment while in jail. Therefore a defendant who pleads not guilty by reason of insanity may come to trial disadvantaged because an extensive "sanity" evaluation is unlikely to have taken place prior to competency restoration and no relatively neutral record of his/her premedication behavioral, perceptual, cognitive, affective, and judgmental capacities at the time of the offense will exist.

respect to whether the data, methods, and procedures are "of a type reasonably relied upon by experts." The guidelines proposed by Golding and Grisso (1988) introduce this concept as follows:

> Forensic psychologists have an obligation, flowing both from their competence and their special status as a person qualified as an expert to the court, to employ the highest clinical and scientific standards of their profession when selecting data collection methods and procedures for an evaluation, treatment, consultation or scholarly/empirical investigation.
>
> Forensic psychologists fully inform prospective clients, relevant parties to a legal proceeding, and other consumers of their professional products and services of the known scientific bases and limitations of the methods and procedures which they employ. (Sections 6[a–b]).

Thus, the forensic expert incurs the affirmative responsibility to justify why their methods or procedures in a particular context might deviate from the "highest clinical and scientific standards." If one is offering diagnostic testimony, it will no longer do to conduct a "seat of the paints" mental status interview and offer testimony about the increased reliability of DSM-IIIR. If the expert is to rely upon DSM-IIIR, then he or she would bear the responsibility of demonstrating why the associated semi-structured elicitation interviews were not used, and how this limited the reliability and validity of their testimony.

It is not assumed, naively, that no controversy exists as to the "highest standards" or the "scientific basis" of various procedures. Considerable dispute exists about most of the methods and procedures we employ. However, guidelines of this type put the responsibility for justification where it belongs and it further legitimates putting the expert to the test of expertise. As we have seen in other contexts, our legal system invites expert testimony based upon critical assumptions, and we need to assume more responsibility in assuring that the assumptions are met.

While all of the existing ethical codes address the legal and ethical necessity of obtaining informed or substitute consent for the pretrial evaluation of defendants,[30] there remain serious problems because of the rules that concern disclosure of such information. As several authors have observed (Golding and Roesch, 1987; Melton et al., 1986; Showalter, 1990), forensic professionals often include in their reports information which can produce adverse "fruits." Until most jurisdictions adopt rules of evidence similar to the procedure in Virginia (reviewed by Melton et al., 1986) which provides for elaborate protection, some set of guidelines is needed. Golding and Grisso (1988) have proposed the following:

[30]Virtually identical language can be found in the codes from the American Bar Association (ABA, 1984) as well as the codes previously referenced by the American Psychological Association, American Psychiatric Association, American Academy of Psychiatry and Law, American Academy of Forensic Psychology, and the code proposed by Golding and Grisso (1988).

Forensic psychologists are aware that "no statement made by the defendant in the course of any (forensic) examination . . . with or without the consent of the defendant, no testimony by the expert based upon such statement, and no other fruits of the statement shall be admitted in evidence against the defendant . . . in any criminal proceeding except on an issue respecting mental condition on which the defendant has introduced testimony" (Federal Rules of Criminal Procedure, 12.2(c), 1985). Forensic psychologists have an affirmative duty to ensure that their written products and oral testimony conform to this rule of procedure.

Because forensic psychologists are often not in a position to know what evidence, documentation or element of a written product may be or may lead to a "fruit of the statement," they exercise extreme caution in preparing reports or offering testimony prior to the defendant's assertion of a mental state claim or the defendant's introduction of testimony regarding a mental condition. Consistent with the reporting requirements of state or federal law, forensic psychologists avoid including statements from the defendant relating to the time period of the alleged offense.

Once a defendant has proceeded to the trial stage, and all pretrial mental health issues such as competency have been resolved, forensic psychologists may include in their reports or testimony any statements made by the defendant that are directly relevant to supporting their expert evidence, providing that the defendant has "introduced" mental state evidence or testimony within the meaning of Federal Rule of Procedure 12.2(c). (Section 6[g]; see also Section 6[f] discussed previously).

Expertise for Hire? – A Brief Proposal for Reform

No problem with forensic expertise produces as much emotionality as the challenge that forensic mental health professionals are "whores for hire." Those of us who take pride in our profession and who are associated with internal reforms having to do with training (Blau, 1984; Brodsky & Robey, 1972; Ciccone & Clements, 1984a, 1984b; Fitch, Petrella, & Wallace, 1987; Gutheil & Appelbaum, 1982; Melton et al., 1986; Pollack, Gross, & Weinberger, 1982a, 1982b; Poythress, 1978, 1979) and revision of ethical standards (Golding & Grisso, 1988; Rappeport, 1981; Rogers, 1987; Sadoff, 1984; Slovenko, 1987; Weiner, 1984; Weinstein, 1984; and many of the codes previously cited) are particularly stung by such continuing accusations. Leaving aside the emotionality, we need to take the challenge seriously and ask what reforms might be needed and whether or not they will be effective.

This article has suggested a number of steps to improve the *internal self-regulation* of the profession with regard to ethical standards and guidelines.

Reforms of this type are preferable in comparison to the "blunt axe" of legislative reform.[31] One may legitimately ask, however, why such internal self-regulation is likely to succeed. As an educator and trainer, my biases lead me to put most faith in educationally based reform that strongly emphasizes the sort of ethical and professional standards emphasized here. Why or how can this sort of reform overcome the inertia or the financial motives which seem to inhibit reform?

It is clear that the fundamental rules of evidence, discussed in detail in this article, provide the basis for the trier of fact to exercise considerable control and discretion over the process of expert evidence production. It is equally clear that our colleagues in the legal system need to exercise the authority that they already have more consistently and forcefully. Several reasons account for their failure to do so. First, the typical law school curriculum places little or no emphasis on learning the relevant aspects of the behavioral and psychological sciences that would equip trial attorneys and future judges with a firmer basis to pursue their own rules of evidence, better cross-examination, and the like. Secondly, the mental health professions have acted more like guilds than scientific professions, and have been reluctant to promulgate and enforce detailed standards. Thus, when the legal system looks for help in interpretation of customary procedure, or the range of acceptable interpretation or training, they find little to guide them. Third, the American legal system, notwithstanding its adversarial reputation, is remarkably passive in its attitudes toward expertise. For example, Rule 706 of the *Federal Rules of Evidence* was designed to give a trial judge discretionary authority to appoint experts to the court. This rule was adopted after considerable study and was strongly supported by the American Bar Association (1971).[32] Nevertheless, for unclear reasons, judges rarely seem to exercise this authority in cases involving mental health issues. In part this may be attributable to their belief that "impartiality" is a fallacy (Diamond, 1959), to a judicial reluctance to "interfere," or to lack of training as to what can or should be expected of a well-trained mental health expert. On all grounds, an articulated interdisciplinary educational system in both law schools and mental health training programs can overcome these problems. The "impartiality as fallacy" argument wasn't very accurate 30 years ago[33] and as the forensic training programs now available come into their maturity and promulgate the standards described here, the ideal goals set forth in tough standards will increasingly become the norm. Moreover, the judiciary can be "nudged" in this direction if trial attorneys, based upon interdisciplinary training in law school, push the issue by raising the various evidentiary objections at trial in a vigorous and well-informed manner. Thus, while the motion to bar Dr. Grigson's testimony may have failed, most trial judges, seeking to avoid reversible error, could be per-

---

[31]For example, attempts to abolish the insanity defense or to exclude mental health professionals from the courtroom.

[32]Even earlier, the National Conference of Commissioners on Uniform State Laws had advocated the essence of Rule 706 as an attempt to make impartial medical testimony routine practice.

[33]See the Special Committee of the Association of the Bar of the City of New York (1956). When the bar and the judiciary set their minds to it, considerable progress towards finding and using more impartial experts works.

suaded that the scientific basis of prediction of future dangerousness was sufficiently "dicey" that prudence, if not constitutionally mandated reliability considerations, in a death penalty case would call for appointing neutral experts under Rule 706.

Proposals to reform the financial basis of the expert system are inherently difficult. For decades numerous proposals to establish neutral panels or lists of "unbiased" experts have emerged. As those of us who work in the system know all too well, enormous financial pressures exist, especially if one is in full-time private practice (Modlin, 1984). Grisso (1987) provides a useful and insightful analysis of the complex economic and guild forces which act negatively upon the development of a more rigorous and scientifically acceptable procedure. Given the current economic structure of our society and the widely based need for forensic evaluations in our criminal and civil justice systems, this is unlikely to change. Creating panels of relatively more impartial experts will help break the link between source of funding and the nature of opinions, but it will not directly eliminate economic competition and financial incentives. In my view, while various procedural reforms can have some impact, the only long-term solution to the problem lies in strengthening the internal reform, the ethical standards, and the quality of training within our profession and in the legal profession. This type of solution will not produce dramatic change in the near future. Very few high quality, coherent, and adequately funded forensic training programs exist. The economic forces which distort the quality and ethicality of expertise are very real and very strong, and some of those whose fundamental financial support is based in exclusive private practice are likely to resist strongly the reforms advocated in this article. Finally, the legal profession, for all of the reasons suggested here, has been reluctant to adopt a more activist stance, utilizing the powers which are inherent in the rules of evidence. Nevertheless, without minimizing these reasons for pessimism, we have no choice other than to pursue the arduous task of internal reform. Our professional situation is not historically unlike that confronted by other, now respected, professions. Our ethical imperative is to vocally and strenuously pursue such options and actively present the justice system with an articulated basis for forensic expertise; by doing so we place our bets on the reverse of Gresham's law—good, well founded expertise will drive out inadequate (bad) expertise.

References[34]

Ake v. Oklahoma, 470 U.S. 68 (1985).

American Academy of Forensic Psychology (1988). *Draft Standards for providers of forensic psychological services*. Unpublished draft.

American Academy of Psychiatry and the Law (1987). Ethical guidelines for the practice of forensic psychiatry. *AAPL Newsletter, 12*, 16–17.

American Bar Association (1984). *Criminal Justice Mental Health Standards*. Chicago, IL: Author.

American Bar Association (1971). *Handbook on the improvement of the administration of justice*. Chicago, IL: Author.

American Psychiatric Association (1981). *The principles of medical ethics with annotation especially applicable to psychiatry*. Washington, DC: Author.

[34]An extensive bibliography on ethics and forensic mental health expertise is available from the author.

American Psychological Association (1981). Ethical principles of psychologists. *American Psychologist, 36*, 633-638.

American Psychological Association (1980). Bibliography on ethics in criminal justice. *Who is the client? The ethics of psychological intervention in the criminal justice system*. Washington, DC: Author.

American Psychological Association (1978). Report of the task force on the role of psychology in the criminal justice system. *American Psychologist, 33*, 1099–1113.

Anderten, P., Staulcup, V., & Grisso, T. (1980). On being ethical in legal places. *Professional Psychology, 11*, 764-773.

Anonymous. (1988). Admissibility of expert testimony under Federal Rule of Evidence 403. *76 ALR Fed 700*.

Appelbaum, P. S. (1983). Death, the expert witness, and the dangers of going Barefoot. *Hospital and Community Psychiatry, 34*, 1003–1004.

Appelbaum, P. S. (1984a). Hypotheticals, psychiatric testimony, and the death sentence. *Bulletin of the American Academy of Psychiatry and Law, 12* 169–177.

Appelbaum, P. S. (1984b). Psychiatric ethics in the courtroom. *Bulletin of the American Academy of Psychiatry and Law, 12* 225–231.

Appelbaum, P. S. (1987). In the wake of Ake: The ethics of expert testimony in an advocate's world. *Bulletin of the American Academy of Psychiatry and Law, 15*, 15–25.

Barefoot v. Estelle, 460 U.S. 880 (1983).

Bazelon, D. L. (1974). The perils of wizardry. *American Journal of Psychiatry, 131*, 1317–1322.

Bazelon, D. L. (1978). The role of the psychiatrist in the criminal justice system. *Bulletin of the American Academy of Psychiatry and Law, 6*, 139–146.

Bazelon, D. (1982). Veils, values, and social responsibility. *American Psychologist, 37* 115–121.

Bersoff, D. N. (1986). Psychologists and the judicial systems: Broader perspectives. *Law and Human Behavior, 10*, 151–166.

Blau, T. H. (1984). *The psychologist as expert witness*. New York: John Wiley.

Bonnie, R. J. (1984). Morality, equality, and expertise: Renegotiating the relationship between psychiatry and the criminal law. *Bulletin of the American Academy of Psychiatry and Law, 12*, 5–20.

Bonnie, R. J., & Slobogin, C. (1980). The role of mental health professionals in the criminal process: The case for informed speculation. *Virginia Law Review, 66*, 427–522.

Brodsky, S. L., & Robey, A. (1972). On becoming an expert witness: Issues of orientation and effectiveness. *Professional Psychology, 3*, 173–176.

Carlson, R. L. (1987). Policing the bases of modern expert testimony. *Vanderbilt Law Review, 39*, 577–593.

Ciccone, J. R. (1986). A new look at an old problem: Expert witnesses and criminal responsibility. *Psychiatric Annals, 16*, 408–410.

Ciccone, J. R., & Clements, C. D. (1984a). The ethical practice of forensic psychiatry: A view from the trenches. *Bulletin of the American Academy of Psychiatry and Law, 12*, 263–277.

Ciccone, J. R., & Clements, C. D. (1984b). Forensic psychiatry and applied clinical ethics: theory and practice. *American Journal of Psychiatry, 141*, 395–399.

Clements, C. D., & Ciccone, R. (1984). Ethics and expert witnesses: The troubled role of psychiatrists in court. *Bulletin of the American Academy of Psychiatry and Law, 12*, 127–136.

Cohen, A. (1985). The unreliability of expert testimony on the typical characteristics of sexual abuse victims. *Georgetown Law Journal, 74*, 429–456.

Criss, M. L., & Racine, D. R. (1980). Impact and change in legal standard for those adjudicated not guilty by reason of insanity 1975–1979. *Bulletin of the American Academy of Psychiatry and Law, 8*, 261–271.

Dahl, P. R. (1985). Legal and psychiatric concepts and the use of psychiatric evidence in criminal trials. *California Law Review, 73*, 411–442.

Diamond, B. L. (1959). The fallacy of the impartial expert. *Archives of Criminal Psychodynamics, 3*, 221–236.

Diamond, B. L., & Louisell, D. W. (1965). The psychiatrist as an expert witness: Some ruminations and speculations. *Michigan Law Review, 63*, 1335–1354.

Dix, G. E. (1983). A legal perspective on dangerousness: Current status. *Psychiatric Annals, 13*, 243–256.

Ennis, B. J., & Litwack, T. R. (1974). Psychiatry and the presumption of expertise: Flipping coins in the courtroom. *California Law Review, 62*, 693–752.

Estelle v. Smith, 451 U.S. 454 (1981).

Faust, D., & Ziskin, J. (1988). The expert witness in psychology and psychiatry. *Science, 241*, 31–35.

Federal Rules of Criminal Procedure. (1985).

Fitch, W. L., Petrella, R. C., & Wallace, J. (1987). Legal ethics and the use of mental health experts in criminal cases. *Behavioral Sciences and the Law, 5*, 105–119.

Fukunaga, K., Pasewark, R., Hawkins, M., & Gudeman, H. (1981). Insanity plea: Interexaminer agreement and concordance of psychiatric opinion and court verdict. *Law and Human Behavior 5*, 325–328.

Garrett, S. M. (1982). People v. Murtishaw: Applying the Frye test to psychiatric predictions of dangerousness in capital cases. *California Law Review, 70*, 1069–1090.

Giannelli, P. C. (1980). The admissibility of novel scientific evidence: Frye v. United States, a half-century later. *Columbia Law Review, 80*, 1197–1250.

Giannelli, P. C., & Imwinkelried, E. J. (1988). *Scientific evidence*. Charlottesville, VA: Michie.

Golding, S. L., Eaves, D., & Kowaz, A. (1989). The assessment, treatment, and community outcome of insanity acquittees: Forensic history and response to treatment. *International Journal of Law and Psychiatry, 12*, 149–179.

Golding, S. L., & Grisso, T. (1988). *Specialty guidelines for forensic psychologists*. Unpublished discussion draft, 4/1/90.

Golding, S. L., & Roesch, R. (1987). The assessment of criminal responsibility: A historical perspective. In I. B. Weiner & A. K. Hess (Eds.), *Handbook of forensic psychology* (pp. 395–436). New York: Wiley.

Grisso, T. (1987). The economic and scientific future of forensic psychological assessment. *American Psychologist, 42*, 831–839.

Gutheil, T. G., & Appelbaum, P. S. (1982). *Clinical handbook of psychiatry and the law*. New York: McGraw-Hill.

Halleck, S. L. (1980). *Law in the practice of psychiatry: A handbook for clinicians*. New York: Plenum Medical Books.

Halleck, S. L. (1984). The ethical dilemmas of forensic psychiatry: A utilitarian approach. *Bulletin of the American Academy of Psychiatry and Law, 12*, 279–288.

Hans, V. P., & Slater, D. (1983). John Hinckley, Jr. and the insanity defense: The public's verdict. *Public Opinion Quarterly, 47*, 202–212.

Jenkins v. United States, 307 F. 2d 637 (D.C. Court of Appeals, 1962).

Jurek v. Texas, 428 U.S. 262 (1976).

Kaplan, L. V., Miller, R. D. (1986). Courtroom psychiatrists: Expertise at the cost of wisdom? *International Journal of Law and Psychiatry, 9*, 451–468.

Kelly, J. (1985). Legislative responses to child sexual abuse cases: The hearsay exception and the videotape deposition. *Catholic University Law Review, 34*, 1021–1054.

Landis, D. T. (1988). When will expert testimony "assist trier of fact" as to be admissible at federal trial under Rule 702 of Federal Rules of Evidence. *75 ALR Fed 461*.

Loftus, E., & Monahan, J. (1980). Trial by data: Psychological research as legal evidence. *American Psychologist, 35*, 270–283.

MacFarlane, K. (1985). Diagnostic evaluations and the use of videotapes in child sexual abuse cases. *University of Miami Law Review, 40* 135–165.

Melton, G. B., Petrila, J., Poythress, N. G., & Slobogin, C. (1986). *Psychological evaluations for the courts: A handbook for mental health professionals and lawyers*. New York: Guilford Press.

Miller, R. D., & Weinstock, R. (1987). Conflict of interest between therapist-patient confidentiality and the duty to report sexual abuse of children. *Behavioral Sciences and the Law, 5*, 161–174.

Modlin, H. C. (1984). The ivory tower v. the marketplace. *Bulletin of the American Academy of Psychiatry and Law, 12*, 233–236.

Moenssens, A. A., Inbau, F. E., & Starrs, J. E. (1986). *Scientific evidence in criminal cases (3rd ed.)*. Mineola, NY: Foundation Press.

Monahan, J. (1980). *Who is the client? The ethics of psychological intervention in the criminal justice system*. Washington, DC: American Psychological Association.

Monahan, J., & Walker, L. (1986). Social authority: Obtaining, evaluating, and establishing social science in law. *University of Pennsylvania Law Review, 134*, 477–517.

Morris, N. (1982). *Madness and the criminal law*. Chicago: University of Chicago Press.

Morse, S. J. (1978a). Crazy behavior, morals, and science: An analysis of Mental Health Law. *Southern California Law Review, 51*, 527–654.

Morse, S. J. (1987b). Law and mental health professionals: The limits of expertise. *Professional Psychology, 9*, 389–399.

Morse, S. J. (1985). Excusing the crazy: The insanity defense reconsidered. *Southern California Law Review, 58*, 777–836.

Morse, S. J. (1986). Psychology, determinism and legal responsibility. In G. B. Melton (Ed.), *Nebraska symposium on motivation: Vol. 33. The law as a behavioral instrument* (pp. 35–85). Lincoln, NE: University of Nebraska Press.

Neumeg, R. (1988). What information is of a type "reasonably relied upon by experts" with Rule 703, Federal Rules of Evidence, permitting expert opinion based on information not admissible in evidence. *49 ALR Fed 363.*

O'Toole, M. B. (1977). Hearsay bases of psychiatric opinion testimony. A critique of Federal rule of evidence 703. *Southern California Law Review, 51*, 129–162.

Otto, R. K., & Melton, G. B., (1990). Trends in legislation and case law in child abuse and neglect. In R. T. Ammerman and M. Hersen (Eds.), *Children at risk: An evaluation of factors contributing to child abuse and neglect.* (pp. 55–83). New York: Plenum.

Petrila, J. (1982). The insanity defense and other mental health dispositions in Missouri. *International Journal of Law and Psychiatry, 5*, 81–101.

Pollack, S., Gross, B. H., & Weinberger, L. E. (1982a). Principles of forensic psychiatry for reaching psychiatric-legal opinions: Introduction. *New Directions for Mental Health Services, 16*, 15–23.

Pollack, S., Gross, B. H., & Weinberger, L. E. (1982b). Principles of forensic psychiatry for reaching psychiatric-legal opinions: Application. *New Directions for Mental Health Services, 16*, 25–44.

Poythress, N. G. (1978). Psychiatric expertise in civil commitment: Training attorneys to cope with expert testimony. *Law and Human Behavior, 2*, 1–23.

Poythress, N. G. (1979). A proposal for training in forensic psychology. *American Psychologist 34*, 612–621.

Poythress, N. G. (1982). Concerning reform in expert testimony. An open letter from a practicing psychologist. *Law and Human Behavior, 6*, 39–43.

Rappeport, J. (1981). Ethics and forensic psychiatry. In S. Bloch & P. Chodoff (Eds.), *Psychiatric ethics* (pp. 255–276). Oxford: Oxford University Press.

Resnick, P. J. (1986). Perceptions of psychiatric testimony: A historical perspective on the hysterical invective. *Bulletin of the American Academy of Psychiatry and Law, 14*, 203–219.

Rice, P. R. (1987). Inadmissible evidence as a basis for expert opinion testimony: A response to Professor Carlson. *Vanderbilt Law Review, 40*, 583–596.

Roe, R. J. (1985). Expert testimony in child sexual abuse cases. *University of Miami Law Review, 40*, 97–113.

Rogers, R. (1987). Ethical dilemmas in forensic evaluations. *Behavioral Sciences and the Law, 5*, 149–160.

Rogers, R., Wasyliw, O. E., & Cavanaugh, J. L. (1984). Evaluating insanity: A study of construct validity. *Law and Human Behavior, 8*, 293–304.

Sadoff, R. L. (1984). Practical ethical problems of the forensic psychiatrist in dealing with attorneys. *Bulletin of the American Academy of Psychiatry and Law, 12*, 243–252.

Showalter, C. R. (1990). Psychiatric participation in capital sentencing proceedings: Ethical considerations. *International Journal of Law and Psychiatry, 13*, 000–000.

Shuman, D. W. (1986). *Psychiatric and psychological evidence.* Colorado Springs, CO: Shepard's/McGraw-Hill.

Slovenko, R. (1987). The lawyer and the forensic expert: Boundaries of ethical practice. *Behavioral Sciences and the Law, 5*, 119–148.

Smith, R. (1981). *Trial by medicine: Insanity and responsibility in Victorian trials.* Edinburgh: Edinburgh University Press.

Special Committee of the Association of the Bar of the City of New York (1956). *Impartial medical testimony.* New York: Macmillan.

Spencer, J. R. (1987). Child witnesses, corroboration and expert evidence. *Criminal Law Review, 1987*, 239–251.

Steadman, H. J., Keitner, L., Braff, J., & Arvanites, M. A. (1983). Factors associated with a successful insanity plea. *American Journal of Psychiatry, 140*, 401–405.

Stone, A. A. (1984). The ethical boundaries of forensic psychiatry: A view from the ivory tower. *Bulletin of the American Academy of Psychiatry and Law, 12*, 209–219.

United States v. Byers, 740 F. 2d 1104 (D.C. Cir., 1984), *cert. denied*, 104 S. Ct. 717.

United States v. Downing, 753 F. 2d 1224 (Third Cir., 1985).

Walker, N. (1968). *Crime and insanity in England, Volume I: The historical perspective.* Edinburgh: University of Edinburgh Press.

Wardle, P. (1984). R. v. Abbey and psychiatric opinion evidence: Requiring the accused to testify. *Ottawa Law Review, 17*, 116–131.

Weiner, B. A. (1984). Ethical issues in forensic psychiatry: From an attorney's perspective. *Bulletin of the American Academy of Psychiatry and Law, 12*, 253–261.

Weinstein, H. C. (1984). How should forensic psychiatry police itself? Guidelines and grievances: The AAPL Committee on Ethics. *Bulletin of the American Academy of Psychiatry and Law, 12*, 289–302.

Weinstein, J. B. (1986). Improving expert testimony. *University of Richmond Law Review, 20*, 473–497.

Ziskin, J. (1981). *Coping with psychiatric and psychological testimony* (3rd ed.). Beverly Hills, CA: Law and Psychology Press.

[24]

International Journal of Law and Psychiatry, Vol. 17, No. 1, pp. 79–97, 1994

0160-2527/94 $6.00 + .00

Pergamon

0160-2527(93)E0004-9

Revisiting the Parable:

Truth Without Consequences

Alan A. Stone*

Introduction

In "The Parable of the Forensic Psychiatrist: Ethics and the Problem of Doing Harm,"[1] Paul Appelbaum offers an interpretation of my "Parable of the Black Sergeant."[2] The "Parable" was part of my formal Presidential Address to the American Psychiatric Association, in which I attempted to demonstrate the complex relationship between psychiatry and morality as manifested in psychiatry's approach to racism, homosexuality, and female psychology. Briefly, the "parable" was an account of an experience I had while an officer in the military years ago. I had performed a psychiatric evaluation of a Black sergeant accused of theft. In the course of evaluation we developed a positive transference/countertransference relationship which led to unguarded and incriminating disclosures on his part. My testimony at his court martial proceeding was instrumental in proving his guilt. He was sentenced to five years at hard labor, and was deprived of all military benefits. My goal in the Presidential Address was to impress on my colleagues that psychiatry, as theory and in practice, inescapably involves human values and should neither claim nor aspire to be "value free science." There was no opportunity in such a paper to explore the ethical dimensions of my testimony in the Black sergeant's court-martial.

Appelbaum speculates that because of my adherence to medical ethics I was primarily concerned about the harm that my testimony at the court martial caused the patient. Appelbaum's opinion is that my understandable concern is a misleading and mistaken basis for drawing any conclusions about the ethics of forensic psychiatry. Appelbaum shares my view that forensic ethics are in a state of disarray, but makes the startling and provocative proposal that the ethics of forensic psychiatrists should not be based on the ethical principles of the medical profession. He allies himself with previous writers[3] who instead propose adherence to the principle of truthfulness.

Appelbaum is correct in stressing my remorse about harming the Black

---

*Touroff-Glueck Professor of Law and Psychiatry, Harvard Law School, Langdell Hall 327, 1545 Massachusetts Avenue, Cambridge, MA, 02138, U.S.A.

sergeant. However, I was equally concerned about the "double agent" problem of betraying his trust. Appelbaum also minimizes my explicit concerns about the conceptual ambiguity of psychiatry. I believe that these oversights in Appelbaum's analysis are crucial limitations both in his interpretation of my ideas concerning the ethical chaos of forensic psychiatry and in his own approach to this subject. Moreover, Appelbaum is simply wrong in his theory that my subsequent paper criticizing forensic psychiatry can be understood as originating in my concerns about causing harm. Nevertheless, it seems to me that it may be possible to avoid a zero sum debate. I have tried instead to find in our interchange of ideas some practical guidance for the ethical quandaries surrounding the issue of capital punishment that currently face forensic psychiatry. I shall first, however, deal with what I consider to be the limitations of Appelbaum's interpretation and his own proposal.

Therapeutic Encounter and Forensic Evaluation

The task of evaluating the sergeant had been one of my assigned duties as a military officer, and once I had reported my psychiatric findings I was literally ordered to testify at the court-martial. Although, as required under military law, I had warned the sergeant that anything he told me could be used against him, we established the kind of psychiatric rapport that leads to unguarded disclosure. Thus, although legally and technically the sergeant had been warned and had given informed consent, my own feeling was that I had unwittingly used my therapeutic skills to extract from him damaging personal revelations. The forensic evaluation had developed into a therapeutic encounter and I had become a "double agent." This clinical problem is one of the potential ethical quagmires of forensic psychiatry as has long been recognized by every responsible practitioner.[4]

Human Values and Diagnostic Evaluation

Less well recognized are the deeper conceptual problems raised by my parable about the Black sergeant. The parable was intended to be more than a case history; it was an attempt to portray a complex human encounter with moral overtones.

The accused, who was in fact a supply sergeant, had confiscated a very large amount of government property, but he was being court-martialed on the specific charge of stealing deodorant from the PX. He had been evaluated by a civilian psychiatrist who was prepared to testify that his behavior had been driven by unconscious kleptomaniacal impulses. The diagnosis of kleptomania[5] and the psychodynamic formulation about the determinism of the childhood on which it was based served to exculpate the sergeant, a result that infuriated the military authorities. They decided the sergeant should be evaluated by military psychiatrists.

When the sergeant and I first met he was suitably wary, and my countertransference, as a newly trained psychiatrist doing his 2 years of required military service, was probably not unusual. I wanted to demonstrate my capacity to empathize across the barriers of race and to find a way to communicate with this Black man. We had, as it turned out, a great deal of common cultural ground. He had gone to a small liberal arts college, majored in literature, and, after a prolonged unsuccessful search for employment appropriate to his learning, had been drafted into the Korean War. Because of his bleak employment prospects in civilian life, he decided that when the war ended he would serve out his 20 years in the Army. His experience was that the United States Army was profoundly racist. He was unable to advance beyond the rank of sergeant while he was forced to serve and pay deference to the less educated and less intelligent White men, most of them Southerners, who were his officers. Bitter about his situation, he stole from the Army whatever and whenever he could, with a sense of entitlement, as reparation for the racial injustices done to him. Psychiatry has no diagnosis and no exculpatory theory of socioeconomic determinism for the victims of such racism. The sergeant's case history and clinical picture were subsequently reviewed by the authors of the *DSM-III-R casebook*, who concluded that he had no mental disorder.[6]

I believed the sergeant's description of the racism he had experienced and I shared his sense of outrage, yet the narrative that emerged from more than ten hours of interviewing could not have been more incriminating to him. Ironically, as the army psychiatrist who had established emotional rapport across the racial divide, I was to be the principal witness against him. After the trial, I was informed that because of my testimony the sergeant was sentenced to five years at hard labor and dishonorable discharge. He lost his pension and everything else of value he had accumulated in his lifetime.

"The Parable of the Black Sergeant" was specifically intended to draw attention to the moral ambiguity of a discipline that accepts the psychic determinism of the Oedipal family but rejects the psychic determinism of lifelong racism. This moral ambiguity, which infects many aspects of psychiatry, is particularly relevant at every juncture of law and psychiatry.

These deeper problems of moral and conceptual ambiguity are also what I emphasized in my subsequent paper on the ethics of forensic psychiatry.[7] Epistemological problems briefly discussed in my earlier paper were: the fact-valued distinction, freewill–determinism, the deconstruction of the self or agency, the mind–brain problem, and the science–morality gap. My purpose was to demonstrate that even the forensic psychiatrist, who resists all of the everyday adversarial inducements to take his testimony to the edge of dishonesty or beyond, proceeds through a further minefield of unrecognized moral hazards. The paper drew responses from a number of distinguished experts,[8] including Appelbaum.[9] Appelbaum later published the paper[10] now under discussion, in which he interpreted my views about the ethics of forensic psychiatry as deriving from a physician's concern about causing harm and expanded on his own ideas about the centrality of truthfulness. In what follows I shall argue that although Appelbaum's principle of truthfulness, as set out in his two papers, might help check some of the arrant dishonesty, it fails to resolve the three problems I have presented.

Moral Sentiments and Professional Ethics

Appelbaum, focusing on my remorseful reaction to the harm I caused, stresses the paragraph in which I wrote, "Do whatever you can to help your patient" and "primum non nocere" (first of all do no harm).[11] These contradictory imperatives constitute the "ethical dialectic of the physician's practice."[12] This dialectic, I suggested, shapes the practical "boundaries" of our struggle to be ethical physicians. However "when we turn our skills to forensic psychiatry, when we serve the system of justice, we can no longer agree on the boundaries of the debate."[13] This "lack of boundaries" was characterized more vividly by Appelbaum as a "slide into ethical chaos."[14]

Appelbaum's thesis is that I have mistakenly assumed that the ethical dialectic (which he refers to as the traditional ethical principles of benevolence and non-maleficence) should apply to the courtroom. He writes, "Can a case be made that beneficence and non-maleficence are not central to forensic ethics, that is, that the ethics guiding forensic psychiatrists differ from those adhered to by their clinical colleagues? Not only do I believe it can, but as we shall see, the failure clearly to make this distinction leads to untold mischief."[15]

Thus, according to Appelbaum, a psychiatrist can and should comfortably wear two hats and keep those hats ethically distinct. In his clinical garb, the psychiatrist is bound by the principles of beneficence and non-maleficence. But as the forensic psychiatrist, that same individual is required to adhere to only the principle of *truthfulness*. In this latter garb, the forensic psychiatrist should not be troubled as I was by the fact that harm may occur as a result of his expert testimony since the dictate primum non nocere does not apply in this context.

Appelbaum understands that as a moral human being I felt profound remorse about the consequences of my testimony. His claim is only that such feelings are not relevant to the ethical imperatives under which the forensic psychiatrist operates. "[P]sychiatrists operate outside the medical framework when they enter the forensic realm, and the ethical principles by which their behavior is justified are simply not the same."[16]

Physicians often confront conflicts between their moral convictions and their professional ethics and in those conflicts we seldom conclude, as Appelbaum has, that we should ignore our moral convictions. Many philosophers and theologians would suggest that our moral obligations generally trump our more narrow professional ethical guidelines.[17]* Thus, I am not convinced that Appelbaum's basic premise of the irrelevance of moral concerns can be ac-

*Applebaum's position exhibits what could be termed *hyperpositivism* or *autopoesis*[18]. It asserts a radical division between disciplines in which values from one discipline simply make no sense and are therefore not applicable in another. However, traditional ethical approaches tend to assert the interrelatedness of interdisciplinary ethics through the medium of an individual's overarching moral scheme; an individual is taken as subscribing to one general moral system, and is not allowed to chop and change his or her ethical preferences at will, or even as the situation demands.[19] This is the view propounded by philosophers from Aristotle,[20] through Aquinas[21] and Kant[22] right up to J. L. Austin. This last was keen to argue that promises (and this would include implied promises arising from the doctor-patient relationship[23]) are not merely objective records of an inward, subjective, spiritual intention to be bound which we can modify inwardly as we move from one discipline (the therapeutic) to another (the forensic). Rather, promising as an institution stands above and apart from those disciplines. When we promise, it is the morality of the institution of promising which obligates us, and "[a]ccuracy and morality alike are on the side of the plain saying that our word is our bond."[24] To subsequently and subjectively modify our promise—that is, to transmogrify the principles of beneficence and non-maleficence into one of truthfulness—would render our professed act of promising hollow, and put it into Austin's category of abuses of promising.

cepted. Furthermore, I believe that the apparent clarity of Appelbaum's argument is purchased at the price of misunderstanding the nature of my moral sentiments. In reality I was concerned that my professional obligations and my unquestioned professional ideology had led me to betray my Black patient and to confirm his worst fears about racism.

Appelbaum recognizes that the physician's principles of beneficence and non-maleficence are binding because of the promises implicit in the doctor-patient relationship.[25] He argues that without a doctor–patient relationship physicians are not bound by those promises. He drives home his point by asking whether the doctor is bound by his professional ethics in selling his house. But the sale of a house does not begin with the doctor examining the patient. And subsequent adherence to the principle of truthfulness does not mitigate the problem of harm that arises when a doctor-patient relationship, with its implicit promises, has developed unexpectedly. Forensic psychiatrists who are well aware of this problem provide formulaic warnings to patients and carefully try to avoid conveying any promises so that they will not be bound by the principles of beneficence and non-maleficence.[26] This is particularly important when the expert has been retained by the adverse side. Specific warnings are also legally required in any situation in which the Fifth Amendment is applicable. The American Psychiatric Association has emphasized in its ethical guidelines the importance of informing patients about the purpose of any psychiatric evaluation.

However, I am not convinced that such procedures are always sufficient to negate the transference/countertransference of the psychiatrist/patient relationship that leads to unguarded disclosure. Moreover, once the forensic examiner has decided that his or her testimony will be helpful to the evaluee, it is not unusual to permit the relationship to become an intensely therapeutic encounter. Thus the expert often enters the deposition or the courtroom deeply involved in a transference/countertransference, wearing both hats and bound by both kinds of ethics, but without any sense of the conflict between them. The experts believe they are serving justice and helping their patients at the same time. This is the forensic psychiatrist's version of being on the "side of the angels." This *over involvement*, I believe, contributes to the "untold mischief" about which Appelbaum complains.

Situational Ethics and Betrayal

If Appelbaum's conception allowed the psychiatrist to gather all information from a patient in the medical situation, while bound by the principles of beneficence and non-maleficence, and then allowed that psychiatrist to serve in the courtroom, while bound only by truth, it would be the ultimate caricature of situational ethics.[27]** Unfortunately, although Appelbaum clearly rec-

**Situational (or act-oriented) ethics require that an act be justified through its direct relation with the situation from which the action arises, rather than a relation mediated through general rules. On this view, general moral rules do not prescribe actions by firmly establishing what is right or wrong, good or bad, obligated or prohibited. Rather, the unfolding demands of the situation are paramount. The standard of justification is a direct appeal to the consequences of a particular action, or a direct perception of one's duty (thought intuition or grace), in a particular situation. General rules, then, would not be determinative or

ognizes the "double agent" problem, including the version I have described, neither of the papers in which he discussed these ideas explicitly confronts it. Because in actual practice the line between a forensic evaluation and a therapeutic encounter is never unambiguous, the problem of broken promises may be incorrigible. In any event, I believe, Appelbaum's failure to confront directly the practical problem of the "Double Agent" constitutes a weakness in the basic premise of his theoretical argument that quite different rules can apply to the different situations. Nonetheless, his willingness to found a different ethics for forensic psychiatrists on the different contexts has convinced me that forensic psychiatrists must even more scrupulously avoid any intermingling of their dual roles. I shall, therefore, propose a more draconic ethical principle in the hope that it will prompt further discussion of these difficult matters.

Based on the above analysis I now believe that it was *ethically as well as morally wrong* for me to have testified at the sergeant's court martial. I am now prepared to argue that, regardless of whether appropriate ethical and legal warnings have been given, whenever an evaluation turns into a therapeutic encounter and produces unguarded disclosures, the psychiatrist should disqualify him- or herself from submitting expert testimony. Before expanding on this idea, I shall further consider the principle of truthfulness as an ethical guideline.

Truthfulness and the Slide into Chaos

According to Appelbaum, the principle of truthfulness that applies in the courtroom situation will serve to prevent any "slide into ethical chaos." As proof that this principle can be effectively applied, he offers (without mentioning names) the example of Dr. Grigson, whose "predictions of dangerousness" helped Texas courts to sentence scores of criminals to death.[28] Appelbaum would say that Grigson's ethical misconduct was in offering untruthful testimony—claiming that he knew with medical certainty that a particular defendant would be dangerous in the future when in fact this is not something an ethical psychiatrist should claim to know. These and other much discussed criticisms of Dr. Grigson's testimony in *Barefoot v. Estelle*[29] were presented to the Supreme Court in an American Psychiatric Association Amicus brief.[30]

Unlike Appelbaum, I have no confidence in the guiding principle of truth as an effective means of preventing the slide into ethical chaos. The standard of truthfulness, as I have said before,[31] has always been imposed by the law on all expert witnesses, who, like all other witnesses, are "sworn to tell the truth, the whole truth, and nothing but the truth."

If truth in psychiatry were a simple and straightforward matter-of-fact rather than a complex question of informed opinion, then Dr. Grigson per-

correct standards of action; they may assist deliberation, but can be set aside at any time as the situation demands. Beauchamp and Childress give the example of a doctor, employing a situation, ethic from whom I have extracted a promise about my future treatment. In their example, the physician would only keep her word if she thought, whether by revelation or balancing the consequences, that what was best, given the situation, was keeping her promise. But since I know that the physician will not necessarily keep her promise, she will know that it matters that much less if she does break it, and so the promise tends to become an idle one, with no obligatory force whatsoever. This holds generally for all moral rules. Moral rules, on this model, can never be absolute; they can be set aside whenever the, in this case, physician decides.

jured himself and for his obvious dishonesty he could be sanctioned by a court. Instead, a majority of the Supreme Court, fully aware of the American Psychiatric Association brief on which the dissent relied, ruled in *Barefoot v. Estelle* that Dr. Grigson's opinion was quite acceptable and expressed doubt about the credibility of the American Psychiatric Association's contradictory opinions. Justice White, writing for the majority, described the American Psychiatric Association as trying to "disinvent the wheel." This ruling was given despite the fact that Appelbaum's views, which were carefully spelled out in the brief, had accurately summarized the professional consensus about predicting future violent behavior.

Perhaps in recognition of this and other similar examples of what is thought to be judicial ignorance about scientific truth, Appelbaum has proposed that the Supreme Court avail itself of a scientific consultant.[32] The legal complications of allowing such an influential scientific insider to advise the court "ex parte" and "in camera" are monumental. The proposal runs contrary to the established norms and traditions of judicial decision-making under our adversarial system of justice. Moreover, Appelbaum's conviction that the Court needs an adviser on the subject demonstrates how arcane and complicated he, himself, believes any scientific criterion of truthfulness can be. That complexity would also be problematic for every other tribunal called on to decide whether an expert's professional opinions were ethical or not. Like Kant's categorical imperative, Appelbaum's criterion of truthfulness is convincing in theory but difficult to apply in practice.

Fully aware of these criticisms, Appelbaum has proposed a definition of truth for ethical purposes that he believes can be applied by the psychiatric profession to expert testimony. Again, although no names are mentioned by him, this formulation also seems to have been inspired by the example of Dr. Grigson, who in *Barefoot* testified in response to hypothetical questions and expressed certainty about his answers without ever having examined the defendant.

Defining Truth in Forensic Psychiatry: Subjective Truth

Appelbaum's definition of truth has a subjective and an objective component. The subjective side of truth is the expert witness's genuine belief in his testimony. It also entails the psychiatrist gathering the maximum possible amount of relevant data in order to be able to have such a genuine belief. I known no reason why Appelbaum would doubt that Dr. Grigson genuinely believed in his testimony. But Grigson had made no attempt to gather his own clinical data. If he had tried to conduct a thorough psychiatric examination, he would have been legally required to warn the defendant, Barefoot, that he was evaluating him for the prosecution in its efforts to secure a death penalty.[33] Instead of pursuing this uncertain course, Grigson answered hypothetical questions put to him by the prosecutor at the sentencing phase of the trial. This alternative strategy, which according to the Supreme Court violates no legal norms, was apparently urged on Grigson by the prosecutor.

Appelbaum may or may not be correct in assuming that Grigson can be faulted ethically for not obtaining the maximum possible information under these circumstances. However, in light of the double agent arguments made in this paper, it may have been more ethical for Dr. Grigson to answer hypothetical questions rather than to provide the necessary warning and then present himself empathetically to Mr. Barefoot and perhaps win his confidence as I had done with the Black sergeant.

Objective Truth

The objective component of Appelbaum's approach to truth requires an "acknowledgement" of limitation. When the expert presents a minority opinion, he has an ethical obligation to justify his deviation from the consensus. Presumably, in obedience to this obligation, Grigson should have informed the fact finder that most psychiatrists believe it is impossible to make the kind of predictions he was making.

Gerald Klerman[34] made similar arguments about ethical standards of care in psychiatric treatment. The essence of both their proposals is to move the psychiatric profession toward authoritative "consensus" and away from divergent schools of thought. Klerman and Appelbaum are both prepared to use emerging "scientific" research to control what is and is not ethical. As a recent paper by Grisso and Appelbaum demonstrates, this approach means that it becomes necessary to make periodic adjustments in our ethical standards in keeping with the changing scientific consensus.[35] Similar "consensus" standards are of course being hammered out in the arena of "Managed Care." These problems have been much discussed elsewhere.[36] It is sufficient for present purposes to indicate that Appelbaum's definition of objective truth is part of the growing trend in the medical profession toward "truth by consensus." There is danger, in my opinion, that such authoritative truth will be indistinguishable from authoritarian truth.

It is important to recognize that our legal system has its own traditional approach to these matters as enshrined in the Law of Evidence. Since divergent expert testimony is often critical for litigation, trial lawyers in particular would be hostile to any systematic effort by the medical profession to exercise quality control over expert testimony in the name of either science or ethics.

The incorporation of professional and scientific norms into the legal standard for admitting expert testimony in epidemiological matters is currently a matter of intense interest in the federal courts. The case of *Daubert v. Merrell Dow*[37] concerns the admissibility of the expert testimony of a plaintiff's witness. The expert was prepared to submit his own non-peer reviewed and unpublished meta-analysis of several studies. The meta-analysis contradicted the findings of the peer-reviewed and published studies.

The Good Clinician and the Truthful Expert

Appelbaum argues that his truth standard converges with the standard of "good clinical practice." The latter standard is based on the premise that whatever is good clinical practice in the office is the basis for good expert testimony in the court. He believes that I have failed to demonstrate any inadequacies in the good clinical practice standard or truth standard as a basis for ethical practice in forensic psychiatry.

It is worth noting that Dr. Andrew Watson, the principal defender of the good clinical practice standard, disagreed with Appelbaum's belief that the prediction of future dangerousness in court would be unethical. Dr. Watson argued that psychiatrists all make and act upon predictions of dangerousness in their offices and therefore should have no compunction about making such predictions in the courtroom.[38] He was therefore in less than total agreement with the criticisms of Dr. Grigson. It should also be noted that the scientific literature on prediction has also taken a discernible shift away from the extreme agnosticism reflected in the American Psychiatric Association brief in *Barefoot*. Appelbaum has, himself, concluded that subsequent research indicates that predictions of future dangerousness might be ethical in some circumstances but not in the Barefoot situation.[39] The quality of research dealing with prediction of future dangerousness is less than an exacting methodology would demand. Attempts to draw scientific conclusions from that research are therefore fraught with difficulty. The subsequent attempt to use those shaky conclusions as the basis for fine tuning the ethics of psychiatry is a fortiori unlikely to have lasting value.

Putting this matter aside, I believe that Applebaum is able to reach his conclusion about the utility of the truth standard only because he deals inadequately with the double-agent dilemma and discounts all of the epistemological problems inherent in the discipline of psychiatry when it presents itself as a value-free science. These problems are certainly not solved in the therapeutic context but they can at least be excused because our intentions are beneficent and non-maleficent. Paternalistic physicians in their ignorance have caused great iatrogenic harm.[40] The moral significance of this harm is mitigated only because we thought that we were doing our best to help our patients. The same mitigation is not available when we cause harm outside the therapeutic sphere in the name of scientific truth and in the service of justice. Appelbaum either ignores these arguments or finds them unpersuasive.

However, he readily acknowledges that I am correct in arguing that neither his truth standard nor the good clinical practice standard provides "true answers" to the "legal and moral questions posed by the law."[41] He explicitly agrees that psychiatrists should not be making moral judgments. But, he believes that this means only that an expert should not respond to ultimate legal questions such as, is this man legally insane? If one thinks, as I do, that many matters in psychiatry, including diagnosis, involve both unrecognized value judgments and moral assumptions, then the problem of making moral judgments arises well before we answer the law's ultimate questions.[42] For example, the sergeant's diagnosis of kleptomania with its determinist theory of uncontrollable impulses involved all of the the moral judgments contained in any answer to the ultimate question. Similarly, if less obviously, the absence of a diagnosis about the effects of life-long subjugation in a racist society is in itself a moral judgment.

Social Perceptions About the Physician's Ethics

Even if Appelbaum is correct in his thesis about a different ethical standard for the legal context, I think that public and even professional perceptions fail to recognize the distinction as one that makes a difference. For example, I see in the American Psychiatric Association's ethical sanctioning of Dr. Grigson, and in the media's bestowing upon him the epithet "Dr. Death," more than a response to his perceived violation of the principle of truthfulness. I believe that the outpouring of criticism stems from the fact that Grigson, a physician, was successfully helping the prosecution send individuals to their deaths. Had Grigson been stretching scientific truth on behalf of clemency for defendants in capital punishment cases, I do not believe that any professional censure would have ensued.

There have been many notorious instances since Grigson's testimony in *Barefoot* in which forensic psychiatrists have given outrageous expert testimony on behalf of defendants and have not been ethically sanctioned. The singling out of Dr. Grigson for ethical sanctions can only be explained by something other than his alleged violation of the truthfulness criterion. It is reasonable to assume that professional and lay observers alike believe that Dr. Grigson was still meant to be wearing the medical mantle of beneficence and nonmaleficence in the courtroom. Such a belief may demonstrate no more than that these social perceptions of the role of the physician and the physician's ethical obligations are incorrect and need to be changed, as Appelbaum's scheme requires. But, right or wrong, these social perceptions would have important professional consequences if forensic psychiatrists were to adopt Appelbaum's approach.

Forensic Psychiatry's Negative Public Image

Appelbaum's standard of objective truth would require each expert witness to acknowledge the limitations of his or her testimony. Clearly the profession has never had a reputation for adhering to such a standard.[43] Over the years, forensic psychiatrists who take extreme positions and claim to be medically certain of their opinions have commanded the highest fees and enjoyed the greatest demand for their services among the trial lawyers who retain them. One veteran attorney summed up his experience as follows, "You don't need to pay that much money to get honest opinions." Equally troubling, it is also commonplace for highly principled non-forensic psychiatrists to lose their clinical balance in the courtroom and become partisan advocates of highly tenuous clinical or scientific opinions. Too often they testify because they have their own axe to grind, e.g., to obtain the court's imprimatur of their own self interest.

Although most experienced forensic psychiatrists pride themselves on avoiding the temptations of dishonesty on one side and the partisanship of inexperienced forensic experts who have some personal axe to grind on the other side, they do not always succeed. Even the impressive expert testimony that was provided in the trial of John Hinckley was far from Appelbaum's standard of modesty as incorporated into the objective dimension of truth.[44]

I am not alone in these observations. Most forensic psychiatrists and most trial lawyers acknowledge the widespread problem of forensic psychiatrists as "hired liars."[45] To the extent that Appelbaum's standard of truth requires the expert to be modest in his claim, it seems to have been honored only in the breach. Indeed it was this apparent lack of truthfulness, and not my concern about harm, that prompted my remark that psychiatrists do not even know the boundaries of the ethical debate when they enter the courtroom. Appelbaum clearly recognizes the problem and has been a leading proponent of peer review of forensic testimony. It remains to be seen whether that approach can be effective and what the legal system's response to such oversight would be. But, if any remedy is to be effective, it is important to understand why "the slide into ethical chaos" of untruthfulness happens so frequently.

There is much empirical evidence demonstrating that the socio-psychological context is at least as important to ethical behavior as is a person's character or ethical principles.[46] When physicians are treating patients, the human realities of that socio-psychological context usually help to reinforce the dialectic of beneficence and nonmaleficence. Although ethical abuses certainly occur, there is a synergy between being a good doctor and being ethical in clinical settings. Turn the physician into a scientific researcher with a different agenda and the socio-psychological context differs. The reinforcement of beneficence and non-maleficence weakens accordingly and patients have been systematically exploited to further scientific goals.[47] The scientific community has painfully learned this lesson and consequently now requires higher ethical standards and external review processes to insure ethical behavior toward patient/subjects during clinical research.

Now consider the physician in a legal setting being led or attacked by zealous advocates, each seeking to manipulate the expert to his own ends. Here the expert's economic and narcissistic self-interest may reinforce the tendency to take extreme positions. The norm of consensus that prevails in the clinical conference room vanishes on the witness stand. If there is any sense of clinical accountability to a patient it usually pushes even further in the extreme direction reinforcing the expert's sense of being on the "side of the angels."

Certainly the courtroom context and the adversarial system routinely induce psychiatrists and other expert witnesses to violate the principle of truth. The ethics of beneficence and non-maleficence may well contribute to the mischief. Whether it is because they themselves want to be helpful witnesses or to beat the lawyers at their own game, or because they have brought their own private agenda to the courtroom,[48] psychiatrists all too frequently fail Appelbaum's test and claim to possess more objective certainty and subjective conviction than they could possibly justify in a clinical context. This writer is certainly not alone in concluding that these powerful incentives induce many psychiatrists to behave in the courtroom as if they had no sense of ethical boundaries. The occupational disease of forensic psychiatry is the tendency to become a zealous and partisan advocate rather than to remain an impartial expert. The search for truth may be the most important goal of justice, but after-the-fact peer review applying Appelbaum's standard of truth seems unlikely to remedy these intense contextual pressures.

Reprising the Double Agent Problem

The foregoing interchange with Appelbaum has led me, as noted above, to believe that forensic psychiatrists should as a first principle eschew any overlap between their clinical and evaluative functions. I would therefore propose that forensic psychiatrists have an ethical duty to excuse themselves from testifying whenever an evaluation for a criminal tribunal has turned into a therapeutic encounter. The fact that the evaluee has been warned, as required by law, is not sufficient to satisfy the ethical requirement. Although the parable of the Black sergeant emphasizes harm, the ethical duty should apply whether or not the resulting testimony would benefit or harm the evaluee.

This more radical rule is particularly necessary for psychiatrists in the criminal justice context because many of the conceptual and epistemological problems of psychiatry cause ethical difficulty only when we move from the therapeutic encounter to the passing of the legal/moral judgments of the criminal courts. A radical rule is also justified by Appelbaum's own advocacy of different ethics for different settings. Finally, a radical rule might help to limit the countertransference pressures that lead experts to stretch the truth. This radical rule, unlike the attempt to fine tune professional ethics, is a return to and reemphasis of the Hippocratic tradition, specifically its dictate, "In every house where I come I will enter only for the good of my patients. . . . All that may come into my knowledge in the exercise of my profession or outside of my profession in daily commerce with men, which ought not to be spread abroad, I will keep secret and will never reveal."[49] In what follows I shall attempt to demonstrate how such a "traditional" approach, that would alter forensic practice as well as forensic ethics, might help to alleviate some of the ethical problems associated with capital punishment.

Capital Punishment and Psychiatric Ethics

A number of difficult ethical problems have surfaced as a result of new developments in the law of capital punishment. Dr. Grigson's questionable testimony was in fact an example of one such legal development. Much has been written about this new statutory and constitutional law and no attempt can be made here to summarize that literature. Stated in an oversimplified way, there have been two major strands in legal-moral objections to capital punishment in the United States. One strand of objections is premised on the idea that execution has become cruel and unusual punishment in contemporary society. The second major strand argues that although capital punishment is in theory acceptable, in our racist society the death sentence is in practice dispensed in a discriminatory fashion and therefore should be abolished.

Many physicians are morally opposed to capital punishment on these or other grounds. Although Dr. Joseph Guillotine might be considered a noteworthy counter-example, physicians have traditionally avoided assisting the state in the performance of executions. Even though a physician-assisted execution might be less painful for the victim, the ethical principle that has come down to us bars such participation. When states adopted lethal injection as the legally prescribed form of execution, the medical profession had little difficulty concluding that it would be unethical for a physician to administer the injection.[50]

The professional objectives behind this ethical principle have not been precisely articulated, but presumably physicians are convinced that they outweigh any countervailing obligation to serve justice or to ease the suffering. In short, the medical profession has decided that the executioner should not be a "man in a white coat."[51]

There are, however, a variety of other legal functions provided by psychiatrists that arguably facilitate the imposition of capital punishment. These include evaluating and restoring competence to be executed. Those issues have produced a great deal of interesting commentary.[52] Psychiatrists who are morally opposed to capital punishment would prefer to limit the profession's involvement in such activities. But most of the recent arguments against such involvement, like those made against Dr. Grigson, have been made on other narrower and supposedly independent ethical and scientific grounds.[53]

The moral condemnation of Dr. Grigson and of other such involvements by abolitionists is more comprehensible than the supposedly neutral professional criticisms. However, neither of these types of criticism is at the center of my own concerns about psychiatry's role in capital punishment. My concerns are centered on the previously mentioned moral and conceptual ambiguity of our supposed medical science. The decision to impose the sentence of execution is an awesome human responsibility. The retributive taking of a life in the name of justice forces the law-givers to reexamine the very concept of justice. Judges and juries should not be led to believe that the discipline of psychiatry has a scientific shoulder on which their terrible burden of decision can rest. I would, therefore, urge psychiatrists, on the grounds of humility if not truth, to inform courts that we have no professional or scientific basis for participating in a capital sentencing hearing. However, as my debate with Appelbaum indicates, I have been unable to convince my colleagues that our epistemological problems create an unbridgeable abyss in the criminal courtroom.

Without some such radical measure, the efforts of psychiatrists to decide what can and cannot be done ethically in the capital punishment area continue to be fraught with difficulty. The bright line between our therapeutic and forensic roles may help us resolve one of the intraprofessional disputes that has arisen in connection with capital punishment. The dispute centers around the psychiatrist's participation in the restoration of competency to be executed by the administration of antipsychotic medication. Leaders of the psychiatric establishment pushed for severe restrictions on the psychiatrist's involvement in restoration of competency to be executed. Their reasoning was based on a complicated extrapolation from the traditional "Do No Harm" ethical grounds prohibiting professional involvement in execution.[54]

Quite unexpectedly, African American psychiatrists within the American Psychiatric Association took a contradictory stance. These minority psychiatrists were "morally" concerned about an ethical rule which even if technically correct might result in the therapeutic neglect of death row inmates. Whatever the establishment's justification for such an ethical rule, for them it came too close to self righteously validating the widespread medical neglect of prisoners among whom African Americans are overrepresented.[55]

The debate quickly went in many other directions. As summarized by Heilbrun et al.,[56] some took the view that once a condemned prisoner became incompetent to be executed, he or she should be given clemency. Others deployed arguments in favor of attempts to restore competency in every case. Finally, there was an intermediate group opposed to absolute rules. The debate proceeded on moral, ethical, and legal grounds and stimulated important discussion about the role of psychiatry in the criminal justice system.

Recently the Supreme Court of Louisiana, in *Louisiana v. Perry*,[57] decided some of the legal questions relevant to this ethical/moral dispute. The Perry Court rejected the so-called "medicate to execute" scheme on state constitutional grounds. The court's discussion of the relevant ethical issues followed the line of analysis set out by the psychiatric establishment's extrapolation from the principle of "Do No Harm" and other recent commentary taking a similar view.[58] The majority thought that the psychiatrist, as an agent of the prosecutorial arm of the state, would, by medicating Perry, become directly involved in preparing the condemned insane prisoner for execution in violation of medical ethics. Thus, according to the court, once medicated, Perry could never be executed. However, if Perry were to recover his sanity without such medication the Court indicated that he might be executed. Although the decision points in the direction staked out by the advocates of clemency, it does not reach that conclusion in all cases.

Unfortunately, the facts of the Perry case did not require the court to resolve the more complicated ethical issues that are of importance to psychiatrists. Perry's treatment had been ordered by a court for legal purposes, i.e., to restore and maintain his competency to be executed. Furthermore, the Louisiana Supreme Court assumed that the medication ordered by the judge was given over Perry's objection and without an independent medical judgment about the appropriateness of the treatment. The Louisiana Supreme Court did not reach the question of what would be the fate of a patient/prisoner like Perry where treatment was instituted on the initiative of psychiatrists because it was deemed medically necessary.

As the ethical dispute demonstrates, many psychiatrists would be deterred from attempting to treat any patient with medication or by any other means if they believed it would lead directly to execution.[59] But, as the African American psychiatrists pointed out, it is also troubling to withhold medically necessary treatment from a psychotically deteriorating patient.

The facts of the Perry case have led commentators to analyze the problem from a particular perspective, which seems to make the ethical issues more insoluble. They imagine court-ordered treatment of a patient with antipsychotic medication. The hypothetical patient achieves a social recovery and is marched off to execution. This scenario imagines the psychiatrist being told what to do by a judge. But, judges do not have a license to practice medicine and no psychiatrist should allow a lay person to order her or him to give a particular treatment. Once the psychiatrist is free of legal coercion the ethical problems are easier to resolve.

The following ethical principles, which are based on suggestions by others[60] as well as on this paper's attempt to separate the domain of treatment from the forensic realm, might then help us find a way through this supposed dilemma. (a) No psychiatrist *treating* a prisoner should provide forensic reports to a court for either the defense or the prosection; (b) no psychiatrist should administer medication or any other treatment to a prisoner solely pursuant to a court order; (c) psychiatrists should provide medically necessary antipsychotic medications to an incompetent prisoner/patient who is under an order of execution only if the court grants a stay of execution sufficient to complete a medically appropriate course of treatment; and (d) during the course of such treatment the psychiatrist must attempt to explain to the patient the medical and non-medical ramifications of accepting treatment—in the case of the death row inmate the consequences of competency being execution. The course of medically appropriate treatment would not be considered complete until the patient is capable of making an informed medical decision about accepting or rejecting medication. By following such guidelines, the treating psychiatrist will build a "Chinese Wall" against judicial incursions. Such an approach would ensure both professional autonomy and will prevent psychiatrist's treatment relationships from being exploited by the interests of the prosecutorial arm of the state.

This solution is not entirely satisfactory. For the psychiatrist who a priori opposes the death penalty, it may not go far enough. Furthermore, there are those who would argue that by requiring the prisoner/patient to choose between endless psychosis and the death penalty, the psychiatrist is still in an ethical quandary. But informed consent, on which this approach depends, always requires that a patient assess the advantages and drawbacks of choosing a particular treatment—in this instance, the consequence of successful treatment is execution.

Such guidelines do not guarantee that all death row inmates who become incompetent to be executed will, with absolute certainty, avoid execution. But they do guarantee both the autonomy of the patient and the professional autonomy necessary to make medical treatment decisions. These ethical proposals, if followed by psychiatrists and respected by the courts, should lead to more opportunity for the psychiatrist to offer medical care unencumbered by drastic legal consequences while the prisoner retains his or her right to accept or reject such care.

Some patients who have been restored to competency through medication may remain competent even if they then exercise their choice to refuse treatment. The psychiatrist-initiated treatment of such prisoners might therefore result in their execution. According to the reasoning here, that result may not be unethical. Such a result may, however, raise State constitutional questions if *Perry v. Louisiana* is followed as a precedent in other jurisdictions.

The Victim Impact Statement

Another ethically troubling situation in capital punishment has arisen out of the Supreme Court's reversal of its prior case law to allow victim impact statements to be introduced at the sentencing phase of trial. In *Payne v. Tennessee*,[61] the court held in a 6-3 decision that the Eighth Amendment's prohibition against cruel or unusual punishments did not act as a per se bar to the admission of victim impact statements during the sentencing phase of trial.

In the wake of *Payne v. Tennessee*, psychiatrists have a potentially substantial role to play in capital sentencing.[62] The victim impact statement is tailor-made for psychiatry's diagnosis of Post-Traumatic Stress Disorder.[63] Every murder victim's family meets the trauma criterion for Post-Traumatic Stress Disorder and most are said to suffer from the condition.[64]

A psychiatrist's testimony or deposition will give scientific weight to the prosecution's argument that the evil deed is worthy of capital punishment. Although this situation fills me with moral trepidation, I recognize that most forensic psychiatrists will have no ethical objections to participating in capital punishment in this manner. Furthermore, unlike the prediction of dangerousness, the psychiatric profession has demonstrated no scientific discomfort with the diagnosis of Post-Traumatic Stress Disorder. Thus, there will be no ethical prohibition against providing such "truthful" testimony which "helps" the victim but "harms" the victimizer. Nonetheless, the approach described in this paper may at least have the minimal value of clarifying the transference/countertransference issues that can complicate expert testimony.

The Ethical Problem of the Victim Impact Statement

Recently I received a letter from a psychiatrist who wanted my advice on this very issue. He was treating a woman whose husband was murdered during an armed robbery. The woman believed that participating in a victim impact statement would help her work through the trauma and have other personal benefits. She wanted her psychiatrist's help and testimony. He had no doubt that his patient suffered from Post-Traumatic Stress Disorder but he wanted to know from me if there were any ethical principles that should keep him from participating in the legal process.

Appelbaum would presumably reason in such a case that neither my conceptual concerns, nor beneficence and nonmaleficence principles, nor the principle of truthfulness would bar this psychiatrist's participation in the legal process. Nonetheless, he and I might agree to the principle that psychiatrists should not intermingle their different roles in the different contexts. I would, therefore, urge the psychiatrist to tactfully inform his patient that, because he was treating her, his professional ethics made it necessary to refer her to a forensic psychiatrist who could do an independent objective evaluation and testify on her behalf.

None of the rules or guidelines proposed here will fully resolve the ethical problems that confound forensic psychiatrists. Nor is any claim intended that these proposals are new or rest on some new foundation. Quite the contrary, they reemphasize our ethical traditions. I believe that this reassertion of our traditional approach may help us to distinguish our therapeutic and forensic roles and, thereby, benefit our patients and our profession. The suggestions made here are expressly directed at the role of the forensic psychiatrist in the criminal courts. It is my impression that the intermingling of the roles of expert and therapist in other legal contexts requires separate consideration but might lead to similar conclusions.***

***A discerning reader has asked how such ethical guidelines might be enforced. Professionals charged with the enforcement of ethical principles have long recognized that there is a general problem. Ethical principles often embrace aspirations of the profession and are not formulated as statutes to be enforced. At a more conceptual level it is possible, following Lon L. Fuller (The Morality of Law 1964) to identify two different ethical standards that an individual should follow. The first marks the threshold of competence; what, if all else fails, we must (are under a duty to) do. This, Fuller termed a 'morality of duty.' However, beyond this threshold, there are a range of acts promoting beneficial outcomes, the omission of which will

Footnotes

[1]Paul S. Appelbaum. *The Parable of the Forensic Psychiatrist: Ethics and the Problem of Doing Harm*, 137 Int'l J. L. & Psychiatry 249 (1990).

[2]Alan A. Stone. *Presidential Address: Conceptual Ambiguity and Morality in Modern Psychiatry* 137 Am. J. Psychiatry 887 (1980).

[3]Halleck, Seymour L., *Psychiatry and the Dilemmas of Crime; A Study of Causes, Punishment, and Treatment*, Berkeley: University of California Press (1971); *See also*, Seymour L. Halleck, *Law in the Practice of Psychiatry: a Handbook for Clinicians*, New York: Plenum Medical Book Company (1980).

[4]Id.

[5]*See, e.g.*, M. J. Goldman, *Kleptomania: Making Sense of the Nonsensical*, 8 Am. J. Psychiatry 986 (1991).

[6]R. Spitzer et al., *DSM-III-R Casebook: A Learning Companion to the Diagnostic and Statistical Manual of Mental disorders* (3rd ed. rev. 1989).

[7]Alan A. Stone *The Ethical Boundaries of Forensic Psychiatry: A View from the Ivory Tower*, 12 Bull. Am. Acad. Psychiatry & L. 209 (1984).

[8]Jonas R. Rappeport. *Editorial: Is Forensic Psychiatry Ethical*, 12 Bull. Am. Acad. Psychiatry & L. 205 (1984); Andrew S. Watson, *Response from a Straw Man*, 12 Bull. Am. Acad. Psychiatry & L. 221 (1984); Herbert C. Modlin. *The Ivory Tower and the Marketplace*, 12 Bull. Am. Acad. Psychiatry & L. 233 (1984); Robert L. Sadoff, *Practical Ethical Problems of the Forensic Psychiatrist in Dealing with Attorneys*, 12 Bull. Am. Acad. Psychiatry & L. 243 (1984); Barbara A. Weiner, *Ethical issues in Forensic Psychiatry: From an Attorney's Perspective*, 12 Bull. Am. Acad. Psychiatry & L. 253 (1984); J. Richard Ciccone and Colleen D. Clements, *The Ethical Practice of Forensic Psychiatry: A View From the Trenches*, 12 Bull. Am. Acad. Psychiatry & L. 263 (1984): Seymour L. Halleck, *The Ethical Dilemmas of Forensic Psychiatry: A Utilitarian Approach*, 12 Bull. Am. Acad. Psychiatry & L. 279 (1984).

[9]Paul S. Appelbaum, *Psychiatric Ethics in the Courtroom*, 12 Bull. Am. Acad. Psychiatry & L 225 (1984).

[10]Appelbaum, *supra* note 1.

[11]This dictate comes from the Hippocratic Oath. *Dorland's Illustrated Medical Dictionary* 767–768 (27th ed., 1988).

[12]Alan A. Stone, *The Ethics of Forensic Psychiatry: A View from the Ivory Tower*, in *Law Psychiatry and Morality*, 57–75, 7 (1984).

[13]Id.

[14]Appelbaum, *supra* note 1 at 255.

[15]Id. at 251.

[16]Id. at 258.

[17]*See, e.g.*, Simon Yeznig Balian, *Personal Responsibility for Professional Actions* 32 Cath. Law. 337 (1988).

[18]*See, e.g.*, Gunther Teubner, *Autopoiesis in Law and Society: A Rejoinder to Blankenburg* 18 Law and Society Review 291 (1984).

[19]*See* Footnote 27.

[20]Aristotle, *Nicomachean Ethics* VI, 5: 1140b6–8.

---

not result in sanction, but the commission of which will result in more or less praise. While we do not see fit to punish the omission of these acts, we do recognize that they act as a guide for appropriate action to which we should all aspire; Fuller terms this standard the 'morality of aspiration' (ibid.). Some professional ethical standards are much more readily expressed as aspirational standards than ones imposing a direct duty. One example is §2 of the Principles of Medical Ethics of the American Medical Association: "Physicians should strive continually to improve medical knowledge and skill . . . " However, the difference between the two standards of aspiration and duty, Fuller points out, is not qualitative, but quantitative; it is a matter of where on the scale of morality the act in question is placed that determines which sanction is appropriate, in much the same way as the maker of a test determines what is to count as an unacceptable and, therefore, failing mark, what is a pass, and what is a distinction. To set a standard which requires that once an examination has passed from the realms of evaluation into those of a therapeutic encounter, the physician should refrain from testifying against the patient, is thus simply to determine that although failing to do so is not criminal, it is unethical. This may require some precise criteria determining when 'the therapeutic' begins, or rely on professional judgment in scrutinizing such criteria, but so do most professional negligence requirements. It is certainly no more difficult a standard than that which requires us to "improve medical knowledge and skill." And any difficulties in policing this standard may be eased by the fact that it is anticipation of the move from the therapeutic to the forensic – from one "ethic" to another – that would count as a criterion triggering consideration of the standard in the first place.

[21]Aquinas, *Summa Theologiae* II-II, q 47, aa. 1-7. For Aquinas, knowledge of how to act in a given situation depends upon rationally discovering the correct general principles and rules of action – these apply universally – and then learning to apply them correctly in concrete situations.

[22]Kant *Foundations of the Metaphysics of Morals* 47 (1959). Kant tests the validity of every action by inquiring whether the reason (or "maxim") for action can be conceived and willed without contradiction as universal law. This is one of his versions of the "categorical imperative."

[23]*See* text at foot note 25.

[24]J. L. Austin, *How to do Things With Words* 10, Cambridge, MA: Harvard University Press (2nd ed. 1975).

[25]Appelbaum, *supra* note 1 at 251–252.

[26]Douglas Mossman, *Assessing and Restoring Competency to Be Executed: Should Psychiatrists Participate*, 5 Behav. Sci. & L. 397 (1987).

[27]*See, e.g.*, T. Beauchamp & J. Childress, *Principles of Biomedical Ethics* 25–66 (1989).

[28]Stone, *supra* note 12 at 69–71.

[29]*Barefoot v. Estelle*, 463 U.S. 880 (1983). *See also* Gerald T. Bennett and Arthur F. Sullwold, *Qualifying the Psychiatrist as a Lay Witness: a Reaction to the American Psychiatric Association Petition in Barefoot V. Estelle* 30, Journal of Forensic Sciences 462 (1985).

[30]Brief for American Psychiatric Association as *Amicus Curriae*, in *Barefoot v. Estelle*, 463 U.S. 880 (1983); *See also* American Psychiatric Association, *The Principles of Medical Ethics: With Annotations Especially Applicable to Psychiatry* 10–17 at § 1, Annot. 4 (rev. ed. 1989).

[31]Stone, *supra* note 12 at 70.

[32]Paul S. Appelbaum, *The Empirical Jurisprudence of the United States Supreme Court* (Justice Henry A. Blackmun: *The Supreme Court and the Limits of Medical Privacy*) 13 Am. J. L. & Med. 335 (1987).

[33]Stone, *supra* note 12 at 69–71.

[34]Gerald L. Klerman, *The Psychiatric Patient's Right to Effective Treatment: Implications of Osheroff v. Chestnut Lodge*, 147 Am. J. Psychiatry 409 (1990).

[35]Thomas Grisso & Paul Appelbaum, *Is it Unethical to Offer Predictions of Future Violence?* 16 L. & Hum. Behav. 621 (1992).

[36]M. Goodman *et al.*, *Managing Managed Care* (1992).

[37]In *Daubert v. Merril Dow Pharmaceuticals*, 61 U.S.L.W. 4805 Decided on June 28, 1993, the Supreme Court held that "general acceptance is not a necessary precondition to the admissibility of scientific evidence under the Federal Rules of Evidence, but the Rules of Evidence – especially Rule 702 – do assign to the trial judge the task of ensuring that an expert's testimony both rests on a reliable foundation and is relevant to the task at hand. Pertinent evidence based on scientifically valid principles will satisfy those demands."

[38]Watson, *supra* note 8.

[39]Grisso & Appelbaum, *supra* note 28.

[40]Elliot S. Valenstein, *Great and Desperate Cures: The Rise and Decline of Psychosurgery and other Radical Treatments for Mental Illness*, New York: Basic Books (1986).

[41]Appelbaum, *supra* note 9 at 228.

[42]*See* Alan A. Stone, *The Trial of John Hinckley*, in *Law Psychiatry and Morality*, 77–98 (1984).

[43]Id.

[44]Id.

[45]S. J. Morse, *Reforming Expert Testimony*, 6 L. & Hum. Behav. 39 (1982); D. Faust & J. Ziskin, *The Expert Witness in Psychology and Psychiatry*, 241 Sci. 31 (1988).

[46]*See, e.g.*, Philip G. Zimbardo & Michael R. Leippe, *The Psychology of Attitude Change and Social Influence* (1991); Lawrence Kohlberg, Charles Levine, & Alexangra Hewer, *Moral Stages: A Current Formulation and a Response to Critics* (1983); David Rosenhan, *Moral Character*, 27 Stan. L. Rev 925 (1975); David Rosenhan, *On Being Sane in Insane Places*, 179 Science 250 (1973).

[47]Jay Katz, *Experimentation with Human Beings: The Authority of the Investigator, Subject, Professions, and State in the Human Experimentation Process*, New York: Russell Sage Foundation (1972).

[48]Alan A. Stone, *Law, Science, and Psychiatric Malpractice: A Response to Klerman's Indictment of Psychoanalytic Psychiatry*, 147 Am. J. Psychiatry 419 (1990).

[49]*See* the Hoppocatic Oath, *supra* note 11.

[50]Curran and Cascells, *The Ethics of Medical Participation in Capital Punishment by Intravenous Injection*, 302 New Eng. J. Med. 226, 227 (1980) (*quoting from Ethics in Medicine: Historical Perspectives and Contemporary Concerns* 5 (S. Reiser, A. Dyke, & W. Curran eds., 1977).

[51]Council of Ethics and Judicial Affairs, American Medical Association, Current Opinions § 2.06 (1986). The APA has interpreted this opinion as a prohibition against psychiatrists participation in such proceedings. *See* David L. Katz, *Perry v. Louisiana: Medical Ethics on Death Row—Is Judicial Intervention Warranted?* 4 Geo. J. Legal Ethics 707, 714n.65 (1991) (*citing* Brief for American Psychiatric Association and American Medical Association as *Amici Curiae* at 17).

[52]*See, e.g.*, Richard J. Bonnie, *Dilemmas in Administering the Death Penalty*, 14L. & Hum. Behav. 67 (1990); Katz, *supra* note 44; Mossman, *supra* note 19.

[53]K. Heilbrun, M. Radelet, & J. Dvoskin, *The Debate on Treating Individuals Incompetent for Execution*, 149 Am. J. Psychiatry 596 (1992).

[54]*See* Katz, *supra* note 44 at 714.

[55]Personal communications with the APA committee of Black Psychiatrists.

[56]Heilbrun *et al.*, *supra* note 46 at 598.

[57]*Louisiana v. Perry*, No. 91-KP-1324, 1992 LEXIS 3170 (La. Oct. 19, 1992).

[58]Katz, *supra* note 44; G. Linn Evans, *Perry v. Louisiana: Can a State Treat an Incompetent Prisoner to Ready Him for Execution?* 19 Bull. Am Acad. Psychiatry & L. 249 (1991; Michael L. Radelet & George W. Barnard, *Treating Those Found Incompetent for Execution: Ethical Chaos With Only One Solution*, 16 Bull. Am. Acad. Psychiatry & L. 297 (1988); Charles Patrick Ewing, *Diagnosing and Treating Insanity on Death Row: Legal and Ethical Perspectives*, 5 Behav. Sci. & L. 175 (1987); Rochelle Graff Salguero, *Medical Ethics and Competency to be Executed*, 96 Yale L. J. 167 (1986).

[59]Heilbrun *et al.*, *supra* note 45.

[60]*See supra* note 51. *See also* Heilbrun, *supra* note 45; Mossman *supra* note 19; Bonnie *supra* note 44; Stanley L. Brodsky, *Professional Ethics and Professional Morality in the Assessment of Competence for Execution: A Response to Bonnie*, 14 L. & Human Behav. 91 (1990); Michael L. Gadelet and George Barnard, *Ethics and the Psychiatric Determination of Competency to be Executed*, 14 Bull. Am. Acad. Psychiatry & L. 37 (1986).

[61]*Payne v. Tennessee*, 111 S. Ct. 449 (1990).

[62]Alan A. Stone, *Report on the Supreme Court Decision in Payne V. Tennessee*, 16 Am. Acad. Psychiatry & L. Newsletter 79 (1991).

[63]Alan A. Stone, *Post-traumatic Stress Disorder and the Law: Critical Review of the New Frontier*, 21 Bull. Am. Acad. Psychiatry & L. (April 1993).

[64]Arthur J. Lurgio, Wesley G. Skogan, & Robert C. Davis, (eds) *Victims of Crime: Problems, Policies, and Programs*, Newbury Park, CA: Sage Publications (1990).

[25]

ARTICLES

The role of psychiatric evidence in passing 'longer than normal' sentences

BOHDAN SOLOMKA

ABSTRACT Under s.2(2)b of the Criminal Justice Act 1991 crown courts have the power to give violent and sexual offenders custodial sentences longer than would be justified by the seriousness of the offence if this is necessary to protect the public from serious harm. In this study, the first 35 Appeal Court hearings involving this power are examined. In 22 of these cases, psychiatric evidence was available, as required under statute, where the offender was, or appeared to be, mentally disordered, in order to exclude medical disposal. Sentencing guidance arising from these Appeal Court decisions has held that psychiatric opinion evidence is relevant in determining the applicability of s.2(2)b. Particularly significant, in the Appeal Court's view, are certain features of personality, untreatability and psychiatrists' opinions regarding risk of serious harm. The boundaries of admissible psychiatric opinion evidence and the possible implications for psychiatrists giving evidence at the sentencing phase are discussed.

Keywords: Criminal Justice Act 1991, medical evidence, sentencing, sexual offenders, violent offenders

The Criminal Justice Act 1991 (CJA 1991) introduced the possibility of a 'longer than normal sentence' (LTNS) for offenders convicted of violent or sexual offences. The powers under s.2(2)b of the Act allow a sentence that is longer than would be commensurate with the seriousness of the offence (Thomas, 1994a).

The Journal of Forensic Psychiatry Vol 7 No 2 September 1996 239–255

ISSN 0958-5184

Section 2(2)b states that the custodial sentence shall be 'Where the offence is a violent or sexual offence, for such longer term (not exceeding the maximum) as in the opinion of the Court is necessary to protect the public from serious harm from the offender'. Cases involving this power are now coming before the Court of Appeal, and the role of psychiatric evidence in the assessment of offending behaviour, dangerousness and treatability has raised some ethical issues which are reviewed in this survey. The objective of the study was to examine the role of psychiatric reports in providing evidence towards evaluating the degree of risk to the public and the appropriateness of applying s.2(2)b. Some cases are discussed in detail to highlight areas of concern.

METHODS

Cases in which LTN sentence had been passed under s.2(2)b and which had been considered by the Court of Appeal between 13 March 1994 and 1 August 1994 were collected. The two sources included Criminal Appeal Reports (sentencing) and the unpublished transcripts of hearings, kindly provided by Dr D. A. Thomas. Court of Appeal hearing transcripts were studied in all cases. Information collected from the reports and transcripts included demographic details, offence, plea, original sentencing description, previous convictions, psychiatric report conclusion as reported in the hearing and the appeal judgment.

RESULTS

Between 13 March 1994 and 1 August 1994, 35 Court of Appeal cases were identified where a longer than normal sentence (LTNS) had been passed under the powers of s.2(2)b of the Criminal Justice Act 1991.

In 30 cases, the original sentencing judge had passed such a sentence. In 5 cases, a LTNS was imposed by the Court of Appeal after the cases had been referred by the Attorney General. In 2 of these cases the original sentence was a discretionary life sentence, and the remaining 3 were referred because the original determinate sentence was regarded as unduly lenient. The age at the time of the Appeal Court hearing was recorded in only 26 cases. The known ages ranged from 21 years to 67 years (median 37 years). Only one appellant was female. A plea of guilty was recorded in 27 cases at the original trial. Fifteen offenders were convicted of multiple charges (ranging from 2 to 8 offences). All but 7 cases had received previous convictions of violent or sexual offences.

Outcome of appeal

There were four possible outcomes of the hearing. (1) In 16 cases, the appeal was dismissed, LTNS and length of sentence remaining unchanged. (2) In 2 cases, the sentence was reduced but remained as a LTNS. (3) In 12 cases, the application of s.2(2)b was considered inappropriate; and (4) in 5 cases, as previously mentioned, an LTNS was imposed where the original sentence had been made without using the powers of s.2(2)b.

Psychiatric reports

In 22 cases (65 per cent), a psychiatric report was considered as information before the sentencing (and Appeal) court. Section 3(3)b of the CJA 1991 states that 'In forming any such opinion as is mentioned in subsection (2) of section 1–2 above a court in the case of any such opinion as is mentioned in paragraph (b) of that subsection, may take into account any information about the offender which is before it'. Psychiatric reports that were available to the sentencing judge were available to the Appeal Courts. In addition the Appeal Courts are able to commission further psychiatric reports. In 2 cases a report by a clinical psychologist was considered, both with reference to sexual offences. As the interest of this study was in statements of diagnosis, treatability and suitability for medical disposal under the Mental Health Act 1983, these psychological reports were excluded from further study. In one case, the psychologist's report was the only clinical report quoted.

Diagnosis

In 9 cases, the psychiatric report identified personality abnormalities. These ranged from descriptions of 'bizarre', 'inadequate', or 'immature' personalities, to diagnoses of personality disorder in 6 cases. In one of these cases diagnoses of chronic schizophrenia and alcohol dependency were also made. There were 8 reports which described the offender as having a disorder of sexual preference. In all these cases, the offender had been convicted of a sexual offence against children. In one case there was an additional diagnosis of generalized anxiety disorder. One case displayed signs of both personality disorder and disorder of sexual preference, together with low intelligence. One man was reported to have brain damage in addition to hypersexuality and paraphilia. There were 5 cases where the defendant was described as not suffering from any mental disorder and 1 case where drug and alcohol abuse alone was noted.

Treatability

In 7 out of 22 psychiatric reports considered, the Court of Appeal transcript gave no mention of whether treatment was likely to be of benefit. In 5 of these cases, no mental disorder had been found. In 12 cases, the psychiatric opinion stated that treatment would not benefit the offender. In cases of violent offences, the reasons included 'unsuccessful hospital treatment in the past', 'Very limited possibility that counselling would help', 'Previous drug and alcohol counselling failed'. In cases of sexual offenders, reasons included 'unwilling to accept responsibility', 'denial and minimization', 'no benefit from previous group therapy', 'refused drug treatment', 'not mentally disordered' under the meaning of the Mental Health Act 1983.

Treatment was indicated as possible in 3 cases. All of these were cases where a disorder of sexual preference had been identified, and in 2 of them treatment was taking place by the time of the Court of Appeal hearing. In 1 case, a view was expressed by clinicians that, whilst treatment directed at sexual offending would be of benefit in a community setting, such a programme would pose too great a risk of serious harm to the public. Treatment in a prison setting was not considered to be of any benefit and according to the appeal hearing transcript, not offered as an alternative. The appeal against a 5-year LTNS was not successful.

Likelihood of reoffending

In 17 of the 22 psychiatric reports an opinion regarding likelihood of re-offending was cited in the transcripts. Of these, 4 were judged not to represent a risk for reasons that included 'offence out of character', 'no suggestion that appellant would indefinitely remain a danger to the public', 'no likelihood of acquiring another family circle', 'low flash-point but otherwise no further concerns about dangerousness'. The remaining 13 cases were considered, according to psychiatric reports, to represent 'high risk of re-offending', 'a danger to women/children', 'a likelihood that behaviour will continue'.

There did not appear to be evidence of psychiatric reports as a whole being over-represented in cases where LTNS were passed at the end of the appeal process. Out of 23 cases where an LTNS was the outcome, 15 had a psychiatric opinion quoted (65.2 per cent) whilst 7 out of 12 cases where LTNS was judged not applicable had a psychiatric report taken into consideration (58.2 per cent).

DISCUSSION

There are methodological shortcomings that limit the extent to which results from this study can be generalized. First, the sample consists of Appeal Court cases which may not be representative of all cases where a LTNS was passed. Secondly, the sources of data were Appeal Court transcripts which were collected retrospectively and did not systematically record information that might have been of interest. Thirdly, original psychiatric reports were not viewed and so there is a risk that the psychiatric evidence quoted in the court transcripts would have been out of context and their meaning thereby altered. For a full study of sentencing patterns and the role of psychiatric evidence, these shortcomings would be addressed. Nevertheless, the aims of this study are to explore Appeal Court sentencing guidance and the legal framework within which psychiatric evidence is used at the sentencing phase, so from that point of view the observations may still be valid.

Under s.2(2)b crown courts have powers to pass a sentence longer than would be commensurate with the seriousness of the relevant offences. This makes a significant change in sentencing practice, freeing the sentencer from the restrictions imposed by a long series of Court of Appeal decisions holding that the dangerousness of the offender does not justify a sentence longer than the offence warrants. Stockdale and Devlin (1987) cite the cases of *Scanlon* and *Gouws* to illustrate Appeal Court decisions that did not follow the principle of proportionality, and these seem to have echoes in current preventative sentencing. In *R.* v *Scanlon* (1979) Waller, L. J. upheld a disproportionately long sentence to protect the public, seeing it as the only option when faced with an offender 'who is suffering from a disorder which cannot be conveniently treated in a local mental hospital, but does not warrant detention in special hospital'. The appellant had a history of multiple hospital admissions including a hospital order, and had previously been convicted of manslaughter of a child. In *R.* v *Gouws* (1981), Skinner, L. J. stated that although 6 years' imprisonment for simple arson was 'severe', it 'was justified on the basis of medical evidence'. The appellant had a history of disturbed behaviour since childhood, with numerous psychiatric hospital admissions (including admission to a Special Hospital), and was diagnosed at trial as suffering from 'severe psychopathic disorder which renders him incapable of coping in open society'. He was not accepted for further treatment in a secure setting and so fell to be dealt with by a custodial sentence. When faced with 'dangerous' violent and sexual offenders, the courts can now take the risk of serious harm into account when sentencing. Thomas (1994a, 1994b) has discussed many of the practical difficulties in applying this section. This discussion will concentrate on the psychiatrist's role in this process.

Criminal Justice Act 1991 and psychiatric evidence

Before passing a custodial sentence, under the Criminal Justice Act 1991 there is a statutory requirement to obtain a medical report on an offender *who is* or *appears to be* mentally disordered (s.4(1)). This medical report can be made orally or in writing, and must be prepared by a registered medical practitioner approved for the purposes of s.12(2) MHA 1983. However, if the court believes a report to be unnecessary, s.4(1) can be disregarded (s.4(2)), and a custodial sentence may still be passed; for instance, if the court already has sufficient information on the defendant's mental condition from other sources. On an appeal against sentence an offender who fulfilled s.4(1) must have a medical report prepared whether or not one was obtained by the trial court.

In 22 of the 35 cases described above, a psychiatric report was available to the court as information to take into consideration. None of these cases led to a hospital disposal. This is not surprising considering that those diagnosed as mentally disordered and treatable at the trial would be expected to have received the appropriate disposal. Following sentencing and at the time of appeal, the 22 cases represented those individuals who had received psychiatric assessment, but for whom it had been concluded that they were not suitable for a treatment under the MHA 1983.

The use of psychiatric evidence in the context of s.2(b) sentencing was considered in *R.* v *Fawcett* [1994], a 33-year-old woman who attacked an 86-year-old lady with a brick. Having pleaded guilty to wounding with intent to cause grievous bodily harm, the defendant was sentenced to 7 years' imprisonment, passed as a longer than normal sentence under the CJA 1991 s.2(2)b. A psychiatric report was taken into consideration (indeed, was heavily praised for its usefulness and detail), which pointed out that she suffered severe personality disorder, had a long history of unsuccessful hospital treatment, was unlikely to change and did not fulfil criteria that would allow a hospital order to be made. In considering the case, the Court of Appeal commented:

> The Court should consider all information about the offender, and should call for a medical report before passing sentence under section 2(2)b if the danger was due to a medical or personality problem, in order to exclude a medical disposal.

The comment continues:

> If the danger was of a recurrent nature, by offending in a particular way, the Court should identify the common strands, by hearing evidence of previous convictions and other relevant previous conduct.

In *R.* v *Utip* (1993), it was stated that a repetition of similar offending may reveal the need for a sentence under s.2(2)b CJA 1991. In this survey, 28 cases (80 per cent) had received a previous conviction of a violent or sexual offence. However, in *Fawcett*, Garland, J. commented that a history of previous convictions need not necessarily in itself be a qualifying factor, particularly where there is a mixture of minor offending and severe personality disorder or other mental abnormalities. To date, there have been 7 appeal cases where previous convictions have been of a minor nature, or where no previous convictions were recorded. In 5 of these cases, a psychiatric report was available. So whilst there is no absolute statutory requirement of a report from a psychiatrist, such a report is seen as highly desirable by the courts (Ashworth, 1992). The boundaries of psychiatric opinion evidence will be discussed in a separate section.

Gunn (1993) discusses the sometimes powerful position in which psychiatrists find themselves at the sentencing phase, and states that it is not in the role of a medical expert to recommend type or length of sentence. He quotes the Streatfield Report (Home Office, Lord Chancellor's Office, 1961) on the 'Business of the criminal courts', which states that '[a] medical report on an offender can be relevant in a number of ways to the court's consideration of a sentence'.

The Streatfield Report considered that psychiatric evidence 'can help pass a sentence designed to stop [the offender] offending again (by indicating treatment which could usefully be given whether in custody or not); it can help pass a sentence designed to protect society from him (e.g. by indicating tendencies which might be thought by the court to justify restrictive action under the Mental Health Act 1959)'. The purpose of s.4 of the 1991 Act mirrors these long-standing roles, in that it ensures that the courts acquire necessary information to allow, whenever appropriate, mentally disordered offenders to receive treatment under mental health act legislation. In this context the issue of dangerousness is linked with discussion about treatment provision and no other aspect of sentencing.

The Streatfield Report also stated that the medical expert 'can help the court to assess the defendant's culpability (by indicating facts which affect his culpability or responsibility)'. Under s.3(3)(a) aggravating circumstances and mitigating factors which affect the seriousness of the offence may be taken into account, based on any information that the court has before it (presumably previous cinvictions and professional reports). Commentators on the 1991 Act list 'mental impairment' (alongside physical impairment) as a possible mitigating factor where it resulted in the offender lacking substantial capacity for judgement at the time of the offence (Leng and Manchester, 1991). The medical report is envisaged in the CJA 1991 as providing information with regards to medical disposal and realistic mitigation. However, the evolving case-law involving the sentencing powers under s.2(2)b is establishing a different use of psychiatric evidence.

Content of psychiatric reports

In *Fawcett*, Garland, J. listed factors that would 'assume prominence' in qualifying for a determinate LTNS. These included

> irrationality of the behaviour, the selection of vulnerable persons, or a particular class of persons or target, unexplained severe violence,

unusual obsessions or delusions, and any inability on the part of the offender to appreciate the consequences of his or her actions. Lack of remorse or unwillingness to accept medication would be a relevant consideration.

These factors may be divided into 'diagnostic', 'treatability' and 'dangerousness' domains. These domains are discussed and cases are highlighted where the role of psychiatric evidence features in the judgment.

Diagnostic factors

In the reports quoted, the two main diagnoses put forward were 'personality disorder' and 'disorder of sexual preference' (most commonly paedophilia). The effect of a diagnosis of personality disorder can be demonstrated in a recent case where disparity in sentences formed the basis for an appeal. In *R.* v *Bestwick and Huddlestone* [1994] two co-defendants pleaded guilty to offences of arson. A psychiatric report spoke of Bestwick's stable family background, his normal psychiatric condition and normal personality. Having pleaded guilty to one count of arson with nine offences (eight arson, one burglary) taken into account, Bestwick was sentenced to 30 months' detention. The sentencing judge, and the Appeal Court, accepted that Bestwick was not a man 'likely to commit further offences of this nature'. He, therefore, fell to be sentenced in accordance with the seriousness of his offending. In Huddlestone's case, a number of psychiatric reports indicated a seriously disturbed personality, which, according to one report, amounted to psychopathic disorder within the meaning of the Mental Health Act. This report went on to say that he had an obsession with lighting fires, arising probably from an early interest in fires and a thwarted ambition to join the fire service. Huddlestone was described as immature and having impaired understanding of the impact of his behaviour on others. He gained excitement from setting fire to property and so was likely to continue doing so. The sentencing judge, and the Court of Appeal, in considering Huddlestone's application for leave, concluded that Huddlestone was a danger and presumably fulfilled relevant criteria ('unusual obsessions', 'inability to appreciate consequences of actions'). He received 5 years' imprisonment as a LTNS under s.2(2)b.

Treatability

The three appellants considered to be treatable according to the psychiatric opinions were sex offenders. In one case, *R.* v *S* (1994), a 49-year-old man who had pleaded guilty to 4 counts of indecent assault on boys, 2 counts of indecency with a child and 1 indecent assault on a girl, had his 7-year LTNS reduced to a 5-year commensurate sentence. The sentencing judge had before him psychiatric reports describing this man as having been sexually abused himself, experiencing paedophiliac fantasies and suffering from generalized anxiety disorder. The Court of Appeal had before it a further report saying that the appellant was attending a treatment programme in prison. It was concluded that the appellant was not likely to acquire another family circle, that he had limited his victims to a narrow range, and did not represent a risk to the public.

Of the 12 cases where the psychiatric opinion quoted was that the defendant was untreatable, 6 were diagnosed as having an abnormal personality, 5 as having disorders of sexual preference, and 2 as suffering drug and/or alcohol abuse. One case, *R.* v *Crow and Pennington* [1994], had three pre-trial psychiatric reports, which disagreed on diagnosis, but which were uniform in deciding that he was untreatable. Pennington was a 57-year-old man who pleaded guilty to a charge of arson; he had a previous conviction for arson with intent to endanger life and a 25-year history of unsuccessful hospital treatment. He was known to be violent during hospital admissions. One psychiatric report stated that the defendant had an inadequate psychopathic personality disorder, coupled with alcohol abuse, and seemed to manipulate admission to prison and hospital in order to get a roof over his head. His complaints of 'voices' were not felt to be true hallucinations. Another report expressed the view that the defendant was suffering from chronic schizophrenia, that he was likely to start another fire, but that there was serious doubt as to whether he would respond to treatment. A plea of not guilty by reason of insanity was felt to be appropriate. A third report considered all the diagnoses, agreed with the diagnosis of inadequate personality disorder and diagnosed alcohol dependency. The defendant was reported as clearly unwilling to receive treatment. Whatever his diagnosis, his disorder was not of a nature or a degree to require detention in psychiatric hospital. A sentence longer than commensurate with the seriousness of the offence was passed. The appeal against the 8-year imprisonment LTNS was dismissed. The sentencing judge stated:

> The reason for that is that I am satisfied that I have got to protect the public from serious harm from you. I form the opinion on the basis of what the doctors say about what your condition is and your unwillingness or inability to co-operate with them and your unsuitability for treatment.

The presence of lack of insight, denial, minimization, refusal to accept treatment and repeated failure of hospital treatments are factors that have been taken into account by the court when considering an LTNS. In the court's view, a psychiatrist's assessment of treatability contributes towards evidence of risk of future harm. Two broad questions arise from such a view. First, to what extent does untreatability constitute a risk factor? Second, is a court justified in using psychiatric evidence for a purpose not foreseen by the author?

The assumption underpinning the decision in *Crow and Pennington* appeared to be that a willingness, ability to co-operate and suitability for treatment would be in themselves helpful towards reducing a risk of future harm. The case of *R.* v *S* (1994) as described above perhaps illustrates this point. Such an assumption, however, does not take into account the basis upon which defendants accept or reject offers of treatment, nor the basis upon which psychiatrists offer intervention (Grounds, 1987). It may alternatively be that the court does not hold such an assumption; rather, that the 'treatability' criteria are the vestigial remains of the original purposes of the psychiatric report, namely assessment of suitability for a medical disposal. Given the predominant diagnoses and the nature of the index offences, it would be reasonable to suggest that the possibility of psychopathic disorder was considered by the reporting psychiatrists. None of the individuals in this study, by definition, fulfilled criteria for psychopathic disorder for purposes of MHA 1983 disposal. However, the disorders described by psychiatrists were of a severity to allow the courts to impose an LTNS in some cases, without previous serious violent or sexual offending. In cases such as *Crow and Pennington, Fawcett*, or *Bestwick and Huddlestone*, 'untreatability' was the factor that closed the option of a hospital order and therefore did not allow the defendants' dangerousness to become a factor in disposal under s.41 MHA 1983. Prior to CJA 1991, this would normally have been the end of the matter, and a sentence proportionate to the offence passed. Under s.2(2)b, the 'risk of serious harm' opinion is given new life in sentencing decisions, which may or may not have been foreseen or intended by the psychiatrist. In *Fawcett* it is clear that any statement regarding untreatability may be used as a 'prominent factor' in passing a sentence under the powers of s.2(2)b, even though the original purpose of the report and the inherent considerations of dangerousness in the context of receiving medical care, would have been to 'exclude medical disposal'.

Risk of reoffending

Prior to the CJA 1991, psychiatric evidence regarding future risk could be used as evidence which reduced mitigation in some cases, but had no direct effect on sentencing. The 'dangerousness' of an offender could affect disposal only in two well-defined circumstances. These were: (1) if the offender committed an offence punishable with life imprisonment (*R.* v *Ashdown*) and was mentally unstable to such a degree that, if at liberty, he would probably reoffend and be a grave danger to the personal safety of members of the public (*R.* v *Blackburn*), and if he were likely to remain so for a long and/or uncertain time, the courts might seek to impose a discretionary life sentence; (2) if the offender was suffering from a mental disorder he might qualify for a hospital order with an indefinite restriction order.

The powers under s.2(2)b do not allow longer than commensurate custodial sentences to be passed which are aimed at deterring others, nor do they permit retribution. The primary purpose of the new provisions is to enable a court to pass a custodial sentence where the offender poses a future risk of serious harm. The longer sentence is a means of preventing such harm. The definition provided under s.3(3) makes it apparent that the court must be satisfied that there is a need to protect the public from 'death or serious personal injury, whether physical or psychological'. In practice, this appears to mean futher sexual or violent offences which are more than minor assaults. In 13 of the 22 cases where psychiatric evidence was quoted, the defendant was felt to be 'dangerous' or 'likely to reoffend'. Where the report of a consultant forensic psychiatrist 'reinforced the [judge's] view that the appellant was a serious danger' (*R.* v *Zoszco*, Hirst, L. T., Auld and Longmoor, JJ., 15 July 1994), an LTNS under s.2(2)b could be passed.

In *R.* v *Spear* [1994] the appellant fell just short of traditional criteria for an indeterminate sentence. He had pleaded guilty to s.18 wounding and received a sentence of life imprisonment. The medical reports noted severe personality disorder with a tendency to react with violence if slighted or wronged, but he was not suffering from mental illness. At the Court of Appeal hearing, with the benefit of a further medical report, the life sentence was quashed and replaced with a 10-year LTNS s.2(2)b. Reference was made to *R.* v *Wilkinson* (1983), where it was said that life imprisonment was reserved for offenders who were in a mental state which made them dangerous to the public, and in relation to whom it was impossible to say when that danger would subside. In the commentary on *Spear* the question was posed whether the Court of Appeal decision meant that if a s.2(2)b determinate sentence was given, the assumption was of dangerousness that would cease in a finite time. It is suggested that this is not the case, rather that evidential requirements to establish dangerousness to justify the imposition of a determinate LTNS are lower and more easily satisfied than those for an indeterminate sentence.

Boundaries of psychiatric expert evidence

On the basis of the 35 Appeal Court cases studied, an opinion regarding the risk of serious harm in a personality disordered or sexually deviant offender *is* regarded by the courts as within the expertise of a psychiatrist, whether it is a restriction order being considered or a longer than normal sentence. In either case, the mental abnormalities are judged as a matter for medical experience and so opinion evidence regarding prognosis, including recidivism within the context of the disorder, must be relevant.

As many commentators point out, the expert witness is an exception to the rule that opinion evidence is inadmissible. Where a matter calls for expertise (from knot-tying to genetic fingerprinting) it is acknowledged that the drawing of certain inferences requires knowledge and experience which the tribunal of fact does not possess (Keane, 1994). There are five points which to some extent identify the limit of psychiatric testimony in the context of s.2(2)b sentencing case-law.

First, it should be considered that where the judge or jurors can form their own opinion without the benefit of an expert, the expert's opinion is irrelevant and therefore inadmissible (*R.* v *Turner* [1975]). In terms of psychiatric evidence, the cases of *R.* v *Chard* (1971) and *R.* v *Wood* [1990] are cited. The latter is perhaps more relevant to this discussion because at the trial medical evidence was excluded even though it stated that the defendant had a 'personality which was to some extent abnormal and was liable to give way to excesses of behaviour under stress'. The Court of Appeal upheld such an exclusion, stating that such matters are not beyond the ordinary experience of the average juror. In *R.* v *Lyons* (1994), the defendant is described as having an 'abnormal' personality. Both psychiatrists' reports avoid the use of specific diagnoses and refrain from identifying him as suffering from a 'disorder'. The medical evidence concluded that this offender was 'not either in need of, or capable of gaining any benefit from, psychiatric treatment'. The Appeal hearing transcript goes on to quote the psychiatric expert's inference that this man is a danger to women, which formed part of the evidence that allowed the court to impose a longer than normal sentence. According to s.2(2)b case-law, therefore, 'abnormal' personality not requiring psychiatric input is within psychiatric expertise.

Secondly, on a similar theme, it is perhaps appropriate to recall the 'prominent factors' in *Fawcett*. These amount to a wide range of behaviours that may be found not only in those suffering with mental disorders, but in many unusual personalities. It is likely that a thorough psychiatric report would address many of the *Fawcett* 'factors' but not necessarily include them within a recognizable mental disorder. It would follow then that full weight would be given to such mention for the purposes of passing an LTNS even though the factors might occur outside the context of mental disorder, and therefore arguably outside medical expertise.

Thirdly, the status of sexual deviancy in the absence of mental disorder as a matter for psychiatric expertise should be examined. The debate regarding continuing detention of sexually deviant patients classified under psychopathic disorder within the mental health review tribunal (MHRT) setting brings s.1(3) MHA 1983 exclusion criteria into relief. However, psychiatric expertise in such matters for s.2(2)b sentencing purposes is unquestioned. In *R.* v *Crow and Pennington* [1994], psychiatric opinion evidence was admissible despite the absence of mental disorder (or 'psychiatric disturbance'). Expertise was available in the evidence of a probation officer specializing in psycho-sexual counselling. Indeed, it was after discussion with this expert that new facts were taken into account and the psychiatrist reversed the conclusions of the original report. It is difficult for a psychiatrist to see the relevance of medical expertise in such a case (beyond excluding mental disorder) and yet the psychiatric opinion counted as further evidence regarding the risk of serious harm.

Fourthly, it would be worth considering the more consistent approach by the court with regards to length of sentence in 'social nuisance' cases. The comment in *Fawcett* on the mixture of minor offending and mental abnormalities is relevant here. Stockdale and Devlin (1987) discuss the temptation (prior to 1991) for courts to impose longer sentences when faced with a mentally abnormal offender displaying bizarre, antisocial, or dangerous behaviour for whom no treatment option was available. In *R.* v *Clarke* (1975) a young woman suffering from 'gross personality deficit' was sentenced to 18 months' imprisonment following the breakage of a pot valued at £1. She had a record of relatively minor offences and multiple hospital admissions, including a hospital order to Special Hospital. On appeal, Lawton, L. J. stated that 'Her Majesty's Courts are not dustbins into which the social services can sweep difficult members of the public. Still less should Her Majesty's judges use their sentencing powers to dispose of those who are socially inconvenient.' The comments of Waller, L. J. in *Scanlon* are perhaps also relevant here. One study appears to draw similar conclusions in a similar context but from a clinician's perspective. Coid (1988) examined 362 mentally abnormal prisoners on remand and drew attention to variations in rejection or acceptance by the NHS according to the range of local facilities. He observed that although only a small proportion of cases warranted an opinion from medium secure or Special Hospital environments, a large proportion of the study population were described by catchment area psychiatrists as too disturbed or potentially dangerous. Coid states that in his view, the rejected men posed least threat to the community in terms of their criminal behaviour. The relevance to the context of s.2(2)b sentencing lies in Coid's suggestion that the diagnoses of personality disorder or psychopathic disorder may have acted as 'convenient excuses' to exclude medical disposal. Unfortunately, the current rate of acceptance or rejection of mentally abnormal offenders by the NHS is not known, nor is the rate at which 'rejecting' reports are used for purposes of 'longer than normal' sentences. Clearly, therefore, only theoretical possibilities can be put forward in this discussion. One important possibility is that such 'convenient excuses' may carry further implications under the CJA 1991 beyond what was intended as simply a 'rejecting' report. Therein lies the risk of courts relying on personality factors in combination with minor offending histories to determine the applicability of 'longer than normal' sentences; a risk that the rulings in 'social nuisance' appeal cases had previously recognized and attempted to guard against.

Fifthly, as in any discussion involving dangerousness, it must be acknowledged that a psychiatrist's tools for prediction in individual cases are imprecise. As pointed out by Quinsey (1995), clinical judgement can at times be proven to be a poor predictor of future violence, depending as it does on 'unreliable', or 'over-restrictive', or 'frankly false' presumptions. However, psychiatrists are regularly faced with examining patients with a view to dangerousness and are prepared, under certain clearly defined situations, to give evidence on such matters. With the introduction of the new powers under s.2(2)b, psychiatric opinion evidence can help, at the post-conviction phase of the trial, to answer two questions which put the same phrase: the 'risk of serious harm'. In the case of a mentally abnormal violent or sexual offender, this allows the same opinion to be used for two very different purposes, namely treatment or punishment. Under s.41 of the MHA 1983, statute exists which requires an approved psychiatrist to give oral evidence in court – evidence that can be tested, and evidence given where the possible consequences are clear. In *R.* v *Birch* [1989] important guidelines were set out that are relevant to the use and interpretation of a psychiatric opinion on the 'risk of serious harm'. The similarity in wording between definitions of dangerousness in CJA 1991 and MHA 1983 was noted in *R.* v *Hashi* [1994]. In this Court of Appeal hearing, consideration was made of the principles established in *Birch* (in particular the understanding of 'public at risk'). However, from a psychiatric point of view, the applicability of *Birch* to s.2(2)b sentencing must be questioned. Those guidelines apply to a context where appropriate checks and balances to the psychiatrist's powers exist for the examining of psychiatric oral evidence, a defined role exists for the psychiatrist in risk assessment and the consequences of a 'dangerous' opinion vary markedly from those well known under the Mental Health Act. Ashworth (1992) expressed concern at the lack of 'procedural or other restrictions, either to protect individual defendants against the sincere but fallible predictions of individual psychiatrists (or even individual judges), or to cause the judge to take steps to ensure, so far as is possible, that the prediction has a sound basis'. As anticipated by Ashworth, it appears that one effect of the 1991 Act is to place great power in the hands of individual psychiatrists, and yet make the restraint and balance in the giving of evidence a matter for a clinician's personal judgement.

The final point to make relates more directly to the purpose of this paper, that is, to generally heighten awareness of the role of psychiatric evidence and the powers under s.2(2)b CJA 1991. On a case-by-case basis a medical expert's awareness of sentencing issues appears difficult to achieve, yet, in theory at least, it should be possible. In *R.* v *Baverstock* (1993), the ruling stated that '[t]he sentencer should . . . give an express indication to counsel before imposing a longer sentence than was commensurate with the seriousness of the offence under section 2(2)b of the Act. Fairness to the defendant required that a proper opportunity be given for this purpose.' However, by this late stage of the trial process it would seem that psychiatric input in the form of a written report would have already been serviced. In practical terms, the potential of a s.2(2)b sentence should be seen in all violent or sexual offenders, and this awareness should be taken into account no matter what the proposed conclusions and recommendations of the report are. This clearly has implications in the gaining of consent from defendants for the purposes of preparing a report to the Courts. This issue has been explored before (Chiswick, 1985) and it could be argued that on the basis of the cases examined here, the difficulties in finding a workable balance have been increased.

CONCLUSIONS

The structure and purpose of the CJA 1991 statute with regard to psychiatric evidence appears to reinforce the long-standing role of assessing the need for medical disposal and provision of realistic mitigation. Psychiatric opinion evidence regarding diagnosis, treatment and risk of reoffending is used in sentencing decisions and plays an important role in allowing the imposition of longer than normal sentences for the purpose of protecting the public from serious harm.

The boundaries of psychiatric evidence in s.2(2)b sentencing have to date not been tested by the appeal process. Indeed medical expertise is relied on in predicting behaviour of personality disordered offenders with no history of convictions of a violent or sexual nature, in sex offenders with no psychiatric disorder, and in offenders with 'abnormal' personality not requiring psychiatric intervention. It cannot be assumed that a report excluding medical disposal is thereby irrelevant to the sentencing process, and all reports prepared pre-sentence should take into account this significant role.

In many ways, this paper reaffirms the concerns of Chiswick (1985), particularly where the defendant's consent to divulge potentially damaging information is involved. It is, of course, up to each individual clinician to define his or her boundaries of expertise. Chiswick urges the limitation of opinion-giving to matters of mental illness and warns that stepping beyond such limits increases the chance of misuse. However, where, prior to the 1991 Act, the restriction of psychiatric evidence to the post-conviction stage may have been welcomed, the evolving case-law reviewed in this paper shows that such a restriction would no longer prevent the abuse of psychiatric testimony.

ACKNOWLEDGEMENTS

I wish to thank Dr D. A. Thomas at the Institute of Criminology, Cambridge for allowing access to court transcripts, Dr A. T. Grounds for valuable discussion and comments, and Mrs Maureen Fry for secretarial help.

Dr Bohdan Solomka, MRCPsych, senior registrar in forensic psychiatry, Norvic Clinic, St Andrew's Business Park, Norwich NR2 0SS

REFERENCES

Ashworth, A. (1992) *Sentencing and Criminal Justice*. London: Weidenfeld & Nicolson.

Chiswick, D. (1985) 'Use and Abuse of Psychiatric Testimony'. *British Medical Journal* 290: 975–7.

Coid, J. W. (1988) 'Mentally Abnormal Prisoners on Remand: I – Rejected or Accepted by the NHS?' *British Medical Journal* 296: 1779–82.

Grounds, A. T. (1987) 'Detention of "Psychopathic Disorder" Patients in Special Hospital – Critical Issues'. *British Journal of Psychiatry* 151: 474–8.

Gunn, J. (chapter ed.) (1993) 'Criminal Law in England and Wales'. In Gunn, J. and Taylor, P. J. (eds) *Forensic Psychiatry: Clinical, Legal and Ethical Issues*. London: Butterworth/Heinemann.

Home Office and Lord Chancellor's Office (1961) *Report of the Interdepartmental Committee on the Business of Clinical Courts*. Cmd 1289 (Streatfield Report) London: HMSO.

Keane, A. (1994) 'Opinion Evidence'. In *The Modern Law of Evidence*, 3rd edn. London: Butterworth.

Leng, R. and Manchester, C. (1991) *A Guide to the Criminal Justice Act 1991*. London: Fourmat.

Quinsey, V. L. (1995) 'The Prediction and Explanation of Criminal Violence'. *International Journal of Law and Psychiatry* 18(2): 117–27.

Stockdale, E. and Devlin, K. (1987) 'Mentally Abnormal Offenders'. In *Sentencing*. London: Waterlow.

Thomas, D. (1992) *Archbold News*, issue 19 (30 October): 5–7.

Thomas, D. (1994a) *Sentencing News*, issue 4 (25 October): 8–11.

Thomas, D. (1994b) *Sentencing News*, issue 2 (26 April): 7–11.

LAW REPORTS

R. v *Ashdown* [1974] All ER 800

R. v *Baverstock* (1993) 14 Cr App R (s) 471

R. v *Bestwick and Huddlestone* [1994] Crim LR 771

R. v *Birch* [1989] Crim LR 757

R. v *Blackburn* (1979) Crim App R (s) 205 (76)

R. v *Chard* (1971) 56 Cr App R 268

R. v *Clarke* (1975) 61 Cr App R 320

R. v *Crow and Pennington* [1994] Crim LR 958

R. v *Fawcett* [1994] Crim LR 704

R. v *Gouws* (1981) 3 Cr App R (s) 325
R. v *Hashi* [1994] Crim LR 618
R. v *Hodgson* (1967) 52 Cr App R 113
R. v *Lyons* (1994) Crim App R (s.) 460
R. v *S.* (Hirst, L. J., Auld and Longmore, JJ., 7 July 1994)
R. v *Scanlon* (1979) 1 Cr App R (s) 60
R. v *Spear* [1994] Crim LR 770
R. v *Turner* [1975] QB 834
R. v *Utip* (1993) 14 Crim App R (s) 746
R. v *Wilkinson* (1983) 5 Cr App R (s) 105
R. v *Wood* [1990] Crim LR 264
R. v *Zoszco* (Hirst, L. J., Auld and Longmore JJ., 15 July 1994)

[26]

[1988]

Dangerous Offenders, and the Morality of Protective Sentencing

By David Wood

Lecturer in Law, University of Melbourne

Recent years have seen a tremendous growth of interest in the topic of dangerous offenders. It is widely argued that the general trend towards briefer prison sentences has made the problem posed by such offenders particularly pressing. To quote one influential commentator, "[t]he shorter prison sentences become, the more difficult it seems to be to argue that there should not be a special protective sentence for the small number of exceptional offenders judged to present an unacceptable risk of further serious harm."[1]

This article is concerned with the justifiability of protective sentencing. Three broad approaches need to be distinguished. The first holds that such sentences are in principle supportable. Where offenders genuinely constitute a threat to the physical well-being of members of the public, their continued detention is warranted despite their having served their normal sentence. According to the second approach, protective sentences are on the contrary unjustifiable. The dangerous offender should be treated no differently from other offenders and released once his ordinary sentence has been served. To detain him further is to punish him not for offences he has committed, but for those he might commit in the future. The third approach seeks a *via media* between the other two. This approach appeals to a distinction between imprisonment on the one hand and forms of detention such as quarantine which do not constitute punishment on the other. It claims that although the continued imprisonment of dangerous offenders is quite unjustified, detaining such offenders further in some form of civil institution may be warranted.

This article argues for the third approach, and claims that it can be extended to dangerous persons generally. It defends two main propositions. The first is that, subject to certain constraints, particularly concerning the identification of such persons, the civil detention of individuals properly classifiable as dangerous is justified, even if they have not already committed any violent offences. The second proposition is that the protective sentencing of dangerous offenders is never justified. These two propositions are defended in the course of examining the case for protective sentencing put forward by Nigel Walker[2] on the one hand (section 1) and Jean Floud and Warren Young[3] on the other (section 2). Section 2 also investigates the latter's

---

[1] Jean Floud, "Dangerousness and Criminal Justice" (1982) 22 *British Journal of Criminology* 213, 215. *Cf.* Floud and Young, *Dangerousness and Criminal Justice,* 38 (Heinemann, London, 1981).

[2] *Supra,* n.1, especially Chap. 5; "Unscientific, Unwise, Unprofitable or Unjust?" (1982) 22 *British Journal of Criminology* 276; *Sentencing: Theory, Law and Practice* (Butterworths, London, 1985), Chap. 22. See also Walker (and others), *The Violent Offender: Reality or Illusion?* (Blackwell, Oxford, 1970).

[3] *Supra,* n.1.

argument against preventive detention, and considers the second option of simply releasing dangerous offenders once they have served their normal sentence.

1. Walker's Defence of Protective Sentencing

Rather than treating incapacitation as in some way an inferior reason for imprisoning someone, Walker asks why, on the contrary, it should not "be regarded as a justification which is quite as sound as retribution, deterrence, or the need for treatment."[4] The major objection to protective sentencing is that "incapacitation as a reason for penal interventions means that a person is punished, not for what he has done but for what it is believed he may do in the future."[5] After stating that this objection assumes that "the only justifiable aim of a sentence must be retributive punishment,"[6] Walker goes on to claim that, insofar as incapacitation is concerned, the "sterility" of a purely retributive approach to sentencing can be "la[id] bare" by considering what a proponent of such an approach would approve in two hypothetical situations. These situations warrant close attention, for they turn out to be very different from the simple knock-down arguments Walker takes them to be.

To start with the first hypothetical situation:

> "In Situation A the offender to be sentenced is certain to commit a crime of serious violence unless detained for longer than the 'just deserts tariff' would allow. Must he be released and reincarcerated only when he has committed the crime he was certain to commit? Or would certainty justify incarcerating him before he commits it? To be consistent the pure retributivist must insist on the former answer. He might protest that the case as posed is unreal and artificial; but the answer to that is that an uncompromising philosophical position must be defensible in any conceivable situation."[7]

Certainly the pure retributivists must hold (as must any retributivist) that the offender cannot be punished for a crime he has not committed, even if *ex hypothesi* there is no doubt about his committing a further crime. But this does not mean that the retributivist, of any sort, is committed to the offender's being released once he has served his tariff sentence. The retributivist, *qua* retributivist, offers only a theory of punishment, not a comprehensive account of the circumstances and conditions under which individuals can be forcibly detained. It is absurd to suppose that he is committed to the view that every social measure, or even every preventitive measure, must be justified on retributive grounds. If this were the case, he would be required to hold that the epileptic could only be denied a driving licence if this was something he rightfully deserved, or homes could only be compulsorily purchased in order to build a new motorway if this were somehow to give their occupants their due. In a whole range of cases, questions of desert are simply irrelevant. However, Walker seems to see the

[4] *Supra,* n.1 p.94.
[5] "Unscientific, Unwise, Unprofitable or Unjust?" *supra,* n.2 p.280.
[6] *Ibid.*
[7] *Supra,* n.2 p.281.

retributivist precisely as offering an account according to which desert is always relevant, and therefore he sees him as being unable to justify, for example, the compulsory commitment of psychotics, or the quarantining of those carrying life-threatening diseases.[8] Why, otherwise, does Walker suppose in the above example that detention or incarceration of any form can be justified only as a form of punishment? To portray the retributivist as Walker does is merely to caricature him.

It might be claimed, however, that Walker's point is not that the retributivist cannot accept the principle that social protection is a justifiable ground for intervention. Rather his point is that it is inconsistent for the retributivist not to extend this principle to the sphere of punishment, given that he is forced to accept it quite generally outside this sphere. (Consider the examples in the previous paragraph.) Walker says, after all, that "[t]he traditional retributivist, who asserts that the law enforcement system ought not to take account of the harm which people might do, must either explain why it should be subject to a restrictive principle which we do not apply outside the system, or else argue that we should apply the same principle outside it."[9] But the retributivist's reply here is obvious. He can acknowledge quite openly that considerations of social protection are just as relevant in the law enforcement system as they are outside it, and go on to say that they are not relevant so as to justify further imprisonment as opposed to merely detention. Beyond that which is required on normal tariff grounds, punishment is just as much out of place in the case of the dangerous offender as it is in the case of the typhoid carrier. It is equally unjust to continue to imprison the dangerous offender once he has served his tariff sentence as it is to imprison, as opposed to merely quarantine, the typhoid carrier in the first place. (The term "imprisonment" is used here in its everyday sense, rather than in the broader legal sense in which any deprivation of liberty constitutes imprisonment.) In both cases, isolation alone is required, and no harsher treatment is defensible.

This criticism of Walker can be reinforced by comparing the case of two persons who are equally dangerous but only one of whom has committed violent offences in sufficient number of sufficient gravity to be classified as a dangerous offender. Social protection requires that they be treated similarly and both incapacitated. But if dangerousness is a reason for punishing the dangerous offender beyond whatever is justified on normal tariff principles, why is not dangerousness similarly a reason for punishing the equally dangerous person who is yet so to qualify? (Let's call him "the dangerous non-offender.") It seems that Walker is forced to hold either that dangerousness constitutes a sufficient reason for punishment in the case of the dangerous offender and dangerous non-offender alike, or in neither of these cases. Of course, Walker does not see the matter this way. He categorically rejects the idea that subjecting a prisoner to further restraint once he has served his tariff sentence is like punishing the innocent. He claims that in no sense does a person "regain his innocence" once he has

[8] *Supra,* n.1 pp.94–95, n.2 p.281.
[9] *Supra,* n.1 p.95.

served his tariff sentence: "One is innocent of a crime until one commits it, after which one is guilty of it for ever. One may be pardoned, or have one's conviction quashed, or eventually become 'rehabilitated' . . . but one does not become innocent in any literal sense."[10] According to Walker, to suppose that the dangerous offender cannot be subjected to a protective sentence is again to beg the question of "whether a sentence should ever be anything but retributive punishment."[11] The point remains, however, that the connection between guilt and dangerousness is yet to be explained. How does the dangerous offender's record of violence make him liable to social protection measures in a way in which the non-offender is not so liable? The frequently raised criticism that the dangerous offender is being regarded as a second-class citizen, that he has lost his equal status in virtue of being categorised as a dangerous offender, appears highly plausible.[12] Walker accuses the retributivist of begging the question of why punishment should be limited to retributivist grounds—or at least, in the case of the limiting retributivist, the question of why "just deserts" should be regarded as placing a ceiling on penalties. But Walker could equally be accused of begging the question of why being convicted of crimes of a certain degree of violence should be regarded as merely setting a threshold for various forms of intervention. He seems to think that because the fact of conviction can never be changed (once the appeal channels have all been exhausted), there are only uncertain limits to the social protection measures that can be taken against the guilty person. It seems far more reasonable, however, to endorse some principle of commensurability between the seriousness of the offences in question and the severity of the punishment administered in relation to them.

The proposition that the continued imprisonment as opposed to civil detention of dangerous offenders cannot be justified prompts a further criticism of Walker. Even if the required connection between guilt and dangerousness could be established, this would be of no assistance in the case of the dangerous non-offender. We are still left with the question of what action, if any, can be taken against him. The absurdity Walker supposes in simply releasing the offender in Situation A has nothing to do with his being dangerous.[13]

Walker draws a parallel between the quarantining of carriers of life-threatening diseases and the protective sentencing of dangerous offenders. The appropriate analogy, however, is rather with the civil detention of dangerous persons generally, whether dangerous offenders or not. That a dangerous person is also classifiable as a dangerous offender is only epistemically or evidentially significant, and not morally relevant. Walker can only draw his parallel with quarantine on the assumption either that quarantine is a form of punishment and not merely detention, or that a protective sentence is merely detention, and not punishment. Walker can

[10] *Supra,* n.2 p.280.

[11] *Ibid.*

[12] We avoid this conclusion by holding that dangerous offenders and non-offenders alike are liable to preventitive measures.

[13] As we shall see shortly, Floud and Young seem to deny such absurdity. They hold that the risk presented by dangerous non-offenders must be borne by the community at large, and cannot justifiably be restricted by detaining such persons.

hardly adopt the first alternative, as then he would be no better placed to handle the dangerous non-offender than would be the retributivist, according to his own crticism of that position rejected above. That is, Walker could only civilly detain a dangerous offender if it is presumed that such treatment was somehow deserved. The latter alternative is hardly plausible either. If a protective sentence is merely detention, why should it be served in a normal prison as opposed to (what we shall call) a civil detention centre.?[14] If incapacitation is all that is required, the more stringent measure of imprisonment cannot be justified.

Turning to the second of Walker's hypothetical situations, in Situation B:

> "the violent offender declares his intention of committing further violence when he is released, and there is no reason to disbelieve him or to doubt his capacity for doing what he says he will do. Would the retributivist allow him to be kept inside any longer than the just deserts tariff permits, in order to stop him doing what he promises to do? Must his answer in this situation also be 'No'? If so, he is in effect saying that his principles do not allow him to take any steps to save a person from becoming a victim of violence if those steps involve the extension of incarceration. If he is completely consistent he would also be unwilling to allow any non-custodial precautionary measure that would involve even inconvenience for the offender."[15]

In Situation A we know only that it is certain that the offender will commit a further violent crime, not how we are certain of this. One way of taking the offender's declaration of intention in Situation B is as just filling out Situation A, as informing us of the way in which we know that the offender will undoubtedly commit the crime. On this interpretation, rather than presenting a different story, Situation B presents a more detailed version of the same story. If this is how Situation B is to be viewed, it clearly does not warrant separate treatment.

It may seem more reasonable, then, to take the declaration of intention in Situation B as possessing moral and not just epistemic status, as making it plain that the offender is responsible for his future crime. Interpreted this way, however, Situation B provides no additional difficulties for the retributivist. If anything, it makes his position easier, for he is provided with separate grounds for intervention: he has not just a prediction of future conduct to rely upon, but a statement of present intention. A substantive criminal law based more soundly on retributivist principles could well regard this statement itself as an offence. (Of course, this would require the legal concept of assault to be extended to threats of future harm, but there seems to be no reason why the retributivist should not agree to this.) It would still have to be considered, however, whether such an offence would be sufficient to justify detaining the maker of such a statement for so long as he is dangerous. It seems that it would be quite fortuitous if this were to be the

[14] *Cf.* Ferdinand D. Schoeman, "On Incapacitating the Dangerous," in H. Gross and A. Von Hirsch, (*eds.*) *Sentencing* (Oxford University Press, New York, 1981), 175.
[15] *Supra*, n.2 p.281.

case.[16] A further possibility open to the retributivist is to analyse the threatened future harm as a continuing offence. Incarceration might then be justified until the offender can establish that he has withdrawn his threat.

2. Floud and Young's Defence of Protective Sentencing

Floud and Young argue for positions diametrically opposed to the two propositions defended here. Contrary to our first proposition (and also to Walker), they claim that the civil detention of dangerous non-offenders is never warranted. The risk presented by such persons must be borne by the community at large. Concerning our second proposition, they dismiss the option of civil detention, arguing (or at least implying) that the more stringent step of subjecting dangerous offenders to protective sentences is defensible.

Floud and Young defend their first claim, that the civil detention of dangerous non-offenders is never warranted, by appealing to what they call "the right to be presumed harmless." The "crucial objection" to taking protective measures against dangerous non-offenders is that

> "such measures would entail abrogating [this] right . . . which, like the right to be presumed innocent, is fundamental to a free society. In such a society people do not simply expect or hope to be treated as harmless; they have a right to be so treated, even if it is more probable than not that they do intend harm: just as they have a right to be treated as innocent even if it is more probable than not that they are guilty."[17]

Floud and Young's "right to be presumed harmless" raises two important questions, which will be considered in turn. The first question is why it should be supposed that this right is sufficiently powerful to exclude the civil detention of dangerous non-offenders. The analogy with the right to be presumed innocent seems misplaced. Central though it is to the English legal system (although the growing number of reverse onus offences cannot pass without comment), it is at most a procedural right which, in itself, does not justify any substantive position. Floud and Young, however, take the right to be presumed harmless to do just that. It needs to be asked why they should regard this right as excluding civil detention when they do not take it as ruling out quarantining those with life-threatening diseases. Floud and Young hold that the risks presented by disease carriers can fairly be redistributed, so that the disease carriers suffer the burden of quarantine rather than the public at large running the risk of infection. It must be asked, then, why the risks presented by dangerous non-offenders should not likewise be redistributed.

Floud and Young are obviously fearful lest they be misinterpreted as endorsing the idea that people generally should be assessed for dangerousness, and those found to be sufficiently dangerous be made liable to detention even if they have not committed any violent offences, or more exactly, have not committed enough of such offences to satisfy the dangerous offender threshold. They point out that this idea gives substance to the slogan, "the

[16] A connected issue here is the form protective sentences should take, whether they are to be determinate or not.

[17] *Supra*, n.1 p.44.

dangerousness of 'dangerousness.'"[18] On the other hand, however, Floud and Young have no moral objections to the practice of quarantining those suspected of carrying life-threatening diseases. They do not seek to distinguish the two practices merely at the epistemic level, on the grounds that predictions concerning the probability of the spread of such diseases are far more reliable than predictions as to the likelihood of violent behaviour. The question arises, then, of what they take to be the moral difference between the quarantining of such persons and the civil detention of dangerous non-offender. They claim this difference lies in the following "vital distinction":

> "Anyone who accepts the practice of quarantine must acknowledge that it may be permissible, in some circumstances, to detain legally sane and innocent persons for the protection of others from *unintentional* harm; but he is in no way committed to the proposition if it is *wilful* harm that is envisaged. Quarantine as a precaution against unintentional harm is one thing; preventative detention as a precaution against *wrong-doing* is another matter altogether."[19]

Two points are in order. First, it is not clear why the distinction between wilful and non-intentional harm is of any relevance at all. Presumably, it matters little to the person who suffers the harm, who is likely to be far more concerned with whether the harm was preventable than with whether it was wilful. Secondly, even if this distinction is relevant, it seems to count in favour of civil detention rather than against it. It appears reasonable to suggest that there are fewer moral difficulties with confining a person who intends harm, or may intend harm in the future, than with confining a person who could cause harm quite unintentionally. It seems, then, that Floud and Young's appeal to the distinction between wilful and unintentional harm is quite unsuccessful. This distinction cannot be used to justify treating the case of quarantining the carrier of a dangerous disease differently from the case of civilly detaining a dangerous non-offender.

The conclusion that civil detention is morally indistinguishable from quarantining can be arrived at another way. Floud and Young argue that subjecting dangerous offenders to protective sentences is morally unobjectionable because, first, such persons have forfeited the right to be presumed harmless, and secondly, what could be termed "the principle of just redistribution of risks" justifies the redistribution of risks that is entailed by protective sentences. They hold, at least implicitly, that the presence of the right to be presumed harmless provides immunity from the application of this principle. This is why they believe that the risks posed by dangerous non-offenders cannot be redistributed (at least not on the grounds of this principle), but must be borne by the community at large. However, it is not clear why the right to be presumed harmless should be regarded as being more significant than the principle of redistribution of risks and given preference to it. It appears more reasonable to hold (and will be maintained here) that this principle is quite in order so long as no attempt is made to use it to justify measures such as imprisonment which constitute punishment, as

[18] *Supra* n.1 p.42.
[19] *Supra,* n.1 p.41, *cf.* 45. 46. Emphasis, Floud and Young's.

opposed to those as quarantine and civil detention which do not. Outside the area of punishment, or at least, where preventitive measures can be justified according to the principle of just redistribution of risks, rather than retributively, it seems that individuals who are required to carry the burden of such redistribution cannot object that the Kantian constraint on using them merely as means to an end has been violated. Certainly, this constraint is not being violated so as to subvert their moral status in the same way it would be were they to be wrongly punished. (The moral distinction here between forms of incarceration which do and do not constitute punishment is vital.) It seems, then, that the right to be presumed harmless is not sufficient to exclude the civil detention of dangerous non-offenders, as opposed to their imprisonment, where the term "imprisonment" is understood, as in this article, in the ordinary sense as a form of punishment rather than the technical legal sense of any deprivation of liberty.

Whereas the first question raised by the right to be presumed harmless asks whether this right is strong enough for Floud and Young's purposes, the second queries whether it is not too powerful. It may well be that in appealing to this right Floud and Young have bought far more than they bargained for. Why should it be supposed that, once they have been convicted of violent crimes of sufficient number and seriousness to satisfy the dangerous offender threshold, individuals are capable of losing this right, and therefore of being made liable to a protective sentence? Once again, the analogy with the right to be presumed innocent is misplaced, for this right is never lost, irrespective of the defendant's past criminal record. Indeed, in the English legal system at least, it is considered of great importance that the jury is kept ignorant of any such record. To talk of a class of persons who might be treated as having lost this right, or at least the benefit of this right insofar as it provides immunity from liability to protective sentences, raises once again the spectre of a second-class citizenry.

The other main proposition of Floud and Young that we are concerned with here, that it is not merely the civil detention of dangerous offenders that is justified, but their continued imprisonment under protective sentences, can be dealt with more briefly. If it is only the incapacitation of dangerous offenders that is required, civil detention suffices. Floud and Young do not consider this issue explicitly. But they appear to believe that if merely the civil detention of dangerous offenders were to be accepted, there would be a serious risk of the practice spreading to non-offenders. However, this fear appears to be quite misplaced. First, granted our argument above, the practice of civil detention (subject to constraints imposed by epistemic considerations relating to the identification of dangerous offenders and the principle of just redistribution of risks) is to be at least cautiously welcomed rather than dreaded. At a minimum, it seems preferable to the two alternative approaches of imprisoning dangerous non-offenders on the one hand, and not intervening with regard to them on the other. Secondly, even if we were mistaken about civil detention being so preferable, there is no reason to suppose that the practice of detaining dangerous offenders would spread to dangerous persons generally. Floud and Young provide no grounds for thinking that the practice cannot be kept so confined. Thirdly, even if there were a distinct possibility of the practice spreading in this way, this is not a sufficient reason to subject dangerous offenders to the more stringent measure. If dangerous offenders were to be imprisoned rather than merely detained for this reason, they could clearly object that they were merely being used as a means to a social end. They could rightfully complain that they were being imprisoned for the dubious reason that, were they only to be civilly detained, the idea that dangerous non-offenders likewise should be subjected to this measure might become fashionable. The central point remains of why dangerous offenders should be subjected to further periods of imprisonment when civil detention centres could serve the end of incapacitation equally well.

This article has so far been mainly concerned with defending the third option set out at the beginning, namely civil detention, against the first option of protective sentencing. It might be objected, however, that we have not sought to defend civil detention against the second option, that of intervening no further in the case of dangerous offenders once their ordinary tariff sentences have been served. We have done no more in this regard than appeal to the analogy with quarantining. Furthermore we have done so, according to this objection, simply assuming that quarantining is morally quite blameless.

It is not to be supposed, however, that quarantining is completely free of moral difficulties. Certainly the question must be faced as to why it is justified as a forcible measure, given that most carriers of serious diseases would willingly co-operate and remain in a quarantine centre voluntarily. It is the risk of the small minority who cannot be relied upon that seems to justify forcible quarantining. However, the main point to note here is that there is a vital moral difference between quarantining and imprisonment, namely that the latter is a form of punishment, whereas the former is not. Two further points regarding the second option are also in order. First, as already pointed out, Floud and Young are quite happy to let the community at large bear the risk presented by dangerous non-offenders. It could well be asked whether it would not be more consistent for them to endorse the same strategy in respect of dangerous offenders, and drop their argument for protective sentences completely. This seems particularly plausible given that, owing to the general absence of "career paths" among dangerous offenders, the risk presented by this class of persons is scarcely considerable in comparison with that presented by dangerous non-offenders. Secondly, and following on from this point, it needs to be reiterated that, given the epistemic difficulties involved in correctly identifying those likely to commit violent crimes, the option of simply releasing dangerous offenders once they have served their ordinary sentence in practice could well be the most reasonable.

Conclusion

Two main propositions have been defended here. The first is that the civil detention of any person properly classified as dangerous may under certain conditions be justified, irrespective of whether he can also be categorised as a dangerous offender. If protection of the public is a reason for incarcerating the dangerous offender, it is equally a reason for incarcerating the dangerous non-offender. The second proposition is that subjecting dangerous offenders (and dangerous persons generally) to protective prison sentences is never justified. Since prisons and civil detention institutions would serve the end of incapacitation equally well, further justification is required to subject individuals to the more stringent measure of imprisonment, and no such justifications can be provided.

These propositions were defended through examining contrary views advanced by Walker, and by Floud and Young. In his attempt to refute the retributivist objection to protective sentencing, Walker considers the contrast only with non-intervention, that is, simply releasing the dangerous offender once he has served his normal sentence. He fails to realise—indeed denies—that it is open to the retributivist to support civil detention. Since civil detention is not punishment, the objection that the person subjected to the measure is being punished for what he might do in the future cannot stand. Contrary to Walker's claim, the retributivist can consistently hold that there are non-retributivist grounds for incarceration (such as social protection), so long as, of course, such incarceration does not constitute punishment. The practice of quarantine simply does not present the restributivist with the difficulties that Walker imagines. Furthermore, Walker fails to establish the connection between guilt and dangerousness which justifies protective sentencing in the case of the dangerous offender, but not in the case of the dangerous non-offender. His argument for the protective sentencing of the former, then, establishes too much in that it counts equally as an argument in favour of the protective sentencing of the latter.

Floud and Young's contention that the civil detention of dangerous non-offenders is never justified was similarly rejected. This proposition cannot be established by appealing, as they do, to the right to be presumed harmless and the distinction between intentional and unintentional harm. The civil detention of dangerous persons, whether dangerous offenders or not, is morally on a par with the quarantining of carriers of deadly diseases. Their principle of just redistribution of risk is just as applicable in the former case as in the latter. Their other main proposition, which follows from their rejection of civil detention, that dangerous offenders may be subjected to the harsher measure of protective prison sentences, likewise cannot be accepted. Seeing that both equally serve the end of incapacitation, there is no justification for the added suffering and damage to individuals' moral status implicit in the latter measure.

Part V
Dangerousness/Psychopathic Disorder and the Prediction of Violence

[27]

International Journal of Law and Psychiatry, Vol. 1, pp. 1–18, 1978
Pergamon Press. Printed in the U.S.A.

About the Concept of the "Dangerous Individual" in 19th-Century Legal Psychiatry

Michel Foucault*
(translated by Alain Baudot** and Jane Couchman***)

I would like to begin by relating a brief exchange which took place the other day in the Paris criminal courts. A man who was accused of five rapes and six attempted rapes, between February and June 1975, was being tried. The accused hardly spoke at all. Questions from the presiding judge:

"Have you tried to reflect upon your case?"

–Silence.

"Why, at twenty-two years of age, do such violent urges overtake you? You must make an effort to analyze yourself. You are the one who has the keys to your own actions. Explain yourself."

–Silence.

"Why would you do it again?"

–Silence.

Then a juror took over and cried out, "For heaven's sake, defend yourself!"

Such a dialogue, or rather, such an interrogatory monologue, is not in the least exceptional. It could doubtlessly be heard in many courts in many countries. But, seen in another light, it can only arouse the amazement of the historian. Here we have a judicial system designed to establish misdemeanors, to determine who committed them, and to sanction these acts by imposing the penalties prescribed by the law. In this case we have facts which have been established, an individual who admits to them and one who consequently accepts the punishment he will receive. All should be for the best in the best of all possible judicial worlds. The legislators, the authors of the legal codes in the late 18th and early 19th centuries, could not have dreamed of a clearer situation. And yet it happens that the machinery jams, the gears seize up. Why? Because the accused remains silent. Remains silent about what? About the facts? About circumstances? About the way in which they occurred? About the immediate cause of the events? Not at all. The accused evades a question which is essential in the eyes of a modern tribunal, but which would have had a strange ring to it 150 years ago: "Who are you?"

*Professeur d'Histoire et des Systèmes de Pensée, Collège de France, Paris, France.

**Chairman, Département d'Etudes pluridisciplinaires, Glendon College, York University, Toronto, Canada.

***Associate Dean, Glendon College, York University, Toronto, Canada.

Note: Ms. Carol Brown of the French Consulate in Toronto generously agreed, at the request of the organizers of the Law and Psychiatry Symposium, to make an initial translation of this paper for public reading, under extreme pressure of time. We have made a new translation, but we did refer at times to Ms. Brown's version. We wish to acknowledge our debt to her – *Alain Baudot and Jane Couchman.*

And the dialogue which I just quoted shows that it is not enough for the accused to say in reply to that question, "I am the author of the crimes before you, period. Judge since you must, condemn if you will." Much more is expected of him. Beyond admission, there must be confession, self-examination, explanation of oneself, revelation of what one is. The penal machine can no longer function simply with a law, a violation and a responsible party. It needs something else, a supplementary material. The magistrates and the jurors, the lawyers too, and the department of the public prosecutor, cannot really play their role unless they are provided with another type of discourse, the one given by the accused about himself, or the one which he makes possible for others, through his confessions, memories, intimate disclosures, etc. If it happens that this discourse is missing, the presiding judge is relentless, the jury is upset. They urge, they push the accused, he does not play the game. He is not unlike those condemned persons who have to be carried to the guillotine or the electric chair because they drag their feet. They really ought to walk a little by themselves, if indeed they want to be executed. They really ought to speak a little about themselves, if they want to be judged. The following argument used recently by a French lawyer in the case of the kidnapping and murder of a child clearly indicates that the judicial stage cannot do without this added element, that no judgment, no condemnation is possible without it being provided, in one way or another.

For a number of reasons, this case created a great stir, not only because of the seriousness of the crime, but also because the question of the retention or the abolition of the death penalty was at stake in the case. In his plea, which was directed against the death penalty more than in favor of the accused, the lawyer stressed the point that very little was known about him, and that the nature of the man had only barely been glimpsed at in the interrogations and in the psychiatric examinations. And he made this amazing remark (I quote approximately): "Can one condemn to death a person one does not know?"

This is probably no more than one illustration of a well-known fact, which could be called the law of the third element, or the Garofalo principle, since Garofalo was the one who formulated it with complete clarity: "Criminal law knew only two terms, the offense and the penalty. The new criminology recognizes three, the crime, the criminal and the means of repression." In large part, the evolution, if not of the penal systems, at least of the day to day penal practice in many countries, is determined by the gradual emergence in the course of the 19th century of this additional character. At first a pale phantom, used to adjust the penalty determined by the judge for the crime, this character becomes gradually more substantial, more solid and more real, until finally it is the crime which seems nothing but a shadow hovering about the criminal, a shadow which must be drawn aside in order to reveal the only thing which is now of importance, the criminal.

Legal justice today has at least as much to do with criminals as with crimes. Or more precisely, while, for a long time, the criminal had been no more than the person to whom a crime could be attributed and who could therefore be punished, today, the crime tends to be no more than the event which signals the existence of a dangerous element – that is, more or less dangerous – in the social body.

From the very beginning of this development, resorting to the criminal over and above the crime was justified by a double concern: to introduce more rationality into penal practice, and to adjust the general provisions of laws and legal codes more closely to social reality. Probably, it was not realized, at least at first, that to add the notion of psychological symptomatology of a danger to the notion of legal imputability of a crime was not only to enter an extremely obscure labyrinth, but also to come slowly out of a legal system which had gradually developed since its birth during the medieval inquisition. It could be said that hardly had the great eighteenth-century legal reformers completed the systematic codification of the results of the preceding evolution, hardly had they developed all its possibilities, when a new crisis began to appear in the rules and regulations of legal punishment. "What must be punished, and how?" That was the question to which, it was believed, a rational answer had finally been found; and now a further question arose to confuse the issue: "Whom do you think you are punishing?"

In this development, psychiatry and psychiatrists, as well as the notion of "danger," played a permanent role. I would like to draw attention to two stages in what one might call the psychiatrization of criminal danger.

The intervention of psychiatry in the field of law occurred in the beginning of the nineteenth century, in connection with a series of cases whose pattern was about the same, and which took place between 1800 and 1835.

Case reported by Metzger: a retired officer who lives a solitary life becomes attached to his landlady's child. One day, "with absolutely no motive, in the absence of any passion, such as anger, pride, or vengeance," he attacks the child and hits him twice with a hammer, though not fatally.

Selestat case: in Alsace, during the extremely hard winter of 1817, when famine threatens, a peasant woman takes advantage of her husband's being absent at work to kill their little daughter, cuts off her leg and cooks it in the soup.

In Paris in 1827, Henriette Cornier, a servant, goes to the neighbor of her employers and insists that the neighbor leave her daughter with her for a time. The neighbor hesitates, agrees, then, when she returns for the child, Henriette Cornier has just killed her and has cut off her head which she has thrown out the window.

In Vienna, Catherine Ziegler kills her illegitimate child. On the stand, she explains that her act was the result of an irresistible force. She is acquitted on grounds of insanity. She is released from prison. But she declares that it would be better if she were kept there, for she will do it again. Ten months later, she gives birth to a child which she kills immediately, and she declares at the trial that she became pregnant for the sole purpose of killing her child. She is condemned to death and executed.

In Scotland, a certain John Howison enters a house where he kills an old woman whom he hardly knows, leaves without stealing anything and does not go into hiding. Arrested, he denies the fact against all evidence; but the defense argues that it is the crime of a madman since it is a crime without material motive. Howison is executed, and his comment to an official at the execution that he felt like killing him, was considered in retrospect as supplementary evidence of madness.

In New England, out in the open fields, Abraham Prescott kills his foster mother with whom he had always gotten along very well. He goes home and breaks into tears in front of his foster father, who questions him. Prescott willingly confesses his crime. He explains later that he was overcome by a sudden and acute toothache and that he remembers nothing. The inquiry will establish that he had already attacked his foster parents during the night, an act which had been believed to be the result of a fit of sleepwalking. Prescott is condemned to death but the jury also recommends a commutation. He is nevertheless executed.

The psychiatrists of the period, Metziger, Hoffbauer, Esquirol and Georget, William Ellis and Andrew Combe refer tirelessly to these cases and to others of the same type.

Out of all the crimes committed, why did these particular ones seem important; why were they at issue in the discussions between doctors and jurists? First,of all, it must be noted that they present a picture very different from what had hitherto constituted the jurisprudence of criminal insanity. In general terms, until the end of the eighteenth century, the question of insanity was raised under penal law only in cases where it was also raised in the civil code or in canon law; that is when it appeared either in the form of *dementia* and of imbecility, or in the form of *furor.* In both cases, whether it was a matter of a permanent state or a passing outburst, insanity manifested itself through numerous signs which were easy enough to recognize, to the extent that it was debated whether a doctor was really necessary to authenticate it. The important thing is that criminal psychiatry did not develop from a subtle redefining of the traditional question of *dementia* (e.g., by discussing its gradual evolution, its global or partial character, its relationship to congenital disabilities of individuals) nor through a closer analysis of the symptomatology of *furor* (its remissions, it recurrences, its rhythm). All these problems, along with the discussions which had gone on for years, were replaced by a new problem, that of crimes which are neither preceded, nor accompanied, nor followed by any of the traditional, recognized, visible symptoms of insanity. It is stressed in each case that there was no previous history, no earlier disturbance in thought or behavior, no delirium; neither was there any agitation, nor visible disorder as in *furor*; indeed, the crime would arise out of a state which one might call the zero degree of insanity.

The second common feature is too obvious to be dealt with at any length. The crimes in question are not minor offenses but serious crimes, almost all murders, sometimes accompanied by strange cruelties (cannibalism in the case of the woman from Selestat). It is important to note that the psychiatrization of delinquency occurred in a sense "from above." This is also a departure from the fundamental tendency of previous jurisprudence. The more serious the crime, the less usual it was to raise the question of insanity (for a long period, it was not taken into consideration in cases involving sacrilege or lèse-majesté). That there is a considerable area of overlap between insanity and illegality was readily admitted in the case of minor offenses – little acts of violence, vagrancy – and these were dealt with, at least in some countries such as France, by the ambiguous measure of internment. But it was not through the ill-defined zone of day to day disorders that psychiatry was able to penetrate penal justice in full force. Rather it was by tackling the great criminal event of the most violent and rarest sort.

Another common feature of these great murders is that they take place in a domestic setting. They are family crimes, household crimes, and at most neighborhood crimes – parents who kill their progeny, children who kill their parents or guardians, servants who kill their employers' or their neighbors' child, etc. As we can see, these are crimes which bring together partners from different generations. The child-adult or adolescent-adult couple is almost always present. In those days, such relationships of age, of place, of kinship were held to be at the same time the most sacred and the most natural, and also the most innocent. Of all relationships, they were the ones which ought to have been the least charged with material motive or passion. Rather than crimes against society and its rules, they are crimes against nature, against those laws which are perceived to be inscribed directly on the human heart and which link families and generations. At the beginning of the nineteenth century, the form of crime about which it appeared that the question of insanity could properly be raised was thus the crime against nature. The individual in whom insanity and criminality met in such a way as to cause specialists to raise the question of their relationship, was not the man of the little everyday disorder, the pale silhouette moving about on the edges of law and normality, but rather the great monster. Criminal psychiatry first proclaimed itself a pathology of the monstrous.

Finally, all of these crimes were committed without reason, I mean without profit, without passion, without motive, even based on disordered illusions. In all the cases which I have mentioned, the psychiatrists do justify their intervention by insisting that there existed between the two actors in the drama no relationship which would help to make the crime intelligible. In the case of Henriette Cornier, who had decapitated her neighbor's daughter, it was carefully established that she had not been the father's mistress, and that she had not acted out of vengeance. In the case of the woman from Selestat, who had boiled up her daughter's thigh, an important element of the discussion had been, "Was there or was there not famine at the time? Was the accused poor or not, starving or not?" The public prosecutor had said: "If she had been rich, she could have been considered deranged, but she was poverty-stricken; she was hungry; to cook the leg with the cabbage was interested behavior; she was therefore not insane."

At the time when the new psychiatry was being established, and when the principles of penal reform were being applied nearly everywhere in Europe and in North America, the great and monstrous murder, without reason, without preliminaries, the sudden eruption of the unnatural in nature, was the singular and paradoxical form taken by criminal insanity or pathological crime. I say paradoxical since there was an attempt to grasp a type of derangement which manifested itself only in the moment and in the guise of the crime, a derangement which would have no symptom other than the crime itself, and which could disappear once the crime had been committed. And conversely, it entailed identifying crimes whose reason, whose author, whose "legally responsible agent" so to speak, is that part of the subject which is beyond his responsibility; that is, the insanity which hides in him and which he cannot even control because he is frequently not even aware of it. Nineteenth-century psychiatry invented an entirely fictitious entity, a crime which is insanity, a crime which is nothing but insanity, an insanity which is nothing but crime. For more than half a century this entity was called homicidal monomania. I do not intend to go over the theoretical background of the notion, nor to follow up the innumerable discussions which it prompted between men of the law and doctors, lawyers and magistrates. I simply want to underline this strange fact, that psychiatrists have tried very stubbornly to take their place in the legal machinery. They justified their right to intervene, not by searching out the thousand little visible signs of madness which may accompany the most ordinary crimes, but by insisting – a preposterous stance – that there were kinds of insanity which manifested themselves only in outrageous crimes, and in no other way. And I would also like to underline the fact that, in spite of all their reservations about accepting this notion of monomania, when the magistrates of the time finally accepted the psychiatric analysis of crime, they did so on the basis of this same notion, so foreign and so unacceptable to them.

Why was the great fiction of homicidal mania the key notion in the protohistory of criminal psychiatry? The first set of questions to be asked is probably the following: at the beginning of the nineteenth century, when the task of psychiatry was to define its specificity in the field of medicine and to assure that its scientific character was recognized among other medical practices, at the point, that is, when psychiatry was establishing itself as a medical specialization (previously it had been an aspect rather than a field of medicine), why then did it want to meddle in an area where so far it had intervened very discretely? Why did doctors want so badly to describe as insane, and thus to claim, people whose status as mere criminals had up to that point been unquestioned? Why can they be found in so many countries, denouncing the medical ignorance of judges and jurors, requesting pardons or the commutation of punishment for certain convicts, demanding the right to be heard as experts by the tribunals, publishing hundreds of reports and studies to show that this criminal or that one was a madman? Why this crusade in favor of the "pathologification" of crime, and under the banner, no less, of homicidal mania? This is all the more paradoxical in that, shortly before, at the end of the eighteenth century, the very first students of insanity (especially Pinel) protested against the practice followed in many detention centers of mixing delinquents and the mentally ill. Why would one want to renew a kinship which one had taken such trouble to break down?

It is not enough to invoke some sort of imperialism on the part of psychiatrists seeking a new domain for themselves, or even the internal dynamics of medical knowledge attempting to rationalize the confused area where madness and crime mix. Crime then became an important issue for psychiatrists, because what was involved was less a field of knowledge to be conquered than a modality of power to be secured and justified. If psychiatry became so important in the nineteenth century, it was not simply because it applied a new medical rationality to mental or behavioral disorders, it was also because it functioned as a sort of public hygiene.

In the eighteenth century, the development of demography, of urban structures, of the problem of industrial labor, had raised in biological and medical terms the question of human "populations," with their conditions of existence, of habitation, of nutrition, with their birth and mortality rate, with their pathological phenomena (epidemics, endemic diseases, infant mortality). The social "body" ceased to be a simple juridico-political metaphor (like the one in the *Leviathan*) and became a biological reality and a field for medical intervention. The doctor must therefore be the technician of this social body, and medicine a public hygiene. At the turn of the nineteenth century, psychiatry became an autonomous discipline and assumed such prestige precisely because it had been able to develop within the framework of a medical discipline conceived of as a reaction to the dangers inherent in the social body. The alienists of the period may well have had endless discussions about the organic or psychic origin of mental illnesses; they may well have proposed physical or psychic therapies. Nonetheless, through all their differences, they were all conscious that they were treating a social "danger," either because insanity seemed to them to be linked to living conditions (overpopulation, overcrowding, urban life, alcoholism, debauchery), or because it was perceived as a source of danger for oneself, for others, for one's contemporaries, and also for one's descendants through heredity. Nineteenth-century psychiatry was a medical science as much for the societal body as for the individual soul.

One can see why it was important for psychiatry to prove the existence of something as extravagant as homicidal mania. One can see why for half a century there were continuous attempts to make that notion work, in spite of its meager scientific justification. Indeed, if it exists, homicidal mania shows:

First, that in some of its pure, extreme, intense manifestations, insanity is entirely crime, nothing but crime – that is, at least at the ultimate boundaries of insanity, there is crime;

Second, that insanity can produce not just behavioral disorders, but absolute crime, the crime which transgresses all the laws of nature and of society; and

Third, that even though this insanity may be extraordinarily intense, it remains invisible until it explodes; that for this reason no one can forecast it, unless he has considerable experience and a trained eye. In short, only a specialist can spot monomania. The contradiction is more apparent than real when the alienists eventually define monomania as an illness which manifests itself only in crime while at the same time they reserve the right to know how to determine its premonitory signs, its predisposing conditions.

So, homicidal mania is the danger of insanity in its most harmful form; a maximum of consequences, a minimum of warning. The most effects and fewest signs. Homicidal mania thus necessitates the intervention of a medical eye which must take into account not only the obvious manifestations of madness but also the barely perceptible traces, appearing randomly where they are the least expected, and foretelling the worst explosions. Such an interest in the great crimes "without reason" does not, I think, indicate on the part of psychiatry a desire to take over criminality, but a desire to justify its functions: the control of the dangers hidden in human behavior. What is at stake in this great issue of homicidal mania is the function of psychiatry. It must not be forgotten that in most western countries psychiatry was then striving to establish its right to impose upon the mentally ill a therapeutic confinement. After all, it had to be shown that madness, by its nature, and even in its most discrete manifestations, was haunted by the absolute danger, death. The functioning of modern psychiatry is linked to this kinship between madness and death, which was not scientifically established, but rather symbolically represented in the figure of homicidal mania.

However, there is another question to be asked, this time from the point of view of the judges and the judicial apparatus. Why indeed did they accept, if not the notion of monomania, at least the problems that it entailed? It will probably be said that the great majority of magistrates refused to recognize this notion which made it possible to transform a criminal into a madman whose only illness was to commit crimes. With a great deal of tenacity and, one might add, with a certain degree of good sense, they did everything they could to dismiss this notion which the doctors proposed to them and which lawyers used spontaneously to defend their clients. And yet, through this controversy about monstrous crimes, about crimes "without reason," the idea of a possible kinship between madness and delinquency became acclimatized even within the judicial institution. Why was this accomplished, and relatively easily at that? In other words, why did the penal institution, which had been able to do without medical intervention for so many centuries, which had been able to judge and condemn without the problem of madness being raised except in a few obvious cases, why did this penal institution so willingly have recourse to medical knowledge from the 1820s on? For there is no mistaking the fact that English, German, Italian, and French judges of the time quite often refused to accept the conclusions of the doctors. They rejected many of the notions which the doctors proposed to them. After all, the doctors did not take them by force. They themselves solicited – following the laws, the rules, the jurisprudence which vary from country to country – the duly formulated advice of psychiatrists, and they solicited it especially in connection with those famous crimes "without reason." Why? Was it because the new codes written and applied at the beginning of the nineteenth century took into account psychiatric expertise or gave a new emphasis to the problem of pathological irresponsibility? Not at all. Surprisingly enough these new laws hardly modified the previous situation. Most of the codes based on the Napoleonic model incorporated the old principle that the state of mental disorder is incompatible with legal responsibility and thus is immune from the usual legal consequences. Most of the codes also incorporate the traditional notions of *dementia* and *furor* used in the older legal systems. Neither the great theoreticians like Beccaria and Bentham, nor those who actually wrote up the new penal laws, tried to elaborate upon these traditional notions, nor to establish new relationships between punishment and criminal medicine, except to affirm in a very general way that penal justice must cure this illness of societies, i.e., crime. It was not "from above," by way of legal codes or theoretical principles, that psychiatric medicine penetrated the penal system. Rather, it was "from below," through the mechanics of punishment and through the interpretation given to them. Among all the new techniques for controlling and transforming individuals, punishment had become a system of procedures designed to reform lawbreakers. The terrifying example of torture or exile by banishment could no longer suffice in a society where exercise of power implied a reasoned technology applied to individuals. The forms of punishment to which all the late eighteenth-century reformers, and all the early nineteenth-century legislators rallied – that is, imprisonment, forced labor, constant surveillance, partial or total isolation, moral reform – all this implies that punishment bears on the criminal himself rather than on the crime, that is on what makes him a criminal, on his reasons, his motives, his inner will, his tendencies, his instincts. In the older systems, the horror of the punishment had to reflect the enormity of the crime; henceforth, the attempt was made to adapt the modalities of punishment to the nature of the criminal.

In these circumstances, one sees why the great unmotivated crimes posed a difficult problem for the judges. In the past, to impose a punishment for a crime one had only to find the author of the crime, and it was enough that he had no excuse and that he had not been in a state of *furor* or *dementia*. But how can one punish someone whose reasons are unknown, and who keeps silent before his judges, except to admit the facts and to agree that he had been perfectly conscious of what he was doing? What is to be done when a woman like Henriette Cornier appears in court, a woman who has killed a child whom she hardly knew, the daughter of people whom she could neither have hated nor loved, who decapitates the girl but is unable to give the slightest explanation, who does not try for a moment to hide her crime, and who had nonetheless prepared for her act, had chosen the moment, had procured a knife, had eagerly sought an opportunity to be alone for a moment with her victim? Thus, in a person who had given no sign of madness, there arises an act which is at once voluntary, conscious, and reasoned – that is, all that is necessary for a condemnation according to the terms of the law – and yet nothing, no reason, no motive, no evil tendencies, which would have made it possible to determine what should be punished in the guilty woman. It is clear that there should be a condemnation, but it is hard to understand why there should be a punishment, except of course for the external but insufficient reason of setting an example. Now that the reason for the crime had become the reason for the punishment, how could one punish if the crime was without reason? In order to punish, one needs to know the nature of the guilty person, his obduracy, the degree of his evilness, what his interests or his leanings are. But if one has nothing more than the crime on one hand and the author on the other, pure and simple judicial responsibility formally authorizes punishment, yet does not allow one to make sense of it.

One can see why these great unmotivated crimes, which the psychiatrists had good reason to emphasize, were also, but for very different reasons, such important problems for the judicial apparatus. The public prosecutors obstinately referred to the law: no *dementia*, no *furor*, no recognized evidence of derangement; on the contrary, perfectly organized acts; therefore, the law must be applied. But no matter how hard they tried, they could not avoid the question of motivation, for they knew very well that from now on, in practice, the judges would link punishment, at least in part, to the determination of motives. Perhaps Henriette Cornier had been the mistress of the girl's father, and sought revenge; perhaps, having had to abandon her own children, she was jealous of the happy family living near her. All the indictments prove that in order for the punitive mechanism to work, the reality of an offense and a person to whom it can be attributed are not sufficient; the motive must also be established, that is, a psychologically intelligible link between the act and the author. The Selestat case, in which a cannibalistic woman was executed because she *could* have been hungry, seems to me to be very significant.

The doctors who were normally called in only to certify cases of *dementia* or of *furor* began now to be called upon as "specialists in motivation"; they had to evaluate not only the subject's reason but also the rationality of the act, the whole system of relationships which link the act to the interests, the plans, the character, the inclinations, and the habits of the subject. And even though the judges were often reluctant to accept the diagnosis of monomania so relished by the doctors, they were obliged to entertain willingly the set of problems raised by the notion: that is, in slightly more modern terms, the integration of the act into the global behavior of the subject. The more clearly visible this integration, the more clearly punishable the subject. The less obvious the integration, the more it seems as if the act has erupted in the subject, like a sudden and irrepressible mechanism, and the less punishable the responsible party appears. And justice will then agree that it cannot proceed with the case since the subject is insane, and will commit him to psychiatric confinement.

Several conclusions can be drawn from this:

First, the intervention of psychiatric medicine in the penal system starting in the 19th century is neither the consequence nor the simple development of the traditional theory of the irresponsibility of those suffering from *dementia* or *furor*.

Second, it is due to the regulating of two phenomena arising necessarily, one from the functioning of medicine as a public hygiene, the other from the functioning of legal punishment as a technique for transforming the individual.

Third, these two new demands are both bound up with the transformation of the mechanism of power through which the control of the social body has been attempted in industrial societies since the eighteenth century. But in spite of their common origin, the reasons for the intervention of medicine in the criminal field and the reasons for the recourse of penal justice to psychiatry are essentially different.

Fourth, the monstrous crime, both anti-natural and irrational, is the meeting point of the medical demonstration that insanity is ultimately always dangerous, and of the court's inability to determine the punishment of a crime without having determined the motives for the crime. The bizarre symptomatology of homicidal mania was designed at the point of convergence of these two mechanisms.

Fifth, in this way, the theme of the dangerous man is inscribed in the institutions of psychiatry as well as of justice. Increasingly in the nineteenth and twentieth century, penal practice and then penal theory will tend to make of the dangerous individual the principal target of punitive intervention. Increasingly, nineteenth-century psychiatry will also tend to seek out pathological stigmata which may mark dangerous individuals: moral insanity, instinctive insanity, and degeneration. This theme of the dangerous individual will give rise on the one hand to the anthropology of criminal man as in the Italian school, and on the other to the theory of social defense first represented by the Belgian school.

Sixth, another important consequence is that there will be a considerable transformation of the old notion of penal responsibility. This notion, at least in certain respects, was still close to civil law. It was necessary, for instance, in order to impute a violation to someone, that he be free, conscious, unafflicted by *dementia*, untouched by any crisis of *furor*. Now responsibility would no longer be limited only to this form of consciousness but to the intelligibility of the act with reference to the conduct, the character, the antecedents of the individual. The more psychologically determined an act is found to be, the more its author can be considered legally responsible. The more the act is, so to speak, gratuitous and undetermined, the more it will tend to be excused. A paradox, then: the legal freedom of a subject is proven by the fact that his act is seen to be necessary, determined; his lack of responsibility proven by the fact that his act is seen to be unnecessary. With this untenable paradox of monomania and of the monstrous act, psychiatry and penal justice entered a phase of uncertainty from which we have yet to emerge; the play between penal responsibility and psychological determinism has become the cross of legal and medical thought.

I would now like to turn to another moment which was particularly fertile for the relationship between psychiatry and penal law: the last years of the nineteenth century and the first few of the twentieth from the first congress on Criminal Anthropology (1885) to Prinz's publication of his *Social Defence* (1910).

Between the period which I was recalling previously and the one I would like to speak about now, what happened? First of all, within the discipline of psychiatry in the strict sense of the term, the notion of monomania was abandoned, not without some hesitations and reversions, shortly before 1870. Abandoned for two reasons: first because the essentially negative idea of a partial insanity, bearing on only one point and unleashed only at certain moments, was gradually replaced by the idea that a mental illness is not necessarily an affliction of thought or of consciousness, but that it may attack the emotions, the instincts, spontaneous behavior, leaving the forms of thought virtually intact. (What was called moral insanity, instinctive insanity, aberration of the instincts, and finally perversion, corresponds to this elaboration, whose favored example since about the 1840s has been the deviations in sexual conduct.) But there was another reason for abandoning monomania; that is, the idea of mental illness, whose evolution is complex and polymorphous, and which may present one particular symptom or another at one stage or another of their development, not only at the level of the individual but also at the level of several generations; in short, the idea of degeneration.

Because of the fact that these great evolutive ramifications can be defined, it is no longer necessary to make a distinction between the great monstrous and mysterious crimes which could be ascribed to the incomprehensible violence of *insanity* and minor delinquency, which is too frequent, too familiar to necessitate a recourse to the pathological. From then on, whether one had to deal with incomprehensible massacres or minor offenses (having to do with property or sexuality), in every case one might suspect a more or less serious perturbation of instincts or the stages in an uninterruped process. Thus there appear in the field of legal psychiatry new categories, such as necrophilia around 1840, kleptomania around 1860, exhibitionism in 1876, and also legal psychiatry's annexation of behavior like pederasty and sadism. There now exists, at least in principle, a psychiatric and criminological continuum which permits one to pose questions in medical terms at any level of the penal scale. The psychiatric question is no longer confined to some great crimes; even if it must receive a negative answer, it is to be posed across the whole range of infractions.

Now this has important consequences for the legal theory of responsibility. In the conception of monomania, suspicions of pathology were aroused precisely when there was no reason for an act; insanity was seen as the cause of that which made no sense, and legal non-responsibility was established in view of this inconsistency. But with this new analysis of instinct and emotions, it will be possible to provide a causal analysis for all kinds of conduct, whether delinquent or not, and whatever their degree of criminality. Hence the infinite labyrinth in which the legal and psychiatric problem of crime found itself. If an act is determined by a causal nexus, can it be considered to be free? Does it not imply responsibility? And is it necessary, in order to be able to condemn someone, that it be impossible to reconstruct the causal intelligibility of his act?

Now, as background for this new way of posing the problem, I must mention several transformations which were, at least in part, the conditions of its being possible. First the intensive development of the police network, which led to a new mapping and closer surveillance of urban space and also to a much more systematic and efficient prosecution of minor delinquency. It must be added that social conflicts, class struggles and political confrontations, armed revolts – from the machine-smashers of the beginning of the century to the anarchists of the last few years of the century, including the violent strikes, the revolutions of 1848 and the Commune of 1870 – prompted those in power to treat political misdemeanors in the same way as ordinary crimes in order to discredit them. Little by little an image was built up of an enemy of society who can equally well be a revolutionary or a murderer, since after all revolutionaries do sometimes kill. Corresponding to this, throughout the whole second half of the century there developed a "literature of criminality," and I use the word in its largest sense, including miscellaneous news items (and, even more, popular newspapers) as well as detective novels and all the romanticized writings which developed around crime – the transformation of the criminal into a hero, perhaps, but, equally, the affirmation that ever-present criminality is a constant menace to the social body as a whole. The collective fear of crime, the obsession with this danger which seems to be an inseparable part of society itself, are thus perpetually inscribed in each individual consciousness.

Referring to the 9,000 murders then recorded annually in Europe, not counting Russia, Garofalo said in the Preface to the first edition of his *Criminology* (1887): "Who is the enemy who has devastated this land? It is a mysterious enemy, unknown to history; his name is: the criminal."

To this must be added another element: the continuing failure of the penitentiary system, which is very frequently reported. It was the dream of the eighteenth-century reformers, then of the philanthropists of the following period, that incarceration, provided that it be rationally directed, might serve as a true penal therapy. The result was meant to be the reform of the prisoners. It soon became clear that prison had exactly the opposite result, that it was on the whole a school for delinquency and that the more refined methods of the police system and the legal apparatus, far from insuring better protection against crime, brought about a strengthening of the criminal milieu, through the medium of prison itself.

For all sorts of reasons, a situation existed such that there was a very strong social and political demand for a reaction to, and for repression of, crime. This demand had to do with a criminality which in its totality had to be thought of in judicial and medical terms, and yet, the key notion of the penal institution since the Middle Ages, that is, legal responsibility, seems utterly inadequate for the conceptualization of this broad and dense domain of medico-legal criminality.

This inadequacy became apparent, both at the conceptual and at the institutional level, in the conflict between the so-called school of Criminal Anthropology and the International Association of Penal Law around the 1890s. In attempting to cope with the traditional principles of criminal legislation, the Italian School (the Criminal Anthropologists) called for nothing less than a putting aside of legality – a true "depenalization" of crime, by setting up an apparatus of an entirely different type from the one provided for by the Codes.

For the Criminal Anthropologists this meant totally abandoning the judicial notion of responsibility, and posing as the fundamental question not the degree of freedom of the individual, but the level of danger he represents for society. Moreover, it meant noting that the accused whom the law recognized as not responsible because he was ill, insane, a victim of irresistible impulses, was precisely the most seriously and immediately dangerous. The Criminal Anthropologists emphasized that what is called "penalty" does not have to be a punishment, but rather a mechanism for the defense of society, and therefore noted that the relevant difference is not between legally responsible subjects to be found guilty, and legally irresponsible subjects to be released, but between absolutely and definitively dangerous subjects and those who can cease to be dangerous provided they receive certain treatment. They concluded that there should be three main types of social reaction to crime or rather to the danger represented by the criminal: definitive elimination (by death or by incarceration in an institution), temporary elimination (with treatment), and more or less relative and partial elimination (sterilization and castration).

One can see the series of shifts required by the anthropological school: from the crime to the criminal; from the act as it was actually committed to the danger potentially inherent in the individual; from the modulated punishment of the guilty party to the absolute protection of others. All these shifts implied quite clearly an escape from a universe of penal law revolving around the act, its imputability to a *de jure* subject, the legal responsibility of the latter and a punishment proportionate to the gravity of this act as defined by law. Neither the "criminality" of an individual, nor the index of his dangerousness, nor his potential or future behavior, nor the protection of society at large from these possible perils, none of these are, nor can they be, juridical notions in the classical sense of the term. They can be made to function in a rational way only within a technical knowledge-system, a knowledge-system capable of characterizing a criminal individual in himself and in a sense beneath his acts; a knowledge-system able to measure the index of danger present in an individual; a knowledge-system which might establish the protection necessary in the face of such a danger. Hence the idea that crime ought to be the responsibility not of judges but of experts in psychiatry, criminology, psychology, etc. Actually, that extreme conclusion was not often formulated in such an explicit and radical way, no doubt through practical prudence. But it followed implicitly from all the theses of Criminal Anthropology. And at the second meeting of this Association (1889), Pugliese expressed it straightforwardly. We must, he said, turn around the old adage: the judge is the expert of experts; it is rather up to the expert to be the judge of judges. "The commission of medical experts to whom the judgment ought to be referred should not limit itself to expressing its wishes; on the contrary it should render a real decision."

It can be said that a point of break-down was being reached. Criminology, which had developed out of the old notion of monomania, maintaining a frequently stormy relationship with penal law, was in danger of being excluded from it as excessively radical. This would have led to a situation similar to the original one; a technical knowledge-system incompatible with law, besieging it from without and unable to make itself heard. As the notion of monomania could be used to overlay with madness a crime with no apparent reasons, so, to some extent, the notion of degeneration made it possible to link the most insignificant of criminals to a peril of pathological dimensions for society, and, eventually, for the whole human species. The whole field of infractions could be held together in terms of danger and thus of protection to be provided. The law had only to hold its tongue. Or to plug its ears and refuse to listen.

It is usual to say that the fundamental propositions of criminal anthropology were fairly rapidly disqualified for a number of reasons: because they were linked to a form of scientism, to a certain positivist naïveté which the very development of the sciences in the twentieth century has taken upon itself to cure; because they were related to historical and social evolutionism which was itself quickly discredited; because they found support in a neuropsychiatric theory of degeneration which both neurology and psychoanalysis have quickly dismantled; and because they were unable to become operational within the format of penal legislation and within legal practice. The age of criminal anthropology, with its radical naïvetés, seems to have disappeared with the 19th century; and a much more subtle psycho-sociology of delinquency, much more acceptable to penal law, seems to have taken up the fight.

It seems to me that, at least in its general outlines, criminal anthropology has not disappeared as completely as some people say, and that a number of its most fundamental theses, often those most foreign to traditional law, have gradually taken root in penal thought and practice. But this could not have happened solely by virtue of the truth of this psychiatric theory of crime, or rather solely through its persuasive force. In fact there had been a significant mutation within the law. When I say "within the law," I probably say too much, for, with a few exceptions (such as the Norwegian code, but after all it was written for a new state) and aside from some projects left in limbo (such as the Swiss plan for a penal code), penal legislation remained pretty well unchanged. The laws relating to suspension of sentence, recidivism, or relegation were the principal modifications somewhat hesitantly made in French legislation. This is not where I see the significant mutations, but rather in connection with an element at the same time theoretical and essential, namely the notion of responsibility.

And it was possible to modify this notion not so much because of the pressure of some internal shock but mainly because a considerable evolution had taken place in the area of civil law during the same period. My hypothesis would be that it was civil law, not criminology, which made it possible for penal thought to change on two or three major points. It was civil law which made it possible to graft onto criminal law the essential elements of the criminological theses of the period. It may well be that without the reformulation which occurred first in civil law, the jurists would have turned a deaf ear to the fundamental propositions of criminal anthropology, or at least would never have possessed the proper tool for integrating them into the legal system. In a way which may at first seem strange, it was civil law which made possible the articulation of the legal code and of science in penal law.

This transformation in civil law revolves around the notion of accident and legal responsibility. In a very general way, it is worth emphasizing the significance which the problem of accidents had, not only for law but also for economics and politics, especially in the second half of the nineteenth century. One could object that since the sixteenth century, insurance plans had shown how important the idea of risk had already become. But on the one hand, insurance dealt only with more-or-less individual risks and on the other, it entirely excluded the legal responsibility of the interested party. In the nineteenth century, the development of wage-earning, of industrial techniques, of mechanization, of transportation, of urban structures, brought with it two important things. First, risks were incurred by third parties (the employer exposed his employees to work-related accidents; transport companies exposed not only their passengers to accidents but also people who just happened to be there). Then, the fact that these accidents could often be linked to a sort of error – but a minor error (inattention, lack of precaution, negligence) committed moreover by someone who could not carry the civil responsibility for it nor pay the ensuing damages. The problem was to establish in law the concept of no-fault responsibility. It was the effort of Western civil legislators and especially German jurists, influenced as they were by the demands of Bismarckian society – a society characterized not only be discipline but also by security-consciousness. In this search for a no-fault responsibility, the civil legislators emphasized a certain number of important principles:

First, this responsibility must be established not according to the series of errors committed but according to the chain of causes and effects. Responsibility is on the side of cause, rather than on the side of fault. This is what German jurists meant by *Causahaftung*.

Second, these causes are of two orders which are not mutually exclusive: the chain of precise and individual facts, each of which has been induced by the preceding one; and the creation of risks inherent in a type of action, of equipment, of enterprise.

Third, granted, these risks are to be reduced in the most systematic and rigorous way possible. But they will certainly never by made to disappear; none of the characteristic undertakings of modern society will be without risk. As Saleilles said, "a causal relationship linked to a purely material fact which in itself appears as an adventurous fact, not in itself irregular, nor contrary to the customs of modern life, but contemptuous of that extreme caution which paralyzes action, in harmony with the activity which is imperative today and therefore defying hatreds and accepting risks, that is the law of life today, that is the common rule, and law is made to reflect this contemporary conception of the soul, in the course of its successive evolution."

Fourth, since this no-fault liability is linked to a risk which can never entirely be eliminated, indemnity is not meant to sanction it as a sort of punishment, but to repair its effects and also to tend, in an asymptotic way, towards an eventual reduction of its risks. By eliminating the element of fault within the system of liability, the civil legislators introduced into law the notion of causal probability and of risk, and they brought forward the idea of a sanction whose function would be to defend, to protect, to exert pressure on inevitable risks.

In a rather strange way, this depenalization of civil liability would constitute a model for penal law, on the basis of the fundamental propositions formulated by criminal anthropology. After all, what is a "born criminal" or a degenerate, or a criminal personality, if not someone who, according to a causal chain which is difficult to restore, carries a particularly high index of criminal probability, and is in himself a criminal risk? Well, just as one can determine civil liability without establishing fault, but solely by estimating the risk created and against which it is necessary to build up a defense (although it can never be eliminated), in the same way, one can render an individual responsible under law without having to determine whether he was acting freely and therefore whether there was fault, but rather by linking the act committed to the risk of criminality which his very personality constitutes. He is responsible since by his very existence he is a creator of risk, even if he is not at fault, since he has not of his own free will chosen evil rather than good. The purpose of the sanction will therefore not be to punish a legal subject who has voluntarily broken the law; its role will be to reduce as much as possible – either by elimination, or by exclusion or by various restrictions, or by therapeutic measures – the risk of criminality represented by the individual in question.

The general idea of the *Social Defence* as it was put forward by Prinz at the beginning of the twentieth century was developed by transferring to criminal justice formulations proper to the new civil law. The history of the conferences on Criminal Anthropology and conferences on penal law at the turn of the century, the chronicle of the conflicts between positivist scholars and traditional jurists, and the sudden détente which occurred at the time of Liszt, of Saleilles, of Prinz, the rapid eclipse of the Italian School after that, but also the reduction of the jurists' resistance to the psychological approach to the criminal, the establishment of a relative consensus around a criminology which would be accessible to the law, and of a system of sanctions which would take into account criminological knowledge – all of these seem indeed to indicate that at that moment the required "shunting switch" had just been found. This "switch" is the key notion of *risk* which the law assimilates through the idea of a no-fault liability, and which anthropology, or psychology, or psychiatry can assimilate through the idea of imputability without freedom. The term, henceforth central, of "dangerous being," was probably introduced by Prinz at the September 1905 session of the International Union of Penal Law.

I will not list here the innumerable legal codes, rules, and memoranda which carried into effect, in one way or another, this notion of the *dangerous state* of an individual in penal institutions throughout the world. Let me simply underline a couple of things.

First, since the great crimes without reason of the early 19th century, the debate did not in fact revolve so much around freedom, even though the question was always there. The real problem, the one which was in effect throughout, was the problem of the dangerous individual. Are there individuals who are intrinsically dangerous? By what signs can they be recognized, and how can one react to their presence? In the course of the past century, penal law did not evolve from an ethic of freedom to a science of psychic determinism; rather, it enlarged, organized, and codified the suspicion and the locating of dangerous individuals, from the rare and monstrous figure of the monomaniac to the common everyday figure of the degenerate, of the pervert, of the constitutionally unbalanced, of the immature, etc.

It must also be noted that this transformation took place not only from medicine towards law, as through the pressure of rational knowledge on older prescriptive systems; but that it also operated through a perpetual mechanism of summoning and of interacting between medical or psychological knowledge and the judicial institution. It was not the latter which yielded. A set of objects and of concepts was born at their boundaries and from their interchanges.

This is the point which I would like to stress, for it seems that most of the notions thus formed are operational for legal medicine or for psychiatric expertise in criminal matters. But has not something more been introduced into the law than the uncertainties of a problematic knowledge – to wit, the rudiments of another type of law? For the modern system of sanctions – most strikingly since Beccaria – gives society a claim to individuals only because of what they do. Only an act, defined by law as an infraction, can result in a sanction, modifiable of course according to the circumstances or the intentions. But by bringing increasingly to the fore not only the criminal as author of the act, but also the dangerous individual as potential source of acts, does one not give society rights over the individual based on what he is? No longer, of course, based on what he is by statute (as was the case in the societies under the Ancien Régime), but based on what he is by nature, according to his constitution, character traits, or his pathological variables. A form of justice which tends to be applied to what one is, this is what is so outrageous when one thinks of the penal law of which the eighteenth-century reformers had dreamed, and which was intended to sanction, in a completely egalitarian way, offenses explicitly defined beforehand by the law.

It could be objected that in spite of this general principle, even in the nineteenth century the right to punish was applied and varied on the basis not only of what men do, but also of what they are, or of what it is supposed that they are. Hardly had the great modern codes been established when attempts were made to mitigate them by legislation such as the laws dealing with extenuating circumstances, with recidivism, and with conditional release. It was a matter of taking into account the author behind the acts that had been committed. And a complete and comparative study of the legal decisions would no doubt easily show that on the penal stage the offenders were at least as present as their offenses. A form of justice which would be applied only to what one does is probably purely utopian and not necessarily desirable. But since the eighteenth century at least, it has constituted the guiding principle, the juridico-moral principle which governs the modern system of sanctions. There was therefore no question, there can still be no question, of suddenly putting it aside. Only insidiously, slowly, and as it were from below and fragmentally, has a system of sanctions based on what one *is* been taking shape. It has taken nearly one hundred years for the notion of "dangerous individual," which was potentially present in the monomania of the first alienists, to be accepted in judicial thought. After one hundred years, although this notion may have become a central theme in psychiatric expertise (in France psychiatrists appointed as experts speak about the dangerousness of an individual much more than about his responsibility), the law and the codes seem reluctant to give it a place. The revision of the penal code presently underway in France has just barely succeeded in replacing the older notion of *dementia* (which made the author of an act not responsible), with the notions of discernment and control which are in effect only another version of the same thing, hardly modernized at all. Perhaps this indicates a foreboding of the dreadful dangers inherent in authorizing the law to intervene against individuals because of what they are; a horrifying society could emerge from that.

Nonetheless, on the functional level, judges more and more need to believe that they are judging a man as he is and according to what he is. The scene which I described at the beginning bears witness to this. When a man comes before his judges with nothing but his crimes, when he has nothing else to say but "this is what I have done," when he has nothing to say about himself, when he does not do the tribunal the favor of confiding to them something like the secret of his own being, then the judicial machine ceases to function.

[28]

Brit. J. Psychiat. (1977), 131, 127–42

Assessing Dangerousness in Criminals

By P. D. SCOTT

This article formulates a definition of the term dangerousness, indicates why the commission of dangerous offences cannot be reliably predicted, and then reviews the several factors which have been or might be used by those who have to make decisions about dangerousness in criminals. It suggests that these factors are useful insofar as they help to illuminate the individual's capacity to feel sympathy and to learn by experience. Since the accuracy of prediction varies inversely with time, the maintenance of personal relationships and good communication seems the inescapable requirement in the management of potentially dangerous criminals.

Introduction

Dangerousness is a dangerous concept (Shaw, 1973). It is difficult to define, yet very important decisions are based upon it; there is as yet little reliable research in relation to it; it is a term which raises anxiety and which is therefore peculiarly open to abuse, especially to over-response of a punitive, restrictive or dissociative nature. Because we have all experienced dangerous emotions there is the risk of projection and scapegoating. The label, which is easy to attach but difficult to remove, may contribute to its own continuance, or may become a convention for evading responsibility or for jumping treatment queues. To legislate for treatment (which, in the absence of transportation and judicial elimination, usually implies incarceration) before the nature and effect of that treatment is known, is very expensive in terms of liberty as well as services and often falls into disuse; there is a risk that the response will repeat the causes and thus lead to a vicious circle.

Definition of Dangerousness in Criminals

It is easier to say what dangerousness is not than what it is. It is not simply that which is noxious or evil, and it is not necessarily a violent, explosive trait of an individual; the man who smokes on a tanker is dangerous by reason of the explosive potential outside him. Similarly, in social animals, much dangerousness depends upon disturbing the often precarious adjustment of other individuals, especially within a group; hence the importance of behavioural conventions or what are now called good manners, which in effect announce the individual's self-control and his concern for the feelings of others. The media of mass communication besides modifying attitudes to, and expectations of, violence, also change the boundaries of groups. In this sense the dangerous individual is simply one who engenders too much anxiety. Dangerous degrees of anxiety are raised not so much by a single breach of convention as by the failure of the offender to respond to the countermeasures of society, and this is likely to indicate, or to be interpreted as, defiance. If our smoker on the tanker immediately responds to the angry order to 'douse that glim' dangerousness will not be implied, but if he does it again it is likely to be assumed that he is motivated, not by the gentle faults of fecklessness, foolishness or forgetfulness, but by dangerous intentions. Thus perception of a lack of response, or adaptiveness resulting in a tendency to repetition and incorrigibility, are likely to lead to a label of dangerousness in any person who has once demonstrated or threatened destructiveness. The context, nature and degree of this aggression or destructiveness will be important.

As to context, aggression will be most alarming in two situations, when society is totally unprepared for it, i.e. the appearance of a new form of attack; and when, having been painfully bitten, or nearly defeated, in this way on previous occasions, it is over-prepared, and likely to respond with a volley instead of a gesture. The nature of the behaviour which society is likely to label dangerous is that which is violent. Violence is aggression concentrated into brief time, and is not necessarily more destructive than continued aggression of lesser intensity. Possibly among many other reasons for the relative tolerance of this extensive aggression is the feeling that there is time to organize resistance, to call for help, or to take evasive action. The distance of the aggression from the body image is an important criterion of perceived dangerousness. In this sense attacks range between assault on the person on the one hand and destruction of public or unowned objects on the other. Offences in certain areas: burglary of the home, especially invasion of the bedroom, and damage to clothing and motor cars, are inclined to cause very marked distress or anger in the owners. Offences such as these, together with blackmail, are on the borderline of dangerousness and likely to raise impassioned debate when attempts to define the concept are made. Other factors, notably permanence of damage, may be helpful in reaching a conclusion. The question is often posed 'should psychological damage be included as well as personal or material damage and destruction'? Clearly psychological damage is very real and is frequently noted as a result of aggression. The Butler Committee's report (1975) includes 'lasting psychological harm' as well as serious physical injury. Psychological harm, especially that which is lasting, is so very difficult to distinguish from pre-existing idiosyncratic vulnerability, so intangible and so easy to claim or simulate, that it will offer, at present, insuperable difficulties.

A still more difficult problem is the point at which individually non-dangerous offences, if repeated sufficiently often, achieve dangerousness by their threat to the rule of law.

The criteria of degree and permanence of damage are obvious, but nonetheless difficult to quantify unless there is actual loss of function or of life. Walker (1969), in considering sentencing, asks 'How difficult would it be to undo the harm if it happened?' More difficult still is that factor which in a medical analogy would be called infectiousness, and which indicates the belief that others will be inclined to follow suit, to use this loophole in the law, to join the insurrection, to practise this clever form of deceit, or to gain ascendancy or preference in this new way.

The medical analogy is also inescapable in relation to the further criteria of treatability and predictability. If an 'attack' of dangerous violence can be anticipated and aborted, or treated, then it ceases to be dangerous. This emphasizes the further complex inter-relationship of the threatening organism with the responses or defences of the body of society. Society may deal with dangerousness by eradicating its causes, isolating its carriers, or acquiring immunity to its effects.

Dangerousness, then, is an unpredictable and untreatable tendency to inflict or risk serious, irreversible injury or destruction, or to induce others to do so. Dangerousness can, of course, be directed against the self.

This definition may be thought to be so unsatisfactory that it would be better for most purposes to substitute a probability figure of this or that sort of damaging behaviour occurring in this or that expected environment.

Prediction

Prediction of dangerousness is particularly difficult because: dangerousness is the resultant of a number of processes which occasionally may be synergistic amounting to more than the sum of their parts, some within the individual and some in society; it is not static; key factors are the individual's adaptiveness, resistance to change, and his intention (which Emile Durkheim said in 1897 is 'too intimate a thing to be interpreted by another person'): a common mistake is to confuse recidivism with dangerousness, they are not necessarily the same and may be combined in various patterns. Dangerous behaviour lies at the extreme of the aggression parameter, and most standardized tests tend to become unreliable at both their extremities, yet it is in just these areas that the most important decisions lie. Existing predictive scales tend to be over-inclusive; their results may be very useful for administrative purposes but are clinically unreliable; they are an encouragement to attempt treatment and a negation of nihilism, but give little help in the commonly posed distinction, not so much between nuisance and danger as between danger and extreme danger. The prognosis for dangerousness may be independent of the prognosis of coexisting conditions, for example the presence of a florid mental illness; such prognoses may even be reciprocal.

Steadman and Cocozza (1974), from their follow-up of nearly 1,000 supposedly dangerous Baxstrom patients, who had perforce been transferred to civil mental hospitals, wrote: 'If we attempt to distinguish the potentially dangerous patient, we double our error by identifying as dangerous all of a group of patients when only one third of them will live up to their expectations.' This was neatly capped by the medical superintendent of one of our own Special Hospitals who said he was sure half of his patients were not dangerous and could be safely released, but he wasn't sure which half.

Prediction studies should aim not to replace but to complement the clinical approach, and *vice versa*. This is well seen in our parole system, where the prediction score, made for every male candidate, is useful but not central in decision making.

We cannot at present hope, by taking infinitely careful aim, to direct our dangerous patient to safety like an arrow to its target; rather, through effective supervision, we must accompany him, being prepared to adapt to his varying needs, whether encouraging independence, moderating activity or recalling him to start again from the beginning.

Practical Issues

We have to rely on a combination of acumen, prediction and after-care. While this cannot be said to be reliable, it is pragmatic and certainly avoids or abbreviates many long terms of segregation, even though there may be occasional mistakes. If it is done it can be done better. What are the factors that can be looked for and fed to the diagnostic procedure, and from what different aspects should the problem be viewed? The following is an elementary practical guide to the more rational use of intuition.

The plan is to consider a series of factors seriatim, but realizing with Kozol (1972) that there are no direct indicators of dangerousness and that each factor may become important in the presence of other factors or may be neutralized by yet others. For some factors, especially personality traits, their correlation with dangerousness will only be of a high order if their definitions are nearly tautological. A good deal of confusion will be avoided if it is acknowledged that some factors may have positive (or negative) correlations with dangerousness at both ends of their scale (too much or too little). The extremes of some factors which in lesser degree predispose to dangerousness may in fact prevent it, e.g. a mild tendency to incest may permit restoration of the offender to his family and consequent repetition, whereas the children of an offender who showed a grosser tendency are likely to be removed permanently; similarly the severely subnormal person is likely to be under permanent supervision, while the subnormal is free to re-offend.

Before factors can be considered they must be gathered. It is patience, thoroughness and persistence in this process, rather than any diagnostic or interviewing brilliance, that produces results. In this sense the telephone, the written request for past records, and the checking of information against other informants, are the important diagnostic devices.

Having collected the facts under the headings: (1) the offence; (2) past behaviour; (3) personal data; (4) social circumstances it is useful then to scan them from a number of different directions with a view to answering certain key questions relating to dangerousness. The most important of these are concerned with the subject's capacity to feel sympathy with others, and his capacity to learn by experience.

(1) The offence

The legal category, even murder, arson and rape, is not very useful in determining dangerousness. It is axiomatic that all behaviour can be reached by different paths, each of which has different implications for the future. To put it another way, offence entities all tend to comprise a majority of benign cases which have made a single and temporary crossing of the threshold, and a malignant minority which are firmly entrenched across that threshold. Just as some of the major offences do not qualify for dangerousness, some of the lesser offences (theft, drunkenness) may.

The detail of the behaviour, on the other hand, is so valuable that opinions should not be stated until the fullest possible information, including at least the witnesses' statements and the depositions, has been obtained. Such detail helps very much in the essential reconstruction of the equation: offender + victim + circumstance = the offence; each element of the equation is equally important.

It is very difficult to generalize about the significance of offences committed in a group or alone. It will depend on whether the group is a loosely structured one (as occurs in youthful affrays and pack rapes) or a highly organized group of professional criminals. Members of organized groups using fire arms, sometimes re-offend in this way even after a long prison sentence and therefore have to be regarded as dangerous, whereas the youthful group members will very probably mature satisfactorily. Members of a structured gang are very much less likely to have any form of mental illness or any personality disorder, sufficient to prevent them relating to the other members, or sufficient to make their behaviour unreliable or unpredictable, for such qualities would be an embarassment and danger to the other members.

Much behaviour which at first sight seems insane, unadaptive, or inexplicable is seen to be rational when the longitudinal development of the incident is studied—the small steps by which it was reached, encouragement by a partner, the basic anxiety which the behaviour sought to allay (often very much greater than the fear of detection and punishment), the resonance of the provocation with previous, perhaps infantile experience. The impact of a breaking marriage may be very different in a man whose mother deserted when he was five.

It is sometimes difficult to accept that the provision of a rational understanding of behaviour may indicate greater, not less, dangerousness; rational behaviour may be exceedingly difficult to treat and very likely to recur. Explanation of behaviour does not eliminate its dangerousness, nor ensure treatability; it only poses further questions which must be answered before a conclusion can be reached.

Offence detail is informative in relation to the 'impulsive or prepared', 'provoked or spontaneous' questions. These two scales are identical, for a person is not impelled without provocation; provocation is no more than strong or persistent stimulation. The legal concept of provocation is a concession to human frailty and therefore must be strictly limited in its application (English, 1970; White, 1970; Brett, 1970), whereas, psychologically, provocation is a common or even usual element in violent behaviour. The principal differences between legal and lay concepts of provocation depend upon the failure of the law to recognize two sorts of provocation: displacement of aggression from a highly provoking source to an area which may be scarcely provoking at all; e.g. the situation in which the rejected wife kills her baby, saying to her husband (as Medea did) 'that will stab thy heart', and also the extremely common and potent provocation offered by a state of continued uncertainty, e.g. when a reluctant or frightened wife rejects but as it were leaves the door open and permits occasional contact; it is the vacillating rather than the abusing or aggressive wife who is most at risk. To the psychologist a degree of contemplation or even preparation and planning, or the use of apparently disproportionate force does not invalidate provocation as an operative factor in the assessment of dangerousness. But once again, such provocation only raises the further questions: will this situation arise again, are the offender, the victim (if still alive), and the environment open to significant modification?

Where the victim is no longer alive, the reasoning is sometimes heard: 'he has killed his mother and will never have another', or 'she has no further babies'; but, as Dr McGrath of Broadmoor has remarked 'Mothers have surrogates'; and battering mothers are fertile and seem to need babies. It is even more essential to recognize that most killings are domestic and therefore much involved with the quality of the marital relationship; there is much to suggest that assortative mating can lead to the repeated selection of an unsatisfactory or provoking spouse; some individuals may be regarded as life-long injustice or provocation collectors.

'Compulsive' has misleading implications in describing offenders. Unless the offender really feels that the behaviour is foreign to him, unless he resists it, and at no stage gives himself up to enjoying it (however much he regrets it afterwards), then it should be called impulsive, not compulsive. Compulsive offending is a myth.

Many dangerous offenders, believing that they cannot control their impulses, seek help from the police or from doctors. They must be taken seriously, for rejection of their angry dependency seems to facilitate the threatened crime. Some offenders, notably paedophiles, have a tendency to use psychiatric clinics as a sort of insurance policy against the next offence; their responsibility, if they wish to be at large, has to be made clear to them.

The degree of violence used in the current offence is often cited as a factor in predicting dangerousness and is thus used in sentencing. Multiplicity of stabs, blows or shots, as well as combinations of methods of killing have been variously attributed to:

(1) the degree of emotional involvement (Berg and Fox, 1947);
(2) the presence of mental illness (Reichard and Tillman, 1950);
(3) victim resistance (Wolfgang, 1958);
(4) youthfulness of the offender (Wertham, 1941, suggests 15–25 years);
(5) lack of motivation (Satten *et al*, 1960);
(6) intoxication (Wolfgang, 1958).

The present author studied 218 cases of male murderers and amongst them found 38 minimum-violence cases who had killed with a single blow, shot or stab (coup), and 52 who had killed with excessive violence (8 or more coups, range 8–124). Each group was further divided into wife killing and non-wife killing, wife being defined as the woman with whom the subject lived. The excessive violence group contained 19 wife killings, the minimum violence only 2. It was concluded that wife-killers favour use of excessive violence. Since the average ages of the two groups of men were 30·8 years (excessive group) and 27·8 (minimum group) age is not the significant factor. The excessive violence men were more likely to involve multiple killings (15·3 per cent as against 2·6 per cent of the minimum group). There was no significant difference on an impulsive-deliberate scale; more than half of both groups were deliberate. Within the excessive violence group the average number of coups in the wife-killers and non-wife killers was the same (15·7 and 15·6 respectively), which suggests that emotional involvement is not the important factor. All the murdered women (whether wives, prostitutes, or old ladies interrupting robberies) were killed with excessive violence. Low intelligence was rare in both groups but twice as common (5·7 per cent) in the excessive group as in the minimum group (2·6 per cent). Twenty-one per cent of the excessive group and 5·2 per cent of the minimum group were mentally ill or had a history of mental illness, and this was nearly all schizophrenia. Strong men capable of resistance, if they get murdered do not often receive multiple coups, and where the motive for the murder contains an element of fear, then excessive violence becomes rare (1·9 per cent in the excessive group, 18·4 per cent in the minimum violence group). Alcohol intoxication seems important (30·7 per cent excessive and 13·1 per cent minimum). There is a strong indication that defencelessness is an invitation to violence, and that once violence is unleashed it tends to continue to the point of satiation or exhaustion, unless controlled by fear of retaliation.

Excessive violence very doubtfully warrants the importance assigned to it by judges and others who assess dangerousness as a guide to sentencing. We forget that most murderers are amateurs and most victims healthy people with a firm hold on life, so that the killer is often horrified at the difficulty of killing and the awful sight and sounds involved, so that he strives in desperation or panic, to end the process quickly.

Separate from the quantity of violence is *the quality of violence*. Some murders, nearly all by excessive violence, involve bizarre desecration of the body, pushing things into body orifices or slitting them open; cutting off or biting nose, ears, breasts; urinating or masturbating upon the body. Such behaviour indicates either mental illness (Satten *et al*, 1960) or more commonly severe degrees of personality disorder associated with high degrees of deprivation of care or companionship in infancy. Quality of violence is a better indicator of dangerousness than quantity.

Disinhibiting factors, if likely to continue or recur, will contribute to dangerousness. The three major varieties are the depressive drugs (i.e. alcohol and the barbiturates rather than lysergic acid or amphetamine), the presence of companions, and fatigue. Groups of immature offenders, once embarked upon aggressive activity can stimulate one another in circular fashion so that very great and quite unexpected and inappropriate degrees of destruction can be achieved within seconds. Common examples are the activities of 10- or 12-year-olds who have broken into a factory, or adolescents who indulge in the so-called pack-rapes. Fatigue, sleeplessness, low blood sugar, can all lead to irritability and a reduced tolerance to long continued stresses which are so commonly the background of violence.

The detail of the offence should also include information as to the offender's *behaviour after the offence*. There are two areas to be considered. The presence of humane feelings—whether or not he tried to repair the damage, seek help, relieve suffering, or whether egocentric needs for escape or concealment were dominant, but this aspect will be considered later. The subsequent behaviour also sheds light on the state of mind at the time of the offence. Stress is sufficiently great or continued, causes an often quite sudden and dramatic 'breakdown' or change in behaviour, this is loosely called regression. It implies emotion and behaviour which is unrestrained, excessive, out of character and senseless, in that, though directed towards immediate relief (running away, self-injury, total denial in the presence of incontrovertible evidence), it is not realistically adaptive. Such behaviour inevitably invites the comparison with infantile behaviour, and this has been used in some ingenious classifications (Sullivan, Grant and Grant, 1957). Individuals vary greatly in the ease and depth of such regression. At one end of the scale, a few primitive personalities may be said to be more often regressed than not, whereas some resilient and resourceful persons retain their adaptiveness under high degrees of stress, and, when they break down, quickly recover (Lifton, 1957).

Study of murderers shows that 90 per cent of those who use excessive violence and 68 per cent of those who use minimum violence are regressed at the time of the killing. It is very useful to study the susceptibility, circumstances, specificity of stress, depth and duration of this regression. It is often possible to trace the stages, of induction and recovery, much as one does in administering an anaesthetic. The study of regression is one of the most useful modes of approaching the assessment of dangerousness. As ever rules of thumb are not possible; some denials in the face of incontrovertible evidence are adaptive, e.g. the paedophile who fears, not the judicial process, but hostility from other prisoners; or behaviour which is dictated by subcultural loyalties.

(2) Criminal record and past behaviour

All agree that the best indication of future behaviour is past behaviour, and it has long been known that it is the offender against property rather than against the person who has the highest tendency to repeat his offence. Neithercutt (1972) reviews the evidence for this paradox: that the most serious crimes, if you lump them together, have the best statistical predictions. Once a person has broken through the barrier between wish and action in a violent manner (even against himself) he could do so again. If to this is added the factor of age, the prediction becomes even more successful. Steadman and Cocozza (1974) constructed a scale for predicting repetition of dangerous offences, using juvenile record, number of previous arrests, convictions for violence, and severity of the last offence, all these factors being in effect refinements of past criminal behaviour.

If aggression appears early and is widely distributed—at home, at school and in the neighbourhood, and if it is present also in siblings and father, then it is likely to persist (Robins, 1966).

The exceptions to these general conclusions are unfortunately common. Some of the most devastating violence is produced by quiet, inoffensive persons with no previous criminal record, who have been under great stress for a long time and finally explode into a single brief but perhaps very dangerous act. Megargee (1966), Blackburn (1970) and Neustatter (1965) have described this phenomenon. A man of 47 asked the female stores keeper at his place of work for an item; she failed to produce it and treated him with scant respect. He picked up a spanner and beat her about the head in a manner which very nearly killed her. When examined he was not mentally ill, not depressed, not paranoid, and was distressed and perplexed by his behaviour. There was no previous crime of any sort. He was an excellent worker, employed beneath his capacity but had never pressed for advancement. He was married to a dominant lady who nagged him and frequently expressed her dissatisfaction with his wages. He had not had a holiday away from home for 20 years. In the last few weeks he had had bronchitis, which kept him awake. He was tired and not feeling well, and he was taking a prescribed medication containing codeine. The storeskeeper, he had hoped, would treat him with respect; she was an attractive and popular middle-aged women whom he liked but had never tried to make a relationship with. When she behaved like his wife he reacted in a way which could be interpreted as venting all his suppressed resentment of his wife upon her.

Another exception to the general rule is the co-called aggressive psychopath who on follow-up (Gibbens, 1970), is shown to have been much less aggressive than expected. Aggressive psychopaths are of many different varieties; one of the commoner types is the man of tender self-regard who relieves his fears of being deflated, by actual or threatened aggression; such men do not enjoy being violent, they do not attack non-threatening persons (children, hospital staff) and they improve with ageing. This type probably contributes largely to the observed fact that many psychopathic states resolve at about 35–40 years. It is equally striking that aggressive psychopaths with a strong paranoid component, and those showing recurrent bouts of tension, agitation, often with hypochondriacal features together with violent and destructive behaviour, do not resolve; the latter group often commit suicide in their 50s.

A previous record of non-violent crime is less predictive of dangerousness. Stereotyped non-violent crime is unlikely to switch or evolve into violence, but there are plenty of exceptions, as when the career takes a new turn into drug or alcohol abuse, exploitation by others, or some new frustration or alienation arises. If, however, non-violent crimes are interspersed with violent ones the outlook is very poor, particularly if penal or other treatments have been tried and failed.

(3) **Personal data**

Sex

Women are less likely to seek violent solutions to their difficulties, and this is probably because they are, or have been conditioned to believe that they are physically weaker. Support for this argument lies in the fact that mothers are as likely to batter their babies as are men, and when they kill them post mortem examination shows just the same excessive violence (Scott, 1973). The general clinical experience is that women more rarely cross the threshold into dangerousness, but when they do, perhaps by substituting stealth for strength, they offer the same difficulties of prediction and treatment as do men. The battering of babies has been regarded as a syndrome, or a specific variety of violence, but in fact it is more a microcosm of violent crime, demonstrating the same broad factors as crime and delinquency in general. There is the same difficulty in determining causative factors, the same constellation with other inadequacies or insufficiencies, the same wide variety of types with a small intractable hard core, and a large penumbra of cases which are easily helped and unlikely to repeat. Important differences depend upon the family setting, the captive victim, the impact of the spouse, and the domestic secrecy which is possible and which adds to the difficulties of supervision.

Age

This has already been touched upon. It is a difficult area for those who sentence or who serve on parole boards; youth is intolerant of incarceration which, on its own, appears to have little or no reformative function (Cornish and Clarke, 1975), yet it is precisely this age group which is most likely to recidivate. In this respect it is very important not to fall into the common error of failing to differentiate between violent and non-violent offenders in respect of recidivism. Heilbrun and his colleagues (1976), using a new and reliable method of assessing the degree of self-control in crimes, found that paroled convicts who committed violent crimes had a better chance of remaining free from further convictions (as judged by a six-month follow-up) than non-violent convicts. They emphasized that the crimes of violent criminals were less controlled than those of non-violent criminals, and that this was true of young criminals as well. They therefore arrived at the conclusion that 'offenders demonstrated less self-control in crimes of violence than in non-violent crimes'; and that 'offenders committing less self-controlled crimes of violence were more successful on parole than offenders committing more self-controlled crimes of violence'. This they found to be true with young offenders also. Once again we are prevented from making any simple rules such as 'youthfulness is always equated with a tendency to repeat', or 'display of uncontrolled violence is of bad prognosis'. Still less can we put these two predictions together and say 'young, violent offenders must be a very poor risk'. Perhaps what Heilbrun is saying is that violent crimes, even though poorly self-controlled, are mostly once and for all. That is an important message but does not obscure the danger of the repeated, poorly self-controlled individual.

Some of the most difficult problems for the forensic psychiatrist occur in the late adolescent range, when a youth of previously 'good character' (as the lawyers, but perhaps not the psychiatrists, would say) has committed an entirely unprovoked violent assault upon a girl; these attacks have no manifest sexual features but seem to be an expression of the following sequence: strong sexual attraction, total inability to effect contact, consequent frustration and anger, which is then expressed on the object which disturbs him. The usual finding in the youth is a combination of weak control, high sexual inhibition with normal sexual drive. The sexual inhibition (usually shared with the family) prevents any frank discussion either with the youth himself (who is by now thoroughly scared of his own impulses) or with his parents, whose only object is to maintain the myth of family 'normality'. Is this a single incident of adolescence or is the blocking of sexual expression more permanent? Will he be able to share his problems when the storm has died down, and thus alleviate his situation, or will the denial persist? And always there is the awareness that if a pessimistic or cautious view is expressed, this will probably result in a lengthy incarceration in a closed institution which, whatever else it does, will effectively prevent the natural solution of finding a suitable girl friend. Provided there is no gross family history of psychiatric disorder, and provided the youth's personality is not too seriously damaged, experience shows that calculated risks are justified, particularly if initial impressions can be checked through a short period of close observation in a hospital, hostel or Borstal institution.

Do sexual offences cease at the male climacteric? The nearest approximation to an answer in the present state of knowledge is that if the offence is directed towards orgasm it will cease, but if not it can continue with little or no abatement far into the senium. Examples of some sexual offences which are not directed towards orgasm are some indecent exhibitionism (sometimes to children, and sometimes of quite a frightening character), some paedophilic offences, including those with a sadistic element, some retaliations against women, especially prostitutes. The resort to violence does in general diminish with age even though offences continue, and of course the violence becomes increasingly easy to resist, and access to children and other potential victims may become a little less easy. But many sexual perverts are incredibly persuasive and successful in getting their unsuspecting victims to co-operate at least in the initial stages.

Marital status

An offender's marital status gives a valuable insight into whether a close relationship can be or was ever achieved and maintained, and if there are children as well then their adjustment too offers a very useful barometer of parental competence. Once adolescence is passed, persistent failure to achieve a sexual partnership, despite attempts, with a history of at least one violent assault upon a female, is usually ominous.

It has to be accepted that if a sexually active man has never managed a mutually acceptable sexual relationship and has tried to force one violently, he may do so again, despite good intelligence, absence of any psychiatric abnormality (including any other evidence of personality disorder); despite a previously clear record and excellent behaviour during a perhaps long prison sentence; despite the opinion of a psychotherapist that he has cooperated well, gained good insight into his psychopathology and is ready for release; and despite the offender's own expressed confidence that he is cured. This is not to say that recurrence is inevitable, but experience shows that it is frequent.

Personality traits

There is no characteristic profile, either of dangerous violence or of specific patterns of violence so that psychological test results from personality inventories and other sources take their place amongst all the other factors which must be scanned. It may be useful to note a high score on the lie scale or the hostility scale, but such findings must be checked against all the other information. Owing to secondary learning effects and changes in motivation, test-results are particularly unreliable (as are all other modes of assessment) in trying to decide on fitness to end indeterminate detention. There is no magic about a standardized test. Bartholomew (1975) reaches similar conclusions: 'Even testing by the psychologist is likely to produce misleading results, as it is not so very difficult for the intellectually able person to recognize the type of answer that should not be given if an early release is hoped for.'

No doubt the contribution of new forms of standardized test is potentially great, but to date they are not clinically very helpful in this field. One of the possible reasons for this may be that the clinicians are not yet able to tell the psychometrists what it is that they wish to be measured. Another barrier is that the objective of a test must be clear and simple, and if this is so the purpose of the test will quickly be apparent to the subject who has good reason to defeat it.

Space permits only a few considerations of special features.

Deceptiveness and transparency. Deceptiveness may be the response of an intelligent individual bent upon release from a situation, but as a personality trait it often stems from a parent-child learning situation in which there was mutual lack of trust. Perhaps mother and child conspired together in keeping a powerful father-figure 'sweet' (the 'as-if' character of Greenacre, 1945); more commonly untrusting and inquisitorial, punitive parents almost compel their children to lie. If together with this the child emerges into adult life with antagonistic and aggressive impulses, then, when he offends it will be difficult to gain his confidence and difficult for the after-care officer to help him. This antagonism and antisociability will hinder attempts to alleviate the offender's situation. Such individuals tend to have poor relationships with prison staff, so that distrust can progressively develop and bind the offender to the least helpful prison subculture. Slightly different is the factor of transparency. Some individuals, either because they need support and reassurance or because of a sort of verbal incontinence, readily reveal their thoughts and feelings, so that their actions are easily anticipated. This is particularly important in those who suffer periodic psychosis, perhaps of a depressive-suicidal or paranoid-homicidal nature. Some are very skilled at concealing such states, but others readily reveal them. Such factors are, of course, of great importance to the after-care agent. Much greater risks in liberating dangerous subjects are justified if they are transparent and not deceptive.

Jealousy, as Shepherd (1961) has said, 'is a notoriously dangerous passion and constitutes a well recognized motive for crimes of violence . . .'. A mild degree of jealousy is useful in preserving family life and is often a matter of pride to the wife. Higher degrees of jealousy are associated with less and less justification and are ultimately destructive. Jealousy is difficult to differentiate from, and may be combined with an intolerance of rejection, a fear of being deserted, a constant (probably narcissistic) need for admiration and re-assurance; unlike these, jealousy is independent of how the spouse is treating the subject. Jealousy is sometimes frankly delusional or may be part of a psychosis, but pathological degrees of jealousy are not dependent upon delusion (i.e. they are compatible with good insight). Pathological jealousy is often (especially in Continental psychiatry) linked with alcoholism, but the relationship is probably in parallel, for each may be quite independent of the other.

In the present context it is essential to grasp certain features of the natural history of pathological jealousy, otherwise very dramatic and serious errors will be made.

Pathological jealousy is exceptionally difficult to treat. Very intensive and long treatment has been observed to achieve control, through the voluntary return for further help of one or both parties, but the basic pathological tendency is not eradicated. The really essential point is that the most gross and dangerous forms may quickly and dramatically clear up in response to such measures as divorce or enforced separation, but will almost inevitably recur, even after years of apparent well-being, when this or a different relationship is resumed. Very many second murders are due to pathological jealousy.

Other dangerous traits. The personality traits of pathological (paranoid) suspicion, and sado-masochism often have to be considered *inter alia* in problems of dangerousness. While both tend to arise very early and to remain throughout life, it is important to recognize that intercurrent states of anxiety and depression can exaggerate minor degrees of these traits which may then be mistaken for fully-fledged features of the personality and lead to over-pessimistic prediction. This is particularly to be observed in children and adolescents who possibly try to dispel depression by giving themselves up to sadistic or masochistic phantasy which will not be and has not been acted out. In such cases it is unwise to attach the rather emotive label of paranoid or sadistic without taking a very close longitudinal view, if possible with a period of hospital observation.

The sadistic tendency is often revealed through the subject's fascination with dictators, Nazi insignia, horror films (especially if the same film is seen repeatedly). Some sadistic individuals collect, or have collected, weapons and cannot pass a gunsmith's shop. Children's drawings and prisoners' choice and use of pornographic magazines are worth inquiry. The prisoner's 'pin-ups' are often informative, but his fetish drawings and pictures may be carefully hidden at the back of the lowest drawer. The occupational preference will sometimes give a hint (butchering and work in abattoirs). Sadistic children often want to be veterinary surgeons, and show a morbid interest in sick and damaged animals which quickly die in their care, as do their pets. A combination of sadistic phantasy with actual violence is an ominous finding, especially if the violence is discussed in a dispassionate, guilt-free manner, and if there is no manipulative endeavour to impress the examiner. Part of the differential diagnosis of active sadism concerns the person who, knowing that he is going to be incarcerated for a long time, manipulates his way into psychiatric care by claiming abnormal impulses, or perhaps by untruthfully inflating phantasy into reality. Some children find relief from their own anxieties by making others anxious and discover that relating horrific, violent or cruel stories will effect this; these children do not have the same prognosis as those who actually seek relief through such actions.

(4) Historical data

Childhood, 'deprivation', very unsatisfactory parent-child relationships, beatings in childhood, alcoholic fathers, dominant mothers are all features which have often been found to correlate with later violence. Duncan and Duncan (1971) find that 'a history of parental violence remains a significant consideration in evaluating homicidal risk'. Palmer (1960) found that the incidence of childhood frustration was significantly higher among murderers than in their next older brothers. The so-called neurotic traits of childhood are not indicators of violence (nor apparently of anything else), though several authors find that a combination of enuresis, firesetting and cruelty to animals may predict later violence (Hellman, 1966). Battering parents are held, particularly in the American literature, to have experienced physical violence in their own childhoods, but there are many exceptions; clinical and ethological data suggest that other deprivations (of access to mother or to play-fellows) may be equally important.

Jessen and Roosenburg (1971), in assessing recidivism (not necessarily through dangerous violence), found only one factor which effectively distinguished between recidivists and non-recidivists, and that was running away from home after the age of 17 years.

Severe head injuries before the age of 10 are not usually associated with adult violence (Climent and Ervin, 1972), though psychopaths with a history of head injury have worse criminal records than those without head injury (Gibbens, 1955).

A host of genetic and biological factors have been supposed to indicate dangerousness: minimal brain damage, temporal lobe disorder, anomalies of the Y chromosome, testosterone over-production; but as Rubin (1972) says '. . . the presence of these defects in known criminals has no predictive value in their possible future violence . . .'.

Relationship with mental illness

Some studies, for instance that of Giovannoni and Gurel (1967) find that released psychiatric patients are much more likely to commit homicide, and rather more likely to commit aggravated assault than members of the general public. But most studies make it quite clear that the link between both crime and violent crime on the one hand and mental illness on the other is very slender indeed.

A recent study by Guze (1976) of 223 men and 65 women convicted of serious crimes, mainly of violence and theft, finds very high rates of sociopathy and alcoholism but very low rates of psychiatric illness. Sociopathy, alcoholism, and drug dependence are associated with serious crime; 'Schizophrenia, primary affective disorders, anxiety neurosis, obsessional neurosis, phobic neurosis and brain syndromes, are not.' Schizophrenia was diagnosed in only two of the males and one of the females.

Hafner and Boker (1973), in a very large-scale German study find that mental patients and defectives together show no higher an incidence of violence than do mentally sound persons. Schizophrenics, they say, are by far the most likely among psychiatric patients to commit acts of violence, but even so the rate is extremely low (5 in 10,000). The corresponding rate for affective psychoses and subnormals together is 6 in 100,000. The age and sex distribution in mentally disturbed violent offenders is similar to that of mentally sound violent offenders. A stay in hospital is followed by a high risk of violence over a period of six months, and marital partners, lovers and children are most at risk particularly from patients with affective psychoses and delusions.

The incidence of violence amongst hospital patients or prisoners must not be too readily attributed to any psychiatric condition rather than to those grave frustrations which are common to closed institutions (Folkard, 1957).

Of all illnesses, epilepsy, in view of its traditional links with explosive aggression, might be expected to correlate with violence. But in general no such correlation exists either with quantity or quality of violence. It seems that, despite the early textbooks, epilepsy is not especially linked with arson, rape or murder. This field has been well reviewed by Gunn (1969 and 1971). Although the crimes of epileptics can only be directly attributed to the epileptic process extremely rarely, yet when an epileptic acts violently in, or immediately after his fit, then he may do the same in subsequent fits. Two second murders, in my experience, have certainly been of this nature. The degree of violence sometimes shown in these 'ictal' crimes is sometimes extremely great.

(5) Progress in custody

This can be prognostically useful, but also misleading.

The outlook for youthful rebellion which has perhaps involved some violence as part of a well directed and understandable retaliation is nearly always excellent, even if within the institution the subject has had many conflicts with authority and has made a great nuisance of himself or herself. In general, aggressive behaviour which stems from strength and determination resolves itself, especially in the young.

Also hopeful (and of course gratifying) are inmates or patients who are at first rebellious and difficult but later conform; the task then will be to determine whether they have made genuine progress towards self-control, have learnt how to manipulate the system (not necessarily an unfavourable feature), or have deteriorated into institutional dependence.

Less hopeful are those whose violence seems to be based on a weakness. These will be particularly difficult to assess if the expression of their violence involved alcohol, drugs, women, children, possession of money, or access to gambling, because these are not openly available in most secure hospitals and prison establishments.

Consideration also has to be given to the things which *are* present in institutions but not outside: the presence of authority to supplement conscience, to protect, control and make decisions.

A single interview near the time of release by a stranger is not a good basis, on its own, for assessing dangerousness. As already stated most help is to be got from plodding through records, nurses' notes and trial transcripts, and talking to the staff who are in daily contact with the patient. It also helps to know the idiosyncrasies of staff. It is sometimes worrying if a certain staff member does *not* produce his usual unfavourable report. Dr Stürup (1968) of Herstedvester indicates the usefulness of staff of both sexes: 'If several of the women have the same (intuitive) feeling I am inclined to take it very seriously.' The reactions of other patients or inmates can be very useful, as are those of the victim or the victim's family. In serious cases the English parole board habitually makes inquiry about the probable local response before conditionally releasing the offender. The institution cat or dog, particularly in assessing young people, can prove a useful staff member, revealing either carefully hidden capacities for affection or cruelty; animals are not so easily deceived as humans.

(6) After-care

The subject's plans for his life outside (or lack of them) are of course important and may reflect his realism and aspirations. Brown and his colleagues (1972) have shown that schizophrenics are more likely to relapse after discharge from hospital if they are returned to the bosom of their families. Very many dangerous offences are based upon the individual's inability to solve ordinary problems of human relationship, which are, of course, most intense within the family. Thus it is often unwise to return offenders to the very setting in which their problem arose.

After-care, and intermediate placements between secure hospital or prison, together with indeterminacy of detention, or partial indeterminacy offered by borstal sentences and various forms of parole and conditional discharge provide our only means of compensating for our inability to make accurate predictions of dangerousness. The after-care officer's onerous task is relieved if he is introduced to the offender at an early stage, if he is well briefed on his charge's characteristics, if his supervision is supplemented by periodic reassessments of the offender and discussion with the responsible medical officer, and if recall is undertaken quickly when the danger signals appear.

Favourable response to after-care is seen when there is movement towards improvement rather than achievement; and, conversely, complete stasis, with consequent frustration, in any important area of life (especially the ability to love or relate to people) is ominous, the more so if there is a well tried perverse solution at hand.

Consideration of the Data

Every single factor, however promising, fails as an indicator of dangerousness, so that the factors can only be used in answering a number of further questions which may be hoped to approach an answer.

For a start, it is healthy for the investigator to review his own role: has he been strictly neutral in his approach? Has every reasonable attempt been made to collect the necessary information? To what extent did the subject suppress or actively distort the facts? Particularly if the offender emerges as a thoroughly attractive person who ought to be summarily released, or if a complex and fully explanatory psychopathology is instantly apparent, then the chances of some form of deception are high, for those who have committed a violent crime (even with provocation) usually have very marked weaknesses of one sort or another.

Consider the subject's life longitudinally, his existential manner of being in the world, what roles he sought or was pushed into, and by whom. Is the sum of the information consistent? High degrees of consistency or of inconsistency should lead to reappraisal, for most individuals' life stories are in the mid position.

Consider the behaviour from the point of view of as many theoretical standpoints as possible. Learning theory can be particularly helpful where the behaviour has been stereotyped: was it well learnt, but to antisocial standards; was it reparative behaviour to circumvent some basic prohibition; was it a conditioned avoidance response to a specific anxiety, or a non-adaptive response to an insoluble and inescapable problem of discrimination? Each of these quite different responses can lead, if the lesson was implanted sufficiently early, repeatedly and in the requisite emotional turmoil, to the most obstinate repetitiveness, and each should be treated in a different manner.

If the dangerous behaviour was not stereotyped but varied and perhaps mixed with non-violent offences, then we are dealing with incorrigibility of a different nature, probably not mainly due to faulty social learning. Very early, constitutional, perhaps organic or psychotic factors may have prevented or destroyed lessons; and there is a variety of indiscriminate offending seen in children who, coming from chaotic homes, have had no consistent social lessons and are without discernible conscience. Many such cases improve when a stable environment has been experienced, but this disorganized group of people, if dangerous violence has appeared more than once, are likely to continue to be dangerous.

It is useful also to consider whether the repeated dangerous behaviour is directed towards satisfying some (perhaps perverse) appetite, which, like any appetite, will certainly recur, or if it is an attempt to evade or cope with a specific problem, which may not recur.

Motive

This leads to the vexed consideration of motive; a difficult area because it is usually over-determined, is vulnerable to unconscious or deliberate falsification, and especially because, on its own, it gives no indication of choice of behaviour. All our motivations have components at all the levels of our being. In well adjusted persons only the socially approved part of the motivation will appear, and the selected solution will be correspondingly polite. In someone who has been 'driven to distraction' by long exposure to a strong motive and an equally strong set of prohibitions, or in someone whose social adjustment has been destroyed by some process or intoxication, the primitive response to the same motivation may appear. Sending a bunch of red roses, and committing a savage rape, may have the same motive operating at different levels of the personality. The single motive is likely to be labelled differently according to the level at which the personality is operating; at a fairly high level a robbery will be called an urgent need for money; at a lower level it will be admitted that the act relieves intolerable tension; at a lower level it may be ritual retaliation against a parsimonious mother; and at a still lower level there may be no words to express it because at that age the offender could not talk. Motive, therefore, always has to be considered alongside other factors, especially the current level of personality integration and the ease with which regression under stress occurs.

Sarabin (1967) says that there are three ways of meeting a crisis: the autistic, the social and explosive violence. Either one withdraws and does without, suffering the consequent symptoms, or one copes on a realistic basis of new adjustment, or one goes like a bull in a china shop for the simple solution. It is useful to study the way in which the offender made his selection. Did he cast about for practical solutions, and with what degree of resourcefulness; did he try to absorb the problem autistically and how much could he stand; or did he go straight for, or almost straight for the violent solution, in which case he is quite likely to do the same next time? A non-commissioned officer had suffered long conflict with his wife; he went through a period of alcoholism (autistic), tried to get a divorce (social), got himself posted to Ireland and volunteered for dangerous duty (the beginnings of the violent solution, but against himself), he then deserted his post, hoping to be dismissed the service (a variety of suicide), and finally shot his wife with a high velocity rifle in the kitchen (the final violent solution). As Menninger (1938) has observed, every murder includes a wish to kill, a wish to die and a wish to survive. It is perhaps the inability to make a choice between these simultaneous motives which compels a violent solution.

Linking concepts

Are there any key areas in which these protean factors have a common bearing? Again a simple answer eludes us, but most of the factors are best utilized in trying to answer two very basic questions, both concerned more with the future than with the current offence. First, is this person capable of compassionate feelings; is he able to feel sympathy with the sort of persons who may become his victims, or is he so egocentric or so indoctrinated or influenced or damaged that such feelings are absent or lastingly obscured? Unless there is some recognizable sympathy for others, and revulsion at causing suffering, there is always a vulnerability to situational aggressive impulses which are bound to recur. This must be assessed by looking deeply into the subject's life pattern and relationships. The common practice of looking for 'signs of remorse' in relation to the current offence is not a good criterion, for after a horrifying deed there are so many protective mechanisms which may be mistaken for callous indifference.

Second, is this person's capacity to learn by experience still intact? Perhaps this comes close to begging the main question, 'is he going to do it again?', but the question forms a central peg on which many other considerations hang, especially the manner in which the antisocial tendency was acquired, the resources which oppose it, the maturity of the personality, and the ease with which regression occurs under stress of various sorts, or on the other hand the obstinacy or lack of adaptiveness which some people show when passions are aroused.

Conclusion

We strive after accurate prediction of dangerousness because this would quell our anxieties, enable us to draw clear lines between the dangerous and non-dangerous, and avoid the necessity of continuing contact with and concern for them. But no such magical process will be possible.

Our disappointment may be alleviated if we accept that short-term assessment (which permits the scanning of the subject's present environment and associates, and his reactions to these) is likely to be much more reliable than long-term assessment, which, especially in the present setting of a mobile and changeable society, is likely to be totally beyond our reach. The point is illustrated by the introduction into an institution, many years ago, of a pencil and paper test to indicate propensity to abscond (I believe it was called the Chernukin test). At first we were very pleased with it, but we soon realized that it only indicated how the individual was feeling at that moment; tomorrow after a letter from home or an altercation with the staff he might feel and act quite differently; the test, to be useful, would have to be given every day, and anyway could achieve no more than would a friendly conversation. Further, the knowledge that absconding may be imminent is useless unless there is a means of dealing with the problem; to lock the subject up (which only delays, whilst amplifying, his need to abscond), or to reduce the tension through personal contact. It was realized that it is an economy to aim straight for the personal contact, which has the advantage of serving a host of other useful functions simultaneously; it has the further advantage that it can be achieved by non-medical personnel provided they are well supported by a good system of communications. Involvement on a long-term basis and good communications are therefore the inescapable bases for assessment of dangerousness.

References

BERG, I. & FOX, V. (1947) Factors in homicides committed by 200 males. *Journal of Social Psychology*, **26**, 109–10.

BLACKBURN, R. (1970) Personality types among abnormal homicides. Special Hospitals Research Report. No. 1.

BRETT, P. (1970) The physiology of provocation. *Criminal Law Reform*, 634–40.

BROWN, G. W., WING, J. K. & BIRLEY, J. L. T. (1972) *British Journal of Psychiatry*, **121**, 241.

BUTLER COMMITTEE (1975) Report of the Committee on Mentally Abnormal Offenders. Cmnd 6244. London: HMSO.

CLIMENT, C. E. & ERVIN, F. R. (1972) Historical data in the evaluation of violent subjects. *Archives of General Psychiatry*, **27**, 621–4.

CORNISH, D. B. & CLARKE, R. V. G. (1975) Residential treatment and its effects on delinquency. *Home Office Research Studies*, No. 32. London: HMSO.

DUNCAN, J. W. & DUNCAN, G. M. (1971) Murder in the family: a study of some homicidal adolescents. *American Journal of Psychiatry*, **127**, 1498–501.

ENGLISH, P. (1970) What did Section 3 do to the law of provocation? *Criminal Law Reform*, 249–67.

FOLKARD, M. S. (1957) A sociological contribution to the understanding of aggression and its treatment. *Netherne Monographs*, *1*. Coulsdon, Surrey: Netherne Hospital.

GIBBENS, T. C. N. (1970) How should we treat violent offenders. *New Society*, 3 September, 408–10.

—— POND, D. A. & STAFFORD-CLARK, D. (1955) A follow-up study of criminal psychopaths. *British Journal of Delinquency*, **6**, 1–11. See also *Journal of Mental Science* (1959) **105**, 108–15.

GIOVANNONI, J. & GUREL, L. (1967) Socially disruptive behavior of ex-mental patients. *Archives of General Psychiatry*, **17**, 146–53.

GREENACRE, PHYLLIS (1945) Conscience and the psychopath. *American Journal of Orthopsychiatry*, **15**, 495.

GUNN, J. C. (1973) *Violence*. Newton Abbott: David and Charles.

—— (1969) The prevalence of epilepsy among prisoners. *Proceedings of the Royal Society of Medicine*, **62**, 60–3.

—— & BONN, J. (1971) Criminality and violence in epileptic prisoners. *British Journal of Psychiatry*, **118**, 332–43.

GUZE, S. (1976) *Criminality and Psychiatric Disorders*. London: Oxford University Press.

HAFNER, H. & BOKER, W. (1973) Mentally disordered violent offenders. *Social Psychiatry*, **8**(4), 220–9.

HEILBRUM, A. B., KNOPF, I. J. & BRUNER, P. (1976) Criminal impulsivity and violence and subsequent parole outcome. *British Journal of Criminology*, **16**, 4.

HELLMAN, D. S. & BLACKBURN, M. (1966) Enuresis, firesetting and cruelty to animals: a triad predictive of adult crime. *American Journal of Psychiatry*, **122**, 1431–5.

JESSEN, J. L. & ROOSENBURG, A. M. (1971) Treatment results at the Dr Henri van der Hoeven Clinic, Nirecht. *Proceedings of the Fifth World Congress of Psychiatry*. Amsterdam: Excerpta Medica.

KOZOL, H. L., BOUCHER, R. F. & GAROFOLO, R. F. (1972) The diagnosis and treatment of dangerousness. *Journal of Crime and Delinquency*, **18**, 371–92.

LIFTON, R. J. (1957) Chinese communist thought reform. In *Group Processes. Transactions of the Third Conference*, pp 219–312. New York: Josiah Macy Jr Foundation.

MACDONALD, J. M. (1968) *Homicidal Threats*. Illinois: Thomas.

—— (1963) The threat to kill. *American Journal of Psychiatry*, **120**, 125–30.

MEGARGEE, E. S. (1966) Undercontrolled and over-controlled personality types in extreme antisocial aggression. *Psychological Monograph*, **80**, no. 611.

MENNINGER, K. A. (1938) *Man Against Himself*. New York: Harcourt Bruce.

MICHAELS, J. J. & STEINBERG, A. (1952) Persistent enuresis and juvenile delinquency. *British Journal of Delinquency*, **3**, 114–23.

NEITHERCUTT, M. G. (1972) Parole violation patterns and commitment of offence. *Journal of Research in Crime and Deliquency*, **9**, 87–98.

NEUSTATTER, L. (1965) The state of mind in murder. *Lancet*, *i*, 861–3.

PALMER, S. (1960) *A Study of Murder*. New York: Thomas Y. Crowell.

RAPPOPORT, J. R. (1967) *The Clinical Evaluation of Dangerousness of the Mentally Ill*. Springfield, Illinois: Charles C. Thomas.

REICHARD, S. & TILLMAN, C. (1950) Murder and suicide as defences against schizophrenic psychosis. *Clinical Psychopathology*, **11**, 149–63.

ROBINS, L. (1966) *Deviant Children Grown Up*. London: Livingstone.

RUBIN, B. (1972) Prediction of dangerousness in mentally ill criminals. *Archives of General Psychiatry*, **27**, 397.

SARABIN, T. R. (1967) The dangerous individual. *British Journal of Criminology*, **7**, 285–95.

SATTEN, J., MENNINGER, K., ROSEN, I. & MAYMAN, M. (1960) Murder without apparent motive. *American Journal of Psychiatry*, **117**, 48–53.

SCOTT, P. D. (1973) Parents who kill their children. *Medicine Science and Law*, **13**, 120–6.

—— (1973) Fatal battered baby cases. *Medicine Science and Law*, **13**, 197–206.

SHAW, S. H. (1973) The dangerousness of dangerousness. *Medicine Science and Law*, **13**, 269–71.

SHEPHERD, M. (1961) Morbid jealousy: some clinical and social aspects. *Journal of Mental Science*, **107**, 687–753.

STANTON, J. M. (1969) Murderers on parole. *Crime and Delinquency*, **15**, 149–55.

STEADMAN, H. J. & COCOZZA, J. J. (1975) We can't predict who is dangerous. *Psychology Today*, **8**(8), 22–35 and 84.

—— —— (1974) Some refinements in the measurement and prediction of dangerous behaviour. *American Journal of Psychiatry*, **131**(9), 1012–14.

STÜRUP, G. K. (1968) *Treating the Untreatable*. Baltimore: The Johns Hopkins Press.

—— (1968) Will this man be dangerous? *The Mentally Abnormal Offender*, Ciba symposium (eds A. V. S. de Reuk & R. Porter), pp 5–18. London: J. & A. Churchill.

SULLIVAN, C., GRANT, M. Q. & GRANT, J. D. (1957) The development of interpersonal maturity: application in delinquency. *Psychiatry*, **20**, 373.

TENNENT, G. (1971) Dangerousness. *British Journal of Hospital Medicine*, **6**, 269.

WALKER, N. (1969) *Sentencing in a Rational Society*. London: Allen Lane, Penguin Press.

WERTHAM, F. (1941) *Dark Legend*. New York: Duell, Sloan & Pearce.

WHITE, S. (1970) A note on provocation. *Criminal Law Reform*, 446–52.

WOLFGANG, M. E. (1958) *Patterns in Criminal Homicide*. Philadelphia: University of Pennsylvania.

P. D. Scott, *C.B.E.* M.A., M.D., F.R.C.P., F.R.C.Psych., *Consultant Forensic Psychiatrist, The Maudsley Hospital, Denmark Hill, London SE5 8AZ*

(*Received 29 September; revised 9 December 1976*)

[29]

Psychological Medicine, 1974, **4**, 133–140

Psychopathic personality: a most elusive category

AUBREY LEWIS

From the Institute of Psychiatry, De Crespigny Park, London

SYNOPSIS For 150 years the diagnostic concept at first called 'moral insanity' has been troubling psychiatric nosologists. Initially emphasis was laid on the affective disturbance in this condition, which was unaccompanied by intellectual impairment. Then its conformity to the idea of a degenerative process became prominent. At various times its relation to epilepsy, hereditary disease, and vice and crime has held the stage. Latterly little advantage has been taken of the information provided about personality by the investigations of psychologists.

Psychopathic personality is one of a cluster of terms which have been used, interchangeably or successively, in the last 150 years to denote a life-long propensity to behaviour which falls mid-way between normality and psychosis. Mania *sine delirio*, moral insanity, moral imbecility, psychopathy, degenerate constitution, congenital delinquency, constitutional inferiority—these and other semantic variations on a dubious theme have been bandied about by psychiatrists and lawyers in a prodigious output of repetitious articles.

In 1801 Philippe Pinel described a condition which he called *manie sans délire*. Its specific features were absence of any appreciable alteration in the intellectual functions—perception, judgment, imagination, memory—but pronounced disorder of the affective functions, blind impulse to acts of violence, even murderous fury. Illustrative cases which he cited included some which would not now be regarded as explosive forms of psychopathic personality. In 1818 a German psychiatrist, Grohman, delimited 'moral diseases of the mind' which he said depend upon physical anomalies in the brain; he posited three subgroups—moral dullness (*Stumpfsinn*), congenital brutality, and moral imbecility (*Blödsinn*). He subscribed to faculty psychology, and took his stand on the somatic theory of psychopathology in the polemic then prevailing between Nasse and his colleagues on the one hand, and Heinroth, the pan-psychological champion, on the other. In France, Esquirol (1838), after some hesitation, confirmed Pinel's observation that intact understanding in these patients can coexist with periodic excitement, and he included the condition among the monomanias, which were likewise a disputed category at the time.

MORAL INSANITY

The next psychiatrist to deal specifically with this topic was J. C. Prichard. In a textbook of his which appeared in 1822 he gave his reasons for dissenting from Pinel's view regarding *manie sans délire*. When, however, in 1835 he produced a riper work, *A Treatise on Insanity and other Diseases Affecting the Mind*, he declared himself convinced of the rightness of Pinel's opinion. With the designation 'moral insanity' he enlarged and generalized Pinel's '*manie sans délire*'. He saw it as a 'morbid perversion of the natural feelings, affections, inclinations, temper, habits, moral dispositions and natural impulses, without any remarkable disorder or defect of the intellect or knowing and reasoning faculties and particularly without any insane illusion or hallucination'.

The sharp distinction that Prichard drew between 'lesions of the understanding' and 'affective lesions' rapidly became a controversial question. On the one side were authorities like Henry Maudsley, who put their standpoint unambiguously:

'As there are persons who cannot distinguish certain colours, having what is called colour blindness, so there are some who are congenitally deprived of moral sense' (Maudsley, 1874).

Equally weighty opinion to the contrary was expressed by Griesinger, J. P. Falret and others.

A DEGENERATIVE PROCESS

Interest shifted from this argument when in the middle of the century Morel (1839) put forward his persuasive views about degeneration: 'degeneration is a morbid deviation from the normal human type, transmissible by heredity, and evolving progressively towards extinction.' His clinical experience as head of a mental hospital stirred his interest in the theoretical and social aspects of degeneration:

'What are asylums but places where the chief kinds of human degeneration are concentrated. The ever growing number of suicides, crimes, offences against property and the person, the appalling precocity of young criminals, the degradation of the race—these are indisputable facts. I had to find out whether the increasing proportion of the insane (or, if you prefer it, the more hopeless complications of their condition) were the outcome of a complex of general causes.'

Treatment, he found, was mostly ineffectual, especially in his class of patients with 'hereditary insanity' (monomania, 'nervous temperament', eccentricity, 'dissolute immorality').

Degeneration, as Morel conceived it, had two essential features: hereditary transmission, and increasing severity in successive generations, leading to extirpation of affected individuals, families, or groups. It did not carry with it the opprobrium which attaches to the word in common speech. The intrusion of moral judgments, which had been evident in Prichard's terminology and that of many other 19th-century psychiatrists, is partly to be attributed to the equivocal meaning of the word 'moral' in French: though mainly used with the same significance as in English, sometimes it refers to every mental function that can be subsumed under the general term 'affective'. Hence it came about that 'moral insanity' and 'moral imbecility' were often treated as synonyms of emotional abnormality (*délire emotif*) or of constitutional proclivity to vice and crime. English psychiatrists had less linguistic temptation to this, though they were much influenced by Morel. Maudsley, for example, wrote in 1874 that

'there is an insane temperament which without being itself a disease may easily and abruptly break down into actual disease under a strain from without or from within; moral feeling like any other feeling is a function of organization; an absence of moral sense is an occasional result of descent from an insane family'.

As recently as 1932 Henderson and Gillespie wrote:

'Under the term "mental defect" we propose to include not only intellectual defect in its various grades, but also emotional and moral defects which have been present from an early age. . . . For "emotional instability" and "moral deficiency" or "moral imbecility", as it has unfortunately been called, we shall use the wider term "constitutional psychopathic inferiority".'

After Morel, modification of the concept came chiefly from Magnan and his disciples in Paris. He described a large category of '*héréditaires dégénerés*', within which he included idiots, imbeciles, feeble minded, and '*dégenerés supérieurs*' (Magnan, 1893). The latter (*dégenerés supérieurs*) had average or brilliant intellectual powers, but moral defects. Physical stigmata or degeneracy were numerous in all the four subdivisions; the corresponding psychological stigmata were obsessions, irresistible impulses, dipsomania, coprolalia, kleptomania, sexual anomalies, and some other analogous features. Common characteristics of these phenomena were concomitant anxiety, awareness by the affected individual of his abnormality, and satisfaction following the accomplishment of an impulsive act.

Magnan subscribed to Morel's picture of doomed hereditary descent, proceeding from *folie raisonnante* or mania in the first generation to idiocy or imbecility in the fourth.

MEDICOLEGAL ASPECTS

Much controversy centred on these views, especially in France and Germany (Bumke, 1912). In England the medicolegal aspect which had engaged Prichard's interest continued to be the dominant issue. Maudsley (1874) exemplifies this:

'moral insanity', he wrote, 'is a form of mental alienation which has so much the look of vice or crime that many persons regard it as an unfounded medical invention ... the symptoms are mainly exhibited in the perversion of those mental faculties which are usually called the active and moral powers —the feelings, affections, propensities, temper, habits and conduct ... (the individual) has no capacity of true moral feelings; all his impulses and desires, to which he yields without check, are egoistic ... his affective nature is profoundly deranged, and its affinities are for such evil gratifications as must lead to further degeneration and finally render him a diseased element which must either be got rid of out of the social organization or be sequestrated and made harmless in it'.

Maudsley pleaded that when such a person has committed an offence 'the truest justice would be the admission of a modified responsibility'.

The Italian contribution was for a time influential; Tanzi and Lombroso (Wolfgang, 1960) were the standard bearers. Tanzi pointed out the objections to regarding degeneration as a cause of moral insanity—which he preferred to call 'constitutional immorality'. He detached it from the forms of ethical failings which are a symptom of disease supervening in a previously normal person, and from the supposed 'epileptic personality' on which Lombroso and, following him, Maudsley and others laid stress. Tanzi also criticized the so-called stigmata of degeneration, reputed to be especially common in psychopaths.

The impact of Lombroso's boldly proclaimed views was more positive. In the 'anthropological' period of his output (1872–85) he proclaimed that the 'born delinquent' with his physical stigmata was the atavistic incarnation of 'moral insanity'. In his second period pathological criteria (chiefly of epilepsy) were to the fore. The born criminal with his evidence of arrested development and his deficiency of altruistic feelings, exhibits, Lombroso maintained, an 'epileptoid' state, a predetermined adversity of character.

French, German, and Italian psychiatrists vied with each other in proposing alternative names for the condition, but most English psychiatrists continued to call it moral insanity while deploring the shortcomings of such a term. Savage (1881) considered that it was easier to describe what the condition is not than to come to a comprehensive definition of it: moral insanity could be a '"secondary" state or stage of mental disease and not a fixed or permanent condition itself' whereas in the primary or essential form peculiarity of character and eccentric behaviour are present from early childhood. Tuke (1892) declared that the wide difference of opinion on this subject among 'mental physicians' was mainly due to 'the want of definition of the terms employed'.

CLARIFICATION OF TERMS

A determined and sustained effort to clarify the relevant terms was made by Koch (1891). He introduced the plural form 'psychopathic inferiorities' which, he said, would include

'all mental irregularities whether congenital or acquired which influence a man in his personal life and cause him, even in the most favourable cases, to seem not fully in possession of normal mental capacity, though even in the bad cases the irregularities do not amount to mental disorder'.

By the term 'psychopathic' Koch intended to stress the presumptive physical basis of the condition.

'They remain always psychopathic in the sense that they are caused by organic states and changes which lie on the far side of the limits of physiological normality ... they rest on a congenital or acquired inferiority of brain constitution.'

He admitted, however, that this could not be demonstrated anatomically or chemically. He held that congenital psychopathic disposition or diathesis is essentially recognizable as sensitiveness (*Zartheit*); the effect of congenital psychopathic taint (*Belastung*) appears as eccentricity, egotism, violent outbursts; and congenital psychopathic degeneration can take a severely antisocial or asocial form, midway between mental disorders and mental normality: neither fish nor flesh, nor good red herring.

Koch's orderly and emphatically confident presentation led to the adoption during the ensuing 20 or 30 years of some of his terminology and much of his theorizing. Müller in 1899 wrote that moral insanity is only a prominent symptom of a psychopathic state: the term had been under heavy fire but might be retained for forensic use. Tiling in 1896 offered 'perversion of character' as an equivalent for 'congenital moral degeneration'. The term 'inferiority' did not last long, however, probably because it connoted a value-judgment which medical usage repudiated. For a considerable period 'psychopathic' was not open to this objection. As Gruhle (1953) kept repeating, the concept of psychopathy implies nothing more than that a person's disposition or temperament deviates appreciably from the average. Gradually, however, this ethically and socially neutral significance was submerged so that a psychopath came to be classified as 'antisocial', or was renamed 'sociopath'.

KRAEPELIN'S CHANGING EMPHASIS

The plainest indicator of the changing notion of this condition is provided by the successive editions of Kraepelin's textbook. In his second edition (1887) he put insanity in the group of congenital defects (*Schwachsinn*); it consists in 'deficiency of those forces which restrain the individual living in society from reckless gratification of his immediate egotistical inclinations'. Impulsive insanity and obsessions are included in the same group. In considering the role of heredity and predisposition, he gives the views of Morel much weight. Nine years later, in his fifth edition of 1896, Kraepelin places psychopathic states among the constitutional disorders; they are life-long morbid personalities, 'mental dystrophies' (*seelische Entwicklungshemmungen*). In this formulation the influence of Lombroso is discernible. The next edition of Kraepelin's textbook (1899) presents psychopathic states as a form of degeneration, along with 'impulsive insanity', obsessions, constitutional depression, and sexual perversions. Harking back to Koch, Kraepelin enlarges the class of 'psychopathic inferiorities' to fill the extensive intermediate territory between indisputable insanity and mental health.

In the 7th edition (1903–1904) the emphasis is on degeneration.

'In the great area of degenerative insanity (*Entartungsirresein*) it is practicably impossible to delimit definite varieties: the artificially contrived groups overlap at every point. We will therefore keep two big divisions separate—"original states" and "psychopathic personalities". . . . We will designate as psychopathic personalities those peculiar morbid forms of personality development which we have grounds for regarding as degenerative'.

Kraepelin, however, was uneasy about his far-flung concept of degeneration:

'The characteristic of degeneration is a lasting morbid reaction to the stresses of life, an inappropriateness in thinking, feeling or willing throughout life': but, he added, 'if we were to regard degeneration as the source of all those congenital attributes that interfere with the attainment of the general purposes of life, we would find traces of it everywhere.'

The 8th edition (1909–1915) describes psychopaths as showing inferiority in affect (*Gemutsleben*) or in the development of mature volition (*Willensausbildung*). They can be divided into those with the stamp of morbid predisposition (obsessional neurosis, impulsive insanity, and sexual deviation) and those with the stamp of personal peculiarity.

It is plain that Kraepelin found the classification of these conditions defeating, as he frankly admits. Successive editions show him struggling, with little success, to cope with the task of shaping categories out of the rich variety of human character and conduct. His efforts and his failure are characteristic examples of the frustration which besets students of personality when they aim at precision. 'All typologies place boundaries where boundaries do not belong. They are artificial categories . . . each theorist slices nature in any way he chooses, and finds only his own cuttings worthy of admiration' (Allport, 1938).

An approach from the standpoint of dynamic psychopathology has not been helpful. It might be expected that psychoanalytical formulations would be illuminating; but they do not attempt a thoroughgoing classification. Alexander (1952) minimized the difficulty:

'This group of behaviour disorders has long baffled psychiatrists and the diagnosis psychopathic personality has come to be considered a waste-basket diagnosis. From the psychodynamic point of view, however, this diagnosis is not more difficult to make than any other diagnosis of a neurosis. The differential criterion is neurotic acting-out versus neurotic symptoms.'

Edward Glover (1955), on the other hand, regards the condition as prepsychotic or larval; but

'until more detailed subdivisions are effected there is something to be said for the otherwise vague caption psychopathy, provided of course we recognize three main subgroups: (a) sexual psychopathy . . . (b) "benign" psychopathy in which social incapacity is the main feature, accompanied, however, usually by psychosexual disorder, and (c) antisocial psychopathy of a more malignant type in which delinquent outbursts associated with a variable degree of sexual maladjustment develop in an otherwise unstable ego'.

Kraepelin's adoption of 'psychopathic personality' led to general decline in the use of 'moral insanity' and 'moral imbecility', but Prichard's terms did not suffer total extinction. There was, moreover, an appreciable lag before 'psychopathic personality' became the accepted designation in English speaking countries. This occurred in the 1920s.

Mercier in 1914 had contemptuously referred to forms of chronic insanity which 'may be divided into two important classes or subtypes, and a rabble of others which need not be considered here'. But in 1922 Smith, a progressive prison doctor, wrote under the heading 'psychopaths', that

'there exists a class of persons who are not insane nor mentally defective . . . their mental condition is such that they are unable to make proper adjustments to the demands of society . . . the group is of very mixed character and it is not easy to settle on any satisfactory classification. We have practically no form of classification of them in this country. So the author proposes to adopt the classification suggested by the Surgeon General of the United States Army.'

Among the subdivisions of psychopathy, Smith listed inadequate personality, emotional instability, paranoid personality, pathological lying, and sexual anomalies. A separate class of offenders, the 'constitutionally infirm' are 'unbalanced and their power of inhibition is lessened. Their conduct is impulsive and variable'. Smith borrowed from American psychiatrists who in their turn had borrowed from the German writers, especially Kraepelin.

It is not easy to account for the persistence of the term 'moral insanity' (though in a dwindling degree) when so many influential authorities, especially in Germany, pointed to its demerits. The chief sustaining factors seem to have been its use in the courts, and its place in legislation covering the commitment of mentally defective persons (Anderson, 1962). In the 1913 Act 'moral imbeciles' were defined as 'persons who from an early age display some permanent mental defect, coupled with strong vicious or criminal propensities on which punishment has had little or no deterrent effect'. The 1927 Amending Act defined 'moral defectives'. In the Mental Health Act 1960 the slate was wiped clean and 'psychopathic disorder' was given official recognition; it was defined as

'a persistent disorder or disability of mind (whether or not including subnormality of intelligence) which results in abnormally aggressive or seriously irresponsible conduct on the part of the patient, and requires or is susceptible to treatment'.

Among the many criticisms of this definition the most obvious centres on the clause which runs 'requires or is susceptible to treatment'; the opinion of psychiatrists or other competent experts as to who requires or is susceptible to treatment will inevitably tend to be subjective and inconsistent.

THE LAST 50 YEARS

There have been many comprehensive reviews of the state of opinion about psychopathic personality during the last 50 years. In Great Britain Henderson (1939), Curran and Mallinson (1944), and Craft (1966); in Germany Schneider (1958), Birnbaum (1926), Kahn (1936), Dubitscher (1936), and Binder (1960); in France Trillat (1965), and Delmas (1943); in the United States Jenkins (1960), Gurvitz (1951), Robins (1967), Carlson and Dain (1962), Maughs (1941), McCord and McCord (1956). These reveal a preoccupation with the nosological status of the concept (latterly influenced by Jaspers), its forensic implications, its subdivisions and limits;

the propriety of identifying psychopathic personality with antisocial behaviour; semantic niceties—for example, the distinction between dyssocial and asocial; cerebral damage as a cause; genetic factors, especially sex chromosome anomalies. The effect of reading solid blocks of this literature is disheartening; there is so much fine-spun theorizing, repetitive argument, and therapeutic gloom ('to me therefore the psychopath, no matter what his age, is a child delinquent, who has never profited by experience, has rarely been benefited by medical, social or punitive measures. He is so unpredictable in his reactions that he is the most dangerous member of society': Henderson, 1939).

The majority of fairly recent writers on the subject deplore the looseness and bias which vitiate attempts at defining it: 'discussion of the prognosis and treatment of all these various types of vulnerable, unusual, abnormal and sociopathic characters, now all lumped together as psychopathic personalities, must embrace so many factors that it cannot profitably be undertaken before more agreement has been reached on questions of definition and delimitation' (Curran and Mallinson, 1944). The difficulty is not evaded by making the definition short and sweet:

'abnorme Persönlichkeiten die an ihrer Abnormität leiden oder unter deren Abnormität die Gesellschaft leidet [People of abnormal personality who suffer through their abnormality or cause society to suffer through it]' (Schneider); 'der Begriff der Psychopathie besagt nichts weiter als dass die Anlagen eines Menschen vom Durchschnitt erheblich abweichen [The concept of psychopathy amounts to no more than that the predisposition (*Anlage*) of a man deviates appreciably from the average]' (Gruhle, 1953).

Detailed definition is likewise unsatisfactory:

'Diese psychopathischen Konstitutionen hängen ursächlich und wesensgemäss mit jenem Erscheinungskreis zusammen den man biologisch als Entartung zu kennzeichnen pflegt i.e. eine von der Norm ungünstig abweichende biologische Degenerationsform von erblichem Charakter [These "psychiatric constitutions" belong in causation and essential nature, to that class of phenomena which we are accustomed to designate as degenerative—that is, as a form of hereditary degeneration which shows adverse departure from the biological norm]' (Birnbaum, 1926).

An inherent problem is how to agree on the range of the normal personality and the tenable criteria of mental illness. Failure in this is attested by the absurd discrepancies between different people's estimate of the prevalence of psychopathy (Wallin, 1949).

For the purposes of the WHO classification of diseases a provisional definition might run

Psychopathic personality is a condition in which ingrained maladaptive patterns of behaviour are recognizable by the time of adolescence or earlier, and are continuous throughout life; the personality is abnormal in the balance and quality of its components.'

Like every other attempt at defining psychopathic personality this is open admittedly, but perhaps inevitably, to criticism on several counts. Neither 'maladaptive patterns of behaviour', nor 'balance of the components of personality', nor their quality are matters of direct observation: individual investigators will no doubt differ rather widely in judging them. The definition might, moreover, be thought too inclusive; it would, for example, cover the postencephalitic behaviour disorders and might be taken to embrace also sexual perversions. But the main difficulty is occasioned by our unsuccess in nailing normal personality down, either as a whole or in its components.

CONCEPTS OF PSYCHOLOGISTS

It is surprising that psychiatrists have paid little attention to the methods and concepts of psychologists in this field. The reason may be practical:

'Many personality qualities can be measured or diagnosed fairly effectively, but the methods are far too elaborate and time consuming, or far too dependent on the skill and experience of the psychologist, to be generally applicable for any practical purposes, or to be used by anyone not specially trained. True, it is possible to suggest some improvements on the unreliable methods that the layman habitually employs' (Vernon, 1953).

In a similarly cautious and tolerant vein Gordon

Allport concluded that there is no one-and-only method for the study of personality

'in respect to accuracy and reliability some of the segmental methods are to be preferred; in respect to adequacy of approach the various synthetic or relational methods are better . . . it is something of a struggle to strike a balance between excessively rigid and perfectionalistic standards (that accomplish nothing but a sterilization of research, limiting it to worthless fragments of behaviour having no essential bearing upon personality) and loose standards that permit wanton assertions and extravagant claims to go without check or proof' (Allport, 1938).

Some psychologists who have concerned themselves with the measurement of factors affecting psychopathy have, like some psychiatrists, put psychopathy essentially on the same footing as delinquency: 'the psychopath presents the riddle of delinquency in a particularly pure form'. Eysenck, commenting on the tendency of the psychopaths to exhibit traits of extraversion, makes it pungently clear that in his view if there is a failure of correlation between questionnaire and psychiatric ratings, this indicates 'faults in the psychiatric ratings, both as regards validity and reliability, and it might further be suggested, not that the questionnaire has no value as a clinical tool but rather that the psychiatric diagnosis has no value as a clinical tool' (Eysenck and Eysenck, 1969). The extensive studies of Quay and his associates on adolescents yielded two large factors, one of which, betokening impulsiveness, rebelliousness and lack of emotional involvement, they called 'psychopathy': it correlated with recidivism, institutionalization, and crimes against the person.

Another assiduous inquirer into this problem (Foulds, 1965) has maintained that

'egocentricity, lack of empathy, and treating others as objects, in the absence of the necessary and sufficient conditions for making a diagnosis of personal illness, are themselves necessary and sufficient conditions for the identification of psychopaths, at least when they are present in such degree that they lead the individuals concerned to conflict with the law or to their being brought for treatment'.

Foulds touches on a crucial issue when he puts forward his argument that traits and attitudes emphasize the continuity of behaviour, whereas symptoms and signs of illness emphasize the discontinuities. Attacks of illness or violence may punctuate the course of psychopathy, but cannot be intrinsic and necessary features of it.

The conclusion of the whole matter is somewhat gloomy. The diagnostic groupings of psychiatry seldom have sharp and definite limits. Some are worse than others in this respect. Worst of all is psychopathic personality, within its wavering confines. Its outline will not be firm until much more is known about its genetics, psychopathology, and neuropathology.

REFERENCES

Alexander, F. (1952). *Dynamic Psychiatry*. University of Chicago Press: Chicago.

Allport, G. W. (1938). *Personality. A Psychological Interpretation*. Constable: London.

Anderson, E. W. (1962). The official concept of psychopathic personality in England. In *Psychopathologie Heute*, pp. 243–251. Herausg. von H. Kranz. Thieme: Stuttgart.

Binder, H. (1960). Die psychopathischen Dauerzustände und die abnormen seelischen Reaktionen und Entwicklungen. In *Psychiatrie der Gegenwart*, pp. 180–202. Edited by H. W. Gruhle, R. Jung, W. Mayer-Gross, and M. Müller. Springer: Berlin.

Birnbaum, K. (1926). *Die psychopathischen Verbrecher*. 2. Aufl. Thieme: Leipzig.

Bunke, O. (1912). *Über nervöse Entartung*. Springer: Berlin.

Carlson, E. T., and Dain, N. (1962). The meaning of moral insanity. *Bulletin of the History of Medicine*, **36**, 130–140.

Craft, M. (editor). (1966). *Psychopathic Disorders and Their Assessment*. Pergamon: London.

Curran, D., and Mallinson, P. (1944). Psychopathic personality. *Journal of Mental Science*, **90**, 266–286.

Delmas, F.-A. (1943). Les constitutions psychopathiques. *Annales Médico-psychologiques*, 101e année, **1**, 219–232.

Dubitscher (1936). Der moralische Schwachsinn. *Zeitschrift für die gesamte Neurologie und Psychiatrie*, **154**, 422–457.

Esquirol, J.-E.-D. (1838). *Des Maladies Mentales*. 2 vols. J.-B. Baillière: Paris.

Eysenck, H. J., and Eysenck, S. B. G. (1969). *Personality Structure and Measurement*. Routledge: London.

Foulds, G. A. (1965). *Personality and Personal Illness*. Tavistock: London.

Glover, E. (1955). *The Technique of Psycho-analysis*. Baillière: London.

Gröhmann (1818). Psychologie der Verbrecher aus Geisteskrankheiten oder Desorganisationen. *Zeitschrift für psychische Aerzte*, **1**, 174–189.

Gruhle, H. W. (1953). *Verstehen und Einfühlen*. Springer: Berlin.

Gurvitz, M. (1951). Developments in the concept of psychopathic personality (1900–1950). *British Journal of Delinquency*, **2**, 88–102.

Henderson, D. K. (1939). *Psychopathic States*. Chapman and Hall: London.

Henderson, D., and Gillespie, R. D. (1932). *A Text-book of Psychiatry*: 3rd edn. Oxford University Press: London.

Jaspers, K. (1965). *Allgemeine Psychopathologie*. 8. Aufl. Springer: Berlin.

Jenkins, R. L. (1960). The psychopathic or antisocial personality. *Journal of Nervous and Mental Disease*, **131**, 318 334.

Kahn, E. (1936). The psychopathic personalities. In *The Oxford Medicine*, Vol. 7, *Psychiatry for Practitioners*, pp. 239–255. Edited by H. A. Christian. Oxford University Press: New York.

Koch, J. L. A. (1891). *Die psychopathischen Minderwertigkeiten*. Maier: Ravensburg.

Kraepelin, E. (1887). *Psychiatrie*. 2nd edn. Abel: Leipzig.

Kraepelin, E. (1896). *Psychiatrie*. 5th edn. Barth: Leipzig.

Kraepelin, E. (1899). *Psychiatrie*. 2 vols. 6th edn. Barth: Leipzig.

Kraepelin, E. (1903–1904). *Psychiatrie*. 2 vols. 7th edn. Barth: Leipzig.

Kraepelin, E. (1909–1915). *Psychiatrie*. 4 vols. 8th edn. Barth: Leipzig.

Magnan, V. (1893). *Leçons Cliniques sur les Maladies Mentales*. Battaille: Paris.

McCord, W., and McCord, J. (1956). *Psychopathy and Delinquency*. Grune and Stratton: New York.

Maudsley, H. (1874). *Responsibility in Mental Disease*. King: London.

Maughs, S. B. (1941). A concept of psychopathic personality. *Journal of Criminal Psychopathology*, **2**, 329–356; 465–499.

Morel, B.-A. (1839). *Traité des Dégénérescences Physiques, Intellectuelles et Morales de l'Espèce Humaine*. J.-B. Baillière: Paris.

Müller, E. (1899). Ueber 'moral insanity'. *Archiv für Psychiatrie*, **31**, 325–377.

Mercier, C. A. (1914). *A Text-book of Insanity*. 2nd edn. Allen and Unwin: London.

Partridge, G. E. (1930). Current conceptions of psychopathic personality. *American Journal of Psychiatry*, **10**, 53–99.

Pinel, P. (1801). *Traité Medico-philosophique sur L'Aliénaiton Mentale*. Richard, Caille et Ravier: Paris.

Prichard, J. C. (1835). *A Treatise on Insanity*. Sherwood, Gilbert, and Piper: London.

Quay, H. C. (1964). Personality dimensions in delinquent males as inferred from the factor analysis of behavior ratings. *Journal of Research in Crime and Delinquency*, **1**, 33–37.

Robins, E. (1967). *Anti-Social and Dyssocial Personality Disorders. A Text Book of Psychiatry*, pp. 951–958. Edited by A. M. Freedman and H. Kaplan. Williams and Wilkins: Baltimore.

Savage. G. H. (1881). Moral insanity. *Journal of Mental Science*, **27**, 147–155.

Schneider, K. (1958). *Psychopathic Personalities*. Translated by M. W. Hamilton. Cassell: London.

Smith, M. (1922). *The Psychology of the Criminal*. Methuen: London.

Tiling, Th. (1896). Ueber angeborene moralische Degeneration oder Perversität des Charakters. *Allgemeine Zeitschrift für Psychiatrie*, **521**, 258–313.

Trillat, E. (1965). Les déséquilibrés. 3. In *Encyclopédie Medico-Chirurgicale*. Psychiatrie, 37310 A10. Paris.

Tuke, D. H. (editor). (1892). *A Dictionary of Psychological Medicine*. 2 vols. Churchill: London.

Vernon, P. E. (1953). *Personality Tests and Assessments*. Methuen: London.

Wallin, J. E. W. (1949). *Children with Mental and Physical Handicaps*. Staples: London.

Wolfgang, M. E. (1960). Cesare Lombroso. In *Pioneers in Criminology*, pp. 168–227. Edited by H. Mannheim. Stevens: London.

[30]

Mental Disorder and Violent Behavior

Perceptions and Evidence

John Monahan *School of Law, University of Virginia*

Throughout history and in all known societies, people have believed that mental disorder and violence were somehow related. The consensus of modern scholarly opinion, however, has been that no such relationship exists. Recent epidemiological studies cast doubt on this no-relationship position. Evidence now indicates that mental disorder may be a consistent, albeit modest, risk factor for the occurrence of violence. Denying that mental disorder and violence may be in any way associated is disingenuous and ultimately counterproductive. Dire implications for mental patient advocacy, for mental health law, and for the provision of mental health treatment need not follow from candidly acknowledging the possibility of a limited connection between disorder and violence.

Is there a relationship between mental disorder and violent behavior? Few questions in mental health law are as empirically complex or as politically controversial. On the one hand, the general public and their elected representatives appear firmly committed to the view that mental disorder and violence are connected. On the other hand, many social science researchers and the patient advocates who cite them seem equally convinced that no such connection exists. Although I have long been in the latter camp (e.g., Monahan, 1981), I now believe that there may be a relationship between mental disorder and violent behavior, one that cannot be fobbed off as chance or explained away by other factors that may cause them both. The relationship, if it exists, probably is not large, but may be important both for legal theory and for social policy. In this article, I lay before you the evidence and the inferences that have persuaded me to modify my views. I first consider the relationship between mental disorder and violence as it has been perceived by public and professional audiences, and then present an epidemiological framework within which the question can be empirically addressed.

Mental Disorder and Violence: Public and Professional Perceptions

Beliefs that mental disorder is linked to violent behavior are important for two reasons. The first is that such beliefs drive the formal laws and policies by which society attempts to control the behavior of disordered people and to regulate the provision of mental health care. Coherent theories of mental health law can be constructed that are not premised on the assumption that the mentally disordered are more prone to violence than is the rest of the general population (e.g., "Developments in the Law," 1974). But there can be little doubt that this assumption has played an animating role in the prominence of *dangerous to others* as a criterion for civil commitment and the commitment of persons acquitted of crime by reason of insanity, in the creation of special statutes for the extended detention of mentally disordered prisoners, and in the imposition of tort liability on psychologists and psychiatrists who fail to anticipate the violence of their patients (Appelbaum, 1988; Grisso, 1991).

The second and perhaps more important reason why beliefs in the violence potential of the mentally disordered are important is that they not only drive formal law and policy toward the mentally disordered as a class, but they also determine our informal responses and modes of interacting with individuals who are perceived to be mentally ill. An ingenious study by Link, Cullen, Frank, and Wozniak (1987) vividly makes this point. These researchers investigated the extent to which a person's status as a former mental patient fostered social distance on the part of others, measured by questions tapping the willingness of the respondent to have as a co-worker or neighbor someone described in a vignette as having once been a patient in a mental hospital. Consistent with much prior

Editor's note. Articles based on APA award addresses that appear in the *American Psychologist* are scholarly articles by distinguished contributors to the field. As such, they are given special consideration in the *American Psychologist's* editorial selection process.

This article was originally presented as a Distinguished Contributions to Research in Public Policy award address at the 99th Annual Convention of the American Psychological Association in San Francisco in August 1991.

Author's note. My work on this topic has been supported by the MacArthur Research Network on Mental Health and the Law. The views expressed here are my own.

I am grateful to the members of the Network and to Lawrence Fitch, S. Ken Hoge, Deidre Klassen, Bruce Link, Lee Robins, Joan Roth, Jeffrey Swanson, Linda Teplin, and Simon Wessely for their comments on the manuscript.

Correspondence concerning this article should be addressed to John Monahan, School of Law, University of Virginia, Charlottesville, VA 22901.

Vol. 47, No. 4, 511–521

research (e.g., Gove, 1980), Link et al. (1987) found no main effect of the former-patient label. But when they disaggregated their subjects—adults drawn from the open community—by means of a "perceived dangerousness scale" into those who believed that mental disorder was linked to violence and those who did not, strong labeling effects emerged. Remarkably, people who believed that there was no connection between mental disorder and violence exhibited what might be called an affirmative action effect: They responded as if they were *more* willing to have as a co-worker or neighbor someone who had been a mental patient than someone who had never been hospitalized. People who believed that the mentally disordered were prone to violence, however, strongly rejected and wished to distance themselves from the former patient.

Before considering the contemporary nature of public and professional perceptions of the relationship between mental disorder and violence, it may be useful to briefly set the topic in historical and cultural perspective.

Perceptions in Other Times and Other Places

From the very origins of Western civilization, most people's experience with the mentally disordered have led them to assume that there was a connection of some kind between mental disorder and violence (Monahan, in press-a). References in Greek and Roman literature to the violence potential of the mentally disordered date from the fifth century before the Christian era began. As the historian George Rosen (1968) noted, in the ancient world "two forms of behavior were considered particularly characteristic of the mentally disordered, their habit of wandering about and their proneness to violence" (p. 98). Plato, for example, in "Alcibiades II," records a dialogue between Socrates and a friend. The friend claimed that many citizens of Athens were "mad." Socrates refuted this claim by arguing that the rate of mental disorder in Athens could not possibly be very high because the rate of violence in Athens was very low.

> How could we live in safety with so many crazy people? Should we not long ago have paid the penalty at their hands, and have been struck and beaten and endured every other form of ill usage which madmen are wont to inflict? (cited in Rosen, p. 100)

Likewise, Plautus, in a play written about 270 B.C., titled *Casina,* wrote of a maid who had taken up a sword and was threatening to murder a lover. One character describes the situation: "She's chasing everyone through the house there, and won't let a soul come near her; they're hiding under chests and couches afraid to breath a word." To this, her lover asks, "What the deuce has gotten into her all of a sudden this way?" The answer he received seemed to suffice for an explanation: "She's gone crazy" (cited in Rosen, p. 99). Advice to those responsible for the care of the mentally disordered in Greece and Rome often made reference to their dangerousness and to the necessity of keeping them in restraints, lest their caretakers be injured.

It is important to emphasize that even in ancient times, the public perception was not that all or most or even many of the mentally disordered were violent, just that a disproportionate number were. The Roman philosopher Philo Judaeus, for example, divided the mentally disordered into two groups. The larger one was made up of disordered people "of the easy-going gentle style," and the other, smaller one, consisted of those "whose madness was . . . of the fierce and savage kind, which is dangerous both to the madmen themselves and those who approach them" (cited in Rosen, 1968, p. 89).

Such public attitudes persisted throughout the Middle Ages and the Renaissance. Care of the disordered was left to family and friends; "only those considered too dangerous to keep at home . . . were dealt with by communal authorities" (Rosen, 1968, p. 139). An early form of the *dangerousness standard* for civil commitment is illustrated by the 1493 German case of a disordered man who had committed a violent act and was ordered locked up in a tower of the city wall. When he no longer appeared violent, he was released from the tower to the custody of his family,

> upon condition that they would confine him themselves should he again become violent. In this event, his wife would confine him in her house or arrange to keep him elsewhere at her expense. If required, the council would lend her a jail. (Rosen, p. 143)

Little in terms of public attitudes changed as the Renaissance gave way to the modern era. In 1843, the London *Times* publishing the following ditty on its editorial page on the day after Daniel McNaughten was acquitted by reason of insanity of murdering the secretary to the prime minister:

> Ye people of England exult and be glad
> For ye're now at the mercy of the merciless mad!

In the United States, as in Europe, the perception of a link between mental disorder and violence is as old as recorded history. The first general hospital in the American colonies to include a ward for the mentally disordered—the cellar—was founded at the urging of no less than Benjamin Franklin. After arguing in vain that the Pennsylvania colony was morally obligated to provide for the disordered, he switched tacks and petitioned the Assembly in 1751 that

> the Number of Persons distempered in Mind and deprived of their rational Faculties has increased greatly in this province. Some of them going at large are a terror to their Neighbors, who are daily apprehensive of the Violences they may commit. (cited in Deutsch, 1949, p. 59)

This argument hit a responsive chord, and the Pennsylvania Hospital still stands in Philadelphia.

The belief that mental disorder is conducive to violence runs deep in Western culture, but is by no means peculiar to it. Westermeyer and Kroll (1978) studied all persons known as *baa,* or crazy, in 27 villages in Laos, a country that at the time of the research was without a single psychiatrist, psychologist, or mental hospital. They questioned family members, neighbors, and the people seen as *baa* themselves about the occurrence of violence and its relationship to mental disorder. They were told that 11% of their subjects exhibited violent behavior before they began acting in a *baa* manner, whereas 54% were reported to have acted violently once they became *baa*. At approximately the same time, Jones and Horne (1973) studied almost 1,000 people in four isolated aboriginal missions in the Australian desert.

> Frequently, [they concluded,] an aggressive act by the patient causes him to present clinically, but with an explanation that was culturally appropriate—he would claim, for example, that his symptoms have been inflicted upon him by magical means and his aggression was his way of protecting himself. (p. 225)

Finally, Jane Murphy (1976), the noted anthropologist, reviewed in *Science* a great deal of research on responses to mental disorder among a variety of Northwestern Native American and several Central African ethnic groups. She reported great similarities among people in very different traditional societies, societies that had never had contact with one another:

> There seems to be little that is distinctively cultural in the attitudes and actions directed toward the mentally ill, except in such matters as that an abandoned anthill could not be used as an asylum in the arctic or a barred igloo in the tropics . . . . If the behavior indicates helplessness, help tends to be given, especially in food and clothes. If the behavior appears foolish or incongruous . . . , laughter is the response. If the behavior is noisy and agitated, the response may be to quiet, sometimes by herbs and sometimes by other means. If the behavior is violent or threatening, the response is to restrain or to subdue. (p. 1025)

Of course, the anthropological fact that a popular belief has persisted since antiquity and is found in all known societies does not mean that the belief is true. Unfounded prejudices may also be enduring and shared. But if the assumption that mental disorder sometimes predisposes toward violent behavior is a myth, it may still be worth noting that it is a myth that is both culturally universal and historically invariant.

Contemporary American Perceptions

In modern times and in modern societies, of course, we no longer have to rely on historians and anthropologists to tell us what we believe. We have survey researchers to quantify our opinions. One poll conducted by the Field Institute (1984) for the California Department of Mental Health asked 1,500 representative California adults whether they agreed with the statement, "A person who is diagnosed as schizophrenic is more likely to commit a violent crime than a normal person." Almost two thirds of the sample (61%) said that they definitely or probably agreed. In modern as in ancient times, however, the public by no means believes that mental disorder inevitably or even frequently leads to violence. In a survey of 1,000 adults from all parts of the United States, conducted by the DYG Corporation (1990) for the Robert Wood Johnson Foundation Program on Chronic Mental Illness, 24% of the respondents agreed with the statement, "People with chronic mental illness are, by far, more dangerous than the general population," whereas twice as many (48%) agreed with the proposition, "The mentally ill are far *less* of a danger than most people believe."

Although ancient attitudes about the relationship between mental disorder and violence were, of necessity, based on personal observation or word-of-mouth, contemporary opinions no doubt reflect the additional impact of the image of the mentally disordered relentlessly promoted by the media (Steadman & Cocozza, 1978). One content analysis performed for the National Institute of Mental Health (Gerbner, Gross, Morgan, & Signorielli, 1981) found that 17% of all prime-time American television programs that could charitably be classified as dramas depicted a character as mentally ill. Of these mentally ill characters, 73% were portrayed as violent, compared with 40% of the "normal" characters (!), and 23% of the mentally ill characters were shown to be homicidal, compared with 10% of the normal characters. Nor are such caricatures limited to television. A content analysis of stories from the United Press International database (Shain & Phillips, 1991) found that in 86% of all print stories dealing with former mental patients, a violent crime—"usually murder or mass murder" (p. 64)—was the focus of the article.

Professional Perceptions

From reading the literature in this area, it would appear that there are only two identifiable groups in modern society who do *not* believe that mental disorder and violence are associated at greater than chance levels. The first group is composed of advocates for the mentally disordered, both of the traditional and ex-patient schools. The most recent pamphlet of the established National Mental Health Association (1987), for example, stated that "people with mental illnesses pose no more of a crime threat than do other members of the general population" (p. 2). Likewise, a recent volume produced by a leading ex-patient advocacy group for the California Department of Mental Health (Campbell & Schraiber, 1989) stated that "studies show that while, like all groups, some members are violent, mental health clients are no more violent than the general population" (p. 88). In making such statements, patient advocates are clearly and commendably motivated by the desire to dispel vivid homicidal maniac images pandered by the media and to counter the stigma and social distancing that are bred by public fear. Given the findings of Link et al. (1987), they surely are right to be concerned.

The second group in society that apparently believes that mental disorder is not associated with any increase in the risk of violence consists of many sociological and psychological researchers. Henry Steadman and I (Monahan & Steadman, 1983a), for example, reviewed over 200 studies on the association between crime and mental disorder for the National Institute of Justice. This was our summary:

> The conclusion to which our review is drawn is that the relation between . . . crime and mental disorder can be accounted for largely by demographic and historical characteristics that the two groups share. When appropriate statistical controls are applied for factors such as age, gender, race, social class, and previous institutionalization, whatever relations between crime and mental disorder are reported tend to disappear. (p. 152)

I now believe that this conclusion is at least premature and may well be wrong. I say this for two reasons. First, to statistically control for factors, such as social class and previous institutionalization, that are highly related to mental disorder is problematic. For example, if in some cases mental disorder causes people to decline in social class (perhaps because they became psychotic at work) and also to become violent, then to control for low social class is, to some unknown extent, to attenuate the relationship that will be found between mental disorder and violence. "The problem," as Bruce Dohrenwend (1990) has noted, "remains what it has always been: how to unlock the riddle that low SES can be either a cause or a consequence of psychopathology" (p. 45). If, in other cases, mental disorder causes people to be repetitively violent and therefore institutionalized, then to control for previous institutionalization also masks, to some unknown degree, the relationship that will be found between mental disorder and violence.

The second reason that I now think the no-relationship conclusion may be wrong is that new research—by no means perfect, yet by all accounts vastly superior to what had been in the literature even a few years ago—has become available. These new studies find a consistent, albeit modest, relationship between mental disorder and violent behavior. I will now turn to this literature, both old and new. As before (Monahan & Steadman, 1983a), I find an epidemiological framework conducive to clear thinking on this topic.

Mental Disorder and Violence: Evidence for a Relationship

There are two ways to determine whether a relationship exists between mental disorder and violent behavior and, if it does, to estimate the strength of that relationship. If being mentally disordered raises the likelihood that a person will commit a violent act—that is, if mental disorder is a risk factor for the occurrence of violent behavior—then the actual (or true) prevalence rate for violence should be higher among disordered than among nondisordered populations. And to the extent that mental disorder is a contributing cause to the occurrence of violence, the true prevalence rate of mental disorder should be higher among people who commit violent acts than among people who do not. These two complementary ways of estimating relationships with epidemiological methods follow.

1. True prevalence of violent behavior among persons with mental disorder
   a. Among identified mental patients
   b. Among random community samples
2. True prevalence of mental disorder among persons committing violent behavior
   a. Among identified criminal offenders
   b. Among random community samples

Within each generic category, two types of research exist. The first seeks to estimate the relationship between mental disorder and violence by studying people who are being treated either for mental disorder (in hospitals) or for violent behavior (in jails and prisons). The second seeks to estimate the relationship between mental disorder and violence by studying people unselected for treatment status in the open community. Both types of studies are valuable in themselves, but both have limitations taken in isolation, as will become clear.

Violence Among the Disordered

Three types of studies provide data from hospitalized mental patients that can be used to estimate the relationship between mental disorder and violence. One type looks at the prevalence of violent acts committed by patients before they entered the hospital. A second type looks at the prevalence of violent incidents committed by mental patients during their hospital stay. A final type of study addresses the prevalence of violent behavior among mental patients after they have been released from the hospital. (I restrict myself here to remarking on findings on violent behavior toward others and exclude violence toward self, verbal threats of violence, and property damage. By *mental disorder,* I refer, unless otherwise noted, to those major disorders of thought or affect that form a subset of Axis I of the *Diagnostic and Statistical Manual of Mental Disorders,* 3rd edition, revised [*DSM–III–R;* American Psychiatric Association 1987]. Three excellent recent reviews (Mullen, in press; Otto, 1992; Wessely & Taylor, 1991) make my task of summarizing these studies much easier.

Together, these three reviews report on 11 studies published over the past 15 years that provide data on the prevalence of violent behavior among persons who eventually became mental patients. The time period investigated was typically the two weeks prior to hospital admission. The findings across the various studies vary considerably: Between approximately 10% and 40% of the patient samples (with a median rate of 15%) committed a physically assaultive act against another shortly before they were hospitalized; 12 studies with data on the prevalence of violence by patients on mental hospital wards are found in these reviews. The periods studied varied from a few days to a year. The findings here also range from about 10% to 40% (with a median rate of 25%; see also Davis, 1991).

There is a very large literature, going back to the 1920s, on violent behavior by mental patients after they have been discharged from civil hospitals (Rabkin, 1979). The best recent studies are clearly those of Klassen and O'Connor (1988, 1990). They find that approximately 25%–30% of male subjects with at least one violent incident in their past—a very relevant, but highly selective sample of patients—are violent within a year of release from the hospital. The ongoing MacArthur Risk Assessment Study (Steadman et al., 1992) is finding that 27% of released male and female patients report at least one violent act within a mean of four months after discharge.

Each of these three types of research has important policy and practice implications. Studies of violence before hospitalization supply data on the workings of civil commitment laws and the interaction between the mental health and criminal justice systems (Monahan & Steadman, 1983b). Studies of violence during hospitalization have significance for the level of security required in mental health facilities and the need for staff training in managing aggressive incidents (Binder & McNiel, 1988; Roth, 1985). Studies of violence after hospitalization provide essential base-rate information for use in the risk assessments involved in release decision making and in after-care planning (Monahan, 1988).

For the purpose of determining whether there is a fundamental relationship between mental disorder and violent behavior, however, each of these three types of research is unavailing. Only rarely did the studies provide any comparative data on the prevalence of similarly defined violence among nonhospitalized groups. Steadman and Felson (1984) is one study that did. The authors interviewed former mental patients and a random sample of the general community in Albany County, New York. The percentage of ex-patients who reported at least one dispute involving hitting during the past year was 22.3, compared with 15.1% for the community sample. For disputes in which a weapon had been used, the figures were 8.1% for the ex-patients and 1.6% for the community sample. When demographic factors were controlled, however, these differences were not significant. Although the rates of violence by mental patients before, during, or after hospitalization reported in the other studies certainly appear much higher than would be expected by chance, the general lack of data from nonpatients makes comparison speculative. But even if such data were available, several sources of systematic bias would make their use for epidemiological purposes highly suspect. Because these studies dealt with persons who were subsequently, simultaneously, or previously institutionalized as mental patients, none of them can distinguish between the *participation* of the mentally disordered in violence—the topic of interest here—and the *selection* of that subset of the mentally disordered persons who are violent for treatment in the public-sector inpatient settings in which the research was carried out. (There is virtually no research on private hospitals or on outpatients.) Furthermore, studies of violence after hospitalization suffer from the additional selection bias that only those patients clinically predicted to be nonviolent were released. Nor can the studies of violence during and after hospitalization distinguish the effect of the treatment of potentially violent patients in the hospital from the existence of a prior relationship between mental disorder and violence.

For example, to use the prevalence of violence before hospitalization as an index of the fundamental relationship between mental disorder and violence would be to thoroughly confound rates of violence with the legal criteria for hospitalization. Given the rise of the dangerousness standard for civil commitment in the United States and throughout the world (Monahan & Shah, 1989), it would be amazing if many patients were not violent before they were hospitalized: Violent behavior is one of the reasons that these disordered people were selected out of the total disordered population for hospitalization. Likewise, the level of violent behavior exhibited on the ward during hospitalization is determined not only by the differential selection of violent people for hospitalization (or, within the hospital, the further selection of "violence-prone" patients for placement in the locked wards that were often the sites of the research), but by the skill of ward staff in defusing potentially violent incidents and by the efficacy of treatment in mitigating disorder (or by the effect of medication in sedating patients). As Werner, Rose, and Yesavage (1983) have stated,

> To the extent that hostile, excited, suspicious, and recent assaultive behavior is viewed by ward staffing as presaging imminent violence, it is the patient manifesting such behavior who is singled out for special treatment (e.g., additional medications, more psychotherapy); such selection may reduce the likelihood of engaging in violence. Thus, paradoxically, if the patient who "looks" imminently violent in this setting is given effective treatments that forestall violent behavior, he will not in fact engage in violence as predicted. (p. 824)

Because the prevalence of violence after hospitalization may be a function of (a) the type of patients selected for hospitalization, (b) the nature and duration of the treatment administered during hospitalization, and (c) the risk assessment cutoffs used in determining eligibility for discharge, these data, too, tell us little about whether a basic relationship between mental disorder and violence exists. Only by augmenting studies of the prevalence of violence among treated (i.e., hospitalized) samples of the mentally disordered with studies of the prevalence of violence among samples of disordered people unselected for treatment status in the community can population estimates free of selection and treatment biases be offered. Fortunately, a recent and seminal study by Swanson, Holzer, Ganju, and Jono (1990) provides this essential information. Swanson and his colleagues drew their data from the National Institute of Mental Health's Epidemiological Catchment Area (ECA) study (Robins & Regier, 1991). Representative weighted samples of adult household residents of Baltimore, Durham, and Los Angeles were pooled to form a data base of approximately 10,000 people. The Diagnostic Interview Schedule (DIS), a structured interview designed for use by trained lay persons, was used to establish mental disorder according to *Diagnostic and Statistical Manual of Mental Disorders*, third edition (*DSM–III;* American Psychiatric Association, 1980) criteria. Five items on the DIS[1]—four

[1] The items were, (a) Did you ever hit or throw things at your wife/husband/partner? [If so] Were you ever the one who threw things first, regardless of who started the argument? Did you hit or throw things first on more than one occasion? (b) Have you ever spanked or hit a child (yours or anyone else's) hard enough so that he or she had bruises or had to stay in bed or see a doctor? (c) Since age 18, have you been

Table 1
Percentage Violent During Past Year in ECA Sample, by Age

Age group	% violent
18–29	7.3
30–44	3.6
45–64	1.2
65+	0.1

Note. ECA = Epidemiologic Catchment Area. From "Violence and Psychiatric Disorder in the Community: Evidence from the Epidemiologic Catchment Area Survey" by J. Swanson, C. Holzer, V. Ganju, and R. Jono, 1990, *Hospital and Community Psychiatry, 41,* p. 764. Copyright 1990 by the American Psychiatric Association. Adapted by permission.

Table 2
Percentage Violent During Past Year Among 18–29-Year-Olds in ECA Sample, by Gender and SES

SES	Men	Women
1 (lowest)	16.1	9.1
2	11.7	5.0
3	8.1	2.5
4 (highest)	6.1	3.3

Note. ECA = Epidemiologic Catchment Area; SES = socioeconomic status. From "Violence and Psychiatric Disorder in the Community: Evidence from the Epidemiologic Catchment Area Survey" by J. Swanson, C. Holzer, V. Ganju, and R. Jono, 1990 *Hospital and Community Psychiatry, 41,* p. 764. Copyright 1990 by the American Psychiatric Association. Adapted by permission.

embedded among the criteria for antisocial personality disorder and one that formed part of the diagnosis of alcohol abuse/dependence—were used to indicate violent behavior. A respondent was counted as positive for violence if he or she endorsed at least one of these items and reported that the act occurred during the year preceding the interview. This index of violent behavior, as Swanson et al. noted, is a "blunt measure": It is based on self-report without corroboration, the questions overlap considerably, and it does not differentiate in terms of the frequency or the severity of violence. Yet there is little doubt that each of the target behaviors is indeed "violent," and I believe that the measure is a reasonable estimate of the prevalence of violent behavior.

Confidence in the Swanson et al. (1990) findings is increased by their conformity to the demographic correlates of violence known from the criminological literature. As Tables 1 and 2 indicate, violence in the ECA study was seven times as prevalent among the young as among the old, twice as prevalent among men as among women, and three times as prevalent among persons of the lowest social class as among persons of the highest social class.

But it is the clinical findings that are of direct interest here. Table 3 presents the prevalence of violent behavior during the past year by *DSM–III* diagnosis. For these data, exclusion criteria were not used: A subject who met the criteria for more than one disorder was counted as a case of each.

Three findings are immediately evident: (a) The prevalence of violence is more than five times higher among people who meet criteria for a *DSM–III* Axis I diagnosis than among people who are not diagnosable. (b) The prevalence of violence among persons who meet criteria for a diagnosis of schizophrenia, major depression, or mania/bi-polar disorder are remarkably similar. (c) The prevalence of violence among persons who meet criteria for a diagnosis of alcoholism is 12 times that of persons who receive no diagnosis, and the prevalence of violence among persons who meet criteria for being diagnosed as abusing drugs is 16 times that of persons who receive no diagnosis. When both demographic and clinical factors were combined in a regression equation to predict the occurrence of violence, several significant predictors emerged. Violence was most likely to occur among young, lower class men, among those with a substance abuse diagnosis, and among those with a diagnosis of major mental disorder (see Swanson & Holzer, 1991).

One final and equally notable study not only confirms the ECA data but takes them a large step further. Link, Cullen, and Andrews (in press) analyzed data from a larger study conducted by Bruce Dohrenwend and his colleagues (Shrout et al., 1988), using the Psychiatric Epidemiology Research Interview (PERI) to measure symptoms and life events. Link et al. (in press) compared rates of arrest and of self-reported violence (including hitting, fighting, weapon use, and "hurting someone badly") in a sample of approximately 400 adults from the Washington Heights area of New York City who had never been in a mental hospital or sought help from a mental health professional with rates of arrest and self-reported violence in several samples of former mental

Table 3
Percentage Violent During Past Year in ECA Sample, by Diagnosis

Diagnosis	% violence
No disorder	2.1
Schizophrenia	12.7
Major depression	11.7
Mania or bi-polar	11.0
Alcohol abuse/dependence	24.6
Drug abuse/dependence	34.7

Note. ECA = Epidemiologic Catchment Area. From "Violence and Psychiatric Disorder in the Community: Evidence from the Epidemiologic Catchment Area Survey" by J. Swanson, C. Holzer, V. Ganju, and R. Jono, 1990, *Hospital and Community Psychiatry, 41,* p. 765. Copyright 1990 by the American Psychiatric Association. Adapted by permission.

in more than one fight that came to swapping blows, other than fights with your husband/wife/partner? (d) Have you ever used a weapon like a stick, knife, or gun in a fight since you were 18? (e) Have you ever gotten into physical fights while drinking?

patients from the same area. To eliminate alternative explanations of their data, the researchers controlled, in various analyses, for an extraordinary number of factors: age, gender, educational level, ethnicity (Black, White, and Hispanic), socioeconomic status, family composition (e.g., married with children), homicide rate of the census tract in which a subject lived, and the subject's "need for approval." This last variable was measured by the Crowne-Marlowe (1960) Social Desirability scale and was included to control for the possibility that patients might be more willing to report socially undesirable behavior (such as violence) than were nonpatients.

The study found that the patient groups were almost always more violent than the never-treated community sample, often two to three times as violent. As in the ECA study (Swanson et al., 1990), demographic factors clearly related to violence (e.g., men, the less educated, and those from high-crime neighborhoods were more likely to be violent). But even when all the demographic and personal factors, such as social desirability, were taken into account, significant differences between the patients and the never-treated community residents remained. The association between mental patient status and violent behavior, as the authors noted, was "remarkably robust" to attempts to explain it away as artifact.

Most important, Link et al. (in press) then controlled for "current symptomatology." They did this by using the False Beliefs and Perceptions scale of the PERI, which measures core psychotic symptoms via questions such as, "How often have you felt that thoughts were put into your head that were not your own?", "How often have you thought you were possessed by a spirit or devil?", and "How often have you felt that your mind was dominated by forces beyond your control?" Remarkably, *not a single difference in rates of recent violent behavior between patients and never-treated community residents remained significant when current psychotic symptoms were controlled.* The Psychotic Symptomatology scale, on the other hand, was significantly and strongly related to most indices of recent violent behavior, even when additional factors, such as alcohol and drug use, were taken into account. Thus, almost all of the difference in rates of violence between patients and nonpatients could be accounted for by the level of active psychotic symptoms that the patients were experiencing. In other words, when mental patients were actively experiencing psychotic symptoms like delusions and hallucinations, their risk of violence was significantly elevated, compared with that of nonpatients, and when patients were not actively experiencing psychotic symptoms, their risk of violence was not appreciably higher than demographically similar members of their home community who had never been treated. Finally, Link et al. (in press) also found that the Psychotic Symptomatology scale significantly predicted violent behavior among the never-treated community residents. Even among people who had never been formally treated for mental disorder, actively experiencing psychotic symptoms was associated with the commission of violent acts.

The data independently reported by Swanson et al. (1990) and Link et al. (in press) are remarkable and provide the crucial missing element that begins to fill out the epidemiological picture of mental disorder and violence. Together, these two studies suggest that the currently mentally disordered—those actively experiencing serious psychotic symptoms—are involved in violent behavior at rates several times those of nondisordered members of the general population, and that this difference persists even when a wide array of demographic and social factors are taken into consideration. Because the studies were conducted using representative samples of the open community, selection biases are not a plausible alternative explanation for their findings.

Disorder Among the Violent

Recall that there is a second empirical tack that might be taken to determine whether a fundamental relationship between mental disorder and violence exists and to estimate what the magnitude of that relationship might be. If mental disorder is in fact a contributing cause to the occurrence of violence, then the prevalence of mental disorder should be higher among people who commit violent acts than among people who do not. As before, there are two ways to ascertain the existence of such a relationship: by studying treated cases—in this instance, people "treated" for violence by being institutionalized in local jails and state prisons—and determining their rates of mental disorder, and by studying untreated cases—people in the open community who are violent but not institutionalized for it—and determining their rates of mental disorder.

A large number of studies exist that estimate the prevalence of mental disorder among jail and prison inmates. Of course, not all jail and prison inmates have been convicted of a violent crime. Yet 66% of state prisoners have a current or past conviction for violence (Bureau of Justice Statistics, 1991), and there is no evidence that the rates of disorder of jail inmates charged with violent offenses differ from those of jail inmates charged with nonviolent offenses. So I believe that data on the prevalence of disorder among inmates in general also apply reasonably well to violent inmates in particular.

Teplin (1990) reviewed 18 studies of mental disorder among jail samples performed in the past 15 years. Most of the studies were conducted on inmates referred for a mental health evaluation, and thus present obviously inflated rates of disorder. Among those few studies that randomly sampled jail inmates, rates of mental disorder varied widely, from 5% to 16% psychotic. Roth (1980), in reviewing the literature on the prevalence of mental disorder among prison inmates, concluded that the rate of psychosis was "on the order of 5 percent or less of the total prison population" (p. 688), and the rate of any form of disorder was in the 15%–20% range. More recent studies have reported somewhat higher rates of serious mental disorder. Steadman, Fabisiak, Dvoskin, and Holohean (1987), in a level-of-care survey of more than 3,000 prisoners in New York State, concluded that 8% had "severe mental disabilities" and another 16% had "significant mental disabilities" (see also Taylor & Gunn, 1984).

Although the rates of mental disorder among jail and prison inmates appear very high, comparison data for similarly defined mental disorder among the general noninstitutionalized population were typically not available. As well, the methods of diagnosing mental disorder in the jail and prison studies often consisted of unstandardized clinical interviews or the use of proxy variables, such as prior mental hospitalization (see, e.g., Steadman, Monahan, Duffee, Hartstone, & Robbins, 1984).

Recently, however, four studies, one with jail inmates and three with prisoners, have become available that use the DIS as their diagnostic instrument. This not only allows for a standardized method of assessing disorder independent of previous hospitalization, it permits comparison across the studies and between these institutionalized populations and the random community samples of the ECA research.

In the first study, Teplin (1990) administered the DIS to a stratified random sample—one half misdemeanants and one half felons—of 728 men from the Cook County (Chicago) jail. In the most comparable of the prison studies, the California Department of Corrections (1989) commissioned a consortium of research organizations to administer the DIS to a stratified random sample of 362 male inmates in California prisons (see also Collins & Schlesinger, 1983; Hodgins & Cote, 1990; Neighbors et al., 1987). Comparative data from the ECA study for male respondents were provided by Teplin (1990). The findings for current disorder are summarized in Table 4.

It can be seen that the prevalence of schizophrenia is approximately 3 times higher in the jail and prison samples than in the general population samples, the prevalence of major depression 3–4 times higher, the prevalence of mania or bi-polar disorder 7–14 times higher, and overall, the prevalence of any severe disorder (i.e., any of the above diagnoses) 3–4 times higher. Although there were no controls for demographic factors in the prison study, Teplin (1990) controlled for race and age in the jail study, and the jail–general population differences persisted. Although these studies all relied on male inmates, even more dramatic data for female prisoners have been reported in one study (Daniel, Robins, Reid, & Wilfley, 1988).

These findings on the comparatively high prevalence of mental disorder among jail and prison inmates have enormous policy implications for mental health screening of admissions to these facilities and for the need for mental health treatment in correctional institutions (Steadman, McCarty, & Morrissey, 1989). But given the systematic bias inherent in the use of identified criminal offenders, they cannot fully address the issue of whether there is a fundamental relationship between mental disorder and violence. Mentally disordered offenders may be more or less likely to be arrested and imprisoned than are nondisordered offenders. On the one hand, Robertson (1988) found that offenders who were schizophrenic were much more likely than were nondisordered offenders to be arrested at the scene of the crime or to give themselves up to the police. Teplin (1985), in the only actual field study in this area, found the police more likely to arrest disordered than nondisordered suspects. On the other hand, Klassen and O'Connor (1988) found that released mental patients whose violence in the community evoked an official response were twice as likely to be rehospitalized—and thereby avoid going to jail—than they were to be arrested. An individual's status as a jail or prison inmate, in short, is not independent of the presence of mental disorder.

As before, complementary data on the prevalence of mental disorder among unselected samples of people in the open community who commit violent acts is necessary to fully address this issue. And as before, the analysis of the ECA data by Swanson et al. (1990) provides the required information, which is summarized in Table 5.

The prevalence of schizophrenia among respondents who endorsed at least one of the five questions indicating violent behavior in the past year was approximately four times higher than among respondents who did not report violence, the prevalence of affective disorder was three times higher, the prevalence of substance abuse (either

Table 4
Current Prevalence of Mental Disorder (%) Among California Prisoners, Chicago Jail Detainees, and ECA Sample

Diagnosis	Prison	Jail	ECA
Schizophrenia	3.1	2.7	0.9
Major depression	3.5	3.9	1.1
Mania or bi-polar	0.7	1.4	0.1
Any severe disorder	7.9	6.4	1.8

Note. ECA = Epidemiologic Catchment Area. The data in columns 2 and 3 are from "The Prevalence of Severe Mental Disorder Among Male Urban Jail Detainees" by L. Teplin, 1990, *American Journal of Public Health, 80,* p. 665. Copyright 1990 by the American Public Health Association. Adapted by permission. The data in column 1 are from *Current Description, Evaluation, and Recommendations for Treatment of Mentally Disordered Criminal Offenders,* 1989, Sacramento: California Department of Corrections.

Table 5
Current Prevalence of Mental Disorder (%) Among Persons in ECA Sample Who Reported Violence or No Violence During Past Year

Violence	Schizophrenia	Major affective	Substance abuse	Any disorder
Yes	3.9	9.4	41.6	55.5
No	1.0	3.0	4.9	19.6

Note. ECA = Epidemiologic Catchment Area. From "Violence and Psychiatric Disorder in the Community: Evidence from the Epidemiologic Catchment Area Survey" by J. Swanson, C. Holzer, V. Ganju, and R. Jono, 1990, *Hospital and Community Psychiatry, 41,* p. 765. Copyright 1990 by the American Psychiatric Association. Adapted by permission.

alcohol or other drugs) was eight times higher, and overall, the prevalence of any measured DIS diagnosis—which here included anxiety disorders—was almost three times higher.

Implications for Research and Policy

The data that have recently become available, fairly read, suggest the one conclusion I did not want to reach: Whether the measure is the prevalence of violence among the disordered or the prevalence of disorder among the violent, whether the sample is people who are selected for treatment as inmates or patients in institutions or people randomly chosen from the open community, and no matter how many social and demographic factors are statistically taken into account, there appears to be a relationship between mental disorder and violent behavior. Mental disorder may be a robust and significant risk factor for the occurrence of violence, as an increasing number of clinical researchers in recent years have averred (Bloom, 1989; Krakowski, Volavka, & Brizer, 1986; Mullen, in press; Wessely & Taylor, 1991).

Should further research solidify this conclusion, would it mean—to return to the points we began with—that laws that restrict the freedom of mentally disordered people for long periods of time or the pervasive social rejection of former mental patients are justified, or that the media is correct in its portrayal of people with mental disorder as threats to the social order? No, it would not and for two reasons.

First, as the Link et al. (in press) study makes clear, it is only people currently experiencing psychotic symptoms who may be at increased risk of violence. Being a former patient in a mental hospital—that is, having experienced psychotic symptoms *in the past*—bears no direct relationship to violence, and bears an indirect relationship to violence only in the attenuated sense that previous disorder may raise the risk of current disorder.

Second and more important, demonstrating the existence of a statistically significant relationship between mental disorder and violence is one thing; demonstrating the social and policy significance of the magnitude of that relationship is another. By all indications, the great majority of people who are currently disordered—approximately 90% from the ECA study—are not violent. None of the data give any support to the sensationalized caricature of the mentally disordered served up by the media, the shunning of former patients by employers and neighbors in the community, or regressive "lock 'em all up" laws proposed by politicians pandering to public fears. The policy implications of mental disorder as a risk factor for violent behavior can be understood only in relative terms. Compared with the magnitude of risk associated with the combination of male gender, young age, and lower socioeconomic status, for example, the risk of violence presented by mental disorder is modest. Compared with the magnitude of risk associated with alcoholism and other drug abuse, the risk associated with major mental disorders such as schizophrenia and affective disorder is modest indeed. Clearly, mental health status makes at best a trivial contribution to the overall level of violence in society. (But see "Developments in the Law", 1974, on the legal justification—"because [the mentally disordered] are . . . unable to make autonomous decisions" (p. 1233)—for preventively intervening in the lives of disordered people in situations in which we do not intervene with nondisordered people, even when the nondisordered people present a higher risk of violence.)

What, then, are the implications of the conclusion that mental disorder may be a significant, albeit modest, risk factor for the occurrence of violent behavior? I see four principle ones. First, the empirical question of the relationship between mental disorder and violent behavior has only begun to be addressed. That *major mental disorder* as a generic category relates to violence would be important to know, but it is by no means all that clinicians and policymakers need to know. They need to know the specific features of mental disorder that carry the increased risk. Do disordered perceptions (e.g., hallucinations), disordered assumptions (e.g., delusions), or disordered processes of reasoning or affect relate most closely to the occurrence of violent behavior? It is unclear whether mental disorder should be unpacked by diagnosis, by course, by symptom pattern, or by specific types of offender–victim interactions for the purpose of answering these crucial questions. Indeed, the victim's manner of reacting or overreacting to "fear-inducing" aspects of the disordered person's behavior may itself be a mediating factor in the occurrence of violence (Link et al., in press). Violence itself may be only a by-product of a more generic tendency to "norm violation" that accompanies some forms of mental disorder. Epidemiological methods have yielded considerable insights in this general research area to date. "It is questionable, however, whether this group comparison approach can shed a great deal of light on more refined questions that may be posed at this point regarding the relationship between mental illness and criminality" (Mulvey, Blumstein, & Cohen, 1986, p. 60). The use of more longitudinal "career" methods at the individual level of analysis may have much to offer in this regard. Such studies could investigate, for example, how a person's likelihood of violence changes as his or her symptoms and life circumstances change.

Second, the data suggest that public education programs by advocates for the mentally disordered along the lines of "people with mental illness are no more violent than the rest of us" may be doomed to failure, as indeed research shows they have always failed (Cumming & Cumming, 1957). And they should fail: The claim, it turns out, may well be untrue. It will no doubt be difficult for mental health advocates to convey more accurate but more complex information about the relationship between mental disorder and violence in the sound bites and bumper stickers that have come to frame our public discourse. But the flat denial that any relationship exists between disorder and violence can no longer credibly be prefaced by "research shows" (Steadman, 1981). As Swanson et al. (1990), in commenting on their ECA data, stated, public fear of violence committed by the mentally disordered in the community is "largely unwarranted, though not totally groundless" (p. 769). I agree with Bloom (1989): "Few are interested in either heightening the stigmatization of the mentally ill or impeding the progress of the mentally ill in the community. Yet this progress is bound to be critically slowed without a realistic look at dangerousness" (p. 253).

Third, the antipathy toward dangerous to others as one criterion for involuntary hospitalization frequently expressed by mental health professionals and professional organizations may be unwarranted. A concern with violence to others may not be a responsibility arbitrarily foisted on the mental health professions by an ignorant public that would better be left exclusively to the police. A somewhat heightened risk of violence may inhere in the disorders that it is the business of psychologists and psychiatrists to treat. It is not unreasonable of society to ask us to attend to this risk, within the limits of our ability to assess it (Grisso & Appelbaum, in press; Monahan, in press-b).

Finally, the data underscore the need for readily available mental health services in the community and in correctional institutions. If the experience of psychotic symptoms elevates the risk of violence and if psychotic symptoms can usually be controlled with treatment (Krakowski, Jaeger, & Volavka, 1988), then the provision of treatment to people in need of it can be justified as a small contribution to community safety, as well as a telling reflection on our common humanity.

REFERENCES

American Psychiatric Association. (1980). *Diagnostic and statistical manual of mental disorders* (3rd ed.). Washington, DC: Author.

American Psychiatric Association. (1987). *Diagnostic and statistical manual of mental disorders* (3rd ed., rev.). Washington, DC: Author.

Appelbaum, P. (1988). The new preventive detention: Psychiatry's problemmatic responsibility for the control of violence. *American Journal of Psychiatry, 145,* 779–785.

Binder, R., & McNiel, D. (1988). Effects of diagnosis and context on dangerousness. *American Journal of Psychiatry, 145,* 728–732.

Bloom, J. (1989). The character of danger in psychiatric practice: Are the mentally ill dangerous? *Bulletin of the American Academy of Psychiatry and the Law, 17,* 241–254.

Bureau of Justice Statistics. (1991). *Violent crime in the United States* (Report No. NCJ-127855). Washington, DC: Author.

California Department of Corrections, Office of Health Care Services. (1989). *Current description, evaluation, and recommendations for treatment of mentally disordered criminal offenders.* Sacramento: Author.

Campbell, J., & Schraiber, R. (1989). *In pursuit of wellness: The Well-Being Project* (Vol. 6). Sacramento: California Department of Mental Health.

Collins, J., & Schlesinger, W. (1983, November). *The prevalence of psychiatric disorder among admissions to prison.* Paper presented at the meeting of the American Society of Criminology, Denver, CO.

Crowne, D., & Marlowe, D. (1960). A new scale of social desirability independent of psychopathology. *Journal of Consulting Psychology, 24,* 349–354.

Cumming, E., & Cumming, J. (1957). *Closed ranks: An experiment in mental health.* Cambridge, MA: Harvard University Press.

Daniel, A., Robins, A., Reid, J., & Wilfley, D. (1988). Lifetime and six-month prevalence of psychiatric disorders among sentenced female offenders. *Bulletin of the American Academy of Psychiatry and the Law, 16,* 333–342.

Davis, S. (1991). Violence by psychiatric inpatients: A review. *Hospital and Community Psychiatry, 42,* 585–590.

Deutsch, A. (1949). *The mentally ill in America: A history of their care and treatment from colonial times* (2nd ed.). New York: Columbia University Press.

Developments in the law: Civil commitment of the mentally ill. (1974). *Harvard Law Review, 87,* 1190–1406.

Dohrenwend, B. (1990). Socioeconomic status (SES) and psychiatric disorders: Are the issues still compelling? *Social Psychiatry and Psychiatric Epidemiology, 25,* 41–47.

DYG Corporation. (1990). *Public attitudes toward people with chronic mental illness.* Elmsford, NY: Author.

Field Institute. (1984). *In pursuit of wellness: A survey of California adults* (Vol. 4). Sacramento: California Department of Mental Health.

Gerbner, G., Gross, L., Morgan, M., & Signorielli, N. (1981). Health and medicine on television. *The New England Journal of Medicine, 305,* 901–904.

Gove, W. (1980). Labeling and mental illness: A critique. In W. Gove (Ed.), *The labeling of deviance: Evaluating a perspective* (2nd ed., pp. 264–270). Beverly Hills: Sage.

Grisso, T. (1991). Clinical assessments for legal decisionmaking: Research recommendations. In S. Shah & B. Sales (Eds.), *Law and mental health: Major developments and research needs.* (pp. 49–80). Washington, DC: U.S. Department of Health and Human Services.

Grisso, T., & Appelbaum, P. (in press). Is it unethical to offer predictions of future violence? *Law and Human Behavior.*

Hodgins, S., & Cote, G. (1990, September). Prevalence of mental disorders among penitentiary inmates in Quebec. *Canada's Mental Health,* 1–4.

Jones, I., & Horne, D. (1973). Psychiatric disorders among aborigines of the Australian desert: Further data and discussion. *Social Science and Medicine, 1,* 219–228.

Klassen, D., & O'Connor, W. (1988). Crime, inpatient admissions, and violence among male mental patients. *International Journal of Law and Psychiatry, 11,* 305–312.

Klassen, D., & O'Connor, W. (1990). Assessing the risk of violence in released mental patients: A cross-validation study. *Psychological Assessment: A Journal of Consulting and Clinical Psychology, 1,* 75–81.

Krakowski, M., Jaeger, J., & Volavka, J. (1988). Violence and psychopathology: A longitudinal study. *Comprehensive Psychiatry, 29,* 174–181.

Krakowski, M., Volavka, J., & Brizer, D. (1986). Psychopathology and violence: A review of literature. *Comprehensive Psychiatry, 27,* 131–148.

Link, B., Cullen, F., & Andrews, H. (in press). Violent and illegal behavior of current and former mental patients compared to community controls. *American Sociological Review.*

Link, B., Cullen, F., Frank, J., & Wozniak, J. (1987). The social rejection of former mental patients: Understanding why labels matter. *American Journal of Sociology, 92,* 1461–1500.

Monahan, J. (1981). *The clinical prediction of violent behavior.* Washington, DC: U.S. Government Printing Office.

Monahan, J. (1988). Risk assessment of violence among the mentally disordered: Generating useful knowledge. *International Journal of Law and Psychiatry, 11,* 249–257.

Monahan, J. (in press-a). "A terror to their neighbors": Mental disorder and violence in historical and cultural context. *Bulletin of the American Academy of Psychiatry and the Law.*

Monahan, J. (in press-b). Limiting therapist exposure to *Tarasoff* liability: Guidelines for risk containment. *American Psychologist.*

Monahan, J., & Shah, S. (1989). Dangerousness and commitment of the mentally disordered in the United States. *Schizophrenia Bulletin, 15,* 541–553.

Monahan, J., & Steadman, H. (1983a). Crime and mental disorder: An epidemiological approach. In M. Tonry & N. Morris (Eds.), *Crime and justice: An annual review of research,* (Vol. 4, pp. 145–189). Chicago: University of Chicago Press.

Monahan, J., & Steadman, H. (Eds.). (1983b). *Mentally disordered offenders: Perspectives from law & social science.* New York: Plenum Press.

Mulvey, E., Blumstein, A., & Cohen, J. (1986). Reframing the research question of mental patient criminality. *International Journal of Law and Psychiatry, 9,* 57–65.

Mullen, P. (in press). Criminality, dangerousness and schizophrenia. In D. Kavanaugh (Ed.), *Schizophrenia: An overview and practical handbook.* London: Chapman & Hall.

Murphy, J. (1976). Psychiatric labeling in crosscultural perspective. *Science, 191,* 1019–1028.

National Mental Health Association. (1987). *Stigma: A lack of awareness and understanding.* Alexandria, VA: Author.

Neighbors, H., Williams, D., Gunnings, T. Lipscomb, W., Broman, C., & Lepkowski, J. (1987). *The prevalence of mental disorder in Michigan prisons.* Lansing: Michigan Department of Corrections.

Otto, R. (1992). The prediction of dangerous behavior: A review and analysis of "second generation" research. *Forensic Reports. 5,* 103–133.

Rabkin, J. (1979). Criminal behavior of discharged mental patients: A critical appraisal of the research. *Psychological Bulletin, 86,* 1–27.

Robertson, G. (1988). Arrest patterns among mentally disordered offenders. *British Journal of Psychiatry, 153,* 313–316.

Robins, L., & Regier, D. (Eds.). (1991). *Psychiatric disorders in America: The Epidemiological Catchment Area study.* New York: Free Press.

Rosen, G. (1968). *Madness in society: Chapters in the historical sociology of mental illness.* Chicago: University of Chicago Press.

Roth, L. (1980). Correctional psychiatry. In W. Curran, A. McGarry, & C. Petty (Eds.), *Modern legal medicine, psychiatry and forensic science.* Philadelphia: Davis.

Roth, L. (Ed.). (1985). *Clinical treatment of the violent person.* Washington, DC: U.S. Government Printing Office.

Shain, R., & Phillips, J. (1991). The stigma of mental illness: Labeling and stereotyping in the news. In L. Wilkins & P. Patterson (Eds.), *Risky business: Communicating issues of science, risk, and public policy* (pp. 61–74). Westport, CN: Greenwood Press.

Shrout, P., Lyons, M., Dohrenwend, B., Skodol, A., Solomon, M., & Kass, F. (1988). Changing time frames on symptom inventories: Effects on the Psychiatric Epidemiology Research Interview. *Journal of Consulting and Clinical Psychology, 56,* 567–272.

Steadman, H. (1981). Critically reassessing the accuracy of public perceptions of the dangerousness of the mentally ill. *Journal of Health and Social Behavior, 22,* 310–316.

Steadman, H., & Cocozza, J. (1978). Selective reporting and the public's misconceptions of the criminally insane. *The Public Opinion Quarterly, 41,* 523–533.

Steadman, H., Fabisiak, S., Dvoskin, J., & Holohean, E. (1987). A survey of mental disability among state prison inmates. *Hospital and Community Psychiatry, 38,* 1086–1090.

Steadman, H., & Felson, R. (1984). Self-reports of violence: Ex-mental patients, ex-offenders, and the general population. *Criminology, 22,* 321–342.

Steadman, H., McCarty, D., & Morrissey, J. (1989). *The mentally ill in jail: Planning for essential services.* New York: Guilford Press.

Steadman, H., Monahan, J., Robbins, P., Appelbaum, P., Grisso, T., Klassen, D., Mulvey, E., & Roth, L. (1992). *From dangerousness to risk assessment: Implications for appropriate research strategies.* Unpublished manuscript.

Steadman, H., Monahan, J., Duffee, B., Hartstone, E., & Robbins, P. (1984). The impact of state mental hospital deinstitutionalization on United States prison populations, 1968–1978. *The Journal of Criminal Law and Criminology, 75,* 474–490.

Swanson, J., & Holzer, C. (1991). Violence and the ECA data. *Hospital and Community Psychiatry, 42,* 79–80.

Swanson, J., Holzer, C., Ganju, V., & Jono, R. (1990). Violence and psychiatric disorder in the community: Evidence from the Epidemiologic Catchment Area surveys. *Hospital and Community Psychiatry, 41,* 761–770.

Taylor, P., & Gunn, J. (1984). Violence and psychosis: I. Risk of violence among psychotic men. *British Medical Journal, 288,* 1945–1949.

Teplin, L. (1985). The criminality of the mentally ill: A dangerous misconception. *American Journal of Psychiatry, 142,* 676–677.

Teplin, L. (1990). The prevalence of severe mental disorder among male urban jail detainees: Comparison with the Epidemiologic Catchment Area program. *American Journal of Public Health, 80,* 663–669.

Werner, P., Rose, T., & Yesavage, J. (1983). Reliability, accuracy, and decision-making strategy in clinical predictions of imminent dangerousness. *Journal of Consulting and Clinical Psychology, 51,* 815–825.

Wessely, S., & Taylor, P. (1991). Madness and crime: Criminology versus psychiatry. *Criminal Behaviour and Mental Health, 1,* 193–228.

Westermeyer, J., & Kroll, J. (1978). Violence and mentally illness in a peasant society: Characteristics of violent behaviours and 'folk' use of restraints. *British Journal of Psychiatry, 133,* 529–541.

[31]

British Journal of Psychiatry (1987), **151**, 474–478

Detention of 'Psychopathic Disorder' Patients in Special Hospitals

Critical Issues

A. T. GROUNDS

The detention of offenders in the legal category 'psychopathic disorder' in special hospitals for treatment raises a number of critical issues. There are doubts about the nature of the disorder; what constitutes treatment; who is 'treatable'; the effectiveness of treatment; and whether evidence of psychological change implies reduced risk of reoffending. In view of these uncertainties, it is argued that indeterminate hospital orders may provide an unrealistic and unjust legal framework for treating 'psychopaths' in special hospitals, and the use of powers under the Mental Health Act to transfer such patients to hospital during the course of prison sentences is a more appropriate alternative. This provision could be used more frequently, subject to improved safeguards of the right of release at the expiry of sentence.

In general penal policy during recent decades there has been a growing disillusion with rehabilitation and treatment as objectives of sentencing, firstly because of doubts about their effectiveness (Martinson, 1974; Brody, 1976), and secondly because they are held to be unjust (Lewis, C. S., 1953; von Hirsch, 1976; Bowden, 1985). Nevertheless, a small number (under 30 a year) of offenders in the Mental Health Act category 'psychopathic disorder' continue to be sentenced by restricted hospital orders and admitted to special hospitals. They represent a tiny minority – less than 1 in 2000 – of those sentenced in the criminal courts for violent and sexual offences. A current approach to the assessment and treatment of 'psychopaths' in one of the special hospitals has been described by Grounds *et al* (1987). Medical recommendations for their admission under restricted hospital orders may rest on an implicit belief that indeterminate sentencing for psychiatric treatment is appropriate for such individuals, and that treatment can reduce the risk of reoffending. When this view is set against the current climate of opinion in criminology and penal policy it looks anachronistic: it maintains the optimistic spirit of the East & Hubert (1939) report in its assumption that psychotherapy may be effective in reducing the risk of future antisocial behaviour in selected cases.

This paper will consider six critical questions concerning the detention of 'psychopathic' offenders in hospital for treatment: Do such offenders have a definite mental disorder? What constitutes treatment? Who is 'treatable'? Is treatment effective? Does psychological change imply reduced risk of reoffending? Is indeterminate sentencing for treatment a fair exchange for sentencing based on principles of criminal justice?

The category of 'psychopathic disorder'

The legal term 'psychopathic disorder' in the 1983 Mental Health Act is defined as "a persistent disorder or disability of mind (whether or not including significant impairment of intelligence) which results in abnormally aggressive or seriously irresponsible conduct on the part of the person concerned". The troubled historical origins of the legal definition and of the underlying clinical concepts – "semantic variations on a dubious theme" – are documented by Walker & McCabe (1973) and Lewis (1974). Walker & McCabe's (1973) examination of how the legal term is used led them to conclude that as a 'diagnosis' 'psychopathic disorder' had no explanatory, descriptive, prognostic or therapeutic function. In practice it is used as a pseudo-diagnosis; a label attached to offenders with a variety of abnormalities to help the psychiatrist "get his patient through the customs-barrier of the courts if he wants to." The Butler committee (Home Office, 1975) also concluded that: "The class of persons to whom the term 'psychopathic disorder' relates is not a single category identifiable by any medical, biological or psychological criteria"; and studies of 'psychopathic disorder' patients in special hospitals (Blackburn, 1982) confirm the variety of clinical features subsumed under this term. The category of 'psychopathic disorder' "remains ill-defined, circular and does not embrace a homogeneous group of individuals" (Blackburn, 1983).

It is therefore a shaky legal foundation on which to select some offenders for diversion from the penal system into indeterminate hospital care.

What constitutes treatment?

There is little consensus about what constitutes treatment for 'psychopaths'. The interpretation of the term 'medical treatment' in the Mental Health Act is general: "'medical treatment' includes nursing, and also includes care, habilitation and rehabilitation under medical supervision". Traditionally in special hospitals the equally non-specific term 'milieu therapy' has been described as treatment (McGrath, 1966; Royal College of Psychiatrists, 1983); but as Gunn (1978) has pointed out: "it is difficult to argue that in hospitals of any kind a structured disciplined environment is a *medical* strategy; it is simply a prerequisite for making sure that patients stay where they are told to stay." McGrath (1968) also questioned to what extent "a benevolent custodial and expectant regime" could be justified as 'treatment'.

If treatment is defined in more specific terms, what counts as adequate treatment for 'psychopaths' will vary in different contexts. In an out-patient setting it may be justifiable to regard measures such as crisis intervention, and long term support without expectation of substantial personality change, as appropriate psychiatric treatment; but in a hospital setting where 'psychopaths' are detained for an indefinite period in maximum security this is not sufficient. Treatment is expected to produce personality change: the Home Office seeks evidence of this before agreeing to release, and for the offender too this is the promise implied by a hospital order. The therapeutic aims therefore have to be higher; and if they cannot be achieved the patient is being deceived.

'Treatability'

In the 1959 Mental Health Act, the term 'psychopathic disorder' included the clause that the disorder "requires or is susceptible to medical treatment." In the 1983 Mental Health Act the 'treatability' clause was changed and made a condition that had to be met for a long term treatment order to be made. For this purpose it must be held that medical treatment for the patient "is likely to alleviate or prevent a deterioration of his condition".

Medical recommendations for hospital orders under the 1959 Act included a section filled in by the reporting doctors, headed "Information to establish that the disorder or disability of mind requires or is susceptible to medical treatment". The specific items cited in the preadmission medical reports of the 'psychopathic disorder' patients ($n=13$) in one ward in Broadmoor Hospital on 1 March 1986 were examined, and two main features were evident: first the wide variety of items mentioned, and secondly their lack of specificity. Some reports merely asserted that treatment was required, without reasons being given. Factors most frequently cited as evidence that the patient's disorder was susceptible to treatment were, first, the patient's self-concern or wish to have treatment; and secondly, being of a young age.

Even the fullest reports were expressed in general terms. For example: "He is a young man of good intelligence who is potentially capable of benefiting from psychotherapy and other forms of psychological treatment. He is anxious to have treatment". Others were more half-hearted: "In view of his young age it is worth trying treatment and the consultant at Broadmoor Hospital is prepared to undertake his treatment". The contents of the reports suggest there was little agreement about specific factors that indicate a likelihood of benefit from treatment, and they do not indicate what specifically distinguished this tiny group of serious offenders from others.

Lewis (1974) noted that the most obvious criticism of the legal definition of 'psychopathic disorder' centered on the 'treatability' clause. "The opinion of psychiatrists or other competent experts as to who requires or is susceptible to treatment will inevitably tend to be subjective and inconsistent." In an earlier paper, when discussing the role of medical diagnosis in a social context, he argued that, "Unless the criteria of ill health are independent and clear it is difficult or unsafe to use data based on them for purposes of selection" (Lewis, A., 1953). The force of this conclusion was ignored by the Butler committee (Home Office, 1975) and others since (e.g. Ashworth & Gostin, 1984) who, having recognised the uncertainty about what constitutes 'treatability', have nevertheless proceeded to argue that the legal criterion should be tightened up even further, so that doctors would be required to make more specific judgements and predictions about this issue. The proposal is self-contradictory and impracticable.

These difficulties are unlikely to be fundamentally altered by the use of the new Interim Hospital Orders (S.38, Mental Health Act 1983), but it is arguable that they may be useful in enabling prospective patients and hospital staff to make more realistic and informed assessments of whether a treatment alliance is possible than could be done prior to the 1983 Act.

Effectiveness of treatment

The general conclusions drawn from surveys of psychotherapy outcome research (Bergin & Lambert, 1978; Prioleau *et al*, 1983) and research on the effectiveness of corrective and rehabilitation programmes for offenders (Martinson, 1974; Brody, 1976) are gloomy. The available follow-up studies of special hospital patients do not enable us to relate outcome to specific treatment received (Black, 1984); however, such studies do indicate that patients in the category of 'psychopathic disorder' have a poorer outcome in terms of reconvictions than the mentally ill, and a history of prior criminal convictions is the factor most strongly associated with reconviction after release from special hospitals (Bowden, 1981; Black, 1982; Tennent & Way, 1984). These results suggest that, as is the case for offenders in the penal system, it is the pre-admission criminal profile that is the best predictor of reoffending; and it seems unlikely that the effect of hospital treatment is in general sufficient to offset its influence. Thus there is little empirical basis for confidence that, in detaining 'psychopaths' for treatment in special hospitals with the aim of reducing likelihood of reoffending, there is evidence to back up our therapeutic hopes and aspirations.

Does psychological change imply reduced risk?

The next issue is related. If, following treatment, some 'psychopaths' do show evidence of psychological and personality change, does such change imply that the patient's risk of reoffending is reduced? Medical recommendations to the Home Office or to mental health review tribunals for discharge or transfer have to be framed as if such an inference was valid, but there is currently a lack of any detailed empirical study confirming whether this is the case. The evidence from follow-up studies so far is not encouraging. If pre-admission variables such as previous convictions are the best predictors of reoffending, as is case for offenders in penal settings, there has to be doubt about the validity of inferring reduced likelihood of dangerous behaviour from evidence of personality or behavioural change in hospital.

Treatment instead of justice – a fair exchange?

The doubts surrounding the above issues lead to the last question. Is the admission of a 'psychopathic' offender to hospital on an indeterminate treatment order a fair exchange for a sentence determined by the sentencing court on criminal justice principles? The effect of psychiatric involvement leading to a hospital order is to remove the offender's right to have the length of time he spends in custody determined by the court on the principle of proportionality. Apart from the possibility of discharge by mental health review tribunals, discretion over the release of restricted patients lies with the executive, in the form of the Home Secretary, rather than the courts. Furthermore, tribunals have to base their decisions on clinical criteria, and cannot take tariff considerations into account. In general sentencing policy there is a weight of legal opinion opposed to the principle of indeterminate sentencing with release dependent upon the progress of the offender. Scarman (1978), for example, has argued that the determination of how long an offender remains in custody should be a matter for the sentencing court rather than the executive, in the absence of evidence that rehabilitation as a penal policy is effective. The balance of justice between the offender and the public "is best struck in open court". The indeterminate hospital order, under which continued detention depends on clinical criteria, operates on quite different principles. But in the case of 'psychopaths', where are the specific clinical features that justify treating this tiny group of offenders differently from the many thousands of others passing through the criminal justice system each year? The question can be answered more easily in the case of the mentally ill and handicapped than in the case of the 'psychopath'.

The admission of 'psychopaths' on indeterminate treatment orders cannot be validly justified on the sole basis that special hospitals provide more humane environments of care than prisons, or that hospital-based research offers the prospect of major breakthroughs in understanding and treatment. The reality of indefinite detention in conditions of maximum security is not so benign. Critics such as Goffman (1961), describing the destructive social dynamics of psychiatric institutions; Kittrie (1971), with his legal critique of "therapeutic tyranny"; and earlier still C. S. Lewis (1953), in his dramatic argument against the "humanitarian theory of punishment", all perhaps overstated their cases, but they have left a legacy of insights that are too incisive and unsettling to be easily dismissed.

These considerations should not be taken to imply that psychiatric help should not be offered to personality-disordered offenders. Patients in the legal category 'psychopathic disorder' have psychopathology from which they suffer (Craft, 1966; Blackburn, 1975, 1982); further descriptive research is required (Lewis, 1974); and psychiatric care and treatment should continue to be offered (Gunn, 1978). The question is, in the light of current knowledge about treatment and its effectiveness, what is the most realistic and just legal framework within which to carry out these tasks? It would seem preferable to find a way of ensuring that those who require care and treatment receive it but without forfeiting their rights to sentencing according to normal criminal justice considerations. The medical and penal issues need to be separated. This would also protect doctors from having unrealistic roles placed upon them as "medical underwriters of preventive detention" (Chiswick, 1982), with the attendant responsibilities of making judgements about future dangerousness and duration of custody: responsibilities which involve carrying the mantle of the sentencing court. Gunn (1978) has argued that compulsory indeterminate treatment for 'psychopaths' in special hospitals is "not entirely ideal because the same person has to act as custodian and physician in an area where there is doubt as to whether a medical disorder is present and where the criteria for custody may be quite different from the criteria for psychiatric treatment and response". Dell & Robertson (1986) reached similar conclusions in their comparative study of treatment and discharge decisions about mentally ill and 'psychopathic disorder' patients in Broadmoor Hospital.

Transfer to hospital during sentence

One way of enabling psychiatric treatment within the framework of normal sentencing is available under the Mental Health Act provision to transfer prisoners to hospital for treatment during sentence (S.47 of 1983 Act). This allows a proper separation of psychiatric and criminal justice considerations in dealing with such offenders, and Mawson (1983) has argued that it is a preferable option. Until recent years only a minority of 'psychopaths' have been transferred to special hospitals by this means, and most have been admitted under hospital orders (Grounds *et al*, 1987).

However, current legal provisions for the transfer of mentally disordered sentenced prisoners, although preferable, are not ideal from a criminal justice point of view. Those transferred during the course of determinate sentences can remain detained under 'notional hospital orders' at the end of sentence without any formal re-examination and renewal of detention at that time. Most of the 'psychopaths' who were transferred during sentence to Broadmoor under the 1959 Mental Health Act eventually left Broadmoor by being discharged to the community or transferred to local hospitals, but the majority of these cases were detained in Broadmoor beyond the expiry date of their original sentences before being released. Recent proposals by a Home Office & DHSS (1986) working party on 'psychopathic offenders' did not address this issue, and were motivated primarily by a concern with how to specify minimum rather than maximum periods of detention before discharge.

There is a case either for a change in clinical practice or a change in the law to ensure that sentenced prisoners given determinate sentences and transferred to hospital for treatment should normally be entitled to release at the expiry of their sentences. If continuing treatment in conditions of maximum security is required beyond this time, this should be carried out by means of making a new civil order under the Mental Health Act (S.3). This would require a new application and two medical recommendations, and would safeguard against passive continuation of detention under a 'notional hospital order' without recertification as occurs at present. Such a reform was advocated by Gostin (1977) but not incorporated into the new Mental Health Act, although it was agreed that, in the case of restricted patients, Home Office restrictions on discharge should be lifted at the "earliest date of release" (which allows for remission) rather than the "latest date of release".

Discussion

Psychiatric help and care should continue to be offered to serious offenders with personality disorders. The question raised in this paper is what is the most appropriate, realistic and just legal framework for doing so. Provisions in the Mental Health Act to transfer 'psychopathic disorder' offenders to hospital during the course of prison sentences are preferable to the use of indeterminate hospital orders, subject to improved safeguards of the right of release at the end of sentence, which are necessary from a criminal justice point of view. Psychiatric help for such offenders needs to be available, but without involving doctors in an inappropriate role and without the offenders themselves losing the right to sentencing according to 'just deserts' principles. As C. S. Lewis (1953) argued, the consequences can be inhumane if we seek to *substitute* mercy for justice. "Mercy detached from justice grows unmerciful, that is the important paradox."

In the case of 'psychopathic disorder', if there was evidence, first, that we were dealing with a well-defined disorder; secondly, that we had specific treatments for it; thirdly, that we knew who was likely to benefit from treatment; fourthly, that such treatments were effective in producing psychological change; and fifthly, that psychological change implied a reduced risk of dangerous behaviour; then there would be justification for preferring to deal with such offenders by indeterminate treatment orders rather than tariff sentencing. But the evidence at each step is lacking and is insufficient to justify the practice of recommending hospital orders for 'psychopaths'. The view that this practice is appropriate continues to be held within the English special hospital system, but it has to be questioned to what extent the beliefs that sustain this practice can be empirically supported.

Acknowledgements

I am grateful to Mrs E. Parker and Ms A. Newman of the Special Hospitals Research Unit for statistics on admissions, to Professor J. Gunn, Mrs S. Dell, Dr P. McGrath and Dr G. Robertson for discussion and comments, and to Dr J. R. Hamilton for his support and encouragement. The opinions expressed in this paper are those of the author and do not necessarily represent those of Broadmoor Hospital or the Department of Health and Social Security.

References

Ashworth, A. & Gostin, L. (1984) Mentally disordered offenders and the sentencing process. *Criminal Law Review*, **1984**, 195–212.

Bergin, A. E. & Lambert, M. J. (1978) The evaluation of therapeutic outcomes. In *Handbook of Psychotherapy and Behaviour Change: an Empirical Analysis* (eds S. L. Garfield and A. E. Bergin), 2nd edn. New York: Wiley.

Black, D. A. (1982) A five year follow up of male patients discharged from Broadmoor Hospital. In *Abnormal Offenders, Delinquency and the Criminal Justice System* (eds J. Gunn & D. P. Farrington). Chichester: Wiley.

—— (1984) Treatment in maximum security settings. In *Mentally Abnormal Offenders* (eds M. & A. Craft). London: Bailliere Tindall.

Blackburn, R. (1975) An empirical classification of psychopathic personality. *British Journal of Psychiatry*, **127**, 456–460.

—— (1982) On the relevance of the concept of the psychopath. In *Issues in Criminological and Legal Psychology, No. 2* (ed. D. A. Black). Leicester: British Psychological Society.

—— (1983). Are personality disorders treatable? In *Issues in Criminological and Legal Psychology, No. 4* (eds J. Shapland and T. Williams). Leicester: British Psychological Society.

Bowden, P. (1981) What happens to patients released from the special hospitals? *British Journal of Psychiatry*, **138**, 340–345.

—— (1985) Treatment and justice. *British Journal of Hospital Medicine*, **33**, 350–352.

Brody, S. R. (1976) *The Effectiveness of Sentencing – a Review of the Literature* (Home Office Research Study No. 35). London: Her Majesty's Stationery Office.

Chiswick, D. (1982) The special hospitals – a problem of clinical credibility. *Bulletin of the Royal College of Psychiatrists*, **6**, 130–132.

Craft, M. (1966) *Psychopathic Disorders and Their Assessment*. Oxford: Pergamon Press.

Dell, S. & Robertson, G. (1986) *Some Aspects of Treatment and Discharge in Broadmoor Special Hospital*. London: DHSS.

East, W. N. & Hubert, W. H. de B. (1939) *The Psychological Treatment of Crime*. London: Her Majesty's Stationery Office.

Goffman, E. (1961) *Asylums: Essays on the Social Situation of Mental Patients and Other Inmates*. New York: Anchor Books, Doubleday.

Gostin, L. O. (1977) *A Human Condition: the Law Relating to Mentally Abnormal Offenders: Observations, Analysis and Proposals for Reform, Vol. 2*. London: Mind.

Grounds, A. T., Quayle, M. T., France, J., Brett, T., Cox, M. & Hamilton, J. R. (1987) An inpatient unit for 'psychopathic disorder' patients in Broadmoor Hospital. *Medicine, Science and the Law*, **27**, 21–31.

Gunn, J. (1978) The treatment of psychopaths. In *Current Themes in Psychiatry* (eds R. Gaind & B. L. Hudson). London: Macmillan.

Home Office (1975) *Report of the Committee on Mentally Abnormal Offenders*. London: Her Majesty's Stationery Office.

—— & Department Of Health And Social Security (1986) *Offenders Suffering from Psychopathic Disorder*. London: DHSS/Home Office.

Kittrie, N. N. (1971) *The Right to be Different: Deviance and Enforced Therapy*. Baltimore: John Hopkins University Press.

Lewis, A. (1953) Health as a social concept. *British Journal of Sociology*, **4**, 109–124.

Lewis, C. S. (1953) The humanitarian theory of punishment. *Res Judicatae*, **6**, 224–230.

——, A. (1974) Psychopathic personality: a most elusive category. *Psychological Medicine*, **4**, 133–140.

McGrath, P. G. (1966) The English special hospital system. In *Psychopathic Disorders and Their Assessment* (ed. M. Craft). Oxford: Pergamon Press.

—— (1968) The psychopath as a long-stay patient. In *Psychopathic Offenders* (ed. D. J. West). Cambridge: Institute of Criminology.

Martinson, R. (1974) What works? – questions and answers about prison reform. *The Public Interest*, **35**, 22–54.

Mawson, D. (1983) 'Psychopaths' in special hospitals. *Bulletin of the Royal College of Psychiatrists*, **7**, 178–181.

Prioleau, L., Murdoch, M. & Brody, N. (1983) An analysis of psychoanalysis versus placebo studies. *Behavioural and Brain Sciences*, **6**, 275–310.

Royal College Of Psychiatrists (1983) *Report on the Future of The Special Hospitals*. London: Royal College of Psychiatrists.

Scarman, L. J. (1978) Control of sentencing: the balance between judge and the executive. In *Criminal Justice: Selected Readings* (eds J. Baldwin & A. K. Bottomley). London: Martin Robertson.

Tennent, G. & Way, C. (1984). The English special hospitals – 12–17 year follow-up study. A comparison of violent and non-violent reoffenders and non-offenders. *Medicine, Science and the Law*, **24**, 81–91.

von Hirsch, A. (1976) *Doing Justice: The Choice of Punishment*. New York: Hill & Wang.

Walker, N. & McCabe, S. (1973) *Crime and Insanity in England (Vol. 2)*. Edinburgh: Edinburgh University Press.

Adrian T. Grounds, BMedSci, BM, BS, MRCPsych, *Formerly Lecturer, Institute of Psychiatry; now Lecturer, Institute of Criminology, 7 West Road, Cambridge CB3 3DT*

[32]

Law and Human Behavior, Vol. 18, No. 1, 1994

The Dimensions of Dangerousness Revisited

Assessing Forensic Predictions About Violence*

Robert Menzies,† Christopher D. Webster,† Shelley McMain,‡ Shauna Staley,§ and Rosemary Scaglione§

In this article, we extend our previous study on clinical predictions of violence using the Dangerous Behavior Rating Scale by increasing follow-up interval from 2 to 6 years and supplying new data on prediction–outcome correlations for multidiscipline assessors. A total of 162 accused persons remanded for evaluations at METFORS were assessed using three criterion measures: subsequent violence, criminality, and general incidents. Statistical analyses revealed a range of predictive performance, contingent on several conditions including the identities of evaluators, categories of subjects, and length and context of follow-up. Even prognostications yielding the highest magnitude coefficients, reaching .53 in the case of psychometric forecasts of behavior in psychiatric hospitals, failed to account for more than 28% of the prediction–outcome covariance. Implications of the results are considered for the future role of the dangerousness construct.

* The research project described in this article was funded by the Social Sciences and Humanities Research Council of Canada, the Canadian Psychiatric Research Foundation, the Solicitor General Canada, the LaMarsh Research Program on Violence and Conflict Resolution, the Ontario Ministry of Health, Simon Fraser University, the Clarke Institute of Psychiatry, and the psychopathy project supported under the sustaining grant provided by the Solicitor General, Canada, to the Centre of Criminology, University of Toronto. Thanks for their perceptive commentaries to Ronald Roesch and the two anonymous reviewers of *Law and Human Behavior*. Acknowledged as well are the contributions of the many research assistants and representatives of mental health, police, justice, and correctional agencies who collaborated in the compilation of these data. Research assistance was provided by Michelle Grossman, Simon Hanbury, Lily Keoskerian, Ed Tymosiak, and Cheri Wilner. Bill Glackman offered technical help with the data analysis. A version of this paper was originally presented at the 1991 Meeting of the American Society of Criminology in San Francisco. Requests for reprints should be sent to Robert Menzies, School of Criminology, Simon Fraser University, Burnaby, B.C., Canada V5A 1S6.

† Simon Fraser University.
‡ York University.
§ Clarke Institute of Psychiatry.

0147-7307/94/0200-0001S07.00/0

In 1985, we published the results of a two-year follow-up study designed to evaluate the accuracy of dangerousness predictions using semistructured prediction instruments and trained nonclinical raters (Menzies, Webster, & Sepejak, 1985a). The research was conducted at the Metropolitan Toronto Forensic Service (METFORS).

Since 1977, METFORS has been the site of numerous studies focusing on the relationship between clinical practices and the criminal law (Chunn & Menzies, 1990; Jackson, 1986; Menzies, 1989; Menzies, Gillis, & Webster, 1992; Menzies, Webster, & Sepejak, 1885b; Roesch, Webster, & Eaves, 1984; Rogers, Gillis, McMain, & Dickens, 1989; Rogers & Webster, 1989; Webster & Menzies, 1993). A forensic assessment agency situated on the grounds of Toronto's largest mental health facility, METFORS offers both one-day and protracted mental health evaluations of criminal defendants remanded from criminal courts throughout the city's greater metropolitan area (Butler & Turner, 1980; Menzies, 1989; Webster, Menzies, & Jackson, 1982). From its inception, the unit has operated on an interdisciplinary basis, with participation by psychiatrists, clinical psychologists, social workers, forensic nurses, and correctional officers. More than 10,000 accused persons have received assessments at METFORS over the intervening years.

From the outset, a central focus of the METFORS research has been the evaluation of clinical and actuarial predictions of dangerousness. The forensic prominence of dangerousness—and of related constructs such as violent behavior, aggression, self-injurious conduct and risk—has been well documented. No other issue in the realm of law and human behavior has attained such public and professional attention over the past two decades, or been the catalyst for such lasting controversy (Britzer & Crowner, 1988; Foucault, 1978; Hall, 1987; Harris, Rice, & Cormier, 1991; Hinton, 1983; Monahan, 1981, 1984, 1988; Monahan & Steadman, 1994; Otto, 1992; Pfohl, 1978; Prins, 1986, 1991; Rennie, 1978; Steadman & Cocozza, 1974; Webster, Ben-Aron, & Hucker, 1985). Against the backdrop of this continuing debate about the validity of the dangerousness construct, the capacity of clinicians and psychometric scales to assess its presence and potential, and the theoretical and methodological value of existing research, our objective was to assemble some preliminary Canadian data on the levels of dangerousness to self and others manifested by pretrial forensic patients, as well as on the accuracy of professional and research efforts to gauge these phenomena.

The original work on dangerousness at METFORS was conceived as an exploratory test of the Dangerous Behavior Rating Scheme (DBRS). The DBRS was a 22-item assessment instrument, using 7-point Likert scale items, which had been developed in consultation with METFORS clinicians to facilitate predictions of dangerousness among pretrial forensic patients. Based partially on a conceptual framework first developed by Megargee (1976), the DBRS represented a multidimensional approach to the dangerousness construct, including a variety of items measuring personality attributes, situational variables, perceived facilitators and inhibitors of violence, levels of rater confidence, and global estimates of dangerousness to self and others.

Two nonclinical raters,[1] observing the clinical interviews behind one-way mirrors, completed the DBRS for 211 defendants remanded to the METFORS Brief Assessment Unit (BAU) between February and June of 1979. Following interrater reliability tests, item analysis and principal component analysis, scores were collapsed between the two coders, and the initial scheme was reduced to 11 specific items[2] along with four global assessment measures (dangerousness to self and others in present and future). The aggregate factor scores elicited from this refined 15-item scale became the principal DBRS indicator of predicted dangerousness for the METFORS subjects (Menzies et al., 1985a).

These predictions were then matched against the levels of officially recorded dangerous conduct registered by subjects during the 24-month period subsequent to their assessment. Using Ontario correctional service print-outs and the records of six psychiatric hospitals in and around Toronto, behavioral profiles were assembled for each individual and rated for dangerousness by nine independent coders on an 11-point scale.[3] The average rating became the primary dependent measure. Although there was variation among individual DBRS items and categories of subjects, the aggregate factor scores yielded an overall +0.34 Pearson correlation with follow-up dangerousness across the full cohort of METFORS subjects (Menzies et al., 1985a).

These results indicated that less than 12% of the dangerous behavior manifested by subjects during the subsequent two years had been successfully anticipated with the assistance of these semistructured instrumental predictions. Although we stopped short of recommending wholesale abolition of dangerousness predictions in forensic settings—given the limitations of the study and given the complexities of the construct and its measurement—nonetheless the low prediction–outcome correlations compelled a cautionary approach. We advised greater acknowledgment of the many competing forces that shape discretionary danger predictions, a more rigorous clinical self-censorship in ambiguous cases, further attention to the social ecology and interpersonal dynamics of individual violence, and fully interdisciplinary understandings of dangerousness as a multifaceted clinical, legal, criminological, and cultural phenomenon.

Still, these conclusions needed to be qualified in light of the study's many limitations. First, because the DBRS had been employed by nonclinical raters only, the prospect of a superior performance by professional mental health practitioners had not yet been explored. Second, the exclusive use of a single predictive instrument precluded the possibility that alternative measures, or even global

---

[1] For details of the raters' qualifications and the reasons why the sample was reduced from 256 to 211 subjects, see footnotes 6 and 7, Menzies et al., 1985a, p. 55.

[2] These were passive aggressive, hostility, anger, rage, guilt, capacity for empathy, capacity for change, tolerance, environmental support, accurate information, and sufficient information.

[3] All misconducts, violent and otherwise, were extracted from the official records and listed for each patient. Nine external judges then rated the level of dangerousness on a scale of 1 to 11, represented by each profile (where 1 = *not dangerous* and 11 = *most dangerous*). These nine ratings for each subject's 2-year "career" were then averaged to produce a Danger Outcome Score, which became the main dependent variable in the original study.

clinical judgments, might render more accurate dangerousness predictions than those generated in the initial study. Third, the two-year follow-up period was arguably an insufficient time frame, as it excluded violent behavior perpetrated by subjects beyond the 24-month boundary and therefore might have inflated the false negative figures to an unknown extent (see Cocozza & Steadman, 1976; Floud & Young, 1981; Monahan, 1981). Fourth, similar problems were embodied in the study's jurisdictional restriction to the province of Ontario, with the result that conduct registered elsewhere in Canada for this highly mobile cohort was not incorporated into the results. Fifth, whereas the original research had relied on a single indicator of follow-up dangerousness generated from independent ratings of two-year behavior yielded by each METFORS remandee, it was conceivable that a variety of triangulated criteria—including levels of criminality and overall frequency of general incidents and violent transactions—might better capture the complex, multidimensional character of the dangerousness construct.

These considerations were instrumental in our decision to undertake a replication and elaboration of the original prediction project. In what follows, we report in more detail our efforts to expand the research protocol and refine the data sources and methodology along a number of different fronts: to include the danger predictions of forensic clinicians as well as trained nonclinical raters; to employ multiple prediction variables and indices; to compile outcome data on each subject across the full breadth of the country and for an extended period of 6 years[4]; and to operationalize follow-up behavior using three different measures of dangerous conduct.

REPLICATING THE METFORS PREDICTION PROJECT

Amid resurgent forensic interest during the late 1980s and early 1990s in the assessment of dangerousness, violence, aggression, and risk (Castel, 1991; Klassen & O'Connor, 1988; Menzies, Chunn, & Webster, 1992; Monahan, 1988, 1992; Otto, 1992; Steadman, Robbins, & Monahan, 1991; Steadman et al., 1994; Toch

[4] First, we concur with Steadman et al. (1994) that longer follow-ups are essential for research bearing on psychologal policy, especially in data sets such as our own (McMain et al., 1989; Webster & Menzies, 1993) where many patients tend to receive numerous hospitalizations and other institutional interventions over extended time periods. Second, as Walker (1991) has pointed out, short-run follow-ups can yield misleading information, and although brief follow-alongs can answer some kinds of questions (e.g., Do men re-offend more often than women?), it takes extended surveys to answer other questions (e.g., How many rapists ever reoffend?) (p. 752). Third, published evidence from the Baxstrom and Dixon studies demonstrates the utility of extended follow-ups of this kind. Steadman and Cocozza (1974) found that although the bulk of hospitalizations occurred within 6 months of release from civil hospitals, the 44 patients who relapsed did so after 25 months. Whereas Thornberry and Jacoby (1979) observed that the majority of 110 subjects released into the community were arrested within the first year, recidivism did continue over years three and four of their study. Authors in both projects draw attention to the fact that policy needs to be informed by data collected over long intervals. It is important to know the extent to which particular kinds of patient and prisoner groups are *not* likely to recidivate.

& Adams, 1989), we return in this article to METFORS for an enhanced evaluation of dangerousness predictions rendered for the above cohort of pretrial forensic patients. The new project represented our efforts to refine and expand the database that had been compiled for the original study and to discern whether the modified method would engender more favorable results concerning the accuracy of dangerousness predictions. The research design was established to amplify the quantity and quality of all data sources relevant to the prediction assessment process, including the sociodemographic and psycholegal information on the METFORS defendants, the clinical and instrument-driven decision-making practices in the BAU, and the conduct and institutional experiences of subjects following their forensic remand.

Our primary research questions were as follows: Would an improved method and data set marshall more accurate predictions of dangerousness? How would the dangerousness ratings of nonclinical coders fare against both global and instrument-aided ratings by professional clinicians? Are some measures of follow-up conduct (general misconducts, criminality, or violent transactions) more predictable than others? Under what temporal and contextual conditions is predictive validity either enabled or constrained? And finally, do some psycholegal subjects elicit more accurate predictions than others? Each of these questions will be addressed in the analyses below.

The subjects comprised 162 individuals from the original study who received their first clinical evaluation in the BAU between March and June 1979.[5] These people exhibited most of the sociodemographic, clinical, and legal attributes personified by pretrial forensic assessment populations in numerous other studies (see Gibbens, Soothill, & Pope, 1977; Roesch & Golding, 1980; Steadman, 1979; Webster et al., 1982). The majority were male (85.8%), under 30 (60.1%), unmarried and noncohabiting (89.2%), unemployed or unskilled laborers (63.8%), and had less than an 11th grade education (68.1%).[6] About half (73 of 140 for whom data were available) had been previously hospitalized in a psychiatric institution. Nearly three quarters (111 of 152) had a prior criminal record and more than two fifths (57 of 131) had experienced a prison sentence. Fifty-five defendants (34.2%) had on this occasion been referred to METFORS charged with a property offense, 32 (19.9%) were facing accusations of violence, another 32 (19.9%) were remanded on alcohol or drug-related charges, and 26 (16.1%) had allegedly com-

[5] In this replication, assessments conducted during the month of February 1979, were dropped from the analysis. Whereas the initial study enlisted the predictions of nonclinical coders only, which were collected for the entire 5-month span (from February through June), the ratings of the BAU clinicians did not become available until the beginning of March. The current sample therefore consists of the 211 original subjects less 36 who had been assessed in February, 7 for whom outcome data could not be found, and a final 6 for whom complete sets of clinical and nonclinical prediction instruments were unavailable, for a total of 162.

[6] The overwhelming majority of subjects assessed at METFORS in 1979 were White (during the first year of the agency's operation, only 7.5% were African Canadian, 1.9% Native, and 1.9% Asian), and, as a result, statistical analyses of racial variability, as undertaken by most investigators in the United States, were not feasible with this cohort.

mitted a technical violation.[7] In the BAU, the presiding psychiatrists classified 68 people (42.8%) as mentally disordered, 14 (9.0%) as unfit to stand trial, and another 19 (12.2%) as questionably fit; 59 (37.8%) to require further assessment; 54 (34.2%) in need of strict custody; and 33 (27.2%) as candidates for inpatient hospitalization.

The initial research protocol for eliciting dangerousness predictions about the METFORS defendants was presented in our earlier article (Menzies et al., 1985a). In addition to the multidisciplinary BAU team of diagnosticians (consisting of the presiding psychiatrist who led the interview questioning, a second, nonpresiding copsychiatrist, a forensic psychologist, social worker, psychiatric nurse, and correctional officer), three trained nonclinical raters were involved in the dangerousness study. All professional and lay assessors had been previously instructed in the use of prediction instruments (see below). They also collaborated in assembling a wide array of demographic, social, medical, psychological, and behavioral data on research forms specially designed for each profession, and they recorded their decisions on a variety of forensic issues, apart from dangerousness, including general mental condition, fitness to stand trial, treatability, and the need for further custody and assessment.

On a typical day, between two and four accused persons were transported to METFORS from local detention centers, along with their arrest reports and other available documents. Each BAU interview lasted approximately 20–40 min (the modal time was 28 min). One of the three nonclinical coders was located in the interview room with the subject and professional assessors, while the other two raters attended from an adjoining cubicle through a one-way mirror and audio pick-up. These latter coders were exposed to the police report (which was read aloud by the lead psychiatrist) but did not participate in preinterview team discussions. All assessors, both clinicians and laypersons, recorded their dangerousness evaluations independently, immediately subsequent to the patient interview and prior to discussion of the case. There were no systematic criteria for allocating cases to assessment teams.

Though dangerousness prediction ratings were compiled and coded for the entire group of assessors (up to nine in any given interview), we focus primary attention in this article on the presiding psychiatrists and the two external coders as representatives, respectively, of clinical and nonclinical raters. We do, however, also assess below the validity of global dangerousness predictions for all disciplines and individuals (see Tables 5 and 7). The two external coders were the same individuals who recorded DBRS ratings in our original two-year follow-up study (Menzies et al., 1985a). The identities of psychiatrists, as with all other participating BAU practitioners excepting the social worker (who was the same individual for all assessments) varied, with seven different psychiatrists involved in 158 of the 162 assessments. Assessment teams were diversified in membership and mix over the four months of the prediction data collection, and there was no

[7] These included failure to appear, breach of parole, bail, or probation conditions, being unlawfully at large, and escaping lawful custody. The remainder of the BAU subjects had been charged with nonviolent sex offenses (9 or 5.6%), public order infractions (5 or 3.1%), and highway traffic act violations (2 or 1.3%).

systematic assignment of cases according to either subject, clinician, or team attributes. The accuracy of both individual clinician generic predictions and pooled instrument endorsements is considered below. The pooled ratings (where one variable, collapsed across all cases, represents the decisions of the psychiatrists as a disciplinary group) are deployed below for both generic and indexical prognostications of dangerousness.[8] The construction of these prediction variables and indexes is reviewed in the following section.

Developing the Indices of Dangerousness Predictions

Prior to the commencement of data collection, three dangerousness prediction indices had been constructed, revised, and implemented through weekly meetings between researchers and clinicians. Emphasis was placed on the generation of scalar measures that would afford raters the opportunity to assess the dangerousness of pretrial forensic patients against a variety of different criteria and on metric continua (7-point Likert scales ranging from *extremely low* to *extremely high*) rather than dichotomous or categorical items. For each of the prediction indices yielded from these consultations, a manual[9] was drafted which clarified individual items and which provided instruction on the assessment process for the purpose of training raters and maximizing reliability of application (Menzies et al., 1985a; Slomen et al., 1979).

The first indicator derived from this pretesting process was a single-item global rating of "dangerousness to others in future" that was recorded by each professional and nonclinical rater during the four months of the prediction exercise.[10] The presiding METFORS psychiatrists, for example, assigned numbers of

[8] In order to evaluate differences in the level of attributed dangerousness being ascribed by the seven BAU psychiatrists taking part in the study, multiway analyses of variance were run, with psychiatric predictions as the dependent variables and the psychiatrist's identity (among the seven involved) entered as an independent factor, along with dichotomized patient history of violence, psychiatric hospitalization, place of birth (for generic predictions of dangerousness), and gender (for DBRS ratings) as control factors (each of the latter four variables had proven to be significantly associated with dangerousness predictions in bivariate analyses). With these statistical controls in place, the identity of the psychiatrist did not have an influence on the level of generic dangerousness predictions, $F(6,125) = 1.04$, $p = .403$. In other words, all other things being equal, there were no significant differences among psychiatrists in the degree of dangerousness they attributed to patients on the single 7-point predictor item. However, DBRS scores did differ significantly across psychiatrists, $F(6,125) = 4.35$, $p = .001$, and there was one interaction effect, $F(6,96) = 3.53$, $p = .003$, between psychiatrist identity and patient history of violence (indicating that some psychiatrists were more likely than others to link prior manifestations of violence with their dangerousness predictions). These differences should be viewed to limit the interpretation of analyses involving grouped DBRS scores of psychiatrists. What prevails for the cohort of seven may or may not apply to individuals.

[9] The manual is available on request from the first author.

[10] The "general" predictions of dangerousness to others in future, unlike the other DBRS items, were not confined to specific individual dimensions of personality, situational, and other factors. Instead, clinicians and lay raters were required in the manual provisions to offer a "general estimate of the patient's harmful behavior to others in future" without explicit limitations imposed on the term or context of the predicted behavior. For the original study (Menzies et al., 1985a), participants had additionally been informed that the accuracy of their interpretations would be checked after an interval of 2 years.

patients to each category of future dangerousness as follows (where 1 = lowest and 7 = highest): 1 = 1, 2 = 1, 3 = 13, 4 = 58, 5 = 50, 6 = 13, and 7 = 2 (M = 4.46, SD = 1.44).[11] The Pearson correlation coefficients among the two coders and pooled psychiatrists, who are the main focus of the analyses to follow, were as follows: .40 (psychiatrists and Coder 1), .45 (psychiatrists and Coder 2), and .51 (Coder 1 and Coder 2).[12]

The second prediction instrument was the DBRS. This had been the only source of nonclinical dangerousness predictions in the original study, and it was again activated for this reassessment, with two modifications. To begin, 4 of the 22 items constituting the earlier version of the scale, namely, the global evaluations (danger to self and others, in present and future), were this time excluded given their observed redundancy and statistical homoscedasticity with other DBRS elements (Menzies et al., 1985a). Further, scale endorsements by participating clinicians—with particular emphasis in this article on presiding forensic psychiatrists—were recorded and analyzed along with the judgments of the trained laypersons.

Tables 1 and 2 review the statistical operations involved in refining the raw DBRS endorsements into reliable metric dangerousness predictions for both lead psychiatrists and lay coders. In Table 1, the initial inventory of scale elements was subjected to both item analysis and external validity criteria, with the consequence that two items ("dangerousness increased with alcohol" and "dangerousness increased with drugs") which generated more than 25% "Don't know" and "Missing" responses from psychiatrists were excluded, and three more items were deleted for failing to correlate at a significant zero-order level with the global "dangerousness to others in future" indicator. The remaining 13 items were subjected to a principal component analysis, with the four resulting factors (which loaded, respectively, on variables representing anger presentation, controlled aggression, interpersonal irresponsibility, and impulsivity[13]) accounting for 69.7% of the variance in psychiatric endorsements. The four factor scores were then totaled, and the aggregate statistic was used as the psychiatrist's DBRS prediction for each METFORS subject.

Precisely the same process was deployed in generating external coder DBRS predictions, with the exceptions that (1) interrater reliability tests were conducted for each item,[14] and (2) following item and external criterion analyses (from which

[11] "Don't know" = 15, "missing" = 5. For all analyses using metric prediction data, missing cases (where the rater did not respond) were excluded, and "don't know" responses were collapsed to the mean.

[12] It can be seen from Table 1 that these correlations, though highly significant statistically, do reflect a considerable measure of interrater variability in the scoring of patients on this 7-point Likert scale.

[13] These factor score descriptions are meant to canvass, in intuitive terms, the overlapping content of all variables with threshold loadings on that factor (for example, interpersonal irresponsibility would appear to encompass low scores on guilt, capacity for empathy, capacity for change, and environmental support. Similarly, controlled aggression apparently correlates with passive aggressiveness, manipulativeness, and failure to provide accurate information). The labels attached to these factors, however, should be treated as theoretical constructs rather than fixed attributes of the METFORS subjects.

[14] One item, control over actions, failed to meet the .40 interrater product–moment correlation threshold.

Table 1. DBRS Principal Components Analysis: METFORS BAU Psychiatrists

				Loadings[a]				
	Mean	SD	Missing cases	Factor 1 ANG	Factor 2 CAG	Factor 3 IRR	Factor 4 IMP	Communality
DBRS items								
Passive aggressive	4.15	1.19	5		.73			.67
Hostility	4.10	1.17	5	.64				.80
Anger	4.22	1.14	5	.83				.79
Rage	4.14	1.39	6	.82				.72
Emotionality[b]	3.89	1.15	5					
Guilt	4.84	1.53	5			.63		.72
Capacity for empathy	4.76	1.30	5			.62		.75
Capacity for change	4.86	1.72	6			.70		.64
Self-perception dangerous	3.08	1.74	8	.69				.52
Control over actions	4.41	1.35	6				.89	.84
Tolerance	4.43	1.40	7				.75	.72
Environmental stress[b]	4.48	1.34	6					
Environmental support	4.36	1.67	5			.82		.75
Dangerousness increased with alcohol[c]	5.04	1.79	17					
Dangerousness increased with drugs[b]	4.81	1.99	43					
Manipulative	4.42	1.22	6		.60			.47
Accurate information	4.48	1.25	6		.64			.67
Sufficient information[b]	4.08	1.09	5					
Eigenvalue				4.36	2.11	1.52	1.07	
Percent variance				33.6	16.2	11.7	8.2	
General items								
Dangerous self present	3.30	1.52	5					
Dangerous self future	3.88	1.48	6					
Dangerous others present	3.67	1.43	5					
Dangerous others future	4.46	1.44	5					

[a] ANG, anger presentation; CAG, controlled aggression; IRR, interpersonal irresponsibility; IMP, impulsivity.
[b] Deleted from scale: nonsignificant correlation with general dangerousness rating.
[c] Deleted from scale: more than 25% "don't know" and/or "missing."

6 items were expunged[15]), the two coder ratings on each element of the scale were collapsed together, yielding average scores, which were then factor analyzed. Although the four resulting principal components were generally similar in structure and loadings to those generated by psychiatrists[16] (representing, respectively, interpersonal irresponsibility, anger presentation, controlled hostility, and social ineptitude), there were enough differences in the sequencing and magnitude of the factors to suggest that the external coder ratings were at least relatively autonomous from those of psychiatrists.

A third index, the Interview Assessment Scale (IAS), was assembled from items yielded through consultations between researchers and forensic practitioners. The IAS was scored by the three lay coders participating in the project and represented an effort to concentrate evaluations on the presentations of subjects

[15] In addition to control over actions, emotionality, environmental stress, dangerousness increased with alcohol, dangerousness increased with drugs, and sufficient information failed to attain the inclusion standards.

[16] This factor set is slightly discrepant from the analyses reported in our original 1985 paper. This is explained by the fact that global items were excluded in the current example (for reasons indicated above), resulting in a reduced number of entry items from 15 to 12.

Table 2. DBRS Principal Components Analysis: BAU Independent Coders

	Coder 1			Coder 2			Pearson corr	Loadings[a]				
	Mean	SD	Missing cases	Mean	SD	Missing cases	Coder 1 and 2	Factor 1 IRR	Factor 2 ANG	Factor 3 COH	Factor 4 SIN	Communality
DBRS Items												
Passive aggressive	3.66	1.75	6	3.27	1.85	5	.64			.90		.89
Hostility	4.58	1.21	6	3.96	1.49	5	.50			.80		.84
Anger	5.49	1.12	6	4.57	1.52	5	.57		.85			.83
Rage	5.48	1.37	8	3.39	1.50	5	.51		.85			.75
Emotionality[b]	4.32	1.61	13	4.52	1.10	5	.54					
Guilt	5.27	1.70	8	5.55	1.44	15	.65	.83				.73
Capacity for empathy	4.27	1.50	6	4.77	1.18	5	.51	.88				.83
Capacity for change	4.53	1.44	6	4.58	1.22	5	.50	.86				.79
Self-perception dangerous	2.73	1.37	8	3.00	1.12	7	.70		.56			.47
Control over actions[c]	4.95	1.50	7	4.70	1.20	5	.22					
Tolerance	5.25	1.13	6	4.14	1.26	5	.46		.76			.72
Environmental stress[d]	4.98	0.86	6	5.14	1.00	5	.40					
Environmental support	4.43	1.21	6	4.52	1.34	5	.62				.62	.60
Dangerousness increased with alcohol[d]	5.53	1.03	20	4.87	1.39	19	.44					
Dangerous increased with drugs[bd]	5.35	0.73	46	3.84	1.23	52	.45					
Manipulative	3.55	1.57	6	4.12	1.53	6	.49				−.86	.79
Accurate information	4.24	1.40	7	4.00	1.37	5	.60	.80				.68
Sufficient information[b]	4.44	1.18	6	3.24	1.20	5	.54					
Eigenvalue								4.36	2.22	1.25	1.08	
Percent variance								36.4	18.5	10.5	9.0	
General items												
Dangerous self present	3.19	1.41	9	3.27	1.07	5	.72					
Dangerous self future	3.91	1.52	10	3.86	1.15	5	.64					
Dangerous others present	4.19	1.40	9	3.89	1.25	6	.54					
Dangerous others future	4.79	1.28	10	4.41	1.22	6	.51					

[a] IRR, interpersonal irresponsibility; ANG, anger presentation; COH, controlled hostility; SIN, social ineptitude.
[b] Deleted from scale. Nonsignificant correlation with general dangerousness rating.
[c] Deleted from scale. Less than .40 intercoder correlation.
[d] Deleted from scale. More than 25% "don't know" and/or "missing".

and on the interpersonal dynamics of the forensic assessment process itself. The goal was to explore the possibility that subsequent dangerousness might be predicted directly from the verbal and behavioral cues exhibited by pretrial remandees and from their transactions with clinicians during the course of forensic interviews.[17] The 13 items in this instrument, also calibrated on a 1–7 axis, included greeting behavior, grooming-appearance, eye contact (appropriateness), eye contact (extent), affect, posturing, agreeability, verbal responses, patient control over interview, pace of interview, level of tension, level of rapport, and synchrony. As with the DBRS, manual descriptions were developed for each item,[18] and IAS users were trained to enhance interrater reliability of implementation. Only the two external coders completed the IAS; clinicians did not perform the task.

The statistical distillation of IAS scores into their final aggregated factor score derivative is summarized in Table 3. As with DBRS endorsements, these responses were reduced through item analysis and external criterion analysis to 11 items from the original 13. They were then collapsed across the two raters and factor analyzed to yield two principal components (the first being associated with the interpersonal dynamics of the interview and the second loading on items describing the subject's failure to muster a prosocial presentation). The aggregated factor scores, representing 61% of the scale variance, were once again generated for use as predictive indices.

In total, these procedures resulted in a range of prediction statistics, including DBRS factor score ratings for both presiding psychiatrists and pooled nonclinical coders, IAS assessments for coders, and global 7-point metric judgments for all individual and group participants in the study. Table 4 indicates that these various prediction scores did achieve, among psychiatrists and lay raters, an appreciable level of intercorrelation, but not to an extent that would compromise their relative

---

[17] It was our belief that experienced clinical evaluators form impressions about patients and prisoners using cues, some of which lie outside their own awareness (Mahl, 1968). Certainly this aspect of the project was guided by the idea that remandees may in interview "give away" important information at a nonverbal level (Ekman & Friesen, 1969). The items in the IAS were defined with a view to allowing raters a chance to capture, in a preliminary way, data more subtle and less obvious than those typically recorded in assessment interviews. According to this view, forensic clinicians will likely vary appreciably in the amounts and types of information they draw from their subjects. It follows from this outlook that the traditional weight on what the *remandee* says or does may be misplaced. What ought to be emphasized as well is the more-or-less moment-to-moment joint responses of interviewer and interviewee as together they proceed through the session. This of course raises far-reaching and possibly very important questions about the possible error involved in giving disproportionate consideration to the subjects' actions and in leaving unstudied and unreported those of the interviewers.

[18] For example, the guidelines to be followed for rating patient affect appeared in the manual as follows: "Under this category of appropriateness of affect we are looking for the congruence between the content of verbalizations and the emotions expressed. Neutral events may produce a severe affective outburst in the patient, while situations which are usually viewed as emotionally charged do not intensify the patient's emotional expression. At times, a patient's affect in general appears somewhat bizarre and, therefore, inappropriate to the interview setting (e.g., the blunting of affect seen in some schizophrenics). Note that a certain degree of interpretation on the part of the raters may be necessary for this category. That is, well-founded anxiety or embarrassment may be responsible for a seemingly inappropriate affect in some instances" (p. 19).

Table 3. Principal Components Analysis: IAS Assessments by Coders

	Coder 1			Coder 2			Pearson corr	Loading		
	Mean	SD	Missing cases	Mean	SD	Missing cases	Coder 1 and 2	Factor 1	Factor 2	Communality
IAS Items										
Greeting behavior	2.98	1.90	8	3.46	1.31	9	.50		.69	.61
Grooming-appearance	3.24	1.84	6	3.78	1.45	5	.66		.71	.51
Eye contact appropriate	2.00	1.70	7	2.89	1.45	6	.67		.74	.71
Eye contact little–much	4.86	1.08	8	4.54	0.96	6	.63		.74	.58
Affect	3.16	1.58	7	4.14	1.31	5	.60		.52	.62
Posturing	3.33	1.56	14	4.98	1.53	5	.63	.66		.52
Agreeability	5.20	1.40	6	3.91	1.35	5	.38	.50		.46
Verbal responses	2.75	2.16	6	3.53	1.45	5	.73	.73		.71
Subject controlled interview	4.28	1.48	6	2.67	1.47	5	.63	.90		.81
Pace of interview[a]	4.19	1.30	6	4.59	0.98	5	.63			
Tension in interview	3.21	1.25	6	2.59	1.30	5	.52	.74		.56
Rapport	4.78	1.33	6	4.17	1.32	5	.68	.57		.61
Synchrony[b]	5.61	0.69	6	4.61	1.31	5	.31			
Eigenvalue								5.46	1.24	
Percent variance								49.7	11.3	

[a] Deleted from scale. Nonsignificant correlation with general dangerousness rating.
[b] Deleted from scale. Less than .35 intercoder correlation.

Table 4. Correlation Matrix: General and Factor Score Dangerousness Predictions[a]

	PS Global	PS DBRS Factor	C1 Global	C2 Global	CS DBRS Factor	CS IAS Factor
PS Global	—	.54	.40	.45	.36	.17
PS DBRS Factor		—	.25	.32	.62	.54
C1 Global			—	.51	.45	.13
C2 Global				—	.33	.30
CS DBRS Factor					—	.71
CS IAS Factor						—

[a] PS Global, BAU Psychiatrists Raw Dangerousness Predictions (1–7); PS DBRS Factor, BAU Psychiatrists DBRS Factor Scores; C1 Global, Coder 1 Raw Dangerousness Predictions (1–7); C2 Global, Coder 2 Raw Dangerousness Predictions (1–7); CS DBRS Factor, Combined Coders DBRS Factor Scores; CS IAS Factor, Combined Coders Interview Assessment Factor Scores.

autonomy as distinct measures. Pearson product–moment coefficients among the displayed ratings ranged from a low of .13 (between Coder 1 global dangerous to others predictions and coders' pooled IAS factor scores) to a high of .71 (between coders' DBRS and IAS indexes).

The Six-Year Follow-up of METFORS Subjects

The follow-up component of this expanded project involved a detailed exploration of the officially registered conduct and experience of METFORS subjects for a 6-year period subsequent to their initial forensic assessment in 1979. As recounted above, the earlier study had been limited by a 24-month follow-up time frame, and by its exclusive reliance on correctional records from the province of Ontario along with hospital files from six institutions in the province. Here, in contrast, we endeavored to maximize both the temporal and jurisdictional scope of the investigation. The search process began this time in 1985, 72 months after each person's first METFORS assessment, and it was oriented toward a full cross-Canada coverage of general incidents, criminal charges, and violent transactions committed by subjects in general psychiatric hospitals, forensic institutions, jails, penitentiaries, and the streets.

In order to develop comprehensive files for each subject, the following sources were consulted: (1) Canadian Police Information Centre (CPIC) printouts, which yielded information on the nature, location, and date of subsequent criminal charges, along with the resulting court dispositions; (2) correctional service records, including dates of admission and release, along with registered misconducts during incarceration, from seven of the nine provinces[19] in which individuals were imprisoned during the 6-year period[20]; (3) National Parole files for

[19] In Canada, prisoners sentenced to terms of less than 2 years are incarcerated in provincial institutions; the remainder serve time in federally run penitentiaries.

[20] Provincial correctional officials declined to provide information on three persons who were arrested, respectively, in Manitoba and Nova Scotia. No one incurred an officially registered police contact in the province of Prince Edward Island. The provincial correctional data base, therefore, included 13 former METFORS patients arrested during the 6 years in British Columbia, 9 in Alberta, 6 in Quebec, 5 in Saskatchewan, and 1 each in New Brunswick and Newfoundland.

the 43 subjects who served federal time, including materials on prison transfers and misconducts incurred during confinement; (4) Correctional Services Canada computer data on the same group of federal inmates; (5) medical records from 10 of the major psychiatric and forensic institutions in Ontario, plus five general hospitals in the Toronto area[21]; and (6) Ontario Death Registry data banks, to identify individuals who had died during the follow-up term of the study.

After locating and securing of access to these various data sources and after their contents were coded onto standardized research instruments, discrete files were assembled for each of the 162 subjects. Records of all incidents leading to an official police, correctional, or psychiatric entry were transferred onto the instruments. For criminal charges and incarceration misconducts, the dates, locations, and outcomes of each transaction were noted. In the case of hospital documents, accounts of all general incidents, violent transactions, and self-injurious events were registered. Subsequently, time lines were reconstructed for each patient, providing a graphic summary of institutional history and conduct over the 6-year term. A coding manual was prepared and pretested, with the revised draft providing a detailed quantitative synopsis of background attributes, clinical judgments, and dangerousness predictions, and the institutional experiences and officially documented conduct of all subjects during the 6-year follow-up term. The outcome data were categorized by institutional location (prison, hospital, or community), tallied separately for each of the 6 years, and aggregated in cumulative fashion (combining Years 1 and 2; Years 1, 2, and 3; and so on) for the purposes of subsequent prediction–outcome analyses (see Menzies & Webster, 1994).

Subtracting from the follow-up cohort three individuals who had died (two by suicide), the remaining 159 subjects registered a total of 1,334 institutional contacts (M = 8.39) during the 72-month period. Of these, 711 (M = 4.47) were psychiatric contacts, and 623 (M = 3.92) involved in correctional settings. The psychiatric interventions included 199 general inpatient admissions, 189 daycare or drop-in referrals, 122 forensic inpatient hospitalizations, 119 outpatient referrals, and 81 brief forensic assessments. Among the institutional contacts, in turn, 398 comprised provincial prison sentences, 178 were probation orders, and 47 resulted in federal penitentiary dispositions. Altogether, among the 11,177 subject-months which could be accounted for,[22] 8,931 (79.9%) were spent in the community, 1,784 (16.0%) in prison, and 462 (4.1%) in psychiatric hospital. By the conclusion of the 6 years, 145 subjects (91.2%) had experienced at least some

[21] Altogether the 162 subjects were referred for 52 additional brief assessments and 55 inpatient assessments at METFORS during the 6-year outcome period. The nine other psychiatric institutions (with number of inpatient admissions for each in brackets) were Queen Street Mental Health Centre (167), Penetanguishene (28), Whitby (22), Clarke Institute of Psychiatry (18), Lakeshore (9), St. Thomas (6), North Bay (2), Kingston (2), and Brockville (1). Eight admissions to the psychiatric wards of general hospitals in Toronto were also included, as were 18 hospitalizations in provinces other than Ontario (among them were patients from the Forensic Psychiatric Services Commission of British Columbia).

[22] The total number of patients months was 11,448 (159 subjects who survived the 6-year outcome period, times 12 months per year, times 6 years). This left 271 months unaccounted for in the official data sources (where subjects left the country or data were unavailable or otherwise incomplete).

pretrial jail time; 140 (88.1%) had been on probation, parole, or bail; 111 (69.8%) had been sentenced to prison; 91 (57.2%) had been psychiatric inpatients; and 43 (27.0%) had outpatient experience (see McMain, Webster, & Menzies, 1989; Menzies et al., 1992; Menzies & Webster, 1994).

For the purposes of the prediction–outcome analysis to follow, officially recorded incidents were compiled across the entire span of the 72-month tracking period. The aggregate tally of incidents for the entire follow-up was 3,245 (M = 20.41 per subject). Of these, 459 (M = 2.82) were threats of violence and 449 (M = 2.82) were overt violent transactions.[23] Therefore, as measured by both the frequency of contacts with criminal justice and mental health institutions and the number of officially recorded incidents in prisons, hospitals, and the community, this was a high base-rate forensic cohort.

These base rates did, however, also vary according to context. The majority of general incidents and violent transactions (N = 1,940 and 241 respectively[24]) occurred in community settings, with most of these leading to criminal proceedings (1,476 charges altogether, and 180 accusations of criminal violence). Psychiatric inpatient locations generated 743 total incidents (M = 4.67), 337 violence threats (M = 2.12), and 130 violent transactions (M = 0.82). Outpatients registered 162 general incidents (M = 1.02), 31 violence threats (M = 0.19), and 4 violent transactions (M = 0.03). Finally, postsentence prison was the setting for 331 total misconducts (M = 2.08), 68 violent misconducts (M = 0.43), and 15 violence threats (M = 0.43), whereas the corresponding frequencies, with means in parentheses, for pretrial remand detention were 69 overall misconducts (0.43), 6 violent misconducts (0.04), and 2 threats (0.01).

Two main patterns were evident in these follow-up behavioral statistics. First, although in absolute terms the preponderance of incidents were recorded in the community, when expressed as a function of temporal opportunity, psychiatric institutions experienced by far the highest relative base rates. This finding replicates patterns reported in the earlier study (Menzies et al., 1985a). In the expanded data set, the proportionate number of violent transactions registered per patient/year was 0.34 in the community, 0.50 in prison, and 3.38 in hospital. These dramatic differences should not necessarily be interpreted as indicative of elevated violence rates among mental patients; they were very likely a function of the more intensive levels of scrutiny and documentation for all forms of behavior manifested in psychiatric contexts.

---

[23] Of the 159 subjects in the follow-up, 140 registered at least one general incident in either community, prison, or hospital. Ninety-two persons precipitated between 1 and 20 incidents, 39 individuals were involved in 20 to 49 incidents, and 9 individuals between 50 and 99. One subject each was responsible, respectively, for 130, 156, 213, and 238 separate general incidents. The distribution of criminal charges across the 6 years was as follows: no charges (n = 33), 1–9 charges (n = 74), 10–19 charges (n = 29), 20–49 charges (n = 21), with one subject each committing 58 and 137 criminal offenses. Comparable results for the third dependent variable, total number of violent incidents, were: none (n = 60), 1–4 (n = 66), 5–9 (n = 23), 10–14 (n = 6), and 1 each yielding 16, 20, 21, and 50 violent transactions.

[24] There were also 74 community incidents involving threats of violence, most of which resulted in some form of psychiatric hospital contact.

Second, the raw (as opposed to cumulative) annual rates of incidents, criminal charges, and violent transactions tended to decline over the 6-year period, as increasing numbers of individuals appeared to distance themselves from mental health and criminal justice settings. From Year 1 to Year 6, the overall frequency of official incidents declined from 1,005 to 280, criminal charges fell from 352 to 160, and the number of violent transactions similarly descended from 158 to 40. As will become evident in the following section, these two tendencies were to play an important role in circumscribing the accuracy coefficients of dangerousness predictions at METFORS.

Relationship Between Danger Predictions and Outcome Conduct

With the various measures of dangerousness predictions and 6-year outcomes established, it was then possible to undertake a statistical analysis of their correspondences. The first procedure involved a direct bivariate verification of the zero-order correlations between predictions of dangerousness derived from the 1979 BAU assessments and the numbers of criminal charges, general incidents, and violent transactions manifested by subjects on a cumulative annual basis over the course of the subsequent 6 years. The resulting Pearson product–moment statistics are presented in Table 5. These figures represent the predictor relationships with the three selected outcomes tallied in running totals after each of the 6 follow-up years. All coefficients above |.10| are displayed, and the analyses are included for 12 different prediction measures. They are based on generic 7-point ratings of nurses, correctional officers, social workers, psychologists, lead psychiatrists, and copsychiatrists, both nonclinical external coders and the participant coder, as well as the three scales whose development is described above (the psychiatrists' DBRS, along with the coders' DBRS and IAS).

As Table 5 demonstrates, the clinical and psychometric predictions of dangerousness attributed to the 159 METFORS subjects[25] in 1979 were not generally borne out by the officially registered frequencies of criminal charges, general incidents, and violent transactions perpetrated by these people during the subsequent cumulative periods of 1 through 6 years. The generic 7-point metric prognostications were especially tenuous, with most disciplines yielding coefficients either too weak to register (e.g., presiding psychiatrists), or actually in a negative direction (e.g., nurses, correctional officers, psychologists, social worker, and the participating lay coder). More encouraging, if still relatively marginal, results were achieved by the nonpresiding copsychiatrists and the two external coders (for the former, predictions of danger to others in future were correlated with number of violent transactions at a .24 level after one year ($p < .01$), at .19 after 2 years ($p < .05$), and .14 after 3 years ($p > .05$).

The two psychometric scales, for their part, were variably successful. In the hands of psychiatrists as a group, there was no evidence of DBRS utility. With the grouped coders, on the other hand, the modest results demonstrated in the 1985

[25] For all prediction–outcome correspondence analyses, the 3 deceased subjects were deleted from the data base.

Table 5. Correlations Between METFORS Predictions of Dangerousness and Outcome Behavior at 1 Through 6 Years[a]

	One year			Two years			Three years			Four years			Five years			Six years		
	CRM	INC	VIL	CRM	INC	VIL	CRM	INC	VIL	CRM	INC	VIL	CRM	INC	VIL	CRM	INC	VIL
NURSES DOF	−.14			−.11			−.11			−.11			−.11			−.10		
CORROFFS DOF	−.21*			−.19*			−.20*			−.21*			−.23**			−.22**	−.14	
SOCWORKS DOF	−.10	−.13		−.11	−.12		−.13	−.14		−.13	−.16		−.10	−.15			−.14	
PSYCHOLS DOF	−.21**		.10	−.20**		.12	−.20**			−.21**			−.19**			−.18*		
PSYCHIAT1S DOF																		
PSYCHIAT2S DOF			.24**	.14	.20*	.19*		.15	.14		.15			.15			.16	
CODER1 DOF						.11			.10						.12			.14*
CODER2 DOF						.14*	−.15*		.13*	−.13*		.10	−.14*		.10	−.15*		
CODER3 DOF				−.11			−.16*			−.22**			−.20**			−.20**		
PSY1DBRS	−.19**																	
CODERSDBRS	−.14*		.16*		.20**	.24**		.20**	.18**		.14*	.18*		.10	.16*		.10	.15*
CODERSIASS		.20*	.16*	−.10	.31***	.15*	−.11	.26***	.13	−.11	.21**	.11	−.11	.19**		−.12	.18*	

[a] NURSES DOF, Nurses 1–7 Dangerousness Prediction (n = 118); CORROFFS DOF, Correctional Officers 1–7 Dangerousness Prediction (n = 90); SOCWORKS DOF, Social Workers 1–7 Dangerousness Prediction (n = 145); PSYCHOLS DOF, Psychologists 1–7 Dangerousness Prediction (n = 145); PSYCHIAT1S DOF, First Psychiatrists 1–7 Dangerousness Prediction (n = 154); PSYCHIAT2S DOF, Second Psychiatrists 1–7 Dangerousness Prediction (n = 80); CODER1 DOF, First Coder 1–7 Dangerousness Prediction (n = 149); CODER2 DOF, Second Coder 1–7 Dangerousness Prediction (n = 153); CODER3 DOF, Third Coder 1–7 Dangerousness Prediction (n = 140); PSY1DBRS, First Psychiatrist DBRS Score (n = 146); CODERSDBRS, Coders Aggregate DBRS Score (n = 136); CODERSIASS, Coders Aggregate Interview Assessment Score (n = 120); CRM, Number of Criminal Charges During Followup; INC, Number of Total Incidents During Followup; VIL, Number of Violent Transactions During Followup. Pearson coefficents >|.10| only are indicated in table.

*$p < .05$.

** $p < .01$.

*** $p < .001$.

article (Menzies et al., 1985a, pp. 61–66) were replicated, although with generally lower coefficients (the correlations with cumulative violence incidence after 1 through 6 years, respectively, were .16, .24, .18, .18, .16, and .15).[26] There was also moderate positive association between coder IAS factor scores and outcome measures, with the overall highest and second highest magnitude coefficients (.31 and .26, $p < .001$) occurring between IAS ratings and number of general disruptive incidents after 2 and 3 years, respectively. Certainly the IAS instrument, for all its "indirectness," was no weaker than the to-the-point DBRS. Whether it would be effective used singly, rather than in combination with the DBRS, is unknown.

Six main observations emerge from Table 5. First, despite our intensified and diversified assembly of prediction indices and outcome measures over this extended 6-year time frame, the accuracy of both single-item and scalar predictions, as with the original study, remained decidedly unimpressive when validated against aggregate general incidents, criminal charges, and violent transactions. The criminal charges criterion yielded by far the worst results, with only one positive correlation in the entire table, but correlations with the other two outcome measures were not appreciably superior in the aggregate. There would appear to be little justification, based on these findings, for inscribing such decisions into routine forensic practice or for establishing legal or clinical policies that rested on generic and unqualified predictions of dangerousness to others.[27]

Second, multiple-item prediction instruments (DBRS and IAS), though generally limited in predictive power and exceedingly low in clinical utility, did nev-

---

[26] The best prediction–outcome correlation among all those attempted (+.33) was achieved in a multivariate procedure, where the total number of incidents after 3 years was regressed against coders' DBRS and IAS scores along with coders' pooled generic predictions of dangerousness to self in future and others in future. This approximated the earlier study's final DBRS prediction–outcome correlation of .34 (Menzies et al., 1985a). In due course, it will be possible for us to cross-validate (Mullen & Reinehr, 1982) the present data set against predictions rendered by the same group of clinicians for another cohort of some 200 patients initially assessed in 1978 (see Menzies et al., 1985b).

[27] Yet one well-known authority, in response to the presentation of an early draft of these findings (Webster & Menzies, 1993), has pointed out that even correlations of the magnitude presented here may be of considerable scientific importance (Robins, 1991, personal communication). Her point is that, given the difficulties involved in tracking violent behavior in a cohort largely at liberty, *any* statistically significant relationships between prediction and outcome deserve note. Moreover, there remains controversy over the relative power of various statistical methods to reveal prediction–outcome relationships existing in the data. In our earlier study (Menzies et al., 1985a) and in the present article, we argue for the use of correlational techniques, which preserve the quality and continuity of metric variables, in contrast to bifurcation, which forces both clinical decisions and subject behavior into arbitrary "all-or-nothing" categories. Our contention is that the traditional reliance on 2 × 2 tables to represent the relative rates of "false positives and negatives" and "high and low hits" (for a recent illustration, see Otto, 1992) has functioned to preserve statistical cleanliness at the expense of internal and construct validity. It reflects, and may even function to perpetuate, the artificial and dualistic choices that have so long beleaguered forensic practitioners in the clinics and courts alike. Parametric statistics such as Pearson correlations, although more difficult to interpret, far better capture the continuous and indexical quality of these prediction and outcome variables, and when combined (as in this article) with simple univariate measures, can offer both relative and absolute evaluations of prediction–outcome correspondences. This point, however, continues to be hotly debated by researchers in the field (see Rosenthal, 1990).

ertheless in almost all instances inspire more accurate forecasts, on all three criteria, than those offered by single-item clinical judgments alone.

Third, with the possible exception of the nonpresiding psychiatrists, there was no indication that professionals fared better than nonclinical raters when assessed against these outcome standards. Indeed, laypersons demonstrated plainly better accuracy than lead psychiatrists in their application of the DBRS.

Fourth, the differences in correlations did not appear to be in any way systematically related to the absolute (baseline) levels of the group predictions. Those clinical disciplines and lay coders with consistently higher ratings were not discernibly better or worse predictors than others. Among the six clinical groups and three individual lay coders (see Table 5), the only two yielding positive coefficients (Psychiatrist 2 and Coder 1) ranked fifth and second, respectively (M = 4.73 and 5.08), in average attributions of dangerousness to others in future. Conversely, means for the three worst sets of danger predictions ranked first, sixth, and eighth (5.08 for psychologists, 4.60 for social workers, and 4.44 for nurses).

Fifth, the number of violent transactions dependent variable was, in general, the most "predictable" of the three outcome measures for the majority of prediction variables and time periods, whereas no one or no group (with the exception of nonpresiding psychiatrists after 2 years) produced a single positive correlation with rates of criminal charges.

Sixth and last, the addition of 4 years to the outcome data clearly failed to enhance the acumen of dangerousness predictions. The few positive Pearson coefficients tended to peak in magnitude after 2 or 3 years, only to decay thereafter as subjects drifted further in time and space away from the 1979 BAU point of departure and as the annual frequency of institutional interventions and officially registered incidents progressively declined.

A related consideration pertained to the community or institutional context of predicted subject behavior. A supplementary series of analyses was conducted to ascertain whether the single-item, DBRS and IAS assessments were more or less accurate in forecasting general incidents and violent transactions in the community, in hospitals, in prisons, and in hospital and prisons combined. For the 1-item Likert-scale predictions, the resulting context-specific correlation coefficients did not display any appreciable patterns. Social workers, psychologists, and presiding psychiatrists did exhibit a slightly enhanced capacity to predict community violence (r after 2 years = .22, .21, .18, $p < .05$, respectively), and nonpresiding copsychiatrists were able to achieve statistically significant coefficients in predicting general hospital incidents after 1 and 2 years (r = .18 and .20, $p < .05$). Otherwise the disaggregated correlations between single-item dangerousness predictions and general incidents and violent transactions, separately and cumulatively calculated for community, hospital, prison, and prison and hospital contexts after 1 through 6 years, did not vary substantially from the overall results depicted in Table 5. Nor did a single significant coefficient emerge from the same measurements using psychiatrist DBRS scores as predictors.

However, context-specific correlations based on the DBRS and IAS ratings of lay coders were strikingly distinct and represented perhaps the most noteworthy findings of the entire study. There was not a single positive and statistically significant correlation, after any of the six annual tallies, between coder DBRS or IAS scores and either follow-up general incidents or violent transactions taking place in the community. Similarly, when only prison incidents and violent transactions were enlisted as criteria, just a single significant finding emerged, and this was a negative correlation between IAS scores and number of general prison incidents after 1 year ($r = -.19$, $p < .05$).

Conversely, as institutionally specific predictions of in-hospital incidents and violence, the two scales demonstrated far better potential. The IAS, in particular, generated positive coefficients in the .50 range for general hospital incidents and around .40 for violent hospital transactions, and the strength of these relationships was maintained throughout the course of the 6-year outcome period. Though slightly lower in magnitude, DBRS-generated correlations were also enhanced when hospital contexts only were considered, with coefficients peaking slightly above .40 for general incidents and at .35 for violent transactions. At their zenith following the second year of the outcome period, the respective coefficients, all significant beyond the .001 level, were .53 (IAS and general hospital incidents), .39 (IAS and violent transactions), .42 (DBRS and general incidents), and .35 (DBRS and violent transactions). When hospital and prison conduct were pooled, coefficients remained significant throughout, but were somewhat depressed, indicating that the correspondences were being accounted for by coders' relative ability to forecast behavior in psychiatric as opposed to penal institutions. In general, although the power of these associations should not be overstated (even the highest magnitude coefficient of .53 translates into only 28% explained covariance), nonetheless these findings may contain important clues to the content, context, and representiveness of dangerousness decisions and outcomes.[28] There is some irony, for example, in the discovery that it is lay coders, using psychometric instruments, who are best at assessing future behavior in clinical settings. The glaring differences in accuracy ratings when applied to hospital contexts, as opposed to prisons and the streets, may also point the way to future research possibilities. Further, the relatively strong performance of the IAS grounded in the presentations of subjects and in the interactional dynamics of interviews is worth noting.

[28] The full breakdown of correlation coefficients for in-hospital conduct was as follows: (CDIAS = coder IAS scores, CDDBRS = coder DBRS scores, I = number of general incidents and V = number of violent transactions):

	Year 1		Year 2		Year 3		Year 4		Year 5		Year 6	
	I	V	I	V	I	V	I	V	I	V	I	V
CDIAS	.41	.32	.53	.39	.50	.38	.51	.37	.51	.37	.51	.38
CDDBRS	.31	.26	.42	.35	.43	.35	.24	.35	.26	.35	.27	.34

For pooled hospital and prison incidents and violent transactions, they were:

	Year 1		Year 2		Year 3		Year 4		Year 5		Year 6	
CDIAS	.33	.24	.46	.34	.40	.32	.38	.28	.37	.25	.35	.24
CDDBRS	.19	.23	.32	.34	.31	.31	.17	.28	.18	.27	.19	.26

In an effort to determine whether some METFORS defendants were more predictable than others, Table 6 expresses annual prediction–outcome correlations as a function of three subject attributes—age, history of violence, and number of prior psychiatric hospitalizations[29]—which had proven to be significantly related to follow-up behavior in multiple classification analysis, $F(9,114) = 7.67, p < .001, R^2 = .23$. The DBRS scores for presiding psychiatrists and coders, along with psychiatrist 7-point generic ratings, are enlisted as predictors.

As displayed in Table 6, no major differences in predictive accuracy were attributable to patient age, although coder DBRS scores did sustain significant correlations with frequency of violent transactions from Year 2 through Year 5 inclusive. Base rates of prior violence did appear to influence the prediction–outcome coefficients. Although these differences should not be exaggerated, given the low overall magnitude of the correlations, all three prognostication measures did attain significance for those patients who exhibited no prior evidence of violent behavior, whereas no such correspondences could be detected in the violent cohort. Finally, subjects reporting either no previous hospitalizations, or many hospitalizations, were associated with undetectable or negative prediction–outcome correlations, in contrast to those with "a few" contacts for whom coefficients were enhanced to the point of reaching a .40 correspondence with violent incidence after 2 years. According to these statistical control operations, then, DBRS and generic psychiatric forecasts reached their highest levels of validity when patients had not been involved in prior violence and when they had experienced low levels of previous psychiatric intervention.

The final set of analyses, presented in Table 7, disaggregate all global predictions of dangerousness to others by individual clinician identity. Here we explore intraprofession differences in capacity to predict dangerousness. As with Table 5, cumulative frequencies of criminal charges, general incidents, and violent transactions are tallied after each year as dependent variables. Only significant Pearson coefficients and those above $|.20|$ are displayed, and only those clinicians participating in 10 or more predictions are included (for these operations, the distinction between "lead psychiatrist" and "copsychiatrist" was abandoned, and coefficients were calculated for predictions rendered by each individual in either role).

The results demonstrate that some clinicians did produce better results than others, but only within the limits of a relatively narrow band of variation. There were a few outliers—for example, Nurse 1, Psychologist 1, and Psychiatrist 6—who were distinguished by the consistency and magnitude of their negative coefficients. Others exhibited better positive predictive capabilities than their peers, as in the case of Psychiatrist 3 (who consistently yielded statistics in the .30 range throughout the outcome period), Nurse 3 (whose prediction correlation with violent conduct remained at about the .30 level over the first 4 years), and Psychiatrist 4 (whose danger prediction–outcome violence correlations registered .37

[29] There were 95 subjects (60.1%) under the age of 30, and 66 (39.9%) 30 years or older. Fifty-seven individuals (41.0%) disclosed a history of violent conduct. Sixty-seven (47.9%) reported no prior psychiatric hospitalizations, 61 (43.6%) had "a few" contacts, and 12 (7.4%) indicated a history of "many" institutions.

Table 6. Correlations Between Danger Predictions and Cumulative Followup Violence Controlled for Background Attributes[a]

	Number of violent incidents					
	1 Year *r*	2 Years *r*	3 Years *r*	4 Years *r*	5 Years *r*	6 Years *r*
Aged less than 30						
PIDOF						
PIDBRS						.21*
CDSDBRS			.26*			.21
Aged 30 or older						
PIDOF						
PIDBRS						
CDSDBRS		.23*	.21*	.20*	.18*	
No prior violence						
PIDOF			.18*		.18*	.19*
PIDBRS			.22*	.20*	.22*	.22*
CDSDBRS	.24*	.28**	.24*	.21*	.21*	.19*
Prior violence						
PIDOF						
PIDBRS						
CDSDBRS						
No prior hospitalizations						
PIDOF						
PIDBRS						
CDSDBRS						
Few prior hospitalizations						
PIDOF						
PIDBRS						
CDSDBRS	.21	.40***	.31**	.33**	.27*	.26*
Many prior hospitalizations						
PIDOF	−.24	−.24		−.22	−.22	−.23
PIDBRS						
CDSDBRS	.24					

[a] PIDOF, Psychiatrist 1 Danger Predictions (1–7); PIDBRS, Psychiatrist 1 DBRS Factor Scores; CDSDBRS, Coders Aggregate DBRS Factor Scores; Only significant Pearson coefficients, and those above |.20|, are displayed.
* $p < .05$.
** $p < .01$.
*** $p < .001$.

after 2 years and .36 after 3 years). Overall, four of the six psychiatrists, one of the three nurses, two of the five correctional officers, and none of the psychologists or the social worker produced consistently positive results. As with generic group correlations, individual clinicians appeared better able to predict outcome frequencies of violence (19 statistically significant positive coefficients in Table 7) in comparison to general follow-up incidents and criminal charges. The latter criterion was associated with only one positive correlation in the entire table. This especially poor performance in the prediction of criminality—even more so than for the other two outcome indices—may have implications for the validity of forensic contributions to predictive decision making in criminal justice as opposed to clinical contexts.

As with discipline groups, accuracies did not seem directly attributable to the aggregate base line levels of individual clinical predictions of dangerousness. For some raters (Correctional Officers 4 and 1), overall high assessments of subject dangerousness ($M = 5.42$ and 4.75, respectively) resulted in positive coefficients; in other instances, for example, Correctional Officer 3 ($M = 5.33$), Psychiatrist 6 ($M = 4.69$), and Psychologist 1 ($M = 4.62$), high general ratings generated neg-

Table 7. Correlations Between Individual Clinicians Dangerousness Predictions and Outcome Behavior at 1 Through 6 Years[a]

	1 Year			2 Years			3 Years			4 Years			5 Years			6 Years		
	CRM	INC	VIL	CRM	INC	VIL	CRM	INC	VIL	CRM	INC	VIL	CRM	INC	VIL	CRM	INC	VIL
NURSE 1 (n = 37)	−.60***			−.57***			−.57***			−.54***			−.48***			−.47**		
NURSE 2 (n = 42)		.20																
NURSE 3 (n = 34)		.34*	.30*	.20	.42**	.26		.43**	.28*		.31*	.30*		.26	.20		.25	.23
CORROFF 1 (n = 20)		.20	.21			.22			.23	−.20		.23	−.20		.23			.24
CORROFF 2 (n = 26)				−.25			−.23			−.22			−.29			−.30		
CORROFF 3 (n = 10)	−.56*			−.27													−.20	
CORROFF 4 (n = 21)						.39*	.37*	.28	.39*	.20		.20						−.20
CORROFF 5 (n = 23)						.23			.26	−.28		.24	−.28			−.27		
SOCWORKER 1 (n = 90)																		
PSYCHOLOG 1 (n = 11)	−.45		.22	−.36		.20	−.34			−.28	−.20	−.33	−.41	−.25	−.33	−.46	−.22	−.30
PSYCHOLOG 2 (n = 25)																		
PSYCHOLOG 3 (n = 88)	−.24**		.22**	−.21*		.25**									.18*			.19*
PSYCHOLOG 4 (n = 17)		−.28	.20			.20				−.41*	−.31		−.30	−.24		−.39*	−.29	.25
PSYCHIAT 1 (n = 31)				−.23			−.28			−.34*			−.31*			−.30*		
PSYCHIAT 2 (n = 32)					.20			.21			.20			.21			.22	
PSYCHIAT 3 (n = 32)			.37*			.36*			.30*			.31*			.30*			.27
PSYCHIAT 4 (n = 54)		.20	.25*		.28*	.37**		.30**	.36**		.22	.31*		.21	.26*		.22*	.23*
PSYCHIAT 5 (n = 30)					.20			.21			.30*			.32*	.22	.22	.33*	.25
PSYCHIAT 6 (n = 37)		−.28				−.35*		−.21	−.26			−.27*					−.25	

[a] CRM, Number of criminal charges during followup; INC, number of total incidents during followup; VIL, number of violent transactions during followup. All predictions are on a 7-point scale (not at all dangerous to extremely dangerous). Only those clinicians involved in 10 or more cases are displayed. Pearson coefficients of |.20| and greater only are indicated in table, except where a lower coefficient is statistically significant.

* $p < .05$.

** $p < .01$.

*** $p < .001$.

ative prediction–outcome correlations. Similarly, those individuals who ascribed relatively lower dangerousness scores to patients as a whole sometimes fared better (Psychiatrists 4, 3, and 5, M = 4.31, 4.36, and 4.49, respectively) and sometimes worse (Psychiatrist 1, M = 4.19, Correctional Officer 2, M = 4.08) in their predictive capacities.

Even those individual practitioners who did achieve some prognostic success, however, could hardly be characterized as "accurate" predictors of dangerousness, given that the highest positive correlation depicted in Table 7 (r = .43, for Nurse 3 with general incidents after 3 years) translates into only 18% variance accountability.

DISCUSSION AND CONCLUSION

Our earlier article concluded with a series of caveats directed at policymakers, practitioners, and researchers involved in the forensic prediction of dangerousness. Whereas we maintained that any wholesale rejection of the concept was premature, it was still apparent that any progress toward resolution of the dangerousness debate would require a fundamental reframing of theory, policy, and practice in both judicial and clinical quarters. Of cardinal importance would be the recognition that danger, violence, risk, psychopathy, conduct disorder, and related constructs are not discrete or insulated entities amenable to narrow scientific calibration—rather, they are complex, multidimensional, and discursively charged phenomena, with deeply engrained and contradictory connections to human thought and action and to wider social structures and cultural forces. Furthermore:

> The paradox and danger of dangerousness emerge when it is built into the concrete practice of professionals and officials. Dangerousness can be implemented for the purposes of either public protection or individual repression. It can safeguard the correctly identified non-violent, or abrogate the rights of the population of false positives. It is both objective, and vulnerable to capricious, arbitrary judgments of value. It can function as an adhesive for the legal and mental health systems, or reinforce the existing disparities between law and psychiatry. (Menzies et al., 1985a, p. 67)

Over the intervening years, the resurgence of theorizing, statutory and case law, medical and psychological activity, and social research on the subject has been accompanied by some genuine advances in understanding. Authorities, practitioners, and investigators are currently, far more than a decade or two in the past, inclined to exercise some restraint in their claims making and to display sophistication in their decision making about people deemed to be dangerous. Recognition of the analytic and methodological limitations is more pronounced, risk assessments in clinics and institutional settings are more likely today to be expressed in probabilistical and contextual language, and research efforts have been placing a higher premium on alternative constructions of social danger, on new technologies, on more rigorous operationalizations, and on the use of multiple contexts and sources of data (Harris, Rice, & Cormier, 1991; Menzies &

Webster, 1994; Monahan, 1984, 1988; Monahan & Steadman, 1994; Mulvey, Blumstein, & Cohen, 1986; Steadman et al., 1991, 1994). These developments reflect a general enrichment of the field, and the implications are potentially far-reaching.

At the same time, and despite these efforts and innovations, on the critical question—namely, whether experts or instruments can reliably and validly differentiate between potentially violent and innocuous human subjects—the overwhelming body of empirical evidence remains highly equivocal. Apart from the longstanding and relatively prosaic presumption, borne out by various research efforts, that young males with violent histories are more likely than others to remain violent (and to be especially high risks in provocative environments and in close temporal-spatial proximity to aggressive episodes), into the 1990s there continues to be a dearth of statistically verifiable and clinically operational assessment criteria (Castel, 1991; Menzies et al., 1992). However the construct has been transformed over the past two decades, and whatever successes might have been achieved in focused contexts with modest mandates (see Floud & Young, 1981; Hall, 1987; Hinton, 1983; Monahan, 1988; Mulvey & Lidz, 1984; Webster et al., 1985), the objective of a standardized, reliable, generalizable set of criteria for dangerousness prediction in law and mental health is still an elusive and distant objective. And there are no guarantees that it will ever be attained.

The overall pattern of results yielded from our METFORS research, both in its original form and in the elaborated replication described in this article, has increasingly led us to embrace these generally pessimistic conclusions. Deploying the best methods that we could muster and enlisting triangulated prediction and outcome measures along with a variety of experts, instruments, subjects, and contexts, we were in general not able appreciably to elevate the accuracy of forensic forecasts over those achieved in the earlier article. The inclusion of clinical along with trained lay decision makers, the widening of the institutional and jurisdictional framework, and the extension of the time period all had minimal effect. Even in those infrequent instances where predictors managed to approximate and surpass the .40 "sound barrier" (Arthur, 1971; Menzies, Webster, & Sepejak 1985b; Monahan, 1981, 1988)—as with psychometric predictions of in-hospital behavior by trained coders—the error terms remained immense and were only marginally reduced in comparison to our previous findings. Whereas some assessors were able to predict some people, under limited temporal and contextual conditions, some of the time, under no circumstances could even the most encouraging performances be mustered as an argument for clinical or psychometric involvement in the identification of potentially violent clinical or correctional subjects.

Of course, these outcomes may be neither conclusive nor generalizable beyond the conceptual, institutional, and methodological boundaries of this single study. Other projects, present and future, may harbor very different visions of the art and science of dangerousness prediction. Indeed, given recent trends toward its rehabilitation, it is unlikely (nor is it necessarily even advisable) that any one disconfirming set of research findings should inspire a general abandonment of the dangerousness construct or a moratorium on its usage in forensic practice. Such a deconstruction is highly improbable, given the continuing discursive power of dangerousness and related ideas about individual violence and psychiatric pathology, given their continued presence in criminal and civil law, and, especially, given the momentum currently demonstrated by "second generation" work (Monahan, 1988, 1992; Otto, 1992; Steadman, 1992) aimed at the scientification of dangerousness in social research and psycholegal decision making. The controversies will almost certainly persist through the current decade and beyond as the relationship between medicine, psychology, and the judicial apparatus continues to evolve, and as the problem of social violence remains a central preoccupation of experts practicing at the intersection between law and human behavior.

REFERENCES

Arthur, R. (1971). Success is predictable. *Military Medicine, 136*, 539–545.

Britzer, D. A., & Crowner, M. (Eds.). (1988). *Current approaches to the prediction of violence*. Washington, D.C.: American Psychiatric Press.

Butler, B. T., & Turner, R. E. (1980). The ethics of pre-arraignment psychiatric examinations: One Canadian viewpoint. *Bulletin of the American Academy of Psychiatry and the Law, 16*, 368–404.

Castel, R. (1991). From dangerousness to risk. In G. Burchell, C. Gordon, & P. Miller (Eds.), *The Foucault effect: Studies in governmentality* (pp. 281–298). Chicago: University of Chicago Press.

Chunn, D. E., & Menzies, R. J. (1990). Gender, madness, and crime: The reproduction of patriarchal and class relations in a pre-trial psychiatric clinic. *Journal of Human Justice, 2*, 33–54.

Cocozza, J. J., & Steadman, H. J. (1976). The failure of psychiatric predictions of dangerousness: Clear and convincing evidence. *Rutgers Law Review, 29*, 1084–1101.

Ekman, P., & Friesen, W. V. (1969). Nonverbal leakage and clues to deception. *Psychiatry, 32*, 88–105.

Floud, J., & Young, W. (1981). *Dangerousness and criminal justice*. London: Heinemann.

Foucault, M. (1978). About the concept of the 'dangerous individual' in 19th-century legal psychiatry. *International Journal of Law and Psychiatry, 1*, 1–18.

Gibbens, T. C. N., Soothill, K. L., & Pope, P. J. (1977). *Medical remands in the criminal court*. Oxford, UK: Oxford University Press.

Hall, H. V. (1987). *Violence prediction: Guidelines for the forensic practitioner*. Springfield, Illinois: Thomas.

Harris, G. T., Rice, M. E., & Cormier, C. A. (1991). Psychopathy and violent recidivism. *Law and Human Behavior, 15*, 625–637.

Hinton, J. W. (Ed.). (1983). *Dangerousness: Problems of assessment and prediction*. London: Allen and Unwin.

Jackson, M. W. (1986). Psychiatric decision-making for the courts: Judges, psychiatrists, lay people? *International Journal of Law and Psychiatry, 8*, 161–188.

Klassen, D., & O'Connor, W. (1988). A prospective study of predictors of violence in adult male mental patients. *International Journal of Law and Psychiatry, 12*, 143–158.

Mahl, G. F. (1968). Gestures as body movements in interviews. In J. M. Shlein (Ed.)., *Research in psychotherapy* (Vol. 3, pp. 295–346). Washington, D.C.: American Psychological Association.

McMain, S., Webster, C. D., & Menzies, R. J. (1989). The post-assessment careers of mentally disordered offenders. *International Journal of Law and Psychiatry, 12*, 189–201.

Megargee, E. I. (1976). The prediction of dangerous behavior. *Criminal Justice and Behavior, 3*, 3–22.

Menzies, R. J. (1989). *Survival of the sanest: Order and disorder in a pre-trial psychiatric clinic*. Toronto: University of Toronto Press.

Menzies, R. J., Chunn, D. E., & Webster, C. D. (1992). Risky business: The classification of dangerous people in the Canadian carceral enterprise. In K. R. E. McCormick, & Visano, L. A. (Eds.),

Canadian penology: Advanced perspectives and research (pp. 61–93). Toronto: Canadian Scholars' Press.

Menzies, R. J., Gillis, J. R., & Webster, C. D. (1992). Images of law and disorder: A survey of forensic mental health professionals in Ontario, Canada. *International Journal of Medicine and Law, 12,* 93–111.

Menzies, R. J., & Webster, C. D. (1994). Faulty powers: The regulation of carceral and psychiatric subjects in the "posttherapeutic" community. In K. R. E. McCormick (Ed.), *Carceral contexts.* Toronto: Canadian Scholars' Press.

Menzies, R. J., Webster, C. D., & Sepejak, D. S. (1985a). The dimensions of dangerousness: Evaluating the accuracy of psychometric predictions of violence among forensic patients. *Law and Human Behavior, 9,* 35–56.

Menzies, R. J., Webster, C. D., & Sepejak, D. S. (1985b). Hitting the forensic sound barrier: Predictions of dangerousness in a pretrial forensic clinic. In C. D. Webster, M. H. Ben-Aron, & S. J. Hucker (Eds.), *Dangerousness: Probability and prediction, psychiatry and public policy* (pp. 115–143). New York: Cambridge University Press.

Monahan, J. (1981). *The clinical prediction of violent behavior.* Beverly Hills, California: Sage.

Monahan, J. (1984). The prediction of violent behavior: Toward a second generation of theory and policy. *American Journal of Psychiatry, 141,* 10–15.

Monahan, J. (1988). Risk assessment of violence among the mentally disordered: Generating useful knowledge. *International Journal of Law and Psychiatry, 11,* 249–257.

Monahan, J. (1992). Risk assessment: Commentary on Poythress and Otto. *Forensic Reports, 5,* 151–154.

Monahan, J., & Steadman, H. J. (1994). Toward a rejuvenation of risk assessment research. In J. Monahan & H. Steadman (Eds)., *Violence and mental disorder: Developments in risk assessment.* Chicago: University of Chicago Press.

Mulvey, E. P., Blumstein, A., & Cohen, J. (1986). Reframing the research question of mental patient criminality. *International Journal of Law and Psychiatry, 9,* 57–65.

Mulvey, E. P., & Lidz, C. W. (1984). Clinical considerations in the prediction of dangerousness in mental patients. *Clinical Psychology Review, 4,* 379–401.

Otto, R. K. (1992). Prediction of dangerous behavior: A review and analysis of 'second generation' research. *Forensic Reports, 5,* 103–133.

Pfohl, S. J. (1978). *Predicting dangerousness: The social construction of psychiatric reality.* Lexington, Massachusetts: Lexington.

Prins, H. (1986). *Dangerous behavior, the law and mental disorder.* London: Tavistock.

Prins, H. (1991). Dangerous people or dangerous situations: Some further thoughts. *Medicine, Science and the Law, 31,* 25–37.

Rennie, Y. F. (1978). *The search for criminal man: A conceptual history of the dangerous offender.* Lexington, Massachusetts: Lexington.

Robins, L. (1991). Personal communication.

Roesch, R., & Golding, S. L. (1980). *Competency to stand trial.* Urbana, Illinois: University of Illinois Press.

Roesch, R., Webster, C. D., & Eaves, D. (1984). *The Fitness Interview Test: A method for examining fitness to stand trial.* Toronto and Vancouver: University of Toronto Centre of Criminology and Simon Fraser University Research Centre.

Rogers, R., Gillis, J. R., McMain, S., & Dickens, S. E. (1989). Fitness evaluations: A retrospective study of clinical, legal and sociodemographic variables. *Canadian Journal of Behavioural Science, 20,* 192–200.

Rogers, R., & Webster, C. D. (1989). Assessing the treatability of mentally disordered offenders. *Law and Human Behavior, 13,* 19–29.

Rosenthal, R. (1990). How are we doing in soft psychology? *American Psychologist, 45,* 775–777.

Slomen, D. J., Webster, C. D., Butler, B. T., Jensen, F. A. S., Turrall, G. M., Pepper, J., Penfold, M., Sepejak, D. S., Loftus, L., Byers, D., Chapeskie, T., Mahabir, R. J., Schlager, M., Beckett, K., Ronald, M., Shinkoda, A., McDonald, A., Glasberg, R., Jackson, M., Allgood, R., Harman, R., Keeling, K., Taylor, C., Murray, M., Farquharson, D., Lawson, I., Hermanstyne, L., & Bendall,

L. The assessment of dangerous behavior: Two new scales. METFORS Working Paper #14. Toronto: Metropolitan Toronto Forensic Service.
Steadman, H. J. (1979). *Beating a rap? Defendants found incompetent to stand trial*. Chicago: University of Chicago Press.
Steadman, H. J. (1992). Comment on Otto and Poythress. *Forensic Reports, 5*, 155–158.
Steadman, H. J., & Cocozza, H. J. (1974). *Careers of the criminally insane: Excessive social control of deviance*. Lexington, Massachusetts: Lexington.
Steadman, H. J., Robbins, P. C., & Monahan, J. (1991). Predicting community violence among the mentally ill. 50th Annual Conference of the American Society of Criminology. San Francisco, CA.
Steadman, H. J., Monahan, J., Appelbaum, P. S., Grisso, T., Mulvey, E. P., Roth, L. H., Robbins, P. C., & Klassen, D. (1994). Designing a new generation of risk assessment research. In J. Monahan & H. J. Steadman (Eds.), *Violence and mental disorder: Developments in risk assessment*. Chicago: University of Chicago Press.
Thornberry, T. P., & Jacoby, J. E. (1979). *The criminally insane: A community follow-up of mentally ill offenders*. Chicago: University of Chicago Press.
Toch, H., & Adams, K. (1989). *The disturbed violent offender*. New Haven, CT: Yale University Press.
Walker, N. (1991). Dangerous mistakes. *British Journal of Psychiatry, 158*, 752–757.
Webster, C. D., Ben-Aron, M. H., & Hucker, S. J. (1985). *Dangerousness: Probability and prediction, psychiatry and public policy*. New York: Cambridge University Press.
Webster, C. D., & Menzies, R. J. (1993). Supervision in the deinstitutionalized community. In S. Hodgins (Ed.), *Crime and mental disorder* (pp. 22–38). Newbury Park, California: Sage.
Webster, C. D., Menzies, R. J., & Jackson, M. A. (1982). *Clinical assessment before trial: Legal issues and mental disorder*. Toronto: Butterworths.

[33]

THE BRITISH JOURNAL
OF
CRIMINOLOGY

Vol. 23 April 1983 No. 2

ASSESSING EVIL

Decision Behaviour and Parole Board Justice

KEITH HAWKINS (*Oxford*)*

IN this paper I want to suggest a way of thinking about decision behaviour in the administration of criminal law in general, and the parole system in particular. The essay probes into the processes by which judgments are made about people caught up in the arms of the law, and is concerned with the ways in which decisions about the selective lifting of the criminal sanction are made by parole boards, emphasising in particular the symbolic nature of such decisions. My intention is not to advance a theory of parole or criminal justice decision-making,[1] but I do want to draw attention to some of the pervasive features in decision behaviour and to propose that decisions made at other points in the criminal process—by the police, for example, by prosecuting officials, by judges, and so on—are also similarly understandable

*Centre for Socio-Legal Studies, Wolfson College, Oxford.

This paper was supported in part by Grant Number 78-NI-AX-0153 from the National Institute of Justice, U.S. Department of Justice, Washington D.C. Points of view or opinions stated in this document are those of the author and do not necessarily represent the official position or policies of the U.S. Department of Justice. An earlier version of this paper was presented in the Lecture Series on " Law and Deviance " at the State University of New York at Buffalo in November 1980, and subsequently published in H. Laurence Ross (ed.) *Law and Deviance* (Beverly Hills, Calif.: Sage, 1981).

[1] This will be attempted in a monograph which is in preparation. Both the monograph and the present paper are part of a larger study of American parole board practices which I have been engaged in, on and off, for several years. The early part of this work, conducted in four American states in 1967–68, is reported in my Ph.D. dissertation (Hawkins, 1971). Supplementary data from three states were gathered in 1975. The major part of the research, however, is more recent, having been carried out in 1979 in three states with high, middle and low (*i.e.* using guidelines) levels of discretion vested in the paroling authorities. The primary method of data collection in all three phases of the study has been participant observation of parole board hearings, complemented by analysis of case files and structured conversations with parole board members and other officials, some of which were tape-recorded in their entirety. Case hearings as such were not sampled. My approach in effect was to sample board members and prisons. In the case of board members I managed (with very few exceptions) to observe all members of each state parole board in action. In the case of prisons, I organised fieldwork so as to spend time in a representative range of institutions. The case hearings which were studied simply happened to be the ones due for decision during those days I was present at each prison. In the most recent phase of the research I spent on average three or four days a week from the beginning of July to the end of October 1979 observing board members at work. Unless otherwise stated, the examples of parole board behaviour cited in the present paper are drawn from the state jurisdiction which I have called Madison.

in symbolic terms. And since decision-making is one of the most familiar and enduring of matters, many of the processes analysed here may be taken as examplars of the ways in which judgments are made in other social settings.

Though the paper is drawn from a study conducted in the United States, I hope it will be treated as relevant to the interests of British students of criminal justice and penal processes, since in many respects it deals with matters of human decision behaviour which transcend apparent contrasts in legal structure or procedure found in various jurisdictions. There are some, doubtless, who might argue that the traditional (until recently, at any rate) American sentencing and parole model differs so substantially from the British that there is little to be learned from American experience. But this is not the case. It is true that what until recently was a common American sentencing structure of high maximum terms and high discretion vested in the parole board is very different from the British preference for judicially-fixed definite sentences, with the parole authorities operating in the relatively narrow leeway (in most cases) of the middle third of the sentence. But the decision-maker's task—to exercise discretion selectively to release prisoners within that leeway—remains the same. It is true also that the prevailing American preference for personal interviews with eligible prisoners (not to mention immediately giving reasons for the decision to the prisoner in person) also differs substantially from the practice in this country of decision by lengthy and impersonal review of documents. But the decision-maker's task is again the same; the procedural contrast is only one of the forms in which evidence about the prisoner's case is put forward for judgment. Whatever the precise legal structure of their jurisdiction, parole board members share contexts and constraints in common. In Britain and in America, paroling authorities must grapple with the fundamental question of how to deal with those social deviants who prompt greatest concern. In any jurisdiction judgments have to be made about the principles employed to determine how heavily an offender is to be sanctioned, and upon what bases that sanction is to be suspended.

In analysing the exercise of discretion by parole boards in reaching decisions about the release or continued incarceration of prisoners, one point in particular should be kept in mind. In making judgments about release or restraint, a parole board is engaged in the appearance of condoning or condemning criminal behaviour; it is making statements about good and evil, desert and punishment, to the prisoner, the institution, and the wider community. The parole decision, in short, is symbolically significant.

Decisions about the reach of the criminal law are never made, of course, in an ideological vacuum. So far as the parole decision is concerned there are two competing ideologies of intervention which lay claim to informing the exercise of discretion. Most closely associated with the ostensible[2] design and practice of parole is the positivist conception of the criminal sanction as a means of treatment to reform the offender. This utilitarian penology operates on a view of the deviant as a flawed individual in need of repair. Crime is

[2] This word is important in discussions of this kind. The criminal law in practice frequently bears little resemblance to the idealised conceptions of the claims made for it.

regarded here as evidence of pathology or disturbance and as the product of antecedent forces, an approach which—in theory, at least—makes its treatment a matter for the application of professional expertise. Ideally, experts are needed to diagnose the " problem " giving rise to the condition of criminality and to make decisions about treatment needs based on an appreciation of the offender's total personality in its social setting. The requirement of expertise and the presumed predictive character of much of this decision-making demands an administrative model of legal judgment, with both a legal structure and supporting procedures which permit the maximum possible flexibility for individualised discretion. Its protagonists regard the ideology of positivism as benevolent in intent, even though it explicitly conceives the primary aim of criminal law to be one of social control. On this view of the criminal sanction, the task of the parole board is to identify the " changed " offender who can be released to the community under supervision where his rehabilitation may be completed.

Until a few years ago positivism was regarded as central to the design and guiding principles of modern Anglo–American penal systems. It has recently suffered a sharp reverse, however, at the hands of those who have advocated a revival of the so-called classical approach to punishment, whose distinctive characteristic is a commitment to retribution. This is an overtly moral stance in which offenders are regarded as exercising a free choice in committing crimes, for which they deserve punishment. Another important axiom is that wickedness warrants punishment in due proportion to its heinousness. Decisions in a neo-classical penal system are reflective, not predictive, since they are based upon the nature of the act (and, on some views, the criminal record) rather than the positivist's " total picture " of the offender. The notion of early release which is discretionary, selective, and hence uncertain—the central feature of the parole concept—is inconsistent with a neo-classical ideology. Yet punishment has to be determined in kind and degree, whether it be by law, court or administrative agency, and the neo-classicist would argue that the central principle in how long a prisoner should serve is " time for crime," respecting the axioms of commensurability of punishment for harm done and consistency of treatment as between like offenders.

These two conflicting conceptions of the deviant mirror the divergent images of the criminal embodied in the law. In the substantive criminal law human beings in general are implicitly recognised as rational and freely exercising choice. Penal law has for most of this century reflected a predominantly positivist view, with its institutions for the most part having been ostensibly organised to correct criminality, though it has not held to such a stable conception of deviance.

I have drawn caricatures, of course. The actual practice of punishment (as distinct from its ideological overtones) is a product of competing constraints, with moral, political and organisational dimensions. Yet it would be a mistake to see the ideologies of positivism and neo-classicism as largely rhetorical devices only very tenuously linked to the real world. Indeed the connection between such ideological statements and the mundane realities of routine cases is a topic of crucial importance in the sociology of criminal justice. These ideologies inform the design of the institutions of justice. They serve as yardsticks for their evaluation.[3] And, of particular importance in the context of this paper, they provide resources for reasoning by in the process of reaching decisions which may be displayed as rational.

What meaning do positivist or neo-classicist ideas have in practice? Parole boards meet to make judgments about crime and punishment. The board has to decide whether a prisoner has " had enough", and whether he is " ready " for remission of his punishment and restoration of his liberty. The word " readiness " is often used by boards to justify release in positivist terms, but it is equally applicable to the possibility that enough time has been served and the slate wiped clean. I shall try to show something of the ways in which certain prisoners are designated as " ready " for release while others continue to be regarded as " unsuitable ".

The parole decision is formally organised as the occasion for further legal categorisation of the deviant. It is the point at which a prisoner (who by definition has been negatively designated by criminal justice officials in a sequence of decisions reaching back to arrest) may have his identity transformed. Having been the incarcerated deviant, one of society's hard-core, he now has the opportunity to have the label of deviance lifted (or at least replaced by a much paler version) and to be re-designated as having paid the price. In effect he must bargain for the suspension of the criminal sanction not only with the parole board, but also those supplying it with information to be the raw material of decision; and where there are differences of interpretation among the board members they must negotiate further among themselves to achieve a working consensus about the prisoner's readiness for release. To analyse some of these processes and to communicate a little of the character of parole decision-making, I shall resort to the somewhat unusual expedient of discussing one actual case observed in one American state. Though the case is presented by way of illustration, subsequent analysis is based not only on this case but hundreds of others.[4]

The Setting

The parole board in the state of Madison (all names are of course fictitious throughout) consists of seven members. They possess wide discretion: state sentencing law specifies maximum terms of imprisonment in all cases, while minimum terms are imposed in the discretion of the sentencing court. As in most indeterminate sentencing jurisdictions, the statutory maximum terms are rather high, conferring substantial authority on the board to work in the leeway between minimum and maximum to determine, in deciding whether to grant parole, in effect how long a prisoner should actually serve.

[3] Indeed recent critiques of positivist penology which have advocated variants of the so-called " justice model " as an alternative have been based on largely unexamined assumptions of what parole boards—in particular—do derived from positivist ideology. An implication of the argument of this paper is that, to the extent that such critiques are based on an inadequate understanding of routine practice, they are misguided.

[4] See note 1. The case selected clearly raised some of the dilemmas of decision-making in a particularly salient fashion for the two parole board members concerned since each one independently, and quite unprompted by me, discussed the issues raised by it some days later when I happened to have my tape-recorder running.

ASSESSING EVIL

Board members in Madison visit each institution in person to conduct parole hearings of eligible inmates. Decisions are made discreetly, the board working behind closed doors in one of the more spacious and comfortable rooms in each prison. Board hearings in less secure institutions are conducted by single members, while a pair of members sit as a panel in the maximum security prisons. Madison law, however, requires any decision about parole to be made by a vote of the majority (*i.e.* four) of the board members. To adapt to this requirement and the constraints of a burgeoning prison population, the board employs a two-stage scheme of decision-making in which case files are screened and voted on at headquarters a few days before the hearing. The inmates in maximum security are screened by two members and subsequently heard by two different members whose files contain the screening members' comments and their votes. Those prisoners held in conditions of minimum or medium security have their cases screened at headquarters by three members before being heard in the institution by a fourth. Where the four members cannot agree about a decision the case is reserved for discussion by the full board in executive session held regularly (usually weekly) at headquarters.

A parole hearing consists essentially of a series of questions put to the prisoner by the panel. Members generally make some effort to put the prisoner at his ease, while trying also to observe certain formalities, such as referring to the prisoner as " Mister ".[5] Where the panel, for whatever reason, is well disposed to the inmate, the hearing resembles an interview; in other circumstances, however, the questioning can take on the character of an interrogation.

Panel members are almost always unacquainted with the cases to be heard when they arrive at the institution, and have to acquire a knowledge of each prisoner by skimming quickly through the records both before the inmate enters the room and during the hearing. For this reason parole hearings often are not unbroken sequences of question and answer. Frequently there are long periods of silence, disturbed only by the board members shuffling through papers or muttering comments and the muffled noises from the depths of the institution itself. In general there is little of the ceremony of the courtroom in a parole hearing Formality seems lacking since there are few constraints upon the substance of the dialogue or upon the kind of language used by any of the parties—members of the board without exception use prison jargon as a matter of course

Yet there are clear patterns in the conduct of hearings. For example, the topics covered recur with great regularity. Almost always a hearing opens with a discussion in some detail of the inmate's offence and prior record. Incidents of misconduct in the institution are also given particular emphasis.[6] Sometimes the questioning will shift to other matters: a prisoner's problems, his accomplishments during his sentence, or his plans on release; but these topics are given comparatively less attention. Prisoners are routinely invited

[5] The masculine is used throughout the paper since none of the Madison cases involved female prisoners.

[6] This is especially true of the Madison board, though somewhat less explicitly so in some other jurisdictions.

to address the board on any matter which they feel has been neglected. This usually serves to signal the end of the proceedings.

The tenor of hearings varies enormously from placid, amicable discussion to strident argument. An amiable session will often be accompanied by encouragement from the board if the prisoner is being refused parole, while a discordant session will usually provoke exhortations to do better. Here a prisoner's behaviour or attitudes are typically displayed as seriously lacking in some major respect. Whether they engage in exhortation, discussion or argument, however, the board members are always in control of the proceedings. After all, the power to ask the questions at a hearing has implications for its substance and tone, and most members are adroit and articulate in putting questions. They soon become old hands, while the parole hearing is, for most prisoners, an isolated and nerve-racking experience, whether it lasts five minutes or 25.

It was in this setting that the prisoner I shall call Curtis Brown appeared before the Madison parole board.

The Case of Curtis Brown

Curtis Brown is before the board on a special early hearing granted to deserving prisoners in the state of Madison. He is 32 years old and serving a 20 to 40-year term for rape. This is the second time he has been imprisoned, having previously served a six to 10-year term for breaking and entering and assault to rape. He was on parole from this earlier sentence when he was convicted of the second rape. Three months before the assault to rape Brown had been convicted of statutory rape.

A thick file contains an amalgam of facts, evaluations, and recommendations about the prisoner. The major account of his most recent offence covers more than one-and-a-half pages, with corroborative evidence provided by 13 witnesses. Brown is reported to have said on reception into the institution to serve this sentence that he is innocent and extremely bitter at being sent to prison for something he did not do. It was also reported on reception that he intended to appeal, with a claim that the victim picked him out of three mug shots and that the entire prosecution was rigged.

The bulk of the file, however, is given over to reports on Brown's institutional conduct and progress. Most portray him as having changed during his imprisonment: "This man has exerted a considerable effort on his own behalf . . . he has a deep concern for his own behavior and is sincere in wanting to remain free of future criminal involvement when he is returned to society." His therapist reports that "he has developed insight to his behavior . . . he is now able to handle the conflicts that led him into the assaultive behavior. . ." There also appears an account of how the prisoner's mother had a traumatic incident at the age of seven when she was in a car accident with her parents and saw her mother decapitated. In a section entitled "Health and Habits" one simple observation appears: "He also indicated a strong attraction to women."

One board member who screened the case for an earlier hearing has noted that the victim "was walking down street and assaulted at knife point";

his colleague adding tersely " I agree . . . [7] the history bothers me ". The file also contains remarks from another board member who had reviewed the case three years before. His entire note reads: " I have studied file: assault to rape in 1962 at age 14. Single at time. Sex play with six-year-old girl at age *11* in *1957* [*sic*]. Rape 1968. Single (intended to get married). H.R.[8]—no interest at this time." (His emphasis.)

A psychological report written at about the same time continued the theme of change meanwhile, referring to Brown's having " become more meaningfully involved in therapy ". Since " overcoming his basic feelings of inadequacy and his poor self-esteem ", it continued, " it is felt that Mr. Brown is now a much more adequate individual . . . MMPI testing indicates the presence of a latent schizophrenic process, but there seems to be no danger of overt psychosis." The conclusion is that " Curtis' behavior is markedly different from the way it was several years ago and he is seen in a much more positive light."

The most recent report on Brown in the file has been produced for the present hearing and is intended to summarise his progress in general. Accordingly it contains a mixture of social and psychological evaluation and reports of prison conduct. The account notes that Brown had escaped from the minimum security section of the prison but had been recaptured the same day; that he had forfeited six months' good time [remission] for sexually molesting a patient in the psychiatric clinic; and that he had completed the requirements for a four-year degree, having already taken three Associate [two-year] degrees. He had been " incarcerated for more than 9½ years " and had been " terminated from formal group psychotherapy because it was felt that he had achieved the therapeutic goals that were set up for him ". " Mr. Brown ", it concludes, " is a mature and sincere individual in his efforts to improve."

The first page of the case file consists of the most recent screening reports from two of the panel members' colleagues. Neither is disposed to grant an immediate parole. One of them has written: " Charge is very serious in view of prior similar charge on which he was paroled. Reports very good, has achieved well academically and has progressed in therapy. Has now served 10 years. Still prefer to discuss."

A woman, Eve Granger, is one of the two panel members hearing Brown's case. She is sitting with Herman Gold, who is an old hand. The panel establishes at the beginning of Brown's interview that he has already served time for breaking and entering and assault to rape, and that he was on parole from the sentence for assault to rape when he was convicted of the second rape. The board members also draw attention to the sexual misconduct with a patient in the prison hospital a few years earlier. They establish that Brown has spent five and a half years in therapy.

" How's it changed you, Curtis? " Gold asks.

" It's transformed me into an entirely different person, it's helped me to change my relationship with my family and other persons."

[7] I use points (. . .) to indicate omitted material; pauses in talk are signified by two dashes (– –).
[8] H.R. (High Risk) is a classification derived from the board's prediction table.

" What was the reason for the offense? "

" A low self-esteem. A fear of females."

" So why d'ya escape in '78? "

Gold's colleague has been looking at the file while this conversation has been going on and says to him: " It'll be 10 years in October."

Brown meanwhile responds to the question about the escape, mentioning (without elaboration) that he had been involved with someone taking photographs in the prison, for which he lost nine months' good time. He says he escaped because he was afraid of having another sexual incident appearing in his record for the parole board to see. He was accused by the other prisoner involved in the photographs, he claims, because the other man had a parole pending which he was afraid would be rescinded. (As sometimes happens, the details and the import of certain questions and answers only emerge subsequently in the hearing or in the brief post-mortem normally conducted by board members when the prisoner has left the hearing room. Occasionally the thrust of a snatch of dialogue is only evident to those in possession of the case file.)

The conversation switches to the inmate's accomplishments during his imprisonment. Brown describes his B.A. degree work and his three Associate degrees. He announces he has been accepted at a state university graduate school to study psychology; he adds that he wants to do a Ph.D.

The two board members decide on the spot that the case will have to go back to headquarters to be discussed by the full board because they simply do not have a majority (four votes) for any board action. Granger has displayed herself as favouring parole, but Gold has aligned himself with the two screening members and has not hesitated to express his reluctance to release. " There are extremes in your case ", Gold says in explaining the decision to refer the case to the full board. " Academically you've done a helluva job. The other side of the coin is the serious offenses, the escape. This sex thing." Brown puts a number of questions to the board which explore how his institutional misconduct relates to his risk outside. (Gold will say later that Brown comes across as very intelligent and articulate, while adding that he found Brown's questioning of the board to be a rather theatrical display of intellectual prowess to the small audience of five or six custodial and correction staff at the back of the room.) Brown continues to plead his case. He says he was not rehabilitated the first time round. But this time it is different. He has a small scholarship from one of the state universities and he wants ultimately to work in the State's Department of Corrections.

Most of this is directed at Gold who has spent much of the hearing questioning many of the inmate's claims and drawing attention to his deviant behaviour, both inside and outside prison. Granger, however, has played less of a part in the questioning and has at the same time presented a less sceptical attitude. The difference in their positions is subtly re-affirmed just before Brown leaves the hearing room. Gold has been looking through the file without success to find the disciplinary ticket Brown collected in 1975, which prompts Granger, who was also unable to find the ticket, to suggest a view of the misconduct as of no great moment by remarking, " I do know he stayed in the general population." [9]

Brown is told that his case will have to be considered by an executive meeting of the full board.

" *There are Extremes in Your Case* "

Brown's case was decided a few weeks later by the full Madison parole board. Its task was to negotiate a resolution of the differences between Granger on the one hand and Gold, together with two screening members, on the other—to produce, in effect a parole " decision " in the case.

One feature of such judgment by review is that the individual decision-makers who have already been involved in hearing the prisoner have a particular stake, a personal commitment, in the outcome. They seek to persuade their colleagues of the accuracy of their picture of the prisoner: they make a pitch. When I asked Gold before the executive session what he thought would happen to Brown, he replied: " I think he'll go . . . Eve will be selling. Now if it was a male that was taking that position then I think he'd stay in . . . You see it's more than the time for crime that she's going to sell on. And she's right and I will have to support it. There's five and a half years of therapy, y'see."

Gold was right. Curtis Brown was granted parole. " I knew as soon as he went out of the room ", Gold said afterwards, " I'd lost that one. I knew I could count on Jimmy's vote and Grant's vote. I knew Eve was against me. I knew Willard would be for release. How long had he got in? Ten years? I knew with that kind of time Nick would vote for him too. That left Bernard. And—it shows you the kind of man he is—Bernard voted not for Brown, but against me. He hasn't read a case for years. He more or less votes against me regardless of the case."

For the woman I have called Eve Granger, Brown " had enough ability ", she said before the executive session, " to want to change some of the factors; the ability to look at himself, what led to it over the period of time. Don't forget he's served 10 or 11 years. It's a whole lot of time in there. No-one was killed. I am saying—y'know I'm not trying to diminish - - but there is no homicide in there—there's no great, great numbers of sexual assaults . . . he did time on two. And there was contact as a teenager, being involved with a six-year-old. . . . He was involved in the program, it's not something that he . . . just, y'know, changed by himself. And I think his demonstration—my goodness he's served a whole lot of time. . . . "

This sympathetic image of Curtis Brown has as its key the remark " Don't forget he's served 10 or 11 years ", for this reference to how much time has been served recurs quite explicitly in two other passages: " It's a whole lot of time in there " and " my goodness he's served a whole lot of time ". It is noteworthy in this connection that there were also persistent references in Brown's file to the amount of time he had served. On this view, Brown has done—in the phrase familiar to parole board members in Madison and

[9] That is, the prisoner's misconduct was not so serious as to warrant some form of punitive segregation.

elsewhere—" time for crime ". The working philosophy of punishment evident here is the neo-classical one, a moral view emphasising commensurability of punishment with evil—not necessarily harm—done. The decision-maker observes that Brown has paid his debt before she raises the issue of his wrong-doing. And when such reference is made, it is not to rape, but to the fact that " no-one was killed ". Indeed, Granger's next comment—" I'm not trying to diminish "—acknowledges that the man's rule-breaking has not been portrayed in the terms that it might be. Brown, in fact, had been on parole when he committed the subsequent offence, a matter which in most cases invites interpretation by board members as an abuse of their benevolence and the goodwill of the state. Furthermore, to repeat behaviour is usually treated as a matter of extreme gravity—especially when it involves such emotive wrong-doing as rape. Yet Granger says of Brown's record " there's no great, great numbers of sexual assaults ". Indeed, the first incident is described as " a contact ". It is possible for this favourable view of the offender to be presented because for this decision-maker the issue of commensurability has been settled: he has served enough time. The wrong-doer, in other words, *has crossed the moral threshold*. He has atoned for his wrong-doing and in the absence of any powerful disqualifying condition (such as a moral panic in the community demanding extra incapacitation for certain types of offender or institutional management concerns which compel the sanctioning of badly-behaved prisoners), he is now ready.

Since the prisoner has wiped the slate clean according to the decision-maker's evaluation of his deserts, favourable data may be marshalled in support of what is perceived as a controversial matter (hence Granger's references above to involvement in the programme and " his demonstration "), but, more importantly, other potentially condemning data can now be re-assembled so that it becomes more difficult to ascribe unfavourable meanings to them. This tactic of reconstruction ensures that the prior moral decision appears rational.

Thus Granger presented an explanation of the prisoner's institutional misconduct, explicitly referring to the contrary image which her colleague had of the behaviour. Her tactic was to exculpate by displaying this particular deviance as " normal " or " inevitable ": " Now, the misconduct that Herman is centering in on . . . (that '75 misconduct in the hospital . . .) I don't know if it's an assault, maybe it was. I don't care if he's involved in homo – – the distinction that he was trying to make; sex is going to occur in a prison. There's going to be homosexual conduct because that's all there is . . . He is a sex offender so you would have to view that sex misbehavior a little bit more carefully than if it was a B and E [10] who was involved in that kind of contact. . . . We don't even have the original ticket . . . by the officer who saw it; it's missing and that's four or five years old now . . . The business with the pornographic picture in the escape . . . the whole idea was to take pictures to sell, so it's not, it wasn't a typical sex misconduct . . . " These remarks are a response to the emphasis which Granger's colleague had given to institutional misconduct during Brown's parole hearing. Though the

[10] That is, a prisoner convicted of breaking and entering.

prisoner has entered the institution designated as a " sex offender " (a label which he still carries save that it is now recast by Granger to embrace the notion of " the *atoned* sex offender ") he is not to be penalised for this rule-breaking because " sex is going to occur in a prison ". That it is possible for such a penalty to be visited on the sex offender prisoner is evident from the comment that a sex offender guilty of institutional sexual misconduct has to be regarded with greater care than someone convicted of breaking and entering who bears the designation " property offender ". Besides, it is difficult to make the misconduct label stick because it is " four or five years old now ". The more recent ticket involving sex is regarded as " not typical ". because there was a mercenary motive. Reference to a motive, such as making money, which is applauded in other settings (and is hence at least comprehensible to the decision-maker) makes it possible for the image of the atoned sex offender to be maintained.

All these justifications are put forward to support the master status of a prisoner who has done time for crime, upon which the decision ultimately rests, as Granger's response to my question suggests:

Q. " Now what I'm interested in is what magic bit of chemistry has tilted the balance very firmly? Is it the fact that he's got his time in? "

A. " Yeah. That's one of the things that I was going to say is that he served 11 years, so *the punishment factor is for me removed* . . . " (My emphasis.)

The other board member had a very different image of the prisoner. " Now it doesn't bother me how much time Curtis does ", said Gold: " It really doesn't . . . Because he for me [is] a second timer. Both rape charges. As far as I'm concerned all the therapy he's had is just words. They mean absolutely nothing." For Gold then, Curtis Brown presents the image of the persistent sex offender; he is not ready for release, for he has not yet reached the threshold of commensurability. The meaning of Gold's alleged indifference to time served, however, is not immediately evident. In the context of the remarks about therapy, Gold could be saying that time for crime is not the dominant value to be advanced in Brown's case. But a more persuasive view is that time for crime is still very much the heart of the issue. So far as Gold is concerned, Brown is " a second timer. Both rape charges "; and such morally disreputable behaviour deserves a great deal of time for atonement to be effected. The difference between the board members is one of values, in terms of what in Brown's particular case constitutes commensurable punishment for two rapes.

Gold supported his picture of Brown by reference to some of the same evidence that Granger employed. Evidence is utterly malleable and can be bent to serve apparently contradictory purposes: " First of all, that sodomy in '75. I was around at the time and I just know what was going on down at that clinic. O.K. he brushes it off as y'know not really happening, and I guess I feel otherwise. That incident coupled with the dialogue that went on yesterday which somehow, for me, was empty . . . I felt he was trying to show me how academically skilled he was, and I guess I did resent that part, because I guess I would have preferred his saying to me -- expressing some feelings about the crimes, about himself."

There are more brush strokes in this portrait of the prisoner. Not only has Brown yet failed to atone for his wickedness, a matter compounded by his failure to express " feeling about the crimes ", there is also a complex image of the prisoner as untrustworthy. He is accused of brushing off " that sodomy in '75 " as " not really happening ". Such behaviour—" sodomy ", not " misconduct " (as Granger preferred to call it)—is morally disreputable because it signifies an unwillingness to recognise guilt, without which there can be none of the remorse which goes some way towards mitigating the impression of wickedness. But it is more serious than that, for here is a man who has repeated his wickedness not only in the community, but in the institution as well. Such repetition suggests considerable commitment to wrong-doing. And here is a man who is to be seen also as an *institutional troublemaker*, a characterisation which reflects the decision-maker's awareness of the administrative implications of his discretionary behaviour. Concern for prison misconduct is yet another aspect of the symbolic significance of the parole decision, for the board member is particularly careful not to appear to condone wrong-doing in the institution by granting the relief of parole to the troublesome prisoner (see Hawkins, 1972). Brown was alert to these dangers—inmates also know the rules of the game—since he offered as an explanation for his escape his concern about having another incident involving sexual misconduct appearing on his record, combined with the suggestion that he had been dishonestly accused.

Whereas for Granger the prisoner had reached the moral threshold, for Gold he had some way to go. Serving time is the principal means by which prisoners atone, and the " two-time rapist " (rather than Granger's less emotive " sex offender ") deserves a substantial period of imprisonment. If Brown had been a " property offender "—another moral master status—Gold's expectations as to commensurability would have been reduced accordingly and it would have been possible for him to erect some causal theory which could make Brown's behaviour seem more comprehensible: " Now with the two-time B and Eer, I'm willing to say that it's a, it may be the lack of a particular job, or y'know, when he was running with some kids and that kind of pressure."

For Granger and (despite his more complex theorising) for Gold, however, Brown's prison misconduct, his efforts at self-improvement and so on, were secondary images, contingent upon a primary moral evaluation focused upon criminal act. Returning to the theme of the different expectations which flow from attributing the master status of " property offender " to a prisoner rather than the more ominous " sex offender " I asked Gold:

Q. " . . . if Curtis Brown had been a B and E man then you would be more likely, probably, to buy into his – "

A. " Yes. Yeah."

Q. " – verbalizing and everything else? "

A. " Right. Yeah, that's so. That's right . . . Obviously my moral, my value judgments that I make about the man and the crime influence . . . how I end up with whatever decision. And the greater, the nastier the crime, the more it offends my moral judgment, which in effect reverts back to the less likelihood of my dialogue with the man becoming more meaningful . . . The rapes are bad enough. When I add that '75 sodomy—and I *know* what went on up there— . . . then I found myself getting angry . . ." (His emphasis.)

The moral evaluation, then, is the central preoccupation of the parole board member. It acts as a precipitating definition, recasting other designations of items deemed " relevant ". To repeat: *the meaning attached to such frequently employed positivist concepts as " rehabilitation ", " response to treatment ", " maturity ", " insight ", or " change " are contingent upon the moral status of the prisoner.* This obtains in the behaviour not only of the members of parole boards, but also of those who ply the board with information. For example, suggestions of pathology in psychaitric or psychological evaluations seem remarkably dependent upon the passage of time. The condition of a prisoner seems to improve once he has made amends according to the time-norms prevailing in any jurisdiction. Once the moral threshold has been crossed a new identity can be constructed; its nature may be expressed differently, depending on the decision-maker's ostensible ideological preferences, but the process remains the same.

Curtis Brown's is by no means an unusual case. I have selected it from the many hundreds observed because it throws into particularly bold relief many of the features of judgments about deviance made by legal actors. Most striking, perhaps, is that two decision-makers had the same person and the same records before them, but their judgments revealed two very different conceptions of the individual. Brown's liberty, needless to say, depended on whichever of the two board members was able to persuade the others of the accuracy of his or her picture.

Such contrasting images of person and act are continually produced in the routine processing of legal cases. Where the decision-maker is an individual, like the policeman on the street, whose decisions about arrest serve to screen cases for access to the criminal justice system, the images of rule-breaker and wrong-doing which usually determine the outcome of the case are very often those held by the policeman alone. The solitary decision-maker is rather unusual in the criminal process, however, since most of the key decisions affecting the handling of cases are made by a number of individuals, in series or in parallel, or a combination of both. This is not to suggest that the single decision-maker is in some sense less important, since he is typically to be found in the role of gatekeeper commanding access to the system of justice (policeman) or the system of disposal (judge) where the implications of a decision whether or how to invoke the law have potentially profound consequences. One of the characteristics of most key criminal justice decisions is that they usually have binary outcomes where the central issue is whether the deviant should continue to be processed by the system, or should go free.

Where a number of individuals have a stake in decision-making, however, contrasting images have to be resolved for the practical purpose of making a decision " here and now ". Parole decisions, to a greater or lesser degree, involve the judgment of more than one member of the board. Indeed the legal requirement in many American states about the proportion of votes by board members upon which action can be taken is a recognition of the continuing possibilities of competing views of the prisoner and his crime. And parole decisions, like most other criminal justice decisions, also involve the judgment of those supplying recommendations to the board. In this connection it is worth recalling the findings of Nuttall *et al.* (1977, p. 38) about parole decisions in England and Wales. Where an assistant governor recommended in favour of parole, the local review committees made a favourable decision in 81 per cent. of the cases. Where the assistant governor made a negative recommendation, the local review committees reached a similar conclusion in 92 per cent. of such cases. Yet those who supply evaluations and opinions (rather than overt recommendations) to the board also play a part, however subtle, in constructing images which serve as the raw material for the ultimate decision. The act of defining what is " relevant " or " significant " enough to warrant inclusion in the records—quite apart from the actual language employed in the account—is an opportunity for the supplier of " facts " and " descriptions " to absorb the ultimate decision-maker into his or her own moral universe. A " decision " in a legal setting, like other decisions which are made in organisational contexts, is, then, a product of an almost infinite sequence of characterisations, appraisals and " facts " which often reach back many years into the past and which accumulate by accretion in a specific, concrete, individualised form in the case file and in a generalised, intangible fashion in the institutional culture of control agents—those unwritten impressions of " the kind of person " about whom they have to make a decision. This raises the issue of the ways in which knowledge is organised to speak to the central matter in processing the deviant: his moral status and the degree to which it is tainted by evil deserving of punishment.

Organising Knowledge

The decision-maker must always impose order on a potentially disordered world. For the parole board member engaged in judging wickedness, the practical problem is one of organising and thus making sense of the vast amounts of data which are accumulated on each case. In this part of the paper I shall address some of the ways in which a structure is imposed on the knowledge available in any case by techniques of simplification, presumption, characterisation, and patterning. (These techniques are all closely inter-related; it eases the analysis to discuss them separately.) Thus reconstructed, the data can be made by the decision-maker to fit a working theory of crime and punishment. This is how justice in practice "makes sense".

Simplification

The decision-maker's immediate task is to make information manageable. This demands an economy in the use of data, a persistent yet chancy matter. Deviants caught up in the system of control are subjected to close scrutiny (insisted on by their positivist ideology) by professional pathologists whose working assumption in effect is that because the deviant is in prison, something is wrong with him. Reports to the parole board contain both newly-discovered data and other material, some of which seems to be endlessly reproduced. A bulky case file whose contents must be studied in a matter of minutes is only likely to yield certain pieces of data—data which may yet be treated as significant and relevant—by chance. Other kinds of information, however, are designed to be conspicuous and readily accessible either by virtue of their location in the file or the colour of the paper on which they are printed.

Economy in the use of data, however, leads to caricature. Small details can, for example, form the foundations for the construction of major models of personality, or a brief account by a victim or police officer can serve in the absence of a trial (as is normally the case, owing to the prevalence of plea-bargaining) to allocate a prisoner to a crude category of criminal type. The infinite colours and shades of the real world, its nuances and subtleties, are transformed into bold blacks and whites by criminal justice officials—and others, for this is again a feature of human judgment in other contexts. The transfiguration of data is especially noticeable, however, where decisions have the binary outcomes typical of so many legal settings.[11] To handle such contrasting outcomes it appears to be easier to think in binary terms. And a starkly drawn, uncompromising picture is valuable in social negotiations over a decision; it is easier to take a position on, to reason about, and to defend. Herman Gold, for example, described his approach to decision-making as beginning by distinguishing between " a lousy case " and " a bad case ", where the former is negotiable and the latter is not.

But decisions have to be made, and usually on the spot. This compels an utterly simplified use of information and the paring down of issues to a few key items. Moreover, the potential complexities and subtleties of meaning in the data are compacted. The significant features in Brown's case were ultimately reduced and compressed so far as Gold was concerned to " Academically you've done a helluva job. The other side of the coin is the serious offenses, the escape. This sex thing." " The parole decision comes down to one, two, very basic issues for each one of us ", Gold said later, " and each one decides the basic issue."

Given the pressures under which parole boards work and human incapacity to process concurrently more than a few items of information, board members tend to rely on a few master categories of data which they employ in each case to see how any candidate measures up. Case files often bear the physical signs of this approach, for master categories are frequently underlined or highlighted, a practice which, in creating salience, tears the data from their context. The major markers include the nature of crime and record, termer status, hearing status,[12] and institutional conduct and performance. The length of minimum sentence imposed by the court [13] and the identity of the judge are regularly considered—what other discretionary decision-

[11] The policeman, for instance, has to decide to arrest *or not*; the parole board to release in the immediate future *or not*.

[12] It is important for boards to know how many prior prison terms, if any, an inmate has served, and whether he is up on his first hearing for parole or has already been " flopped " (turned down) once or more.

[13] The judicially-fixed minimum is the significant marker in Madison, owing to the state's sentencing structure. In other jurisdictions it may be a judicially-fixed maximum term which is treated as particularly relevant.

makers have done at an earlier stage in processing the same case is often an important guide. Another way in which salient pieces of information are produced occurs when a board member who has had more opportunity to read a case file summarises it for a colleague. This oral highlighting reduces the data to their essence, as the following remarks by Eve Granger on another case suggest. The terse sequence of markers employed may be regarded as a typical means of putting a colleague in the picture: " Burglary in Alabama in '48. Hustling. He shot the son of the woman he was living with in '75—situational crime. Sentenced to 10 to 20. He's 55."

The brevity of the hearing and the nature of the issues involved, especially the preoccupation with evil, mean that the recurrent images tend to be very powerful and starkly drawn, pushing contrast to the point of contradiction. Frequently the decision outcome hinges on one matter only, concerned with the question of wickedness: " Did he have a gun or not? " " Was it a pocket knife or a hunting knife? " " Was it $50 or $5,000? " " Did he know his victim was crippled? " The prevalence of plea bargaining in the United States, however, almost always renders this information problematic. The adversarial nature of the hearing (in fact if not in name) also leads in the fact-finding and decision processes to a production of two competing versions of reality aligned with the binary outcome of the decision. In Brown's case an image of the reformed prisoner who had served his term competed with another image of the repetitive rapist.

Presumption

Decision-making is also dependent upon setting. Setting provides a general and a specific context for judgment, creating expectations and working presumptions among decision-makers. Parole boards work in prisons and confront the worst cases of social deviance. In specific terms, where a prisoner is held affects the decision-maker's moral tolerances. " If they look half-way good " in [Madison's most secure institution], said an experienced board member, " you're impressed with them. But when you get back here [headquarters] you wonder what got into you."

Expectations and tolerances are different when the world is comprised of social outcasts. It is possible for a parole candidate to be judged " a good case " because he presents certain cues, even though a court thought his case bad enough to warrant confinement in the state prison. Deviance, after all, is a relative notion, as writers of the societal reaction school have reminded us. Similarly, something which may appear " normal " in other settings can be made to appear sinister in a prison record: Curtis Brown, rapist, it is interesting to note, " . . . indicated a strong attraction to women ", an observation that would almost certainly not be made of a property offender (or anyone else).

But more important is the working presumption adopted by parole board members that *because* a person is in prison he is at best morally suspect and at worst morally disreputable. Labels generated and applied earlier in the system in the processing of deviants produce in the parole board a *stance of scepticism* when addressing prisoners' cases. People arrive in prison as the ultimate social outcasts, almost always having been defined many times on previous occasions as deviant. Staff views about the behaviour of prisoners are permeated with the suspicion and distrust which also typify the staff images of inmates of other total institutions such as patients in mental hospitals (Goffman, 1961; Grusky, 1968). This leads, in effect, to a dual imagery about prison. Curtis Brown was held in a maximum security institution which was, according to one brand of rhetoric, a place of reform and renewal, while according to another it was also (in one of Herman Gold's many memorable phrases) "a snake-pit".[14] Brown's hearing portrays prison both as a place where he had had an effective education, and as a place where he had allegedly sexually molested another prisoner in the hospital and where he had received a ticket for being involved in the taking of pornographic photographs which he intended to sell.

The board's sceptical stance is fortified by the nature of the knowledge it has of any prisoner. For the most part it consists of documentary evidence, which centres on a biography of wrong-doing. Case-files typically record a succession of troublesome incidents reaching back into the deviant's life. The crime which has brought the inmate to prison is usually described, often in some detail, and the rap-sheet bluntly lists prior crimes in chronological order. Any institutional misconduct and punishment will also be documented.

On the other hand materials amenable to favourable interpretation are usually limited to the prisoner's behaviour and performance during the period of imprisonment (which can, of course, equally be the opportunity for unfavourable evaluation). These data are both narrower in scope and of a different character. Descriptions of wrong-doing (criminal act and record, prison misconduct) have a concreteness and tangibility about them. They smack of *factual accounts*, especially since they are usually linked with some sanctioning procedure. (If misconduct has been punished with a sanction this not only normally settles any doubt in the decision-maker's mind about the guilt or degree of guilt of the individual, but the sanction may often be used as an indicator of the extent of the wrong-doing involved.) Reports of performance during imprisonment, however, are recognised as *statements of opinion*, unless there is some visible criterion of progress (Brown's degrees, for example)—though these are not usually treated as weighty evidence. Occasionally a prisoner may return lost keys, come to the help of a guard during a disturbance, or tip the authorities off about a break-out; sometimes an individual may turn himself in after escaping. But generally such items as are capable of favourable interpretation are vague and amorphous. Statements of opinion are implicitly recognised as open to alternative view, and they do not possess the incontrovertible assertiveness of the "facts" of a criminal act or record. A prisoner can attend so many hours of group

[14] This dual image has parallels in the two ideologies of criminal justice discussed in the first part of the paper. The positivist view of prison as a benevolent place of rehabilitation where skills can be acquired, insights developed, or maturity encouraged contrasts starkly with an image of prison as an unpleasant place of punishment where inmates do "hard time". Here prison is a dark and shadowy world, a brutal and nasty place, a snake-pit of violence, corruption, blackmail and forcible sex. This latter picture is closer to most sociological analyses of penal institutions, such as those presented by Clemmer (1940), Sykes (1958), Cloward (1960), Sykes and Messinger (1960); see also Goffman (1961). Both images of prison emerge in the routine work of parole board members, without any particular discomfiture about their mutual incompatibility being apparent.

counselling or Alcoholics Anonymous; he can undertake a variety of educational programmes, or make claims of greater maturity or insight, as Brown did, but these will do little to mitigate moral disreputability if the threshold has not been reached, even if the decision-maker believes what he hears or reads. Claims from prisoners to be " changed " have a tendency to be regarded as a predictable rhetoric. Some prisoners recognise this by making the claim in a subtle fashion, by " changing "—but only up to a point. (One Madison prisoner with a not inconsiderable sense of humour, for example, decided that extravagance was inappropriate. " I used to steal every day ", he said. " But now I broke the habit I just steal once in a while." When asked what kind of a drug habit he had, he replied, " I didn't. I had an alcoholic habit. That's how I stopped the drug habit.") Besides, such potentially favourable data relate to only a small segment of the prisoner's life—that which has taken place since his wickedness. Items open to favourable interpretation occurring earlier in a prisoner's career (a good education, a steady job) ironically invite the censure of the prisoner for his subsequent moral frailty.

This is not to suggest, however, that, though evidence of wrong-doing has a categorical quality, such evidence is unproblematic. Parole board members are routinely placed in a position of having to decide what the " facts " of any crime or institutional misconduct were, since prisoners almost always present them with different—often dramatically different—accounts. In criminal justice systems which rely heavily on pre-trial negotiations to secure pleas of guilty, conviction labels in the vast majority of cases bear only a tenuous resemblance to the seemingly more serious behaviour which brought the inmate to prison. Whatever working theories of crime and punishment parole boards adopt, they need to know about the prisoner's criminal behaviour. Arrest and conviction produce labels of official processing which are artfully penetrated by the board members to get at the " real facts ", relying on the victim's, complainant's, police, or investigator's reports of what happened—accounts which the law would regard as untried allegations. The " thief " may find himself asked about the gun he used (a practice known in one state as " swallowing the gun ") or the " assaultive " offender asked about his rape.

The prisoner, meanwhile, almost always tries to present a contradictory image of reality to the board. A few claim complete innocence. Most, however, tend not to deny their involvement in some sort of crime, but rather seek to present a picture which diminishes the gravity of the alleged wrong-doing. Some, ironically, seek to vindicate the accuracy of the conviction label. The board members find themselves having to choose between two competing pictures of reality: the prisoner's account and the " official " account reported in the case-file. It is rare indeed that any account other than the official one—in its entirety—is relied upon, owing to the stance of scepticism adopted by parole board members. The prisoner occupies a very different moral status from the victim, which creates in the decision-maker assessing the competing claims made about the wickedness of the act a corresponding presumption in effect that the victim—*because* he or she *is* the victim—is to be relied upon. Besides, the prisoner who wishes to press his version of reality may explicitly or implicitly impugn the competence or integrity of criminal justice officials, a matter which risks violating cultural values about not making denigratory comments about others. When such remarks are made by one in the particularly discredited status of prisoner, this may well be regarded as further evidence of moral disreputability. And here the prisoner opens up the possibility of a double bind, for if at a subsequent hearing he presents a different account of his crime, one which accords more closely with the official record, he runs the risk of being adjudged untrustworthy or manipulative in trying to " con the board ". The cast of moral disreputability heavily stains the prisoner's identity.

The prisoner's discredited status leads to routine official scepticism in other respects. Even where an inmate has an opportunity to present himself in a favourable light—by assisting prison authorities, for example—he will find that board members will habitually treat reports of such events with scepticism, inquiring into the ways in which the prisoner could have engineered the " loss " of keys which he subsequently hands in, or what his precise motives may have been in naming other prisoners who were allegedly planning to escape.

Characterisation

Decision-makers like to create a picture of the kind of person they are facing, also to make the totality of their knowledge more manageable, as the two very different Curtis Browns which emerged at the hearing showed. In doing so, board members rely heavily on characterisations of the prisoner which they assemble from bits and pieces of data in the case-files, and brief comments which prison officials occasionally volunteer about a particular individual. Processes of characterisation are central to human judgments about the world, and are at the heart of decisions made in the criminal process from the policeman on the street onwards. Characterisation is a means of endowing individuals with attributes to make sense of them and to place them; it creates and organises expectations since it embodies a description and a prediction. Embedded in the notion of " the kind of person " is another of " what that person is likely to do ". Characterisation occurs regardless of personal working theories about crime and punishment held by any decision-maker. The positivist (in theory) needs to know what kind of person committed the act for diagnostic and predictive purposes; the neo-classicist, meanwhile, is interested in whether he is judging a " situational " or " provoked " offender, or a " professional " or " persistent " one, for these incorporate differing degrees of wickedness Blameworthiness—hence desert—is equally dependent upon such categorisation.

But with characterisation we confront a seeming paradox in human judgment, for although such interpretative practices display certain patterns they are also precarious. Portraits of prisoners may be painted in vastly different colours, as the Brown case suggests. The prisoner who talks freely about his crime may appear to one decision-maker to be " open ", " honest ", " candid " and " remorseful ".[15] To another he may seem not " open " but " manipulative ", not " honest " but " insincere ", not " candid " but " callous ", not " remorseful " but " remorseless ". A " thoughtful ", " quiet " or " gentle " person can be also regarded as " calculating ", " sullen " or " weak ". Someone who seems " carefree " or " happy-go-lucky " to one can be " irresponsible " and " couldn't-care-less " to another. The prisoner who sticks by his account of his crime or his " problems " may be thought " consistent "—or " stubborn ". But the data have to be compressed in this way to make a binary choice possible, and there are vastly different implications for the object of all of this, of course, depending upon which way the choice falls.

It is true that prisoners can try to redraw their portraits by projecting an image of " the remorseful " or " the reformed " criminal, but the precariousness of human judgment readily leads to the double bind already referred to: a display of remorse or reform risks being characterised at best as " just words " (as Gold said of Brown), at worst as evidence of a " manipulative personality ". The irony is complete. To be regarded as " manipulative " following a display of " remorse " has the utterly opposite effect on the decision-maker of suggesting a total lack of remorse.

The use of such language is a means by which characterisations developed by other criminal justice officials can subtly permeate a prisoner's records and deliberately or unwittingly influence subsequent decision-making. The assessments of prison staff and the evaluations provided by psychologists, psychiatrists and others who lay claim to expertise and a dispassionate judgment informed by the scientific tenets of their discipline all embody moral evaluations transmitted as much in their choice of words as in the substance of their remarks. The report on Curtis Brown's psychotherapy, for instance, not only observes that he had achieved the goals set up for him, but also notes that he has been " incarcerated more than 9½ years " and describes him as a " mature and sincere individual ", neither of which can lay claim to being distinctively psychotherapeutic evaluations. I have read case-files which have described how some prisoners have " torn " or " cut " property; others in which property has been " ripped " or " slashed ". One prisoner " raised in a middle class home " may have " realised drink has been cause of all his problems ", while another has been a " spoilt child " who " blames all his problems on drink ". These instances are all clearly expressions of opinion (and will read as such) even though they conceal deeper values. But values can be made to masquerade as " facts ". " He has been steadily employed, but he recently went on a drunken binge ", to quote an example from the literature (Robison *et al.*, 1971) conveys a different value emphasis—and can be shown to produce different decisions—from " He recently went on a drunken binge but has been steadily employed."

How precariously characterisation can operate is evident in the following case I observed some years ago in a western state, which nicely points up the fine distinction between a " candid " or a " callous " personality:

[15] The words I am using here are all terms I have regularly encountered written in case-files and used orally in board hearings.

ASSESSING EVIL

> The prisoner had been convicted of homicide, first degree, and had served more than 16 years. He had struggled with his victim before killing him by beating him over the head with a baseball bat. According to the official record the struggle came about as the result of an attack by the man on his victim. The prisoner did not dispute the facts of the crime but argued that the victim had persisted in making vigorous homosexual advances towards him which he was trying to repel. The reports on the prisoner's activities in the institution were extremely favourable, as was his most recent psychiatric report. The inmate claimed, during his hearing, to have had a religious conversion while imprisoned, which he described at some length.
>
> When the prisoner had left the hearing room, panel member A (who by the convention operating among the board members had the task, as main interviewer, of nominating the board's decision) began, " Well, he seems to have developed some controls—." At this point, member B grimaced swiftly at member C who was sitting next to him, and before A could continue interrupted to say that he did not accept the prisoner's account of his crime. His view was that the prisoner's version was a complete fabrication, and the idea of a religious conversion was merely a tactic designed to impress the board. Member C then briefly entered the discussion to support this view. Member A did not seek to defend what his colleagues had interpreted as a favourable disposition and parole was denied.

Characterisations of deviant act and deviant personality are reciprocal. Deviance is often regarded as an intrinsic characteristic of the person being confronted. In prison this is the rule rather than the exception since parole boards deal for the most part with people who have rather frequently been processed as deviant in the past. Here a particular act may seem so immersed in a personality as to appear a typical facet of that individual. Where the act is a breach offending deeply-held values it may disfigure the personality like a persistent stain. Here the deviant label is generalisable, the cast of disreputability creating an expectation that there will be other instances of disapproved behaviour. In other cases, however, behaviour which does not offend fundamental values may, if not repeated, be treated as an aberration, and not as an integral aspect of the prisoner's personality. Instead the act may be regarded as " an isolated instance " or " situational ". The biography of the offender in this sort of case will be assembled in such a way as to present the act as a curious lapse, or as the product of an overwhelming provocation or need. The act is severed from personality to be displayed as " uncharacteristic ". In some cases a characterisation of the prisoner may be mobilised not only partially to excuse the deviance, but also to account for it. Sexually molesting one's step-children can be explained (as it was in another Madison case) by the fact that the prisoner is " a real hill-billy ", while examples of assault in the same man's record were explained by him in terms of " Down South that's what you do. If you drink you gotta fight." This led the board to describe the behaviour as " A cultural phenomenon among Southern Whites."

Patterning

Characterisation of personal type to create a moral image implicitly involves the organisation of data in which a pattern is sought in the scraps of socially accumulated knowledge derived from the case-file and personal interaction at the hearing. The image assembled defines a particular response as " appropriate ". Decision-makers frequently structure their data by recourse to precedent, when they categorise a case as possessing features which are normally handled in a particular way (Sudnow, 1965). A variant of this is to structure data by analogy or comparison: the ideas of similarity or dissimiliarity are familiar ones to human beings, and are underpinned in criminal justice by the norm of consistency which demands like punishment for like offenders. Establishing a match with some problem encountered previously is an efficient way of making judgments.

One way in which a pattern is imposed on data to create imagery of a particular sort which deserves closer analysis is the assembly of a biography of the prisoner. The biography is a special one, however, directed to the construction of a *career as deviant*. Meaning is sought in a prisoner's unfolding sequence of criminal acts, a matter which is often carefully explored. The significance of a subsequent act may be recast by reference to earlier behaviour, and earlier behaviour may take on a new or added meaning in the light of subsequent acts. Though a violation of the traditional code of criminality is a discrete and finite thing, blameworthiness attaches to the person and is a continuing, evolving matter. A prisoner's criminal act recedes into the past and as it does notions of desert diminish as the prisoner gradually makes amends by serving time. A display of remorse taken to be " genuine " or claims to be " changed " may help lift the blame a little, although the act is done. Yet blameworthiness can be revived by a subsequent act—such as Brown's sodomy—which represents not simply a general repetition of wrong-doing, but a specific repetition of the same kind of wrong-doing. Such repetition is a serious matter for it signifies persistence in wickedness. If Curtis Brown had been a first offender—albeit a rapist—it is more likely he would have been regarded as a " situational " case in the absence of a career of deviance. However, a number of incidents of sexual rule-breaking by Brown suggested a pattern to one of the board members (Gold) at least, while Granger's remarks may be read as an attempt by her to minimise the suggestion of pattern (" there's no great, great numbers of sexual assaults "). One screening report listed Brown's sexual misconducts almost exclusively (though the entire file was available for study by the screening board member), mentioning the year each occurred. And another screening summary observed: " Charge is very serious in view of prior similar charge on which he was paroled."

Meaning is derived, then, from the distribution of deviance over time, and the juxtaposition of one kind of deviant act with another. A cluster of early offences followed by fewer convictions can be treated as evidence that the deviant has " changed ", " learned his lesson ", " had enough ", and so on (depending on whatever working theory of criminality is employed), while a number of offences committed recently by a person previously without an official record of deviance has the opposite connotation. Brown's repetition of rape as a parolee signified to Gold some sort of commitment to that kind of behaviour, an impression greatly enhanced by the fact that Brown subsequently collected two tickets for sexual misconduct in prison. The deviant career is thus further embellished by knowledge of the kinds of deviance recorded. Brown's second rape conviction took on an ominous significance for Gold in light of an earlier crime of the same sort. Yet if Brown's earlier offence had been a property offence—something which could be regarded as qualitatively different—his second offence might have been open to different interpretation (as an " isolated " case, for example).

Time is very elastic when careers of deviance are constructed. It can be stretched to extreme lengths in certain cases to embrace items which are seemingly trivial. Brown's sex play with a six-year-old when he was a boy might be regarded in another setting as " normal " behaviour, but in a prison record, especially the record of a rapist, it can be made to appear ominous. More striking, perhaps, is the fact that it was considered significant to record that Brown's *mother* had a traumatic incident at the age of *seven* when she was in a car accident and saw her mother decapitated. This displays not only the salience of history and the almost infinite capacity of pieces of supposedly " relevant " data to survive in files, but also the kind of theorising which deems such material to be relevant. The decision-maker may be led into speculating that the traumatic incident may have affected the way in which Brown's mother later brought him up, which in turn had some (unspecified) link with his subsequent sexual misconduct. Or he may be able to adduce a different meaning from the information. At the very least it is likely that the board member will be led to believe that its very presence in the file *must mean something*.

One clear pattern which seems to emerge in this connection is that salience is reciprocally tied to the dominant moral evaluation. The more morally disreputable the act, the more likely old data are to be regarded as relevant. The old data in turn cast a shadow over what happens later. In one case I observed in a western state in 1979, for example, an elderly prisoner claimed an unblemished record as a law-abiding citizen. The board disputed this, pointing out to him that he had been discharged from his city police force 41 years earlier for " corruption ". According to the record the prisoner had accepted a gift of a cigar from a motorist as an inducement to drop a speeding charge. The prisoner, significantly, was serving time for many acts of indecency with small boys.

Patterns of deviance—or non-deviance—can be discerned in a prisoner's record permitting pictures to be drawn of a " professional " or " persistent " criminal, for example, or an " occasional " or " situational " one. The former are condemning conditions because they suggest a fully voluntary commitment to deviance, where the latter are condoning conditions suggesting less wickedness which are applied in cases where it seems that the offender in some sense had less choice to do otherwise. If the career seems lacking in versatility it is a straightforward matter to see a prisoner as a " property offender ", a " con-man ", or as " violent " or " dangerous ".

On the other hand, the career of a versatile offender (with some violence in his record) is liable to characterisation as " unpredictable " or " hardened ", while one whose pattern of behaviour appears divorced from any notion of rationality possessed by the decision-makers risks description as " disturbed " or " pathological ". Purposive offences with a financial motive are understandable as rational, even though they may be vigorously condemned. But the burglary with a seemingly gratuitous display of malicious damage will appear to be much less rational than a straightforward offence for gain. Bizarre embellishments to the crime or offences lacking any apparent motive seem " senseless ". In general, the more morally disreputable the act, the more difficult it becomes to regard it as " rational ". And a career of wickedness suggests a pathological personality; as Gold said, speaking of Curtis Brown, " I guess I see the guy . . . with a history of rapes as internally a pretty fouled-up man . . . "

Judgments of wickedness, however, like characterisations of person, are very subtle and shifting things which turn on matters that in other settings would seem commonplace or banal. A gesture, a word, a touch, a glance, an omission can all take on an immense significance. Inmates recognise that certain kinds of acts are more readily recognisable as "rational" or " comprehensible ", hence their frequent efforts to neutralise the impression of wickedness by claiming, in explanation of their crime, that they were drunk, for example; that they were in need, or provoked; or that they were not already in possession of the knife they used (it was the victim's, or it was already in the room, on the table); or that it was not a heavy hunting-knife with a sharp six-inch blade (but a pocket-knife with a broken three-inch blade).

Careers of deviance possess, however, an almost infinite pliability which can be bent to serve very different interpretations should subsequent events recast the meaning derivable from earlier examples of wrong-doing. When this happens the new master category can be retrospectively validated by re-assembling earlier data not just to conform to it, but to confirm it. Similarly, when a prisoner has reached the moral threshold and atoned by serving his time it is easier to recast judgments of pathology. The effect of this is to tilt a parole board's working presumption against release to one where it looks for good reason to refuse the prisoner.

Conclusion

The act of judgment assigns an individual to a role and creates images and expectations about personal types. The creation of imagery is an essential part of decision-making about deviants (and others), for it provides a means of making a rational decision and for a portrayal of the essential rationality of that decision to the decision-makers themselves, and their interested audiences (including, not least, the deviant).

Most of the studies of the criminal justice system from interactionist or phenomenological perspectives have focused on the establishment and processing of wrong-doers showing how the law selects deviants and casts them into deviant roles and identities.[16] This paper, however, has been concerned with the process by which the criminal sanction is selectively lifted from officially designated deviants. Its theme has been the ubiquity and significance of assessments of moral character in the social construction of crime and punishment. The key is the moral threshold implicitly observed in their own personal ways by all decision-makers. Yet to talk of a threshold is not to suggest a rigid, immutable standard; it is, rather, a subtly movable barrier which may be raised or lowered in response to the imposition or relaxation of wider socio-political or economic constraints. This is how sanctioning practices adapt to changing times.

To draw attention to the shifts in the threshold and to emphasise the moral character of criminal justice decision-making is not necessarily to subscribe to the currently fashionable view of discretionary justice as " arbitrary " or " capricious ".[17] What may more accurately be described as " capricious " is the seemingly random assignment of cases to particular decision-makers or panels of decision-makers who may have contrasting views about desert which produce different outcomes. While I have stressed the precariousness of human judgment, I have also tried to show that discretionary behaviour is patterned behaviour. For example, remarkable consistency is observable in the choice of cues which signify wickedness. A similar consistency is evident in the placing of misconduct in a hierarchy of gravity: the rapist in Madison (and other states), for instance, is treated differently from " the B and E man ". Furthermore, the fact that Gold was able accurately to predict the outcome of the full board's decision in Brown's case—including the position which each of his colleagues would adopt—suggests considerable stability in decision-making behaviour. What is less easily determined, however, is the choice of norms to be adopted to reflect a notion of commensurable punishment. These issues have implications for two matters central to the " problem " of discretion. First, there is the question of introducing some means whereby a greater degree of consensus among decision-makers may be achieved about the moral threshold to be demanded of different offenders, for while each decision-maker may be internally consistent in judging cases, external consistency with one's fellows is another matter. The second question is concerned with developing some workable norms of commensurability, an enduring and essentially insoluble problem not least because it requires choices to be made about whose values are to be adopted.

Labels of deviance are at once plastic and persistent. Labels generated and applied earlier in the criminal process may be compounded by subsequent judgments. Yet the process is an artful one and earlier designations of deviance may be penetrated so that they may be made to conform to transcendent characterisations of wickedness. Here designations of deviance are treated as human artifacts and not as objective descriptions of some reality beyond a legal categorisation. The grant of liberty is not necessarily

[16] In a rich literature see, for example, Cicourel (1968), Emerson (1969), Lemert (1972), Piliavin and Briar (1964), Skolnick (1966), Werthman and Piliavin (1967).

[17] The most recent exponent of this view in connection with parole is David Rothman (1980); his historical analysis of decision-making is entitled " A game of chance ".

made in an obviously arbitrary or irrational way, nor is it founded upon evaluations of reform or rehabilitation (as some of the critics of American criminal justice have assumed [18]). Instead it is a reflection of the compelling human need to make statements about—as well as judgments about—wickedness and desert.

References

AMERICAN FRIENDS SERVICE COMMITTEE (1971). *Struggle For Justice*. New York: Hill and Wang.

CICOUREL, A. V. (1968). *The Social Organization of Juvenile Justice*. New York: Wiley.

CLEMMER, D. (1940). *The Prison Community*. New York: Holt, Rinehart and Winston.

CLOWARD, R. A. (1960). "Social control in the prison." In *Theoretical Studies in Social Organization of the Prison*. New York: Social Science Research Council. Pp. 20–48.

EMERSON, R. M. (1969). *Judging Delinquents: Context and Process in Juvenile Court*. Chicago: Aldine.

GOFFMAN, E. (1961). *Asylums: Essays on the Social Situation of Mental Patients and Other Inmates*. New York: Anchor Books.

GRUSKY, O. (1968). "Role conflict in organization: A study of prison camp officials." In *Prison Within Society*, ed. by L. Hazelrigg. New York: Doubleday.

HAWKINS, K. O. (1971). "Parole selection: The American experience." Unpublished Ph D. dissertation, Cambridge University.

HAWKINS, K. O. (1972). "Some consequences of a parole system for prison management." In *The Future of Parole*, ed. by D. J. West. London: Duckworth. Pp. 96–115.

VON HIRSCH, A. (1976). *Doing Justice: The Choice of Punishments*. New York: Hill and Wang.

LEMERT, E. M. (1972). *Human Deviance, Social Problems and Social Control* (2nd ed.). Englewood Cliffs, N.J.: Prentice-Hall.

MORRIS, N. (1974). *The Future of Imprisonment*. Chicago: University of Chicago Press.

NUTTALL, C. P., with Barnard, E. E., Fowles, A. J., Frost, A., Hammond, W. H., Mayhew, P., Pease, K., Tarling, R., and Weatheritt, M. J. (1977). *Parole in England and Wales*. London: H.M.S.O.

PILIAVIN, I. and BRIAR, S. (1964). "Police encounters with juveniles." *American Journal of Sociology*, **70,** 206–214.

ROBISON, J. O., KINGSNORTH, R., ROBISON, M. N., and INMAN, N. G. (1971). *By the Standard of his Rehabilitation. Information, Decision, and Outcome in Terminations from Parole: The Implementation of Penal Code Section 2943*, California: Department of Corrections Research Division.

ROTHMAN, D. J. (1980). *Conscience and Convenience*. Boston: Little, Brown.

SKOLNICK, J. H. (1966). *Justice Without Trial: Law Enforcement in Democratic Society*. New York: Wiley.

[18] See, for example, American Friends Service Committee (1971), von Hirsch (1976), Morri (1974), Wilson (1975).

SUDNOW, D. (1965). " Normal crimes: Sociological features of the penal code in a public defender office." *Social Problems*, **12,** 255–276.

SYKES, G. M. (1958). *The Society of Captives: A Study of a Maximum Security Prison.* Princeton: Princeton University Press.

SYKES, G. M. and MESSINGER, S. L. (1960). " The inmate social system." In *Theoretical Studies in Social Organization of the Prison.* New York: Social Science Research Council. Pp. 5–19.

WERTHMAN, C. and PILIAVIN, I. (1967). " Gang members and the police." In *The Police: Six Sociological Essays*, ed. by D. J. Bordua. New York: Wiley. Pp. 56–98.

WILSON, J. Q. (1975). *Thinking about Crime.* New York: Basic Books.

Name Index